HUMIDITY AND MOISTURE

Measurement and Control
in Science and Industry

HUMIDITY AND MOISTURE

Measurement and Control in Science and Industry
Arnold Wexler, Editor-in-Chief
National Bureau of Standards

Volume One

Principles and Methods of Measuring Humidity in Gases
Robert E. Ruskin, Editor
Naval Research Laboratory

Volume Two

Applications
Elias J. Amdur, Editor
Honeywell, Inc.

Volume Three

Fundamentals and Standards
Arnold Wexler and William A. Wildhack, Editors
National Bureau of Standards

Volume Four

Principles and Methods of Measuring Moisture in Liquids and Solids
Paul N. Winn, Jr.
University of Maryland

HUMIDITY
and
MOISTURE

Measurement and Control in Science and Industry

ARNOLD WEXLER
Editor-in-Chief
National Bureau of Standards

VOLUME TWO

APPLICATIONS

ELIAS J. AMDUR, Editor
Honeywell, Inc.

Based on papers presented at the
1963 International Symposium on Humidity and Moisture
Washington, D.C.

Sponsored by

National Bureau of Standards
U.S. Weather Bureau
American Society of Heating, Refrigerating and Air-Conditioning Engineers
American Meteorological Society
Instrument Society of America

REINHOLD PUBLISHING CORPORATION, NEW YORK

Chapman & Hall, Ltd., London

Symposium Committees

General Committee

W. A. Wildhack, *Chairman*
National Bureau of Standards
Washington, D. C.

Arnold Wexler
National Bureau of Standards
Washington, D.C.

A. K. Showalter
U.S. Weather Bureau
Washington, D.C.

Lester Machta
U.S. Weather Bureau
Washington, D.C.

A. S. Gates, Jr.
ASHRAE, National Institutes of Health
Bethesda, Md.

J. L. Threlkeld
ASHRAE, University of Minneapolis
Minneapolis, Minn.

G. O. Haglund
ISA, Vitro Corporation
New York, N.Y.

H. S. Kindler
Instrument Society of America
Pittsburgh, Pennsylvania

K. C. Spengler
American Meteorological Society
Boston, Massachusetts

Program Committee

Arnold Wexler, *Chairman*
National Bureau of Standards
Washington, D.C.

B. R. Bean
National Bureau of Standards
Boulder, Colorado

D. M. Gates
National Bureau of Standards
Boulder, Colorado

Christos Harmantas
U.S. Weather Bureau
Washington, D.C.

N. B. Hutcheon
Division of Building Research
National Research Council
Ottawa, Canada

D. A. Mazzarella
Science Associates
Princeton, N.J.

P. E. McNall, Jr.
Honeywell, Inc.
Minneapolis, Minn.

H. D. Parry
U.S. Weather Bureau
Washington, D.C.

C. L. Roberson
Owen-Corning Fiberglass Corporation
Granville, Ohio

R. E. Ruskin
Naval Research Laboratory
Washington, D.C.

v

P. N. Winn, Jr.
University of Maryland
College Park, Maryland

Assisted by:

E. J. Amdur
Honeywell, Inc.
Minneapolis, Minn.

Calvin Golumbic
Agricultural Marketing Service, USDA
Beltsville, Maryland

Anthony Haas
Dryomatic Division
Alexandria, Va.

R. M. Marchgraber
U.S. Army Electronics Research and
Dev. Laboratory
Fort Monmouth, N.J.

R. G. Nevins
Kansas State University
Manhattan, Kansas

K. H. Norris
Agricultural Marketing Service
USDA, Beltsville, Maryland

Edward Penner
Division of Building Research
National Research Council
Ottawa, Canada

P. J. Sereda
Division of Building Research
National Research Council
Ottawa, Canada

Norman Sissenwine
Air Force Cambridge Research Laboratories
Bedford, Massachusetts

H. K. Weickmann
U.S. Army Research and
Development Laboratory
Fort Monmouth, N.J.

R. G. Yeck
Agricultural Research Service
USDA, Beltsville, Maryland

Local Committee on Arrangements

J. W. Morgan, *Chairman*
Johnson Service Co.
Arlington, Va.

R. J. Dillard
York Corporation
Washington, D.C.

G. F. Guenterberg
Harvey W. Hottel Incorporation
Silver Spring, Maryland

Kirby Hanson
U.S. Weather Bureau
Washington, D.C.

F. A. Leser
ILG Electric Ventilating Co.
Washington, D.C.

F. C. Quinn
Hygrodynamics
Silver Spring, Maryland

W. C. Reamy
Meleney Engineering Co.
Washington, D.C.

B. F. Remington
U.S. Weather Bureau
Washington, D.C.

W. R. Tilley
National Bureau of Standards
Washington, D.C.

Julia I. Szabo
ASHRAE
New York, N.Y.

J. H. Cansdale
ASHRAE
New York, N.Y.

Foreword

Humidity is an attribute of the human environment most generally recognized by its important role as a determinant in climate, weather, and personal comfort—"It's not the temperature, it's the humidity!" It is also frequently apparent by its effect on common hygroscopic materials such as wood, textiles, paper and foodstuffs.

Like the other climatic variables—temperature, pressure and precipitation—humidity has long been regularly measured and recorded as a part of the synoptic history which provides some basis for weather prediction and some measure of the problem of climate or weather control. On a small scale, humidity control has long been feasible in the laboratory test chamber, and with the first advent of mechanical refrigeration it was rapidly extended to the whole laboratory as well. On a large scale, dams and reservoirs, irrigation projects and reforestation belts, film-covered or blackened ponds, have some effect on local climate. Proposals for shifting the course of the ocean currents, blocking or widening the ocean straits, and blackening the polar ice caps, envisage man's widespread "control" of climatic humidity. To the extent that these programs progress beyond the proposal stage, more precise and careful measurement of humidity over wide areas will be necessary in order to assess the effects.

Techniques for making these measurements at the National Bureau of Standards have progressed from less to greater precision with perhaps an occasional side trip. I recall one such journey, when one of my first assignments at NBS was calibrating aerographs (time-recorders of temperature, pressure, humidity) for the Aerology Branch of the Navy. The "precision" hygrometric element was a bundle of human hairs, transmitting its variation in length to a pen recorder. To lessen the tedium of many observations of dew point in the test chamber—using an airstream bubbling through ether to cool a metallic mirror and reading a liquid-in-glass thermometer immersed in the ether both when the mist appeared and when it disappeared—I proposed to use the "well-known" fact that the humidity is roughly constant with temperature over saturated salt solutions. I consulted the International Critical Tables, selected four or five salts to cover the relative humidity range of 15 to 95 per cent, visited the storeroom for salts and trays—and cut calibration times to a small fraction! My pride in this achievement was considerably abated when I found, on finally reading in detail the references given in the I.C.T. that the salts had been "calibrated" by use of a hair hygrometer!

It was a long and tedious job to check—or "re-calibrate"—the salt solutions from 0 to 40°C using the dew-point apparatus. Although the results were well within 1 per cent of presently accepted values (except for the saturated solution of LiCl), and the method was routinely used thereafter, publication of the results was postponed for still better accuracy; it was finally redone by Wexler and Hasegawa [*J. Res. Natl. Bur. Std.*, **53**, 19 (1952)]

Some years later, when exploring the utility of the critical flow principle in a variety of devices, including a gas analyzer, it seemed natural to try it in a hygrometer (Wildhack, Perls, Kissinger and Hayes, Vol. I). It worked quite well; but again waited some years to be refined for greater precision as a laboratory standard (Greenspan, Vol. III).

The central province of the National Bureau of Standards is precision physical measurements and measurement standards; its national role is to provide measurement services and data to science, engineering and technology. These services include not only calibrations performed on precision instruments, which are to be used further in the laboratory or in calibration of working instruments for field or factory, but also the publication of research on methods of measurement, or of results of measurement, and the collection and dissemination of information on all areas of measurement science.

A particularly appropriate service is the compilation of papers on the state of the art in the measurement of physical quantities important to science and industry. One of the best ways to achieve a definitive coverage is to get experts in the field to present papers describing both old techniques and new discoveries and developments. Thus, NBS frequently sponsors symposia or conferences, in a variety of fields, usually in cooperation with other organizations having allied interests in particular fields. As an example, NBS has sponsored several Temperature Symposia over the years: in 1938, with the American Institute of Physics; in 1954, with the American Institute of Physics and the Office of Aerospace Research; and in 1961, with the American Institute of Physics and the Instrument Society of America. Thus when it appeared that a Symposium on Humidity would be of value to the technical community, NBS proposed that the Weather Bureau, the American Meteorological Society, the Instrument Society of America, and the American Society of Heating, Refrigerating, and Air-Conditioning Engineers join in planning and arranging the Symposium.

The result of the jointly sponsored Symposium, in which 306 authors presented 229 papers during four days to 850 people, is not only this four-volume definitive record of the present state of humidity measurement and control; it was for the participants—and hopefully will be for our readers—an inspiration and impetus to more extensive work in this area, and it gave them a better appreciation of the many techniques available for application to a host of practical problems.

The Symposium General Committee, composed of representatives of each of the sponsoring organizations, worked harmoniously to achieve a well-planned and well-operated symposium (with an exhibit!) and to publicize it to interested persons. To select papers of high quality, the Committee appointed my colleague, Mr. Arnold Wexler, Chief of the Humidity Measurements Section, to serve as Program Chairman and as Editor-in-Chief for the publication. On his committee also were representatives of each of the sponsors.

After selecting a publisher, Reinhold Publishing Corporation, who had also published the Temperature Symposia volumes, the General Committee has gone into a state of hibernation, to bestir itself some few years hence when further advances in the measurement and control of humidity and moisture make appropriate a return engagement.

My official and personal thanks go to all participants.

W. A. WILDHACK
Chairman, General Committee
1963 International Symposium
on Humidity and Moisture.

General Preface

On May 20-23, 1963, over 850 scientists and engineers from around the world attended the 1963 International Symposium on Humidity and Moisture in Washington, D.C. The Symposium was sponsored by two U.S. Government agencies, the National Bureau of Standards and the U.S. Weather Bureau, and three technical societies, the American Society of Heating, Refrigerating and Air-Conditioning Engineers, the American Meteorological Society and the Instrument Society of America. "Humidity and Moisture" contains most of the papers that were presented at the Symposium, as well as several other papers that were subsequently added to augment the coverage in certain areas.

The measurement and control of humidity —water in the vapor phase—and moisture— water in the adsorbed or absorbed phase— play an important role in such scientific disciplines as physics, chemistry, biology and medicine, in many branches of engineering, in meteorology and in agriculture, and in such diverse industrial fields as air conditioning, drying, refrigeration, cryogenics, storage, food processing, packaging, materials manufacturing and processing, gas transmission, and electronics. The Symposium provided an unique opportunity for representatives from the scientific, engineering and industrial communities to meet at a common forum to exchange information on the latest research and developments and to review the current state of the art.

The organization of the sessions, the invitation of contributions on special topics, and the selection of papers were arranged by the Program Committee. Dr. J. Herbert Holloman, Assistant Secretary of Commerce for Science and Technology, delivered the keynote address. Over 200 papers were presented at 32 meetings in four parallel sessions. Because of the large number of papers and the broad subject matter, there are both duplications and omissions. No attempt was made to edit the written papers so that definitions, terminology and mathematical symbols would be uniform and consistent.

It was impractical to encompass all the papers within one set of covers. The contents were therefore divided into the following four volumes, each under the cognizance of a separate volume editor:

Volume One. Principles and Methods of Measuring Humidity in Gases. Editor, Robert E. Ruskin, Naval Research Laboratory.

Volume Two. Applications (measurements unique or special to various fields or disciplines; studies and investigations in which humidity or moisture is the critical parameter). Editor, Elias J. Amdur, Honeywell, Inc.

Volume Three. Fundamentals and Standards. Editors, Arnold Wexler and William A. Wildhack, National Bureau of Standards.

Volume Four. Principles and Methods of Measuring Moisture in Liquids and Solids. Editor, Paul N. Winn, Jr., University of Maryland.

I would like to express my appreciation and acknowledgment to the members of the General Committee, the members of the Program Committee, the members of the Local Committee on Arrangements, the headquarters staff of the American Society of Heating, Refrigerating and Air-Conditioning Engineers, particularly Miss Julia Szabo, the Office of Technical Information of the National Bureau of Standards, especially Messrs. W. R. Tilley and R. T. Cook, and to Mrs. Rosemary Soler of NBS. Their enthusiastic cooperation and diligent work contributed materially to the success of the Symposium.

ARNOLD WEXLER,
Editor-in-Chief

Preface to Volume Two

The papers in this volume discuss the measurement or control of humidity in various applied scientific and industrial fields, in agriculture and in comfort air-conditioning. No attempt has been made to hold these papers to a preconceived standard of excellence or to mediate the various disagreements which exist in some fields, particularly in upper-air meteorology.

Because of the wide range of problems discussed, the papers vary from descriptive reviews which may be evaluated by any technically trained person having a general familiarity with humidity instrumentation to reports of investigations which can properly be reviewed only by specialists. The assistance of the following persons who reviewed papers in their fields of specialization has been invaluable, and I wish to take this opportunity to thank them for their efforts: Messrs. D. M. Gates, J. R. Meyer Arendt, J. W. Herbstreit, R. E. McGavin, R. O. Gilmer, and Mr. B. R. Bean, N.B.S., Boulder Labs; Mr. Lester Machta, Weather Bureau; Mr. J. L. Threlkeld, University of Minnesota; Mr. R. G. Nevins, Kansas State University; Mr. I. J. Ross, University of Florida; Mr. Norman Sissenwine, AFCRL; Mr. A. W. Straiton, University of Texas; Mr. R. G. Yeck, U.S.D.A., Beltsville; Mr. Lester Leiden, Parametrics, Inc.; Messrs. P. E. McNall, Jr., H. C. Lofgren, and H. A. Cloud, Honeywell, Inc.

ELIAS J. AMDUR,
Editor, Volume Two

Contents

SECTION V: PROCESS CONTROL

SECTION VI: METEOROLOGY

SECTION VII: RADIO PROPAGATION AND ATMOSPHERIC REFRACTION

SECTION I

BIOLOGY AND MEDICINE

1. Humidity Effects on the Comfort and Well-being of People

Ralph G. Nevins

Kansas State University, Manhattan, Kansas

AND

James D. Hardy

John B. Pierce Foundation, New Haven, Connecticut

ABSTRACT

Comfortable environmental conditions are based on the individual's ability to maintain thermal balance with his environment by means of minor physiological adjustments, without sweating or shivering. Evaporation, which plays an important role in maintaining the body in thermal balance, can be divided into two processes—insensible perspiration and sweating. For a resting subject exposed to a comfortable environment, approximately 24 per cent of the total body heat loss is insensible perspiration.

A historical review of comfort work introduces the comfort line and effective temperature. Along a line of constant effective temperature, an increase in relative humidity of 20 per cent requires a decrease in dry-bulb temperature of approximately 2°F.

Recent data indicate that in the range of dry-bulb temperatures of 73 to 77°F, variations in relative humidity from 25 to 60 per cent do not affect comfort sensations, for sedentary or slightly active normally clothed subjects.

The differences reported do not indicate an error. Each must be applied to different conditions. The effective temperature lines indicate a subjective reaction immediately after entering a conditioned space, while the newer data indicate reactions to conditioned spaces when the exposure time is approximately three hours or longer.

Man has long recognized the existence of humidity and its effect on his comfort. "It's not the heat, it's the humidity," is a classical example of man's awareness of humidity as a factor in providing for his comfort and well-being.

The sensation of comfort or lack of awareness of discomfort is a complex subjective reaction resulting from a combination of physical, physiological, and psychological factors. From a thermal standpoint, comfortable environmental conditions are based on the individual's ability to maintain thermal balance with his environment by means of minor physiological adjustments, without sweating or shivering. In the "comfort range," the thermal environment imposes low level stimuli which are within the vasomotor control limits.

In addition to the factors making up the thermal environment, i.e., dry-bulb temperature, relative humidity, air motion, and mean radiant temperature, man's comfort also can be affected by climate and season, activity, clothing, state of health, sex and age.

Historically, man has proposed and used

3

many different methods to achieve and maintain a comfortable air temperature. Only in this century has man had the technical understanding and facilities to achieve and maintain a desired level of humidity. In 1911 at the annual meeting of the American Society of Mechanical Engineers, Willis H. Carrier[1] stated:

"A specialized engineering field has recently developed, technically known as air conditioning, or the artificial regulation of atmospheric moisture. The application of this new art to many varied industries has been demonstrated to be of greatest economic importance."

Prior to this, ventilation to remove heat, humidity and odors had been given engineering consideration as early as 1845.[2] The well-publicized story of the Black Hole of Calcutta was a dramatic example of the effects of bad ventilation and the resulting overheating.

In 1883, a German researcher, J. T. F. Hermans,[3] unequivocally suggested that discomfort, commonly blamed on bad ventilation, in reality was due to excessive temperature and humidity. Experimental evidence to support Hermans came in 1905 from work by Flugge and his associates.[4] Flugge concluded that

"The thermal properties of our atmospheric environment—temperature, moisture, air movement—are of far greater significance for our well-being than the chemical properties of the air. The feelings of freshness which we experience when a closed room is freely ventilated or when we emerge into the outer air, are clearly due to more effective cooling of the body."

German, English and American confirmation of Flugge's results led to complete acceptance of the thermal view of ventilation by 1909.

The thermodynamic processes which govern the exchange of heat between the body and the thermal environment are described by the equation

$$M = \pm C \pm R + E \pm \varDelta S \qquad (1)$$

where

M = rate of metabolism, heat produced in the body (always +), Btu/hr

C = rate of convective heat loss (+) or gain (−), Btu/hr

R = rate of radiative heat loss (+) or gain (−), Btu/hr

E = rate of evaporative heat loss (always +), Btu/hr

$\varDelta S$ = rate of change of stored energy, (+ heat stress, − cold stress), Btu/hr.

When Eq. (1) is balanced with $\varDelta S$ equal to zero without activating the thermoregulatory activities of shivering, sweating and strong vasomotor activity, thermal comfort is achieved. Complete evaluation of Eq. (1) requires analysis and study of each term. This paper is limited essentially to a discussion of the evaporative heat loss term and its effect on comfort assuming other factors constant.

The evaporative heat loss (E) can be divided into two distinct processes, insensible perspiration and sweating. Insensible perspiration is the evaporation of water which diffuses through the epidermis from the deeper layers of the skin and from the moist surfaces of the respiratory system. For a resting subject exposed to a moderate or comfortable environment, approximately 24 per cent of the total heat loss from the body is insensible perspiration, with 16 to 14 per cent evaporating from the skin and 8 to 10 per cent evaporating from the respiratory tract.[5, 6] For non-resting subjects the evaporative heat loss increases and becomes 40 per cent of the total heat loss for light work or walking slowly to 60 per cent for moderately heavy working or moderate dancing.[7]

Evaporation of water from the skin surface and its subsequent cooling and expansion to the surrounding air temperature and vapor partial pressure occurs within a few millimeters of the skin surface so that all of the heat required for evaporation is supplied by the skin. The water lost by evaporation can be expressed by the equation

$$W_v = A'C(P_S - P_V)f(VD) \qquad (2)$$

where

W_v = water loss by vaporization, g/min.

A' = wetted area

P_S = saturated vapor pressure at skin temperature, cm Hg

P_V = vapor pressure at air temperature, cm Hg

C = 0.0003 g/min.-cm Hg (proportionality factor)

$f(VD)$ = a function of velocity V and characteristic body dimension, D.

Equation (2) by Büttner[8] first introduced the concept of a variable wet surface area for determining water loss from the skin. Gagge[9] then introduced the equation

$$E = (W\mu) A(P_S - RH \times P_A) \qquad (3)$$

where

E = heat loss by evaporation, Btu/hr
W = fraction of body area completely wet
μ = coefficient of heat transfer by evaporation containing constants for vaporization, air motion and direction, Btu/sq.ft-hr-in. Hg vapor pressure difference
A = total body area (DuBois Formula), sq ft
P_S = saturated vapor pressure at skin temperature, in. Hg
RH = relative humidity, per cent
P_A = saturated vapor pressure at air temperature, in. Hg.

From Eq. (3), it is seen that when the quantity $(RH \times P_A)$ is equal to the vapor pressure of the skin, P_S, then $E = 0$.

Below an air temperature of 88°F (31°C) for nude men and 84°F (29°C) for clothed men the value of E is essentially constant for a given individual, activity and air motion.[10] This would indicate a minimum value of $W\mu$ which is based on the permeability of the skin to moisture coming from beneath the skin. However, in the absence of sweating it has been found[11] that non-fasting men, lightly clad in union suits, showed a greater evaporative heat loss at 30 per cent RH than at 80 per cent RH for air temperatures of 72, 76 and 80°F.

The evaporative heat loss resulting from moisture evaporated in the respiratory system varies with the inspired volume of air (respiration rate and lung capacity) and its water vapor content. The expired air will be saturated at 90 to 95°F. A man at rest will lose approximately 16 grams of water per hour by this method.

Increased activity resulting in an increased metabolic rate will lower the threshold temperatures for sweating. With the production of sensible perspiration, the skin becomes wetted. By this means the body can maintain its thermal balance with $\Delta S = 0$ until E reaches a maximum rate. This is the zone of evaporative regulation.

Extensive studies by Winslow, Herrington and Gagge at the John B. Pierce Laboratory in the 1930's resulted in better understanding of the physiological responses of the body to the thermal environment. Using the body heat balance equation [Eq. (1)], the operative temperature[12] was defined as a measure of the net thermal effect of radiative and convective heat transfer. It therefore included effects of dry-bulb temperature, air motion, mean radiant temperature and mean skin or body surface temperature. Effects of humidity were not included. When the air movement is less than 30 fpm, the operative temperature is approximately equal to the mean of the dry-bulb temperature and the mean radiant temperature. If the MRT is approximately equal to the dry-bulb temperature, then the air temperature approximates the operative temperature.

Using the operative temperature as a variable, the group at the Pierce Laboratory also defined a zone of evaporative regulation, a zone of vasomotor regulation, and a zone of body cooling.[10] Figure 1 is adapted from their 1938 data for clothed subjects. Thermal comfort exists when the body is in the zone of vasomotor regulation.

In the zone of evaporative cooling, sweat glands wet the skin with water which increases the evaporative heat loss (sensible perspiration). This heat loss (E) balances the decreased radiative and convective heat loss ($R + C$) such that the stored energy term (ΔS) is zero (indicating negligible change in body temperature). There is an upper limit which is dependent on the maximum sweat rate of an individual.

In the zone of body cooling, the radiation and convection components increase as the evaporative heat loss remains approximately constant. As a result, the body temperature and stored energy decrease. At a body temperature of approximately 93 to 94°F, shivering is initiated which increases the metabolism in an attempt to balance Eq. (1) and arrest the lowering of body temperature.

In the zone of vasomotor regulation, the evaporation is essentially constant. The vasomotor system controls the blood flow to the skin thereby increasing or decreasing the skin surface temperature which results in increased or decreased radiative and convective heat losses, balancing Eq. (1) with $\Delta S = 0$.

Efforts to establish or specify conditions

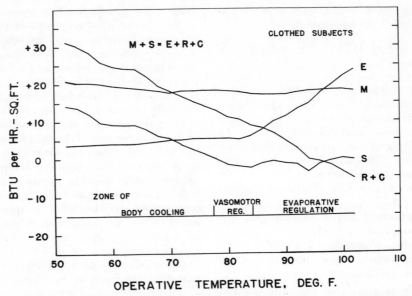

FIG. 1. Evaporation (*E*), radiation and convection (*R* + *C*), metabolism
(M) and storage (S) for clothed subjects.(Adapted from Ref. 10).

which would provide a comfortable environment began during the period 1913 to 1923. During this period, Professor John Sheppard at Teachers' Normal College in Chicago is reported to have introduced the term "comfort zone";[13] the New York State Commission on Ventilation was appointed and began their numerous experiments, which resulted in a report published in 1923;[14] and the American Society of Heating and Ventilating Engineers published the first work of Houghten and Yaglou[15] which established "lines of equal comfort," defined "effective temperature" and determined a "comfort zone."

These latter experiments were conducted under dynamic conditions with the subjects walking from one controlled room (air temperature and humidity) to another. The conditions in the second room were adjusted until the relatively instantaneous reaction of the subjects gave identical comfort sensations or "equal warmth." These results were plotted on a psychrometric chart and were known first as lines of equal warmth. The effective temperature (ET) is defined as "an arbitrary index" which combines into a single value the effect of dry-bulb temperature, humidity and air motion on the sensation of warmth or cold felt by the human body. The numerical value is

that of the temperature of still, saturated air which would induce an identical sensation.[7]

The "comfort zone" and a "comfort line" were determined from a group of tests involving 130 subjects of both sexes, wearing different types of clothing and representing several different occupations. The subjects were seated in comfortable chairs and engaged in light activities such as card playing, reading and writing. Subjective reactions to the environments were obtained by asking

(1) Is this condition comfortable or uncomfortable?

(2) Do you desire a change?

(3) If so, do you prefer warmer or cooler?

Twelve subjects were exposed to the test conditions for 3 hours; 14 subjects for 2 hours; and 100 subjects for 15 minutes or somewhat longer. The comfort zone was defined as including those effective temperatures over which 50 per cent of the people are comfortable. On this basis, the zone limits were found to be 62 and 69°F ET with a comfort line of 64°F ET. Figure 2 is a reproduction of the first comfort chart as it appeared in the introductory material of the *Transactions of ASHVE* published in 1924.

The collection of physiological data needed for a basic understanding of the man-environment process was not neglected by the ASHVE workers. In 1929, Houghten, Teague, Miller and Yant[16] published results showing the heat and moisture losses from the human body as a function of the effective temperature and air motion. These data were similar to the Pierce Laboratory data published in 1938 (Fig. 1), except for the evaporative heat loss curve. For clothed subjects, the ASHVE data showed a minimal and constant evaporative heat loss below 75°F, as compared with 84°F, and showed a greater evaporative heat loss between temperatures of 73 to 97°F.

Modification of the comfort chart resulted from work published in 1929 by Yaglou and Drinker.[17] Their experiments were carried out at the Harvard School of Public Health to determine effects of summer climate on the comfort zone. Some 91 subjects were used (56 men and 35 women) with no restriction in regard to clothing. Most of the men wore two-piece palm beach or light woolen suits. The

women wore silk, linen or cotton dresses. The subjective reactions were obtained using a 5-point scale: (1) cold, (2) comfortably cool, (3) very comfortable, (4) comfortably warm, and (5) too warm. Test periods of 3 hours were used with a pre-test time of approximately one hour.

The summer comfort zone was found to be between 64 and 69°F ET. This zone included all votes indicating comfort, not just 50 per cent or more. Results of similar experiments established a winter zone between 60 and 74°F ET. The comfort lines were respectively 71 and 66°F. It is interesting to note that English people were reported at that time to prefer temperatures 8°F lower than those preferred by Americans. Also contained in this paper was considerable discussion of the relation of climate and season to the type of under-clothing worn by Americans.

The Comfort Chart (Fig. 3) as it appears in the 1961 ASHRAE Guide and Data Book is

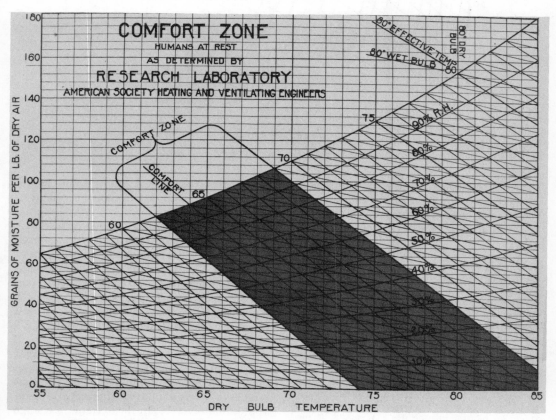

FIG. 2. Original ASHVE comfort chart. [Reprinted from *Trans. ASHVE*, 30 (1924)].

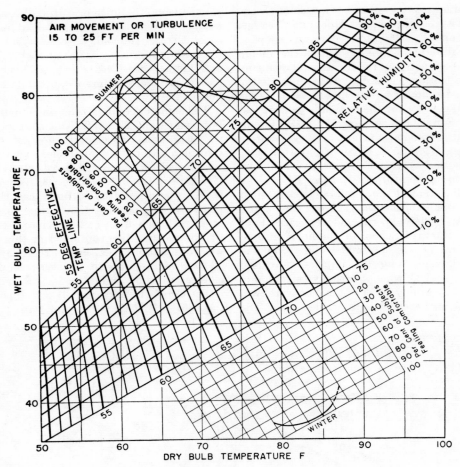

FIG. 3. ASHRAE comfort chart for still air.[7]

basically the same as the chart published in 1925. However, in light of research since that time a note has been added which defines its application.

"Both summer and winter comfort lines apply to inhabitants of the United States only. Application of winter comfort line is further limited to rooms heated by central systems of the convection type. The line does not apply to rooms heated by radiant methods. Application of summer comfort line is limited to homes, offices and the like, where the occupants become fully adapted to the artificial air conditions. The line does not apply to theaters, department stores, and the like where the exposure is less than three hours. The summer comfort line shown pertains to Pittsburgh and to other cities in the northern portion of the United States and Southern Canada, and at elevations not in excess of 1000 ft above sea level. An increase of one deg ET should be made approximately per 5-deg reduction in north latitude."

The areas indicating summer and winter comfort zones have been removed in light of field experience, careful analysis of the original data and laboratory experiments since 1940. Also the winter comfort data from the research prior to 1932 were eliminated and the data of Houghten, Gunst and Suciu[18] have been substituted. These data indicate an optimum condition of 68 ET in place of the 66 ET reported earlier. However, these data cover a range of effective temperature of only 4 ET (65 to 69 ET).

Examination of this chart indicates that along a constant effective temperature line an increase in relative humidity of 20 per cent requires a decrease in dry-bulb temperature of approximately 2°F. (In the extreme, a change from 30 to 70 per cent RH at 68 ET requires a change in dry-bulb from 75 to 70.5°F.) Since 1938, evidence from various sources[19, 20] has indicated that in the zone of thermal neutrality* the effective temperature index overemphasizes the effect of relative humidity on comfort.

In 1947, Yaglou,[21] one of the original ASHVE investigators, proposed that the overemphasis resulted from the use of instantaneous thermal impressions and the resulting adsorption and desorption phenomena, that is, the heat of adsorption giving a sense of warmth as moisture was adsorbed on skin and clothing. Likewise, there was a cooling effect when the moisture evaporated. To correct the effective temperature index, it was proposed

* Zone of vasomotor regulation: heat production equal to the net heat loss by convection, radiation and evaporation with no change in stored energy and without sweating or shivering.

that lines of constant mean skin temperature replace the ET lines. Lines of constant mean skin temperature in relation to effective temperature are shown in Fig. 4. Subjects normally dressed for a given dry-bulb temperature in a range of 30 to 82°F were found to be comfortable when their mean skin temperature averaged between 91 and 93°F, provided subjects were not sweating. Skin temperature as a comfort index fails when subjects are more than slightly active or are sweating.

Current laboratory and field data indicate that in the range of dry-bulb temperatures of 73 to 77°F, variations in relative humidity from 20 to 60 per cent do not affect comfort sensations for sedentary or slightly active healthy men and women normally clothed in uniform environments.[22] Research by Glickman and others[23] using 15 subjects exposed to

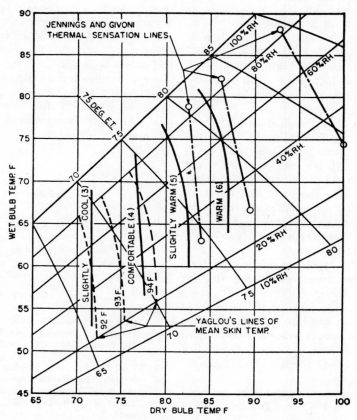

FIG. 4. Thermal sensations for clothed subjects at rest (1960 data) compared with effective temperatures, and lines of constant mean skin temperature.

two levels of relative humidity (30 and 80 per cent RH) found that the effective temperature index appeared to be adequate for subjects in the dynamic state, but for equilibrium conditions the effective temperature index placed too much emphasis on relative humidity. Measurements in these tests included physiological as well as subjective reactions.

In 1960, Koch, Jennings and Humphreys,[24] using the environmental research facilities at the ASHRAE laboratory in Cleveland, conducted a series of experiments using 20 subjects wearing light, indoor clothing and seated at rest. These subjects were exposed for periods of three hours to dry-bulb temperatures of 68 to 94°F with relative humidities from 20 to 90 per cent. Room surface temperatures were held at the same temperature as the room air and the air motion was 20 fpm or less. The results are reproduced in Fig. 4.

The curves show the conditions under which the test subjects indicated sensations of "slightly cool" (3), "comfortable" (4), "slightly warm" (5) and "warm" (6). It may be seen in Fig. 4 that line (3) is vertical indicating that at this temperature level, relative humidity has no effect on sensation of comfort. Line (4) at a comfortable level, is shown as nearly vertical.

Examination of the original data given in Ref. 24 shows that line (4) could be plotted vertically for relative humidities of 30 to 70 per cent. Above 70 per cent, the line would curve slightly to the left (toward a lower dry-bulb temperature). Even so, the effect of relative humidity is small such that the optimum comfort line for these subjects extends from 77.6°F at 30 per cent RH to 76.5°F at 85 per cent RH.

Lines (5) and (6) indicate definite effects of humidity on the thermal sensations, with the greatest effects occurring at the higher values of relative humidity. As conditions become warmer and the control of body temperature becomes increasingly dependent upon evaporative heat loss, the relative humidity would be expected to become an increasingly important factor.

Fig. 4 also indicates agreement between lines (3), (4), (5) and (6), and Yaglou's lines of mean skin temperature as well as the laboratory studies of Jennings and Bivoni.[25]

The thermal sensation lines of Fig. 4 show considerably less effect of relative humidity on comfort than do the effective temperature lines of Fig. 3 (also shown in Fig. 4). Neither set of lines is in error, but each applies to different conditions. The effective temperature lines indicate a subjective reaction immediately after entering a conditioned space, while curves (3), (4), (5) and (6) indicate reactions to conditioned spaces when the exposure time is approximately three hours or longer.

When sedentary or slightly active people are exposed to dry-bulb temperatures in the range of 73 to 78°F, the effect of humidity on their comfort and well-being has been found to be negligible over a range of humidities of 25 to 70 per cent. As the dry-bulb temperature increases above 78°F, humidity effects become very important as evaporation becomes the major avenue of heat loss. Increased activity (metabolism) produces a similar reaction. Below 73°F, evaporation is minimal and constant, and for clothed subjects it is essentially independent of air temperature and relative humidity. The air conditioning industry has grown out of the concern of man for his comfort and feeling of well-being and has become a major segment of industrial America. The 1911 dreams of Willis Carrier and others have been realized, and the control of humidity for comfort is now an everyday occurrence.

References

1. Carrier, W. H., "Rational Psychrometric Formulae," *Trans. ASME*, **33**, 1005 (1911).
2. Bernan, Walter, "History and Art of Warming and Ventilating Rooms and Buildings," London, 1845.
3. Hermans, J. T. F., "Veber die vermeintliche Ausathmung organischer Substanzen durch den Manschen," *Archiv für Hygiene*, **1**, 1 (1883).
4. Flugge, C., "Veber Luftverunreinigung, Wormestauung and Luftung in geschlossenen Raumen," *Zeitschrift für Hygiene*, **49**, 363; Heymann, 388; Paul, 405; Erckleutz, 433 (1905).
5. Wiley, F. H., and Newburgh, L. H., "The Relationship Between the Environment and the Basal Insensible Loss of Weight," *J. Clin. Invest.*, **10**, 689–701 (1931).
6. Bazett, H. C., "The Regulation of Body Temperatures," in Newburgh, L.H., "Physiology of Heat Regulation," p. 116, Philadelphia, W. B. Saunders Co., 1949.

7. ASHRAE Guide and Data Book 1961, Fundamentals and Equipment, pp. 482 and 852, ASHRAE, 1961.

8. Hardy, J. D., "Heat Transfer," in Newburgh, L. H., "Physiology of Heat Regulation," p. 104, Philadelphia, W. B. Saunders Co., 1949.

9. Gagge, A. P., "A New Physiological Variable Associated with Sensible and Insensible Perspiration," *Am. J. Physiol.*, **120**, 277–287 (1937).

10. Gagge, A. P., Winslow, C.-E. A., and Herrington, L. P., "The Influence of Clothing on the Physiological Reactions of the Human Body to Varying Environmental Temperatures." *Am. J. Physiol.*, **124**, 30–50 (1938).

11. Inouye, T., Hick, F. K., Tesler, S. E., and Keeton, R. W., "Effect of Relative Humidity on Heat Loss of Men Exposed to Environments of 80, 76 and 72°F," *Trans. ASHVE*, **59**, 329 (1953).

12. Winslow, C.-E. A., Herrington, L. P., and Gagge, A. P., "Physiological Reactions of the Human Body to Varying Environment Temperatures," *Am. J. Physiol.*, **120**, 1–22 (1937).

13. Hill, E. Vernon, discussion to "Determination of the Comfort Zone" by F. C. Houghten and C. P. Yaglou, *Trans. ASHVE*, **29**, 361 (1923).

14. Report of the New York State Commission on Ventilation, New York, E. P. Dutton and Co., 1923.

15. Houghten, F. C., and Yaglou, C. P., "Determining Lines of Equal Comfort," and "Determination of the Comfort Zone," *Trans. ASHVE*, **29**, 163, 361 (1923).

16. Houghten, F. C., Teague, W. W., Miller, W. E., and Yant, W. P., "Heat and Moisture Losses from the Human Body and Their Relation to Air Conditioning Problems," *Trans. ASHVE*, **35**, 245 (1929).

17. Yaglou, C. P., and Drinker, P., "The Summer Comfort Zone: Climate and Clothing," *Trans. ASHVE*, **35**, 269 (1929).

18. Houghten, F. C., Gunst, S. B., and Suciu, J., "Radiation as a Factor in Sensation of Warmth," *Trans. ASHVE*, **47**, 93 (1941).

19. Rowley, F. B., Jordan, R. C., and Snyder, W. E., "Comfort Reactions of Workers During Occupancy of Air Conditioned Offices," *Trans. ASHVE*, **53**, 357 (1947).

20. Yaglou, C. P., "Indices of Comfort," in Newburgh, L. H., "Physiology of Heat Regulation," pp. 277–287, Philadelphia, W. B. Saunders Co., 1949.

21. Yaglou, C. P., "A Method for Improving the Effective Temperature Index," *Trans. ASHVE*, **53**, 307 (1947).

22. Fahnestock, M. K., and Werden, J. E., "Environment, Comfort, Health and People," *Refrig. Eng.* (February 1956).

23. Glickman, N., Inouye, T., Keeton, R. W., and Fahnestock, M. K., "Physiological Examination of the Effective Temperature Index," *Trans. ASHVE*, **56**, 51 (1950).

24. Koch, W., Jennings, B. H., and Humphreys, C. M., "Environmental Study II—Sensation Responses to Temperature and Humidity Under Still Air Conditions in the Comfort Range," *Trans. ASHRAE*, **66**, 264 (1960).

25. Jennings, B. H., and Givoni, B., "Environment Reactions in the 80F to 105°F Zone," *Trans. ASHRAE*, **65**, 115 (1959).

2. The Role of Humidity in the Evaluation of the Stress Imposed on Men Working in Hot Environments

Paul E. Smith, Jr. and Lucien Brouha

Haskell Laboratory, E. I. du Pont de Nemours & Company, Wilmington, Delaware

ABSTRACT

Heart rate has proved to be a useful measure of the stress imposed on men working in hot environments. When the total number of heart beats for a given period, including work and recovery (cardiac cost), is plotted against the enthalpy of the environment in which the work was performed, a set of linear relations is disclosed—parallel to each other and humidity dependent. When the data are corrected for the radiant heat load, the points fall on a single straight line. Consequently, it is possible to assess the relative importance of the three means of heat loss from the body, i.e., convective, evaporative and radiant. The data presented cover a variety of work levels and environments. They indicate that evaporation, which is humidity dependent, is the most effective means of heat loss.

The use of heart rate as an indicator of thermal stress in workers has been documented by Brouha and his associates.[1,2] Their findings are summarized in Fig. 1.

Time, plotted on the abscissa, indicates that the observation period is divided into two portions: 34 minutes of exercise followed by 65 minutes of recovery. Exercise was by means of a bicycle ergometer at a rate of 540 kilogram-meters per minute (kg-m/min.) for 30 minutes, followed by a 4-minute period at 900 kg-m/min.

Values plotted against the ordinates are averages for the six male subjects who parti-

cipated. These indicate the level of oxygen consumption in liters per minute and heart rate in beats per minute. Data are shown for the same work levels in two different environments: 25°C and 43 per cent RH and 33°C and 82 per cent RH.

We wish to emphasize the fact that the levels of oxygen consumption are essentially the same in both environments and that complete recovery for this function is achieved in 25 minutes following exercise. In contrast, heart rate levels differ markedly, and recovery is incomplete at the end of the observation period. To correlate these heart rate differences with stress-producing factors, it is convenient to integrate the heart rate curves. This integral is referred to as the "cardiac cost." Cardiac cost may be subdivided into work cost and recovery cost. The latter should not be neglected and is usually the clearest indicator of accumulated strain resulting from work in a stressing environment.

Major stress-producing factors in a normal industrial environment include work level, dry-bulb temperature and humidity. The effects of varying these separately are displayed in Fig. 2. Here the exercise consisted of walking for 15 minutes on a treadmill at 3.2 miles per hour. In the first panel are displayed the effect on heart rate when the mill slope is varied from 0 to 5 and 10 per cent with the dry-bulb and relative humidity held constant. Successive panels show the effects when only the dry-bulb is varied and when only the relative humidity is varied. In each case, the

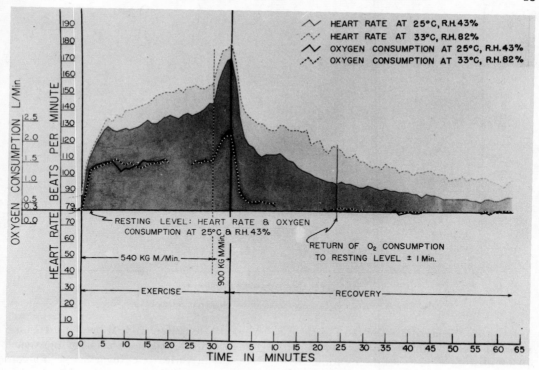

Fig. 1. Physiological responses to heat.

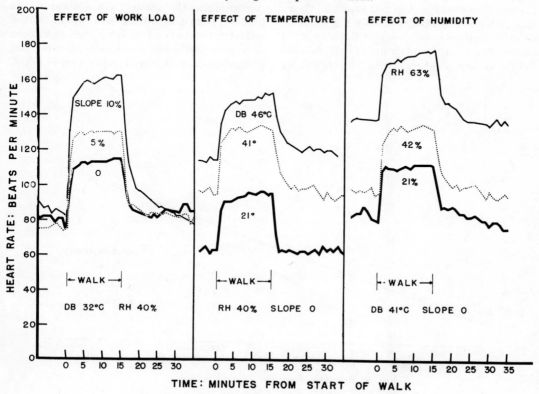

Fig. 2. Heart rate response to various conditions.

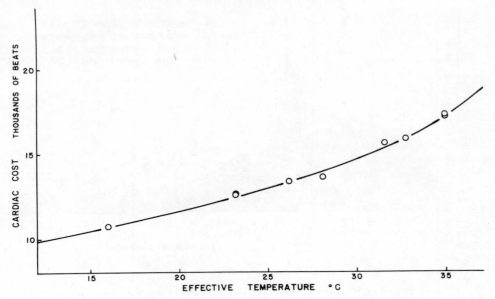

FIG. 3. Relation of cardiac cost to effective temperature.

heart rates displayed are for the fourth of a series of four 15-minute walks separated by 20 minutes of rest in the same environment.

In order to achieve predictive power with information developed in tests such as these, it is useful to plot cardiac cost for a given level of work against some function descriptive of the environment. A widely used function is the "effective temperature" scale developed by Yaglou, Houghten and Miller.[3, 4, 5] Its usefulness in work situations has been questioned by many investigators. Nevertheless, it is convenient to use and, in many cases, informative. Accordingly, the cardiac costs observed on four subjects performing four walks as described in a variety of environments have been averaged for each environment and are plotted against effective temperature in Fig. 3.

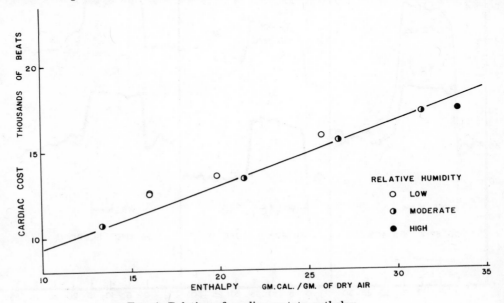

FIG. 4. Relation of cardiac cost to enthalpy.

The resulting curve is exponential in nature, increasing in steepness at high values of effective temperature.

The effective temperature scale is based on the subjective judgments of a large number of individuals concerning the equivalence of two different environments. It is desirable to relate physiological responses to measurable physical properties of the environment. To do this, the following rationale has been followed.

Heat exchange between an individual and the environment is through convection, evaporation and radiation. The first two of these are directly a function of the enthalpy of the environment. Enthalpy may be defined as the heat content of the atmosphere. The units are g cal/g of dry air. It is one of the co-ordinates from which a psychometric chart may be constructed.[6] For this purpose, its base is taken at 0°F for dry air and at the freezing point for the water vapor content of the air-vapor mixture.

If one considers a thin layer of air in contact with the skin to be saturated at skin temperature, then an enthalpy gradient will exist between this layer and the environment. Heat exchange by convection and evaporation will be controlled in part by this gradient.

To test this hypothesis the data of Fig. 3 have been replotted against enthalpy. The result is shown in Fig. 4. The straight line has been fitted by eye to the half solid circles which are the data points for environments having a moderate relative humidity, ranging from 40 to 50 per cent. The low humidity points represented by open circles fall to the left of this line; the single high humidity point is to the right.

Lines of constant enthalpy are approximately parallel to the wet-bulb temperature lines of a psychometric chart. As one moves along such a line from high to low relative humidity, the dry-bulb temperature increases. In the experiments quoted, wall temperatures were the same as dry-bulb temperature. Hence, in these experiments a shift from high to low relative humidity means an increase in the effect to be expected from the radiant component of the heat load.

The magnitude of this effect may be estimated from the following considerations. Radiant heat exchange between objects is a function of the difference between the fourth powers of their absolute temperatures. For a narrow range of values, this may be approximated by the first power difference.[7] Within the limits of this approximation, therefore, the radiant temperature of the environment

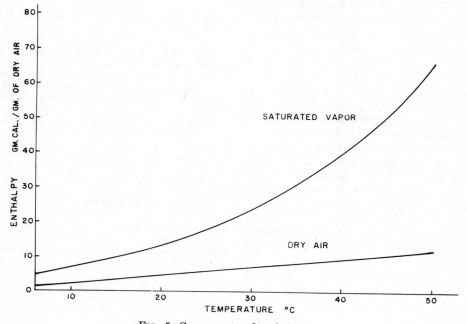

FIG. 5. Components of enthalpy.

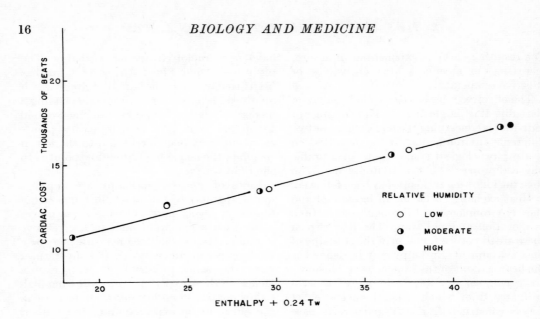

F_{IG}. 6. Relation of cardiac cost to enthalpy corrected for radiant heat.

may be expected to contribute an effect equal in magnitude to that produced by the dry-bulb temperature.

The components which make up enthalpy are shown in Fig. 5. The straight line is a function of the specific heat of dry air. Hence the enthalpy is equal to 0.24 times the temperature. The curve for saturated vapor is a function of both the specific and latent heats of the vapor. Since there is no component of latency in radiant heat, its effect may be taken as equal to that of dry air. Accordingly, a factor equal to 0.24 times the wall temperature has been added to the enthalpy, and the results have been plotted in Fig. 6.

We do not have sufficient data to extend this relationship to levels of higher metabolic work. The data we have suggest a family of parallel lines. Nor have we as yet studied the effect of varying wind velocities. We have examined the relationship between final heart rates and enthalpy. The resulting plots display curvature resembling Fig. 3. This suggests that the linearity displayed in Fig. 6 results from integrating the total effects of the environment.

Reconsideration of Fig. 5 leads to a proper

appreciation of the role of humidity as a factor in assessing thermal stress. Whereas the effects of dry bulb and radiant temperatures are linear, the humidity effect is essentially logarithmic and predominates at higher temperatures.

References

1. Brouha, L., Smith, P. E., Jr., De Lanne, R., and Maxfield, M., "Physiological Reactions of Men and Women During Muscular Activity and Recovery in Various Environments," *J. Appl. Physiol.*, **16** (1), 133 (1960).
2. Brouha, Lucien, and Maxfield, Mary E., "Practical Evaluation of Strain in Muscular Work and Heat Exposure by Heart Rate Recovery Curves," *Ergonomics*, **5**, 87 (January 1962).
3. Houghten, F. C., and Yaglou, C. P., "Determining Equal 'Comfort' Lines," *Trans. ASHVE*, **29**, 163 (1923).
4. Houghten, F. C., and Yaglou, C. P., "Cooling Effect on Human Beings Produced by Various Air Velocities," *Trans. ASHVE*, **30**, 193 (1924).
5. Yaglou, C. P., and Miller, W. E., "Effective Temperature with Clothing," *Trans. ASHVE*, **31**, 89 (1925).
6. "Heating, Ventilating, Air Conditioning Guide," p. 51, 1958.
7. Hutchinson, F. W., "Industrial Heat Transfer," pp. 56, 57, New York, The Industrial Press, 1952.

3. A New Method for Completely Describing Man's Thermal Environment

A. H. Woodcock* and J. R. Breckenridge

U.S. Army Research Institute of Environmental Medicine, Natick, Massachusetts

ABSTRACT

Physical principles of heat and moisture exchange are used to show that the globe thermometer satisfactorily predicts the energy exchange between man and his environment. Such a globe correctly combines effects of air temperature, temperature of the surroundings, and solar radiation if the globe is painted the correct shade of gray. From this analysis, a method is proposed whereby three globes are used to predict the range of heat losses possible in a given environment within which man may adjust his heat loss to match his metabolic heat production. The minimal heat loss, when the man is not sweating, is determined using two globes, one electrically heated, to indicate both temperature and effect of wind. The maximal heat loss, with the skin wet with sweat and being cooled by evaporation, is determined by also including a globe with a wetted surface. Nomograms are provided for determining these limits on heat loss from readings on the globes.

There have been many indices proposed to assess environments. The earliest of these, temperature, is probably based on the correlation between how warm man feels and the position of the mercury in an ordinary mercury-in-glass thermometer. Since then many instruments have been suggested; the wet-bulb thermometer, the kata-thermometer, the globe thermometer, the thermo-integrator of the Pierce Laboratories, the frigorimeter of Morikofer and many others.

* Deceased.

Relationships between the readings of instruments, or between combinations of such instruments, and heat stress in man have been many. There are the Effective Temperature, the Predicted Four-Hour Sweat Rate, Index of Physiological Effect, Heat Stress Index, Humiture Index, and Wet-Bulb-Globe Temperature Index. Some of these are purely empirical, some theoretical and some a combination of the two.

In making any assessment of these indices it is necessary to distinguish between subjective factors, such as comfort, and purely thermal factors. Thermal factors, which will be discussed here, are related essentially only to the ability of the environment to remove heat from the human skin, which is purely a physical problem. Comfort or feeling is a subjective state which is ill-defined and probably involves factors other than purely thermal ones. For example, clamminess contributes to discomfort but may be due mainly to the unpleasant feeling of sweat-moistened clothing clinging to the skin. This is a frictional effect involving adhesion and surface tension, which are not directly related to thermal exchange.

This paper will attempt to show, from a discussion of the basic equations of heat transfer, how the thermal environment as it relates to man can be described. A new method will be proposed for estimating the heat absorbing capabilities of the environment, expressed as a heat loss range over which man can accommodate himself through physiological adjustment of skin temperature and sweat rate. In the development, the various mechanisms of heat transfer will be discussed to provide the reader with a clear picture of the interplay between the factors involved.

In its simplest form, convective heat loss from a surface such as man's skin is given by the equation

$$H_a = B\sqrt{V}(t_s - t_a) \tag{1}$$

where

H_a = the rate of heat loss, kcal/m²hr
B = a constant depending on shape and size
V = the air speed, ft/min
t_s = the surface temperature, °C
t_a = the air temperature, °C.

In this equation heat flow is given by the product of a conductance term $B\sqrt{V}$ and a potential or temperature difference $(t_s - t_a)$.

If to this simple equation an expression for long-wave radiation is added, the equation becomes

$$H = A(T_s^4 - T_r^4) + B\sqrt{V}(t_s - t_a) \tag{2}$$

where

T_s = the surface temperature, degrees Kelvin
T_r = the mean radiant temperature, degrees Kelvin
A = the coefficient of radiant heat exchange.

In this equation, there are two environmental temperatures, namely, mean radiant temperature and air temperature.

The globe thermometer proposed by Vernon has been used with considerable success to estimate a single equivalent environmental temperature for men in indoor situations where mean radiant temperature differed from air temperature. This device is a 6-in. diameter hollow copper sphere painted dull black, with a thermometer bulb located at its center. In essence, it is a thermometer with a 6-in. black spherical bulb for which the equation of heat exchange with the environment is

$$0 = A'(T_g^4 - T_r^4) + B'\sqrt{V}(t_g - t_a) \tag{3}$$

where

T_g and t_g = globe temperatures, degrees Kelvin and Celsius, respectively

A' = its coefficient of radiation exchange
B' = its coefficient of convective exchange.

It should be noted that A' will not generally have the same value as A, the coefficient for man, nor will B' be the same as B since the globe has a different size and shape than the man.

If however

$$\frac{A}{A'} = \frac{B}{B'} \tag{4}$$

then the equation for the globe thermometer can be multiplied by A/A' giving

$$0 = A(T_g^4 - T_r^4) + B\sqrt{V}(t_g - t_a) \tag{5}$$

Subtracting this from the equation for man's heat exchange gives

$$H = A(T_s^4 - T_g^4) + B\sqrt{V}(t_s - t_g) \tag{6}$$

in which the mean radiant temperature t_r (or T_r) and air temperature t_a have been replaced by the single globe temperature t_g.

It is again stressed that the substitution is valid only if the ratio of radiative coefficients is equal to that for the convective coefficients. That this is approximately so may be seen from Table 1, which compares values of A and B for man from the physiological literature with the values of A' and B' for the standard 6-in. globe.

TABLE 1. COEFFICIENTS OF HEAT LOSS

Investigator	Radiation ($A \times 10^8$)	Convection (B)
Winslow *et al.*	3.46	0.743
Nelson *et al.*	4.50	0.53
Burton	3.22	0.793
Newling (copper man)	3.06 (erect)	0.61
Bohnenkamp and Ernst	4.14	
Guibert and Taylor	3.75	
Average	3.688	0.669
Globe	4.634	0.825
Ratio (average/globe)	0.796	0.811

From this Table it will be seen that the values for man vary somewhat. However, the averages divided by globe thermometer coefficients give ratios of A/A' and B/B' which agree within 2 per cent. This then is the reason why the globe thermometer should work so well as an index of temperature in indoor environments.

It was natural that investigators, having had success indoors, should attempt to use the globe thermometer outdoors. However, it has been found that the globe thermometer gave high readings in the presence of sunlight. It was apparent then that the black globe thermometer absorbed too much sunlight. The wet-bulb-globe temperature index is calculated using 70 per cent wet-bulb temperature, 20 per cent globe temperature and 10 per cent air temperature, the latter presumably added to correct for the high effect of sunlight.

The heat exchange for man including sunlight is given by

$$H = A(T_s^4 - T_r^4) + B\sqrt{V}(t_s - t_a) + Y \quad (7)$$

where Y is the heat absorbed from sunlight. For the globe thermometer, the equation is

$$0 = A'(T_g^4 - T_r^4) + B'\sqrt{V}(t_g - t_a) + Y' \quad (8)$$

where Y' is the sunlight absorbed by the globe. The condition for the globe thermometer to be an accurate index in an outdoor environment is then

$$\frac{A}{A'} = \frac{B}{B'} = \frac{Y}{Y'} \quad (9)$$

If this relationship holds then the equation

$$H = A(T_s^4 - T_g^4) + B\sqrt{V}(t_s - t_g) \quad (10)$$

holds in sunlight as well as indoors.

Since paints of different colors absorb different percentages of sunlight or short-wave radiation but are all black to long-wave radiation, Y' can be adjusted to a suitable value by painting the globe an appropriate shade of gray. From measurements of man's shadow area normal to sunlight relative to his total surface area and the absorption coefficient for white human skin, a value of Y could be estimated and the required value of Y'

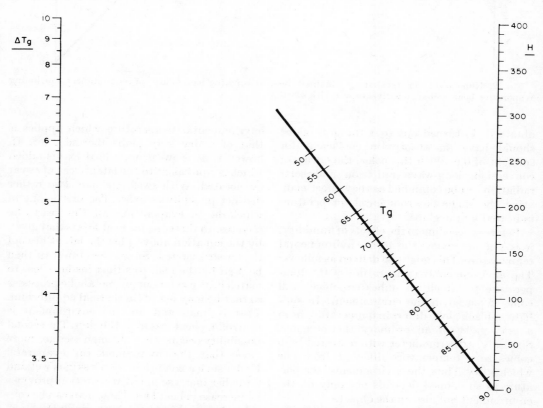

Fig. 1. Nomogram for estimating minimal, or non-sweating, heat dissipating capability of environment; based on input to heated globe of 4 watts.

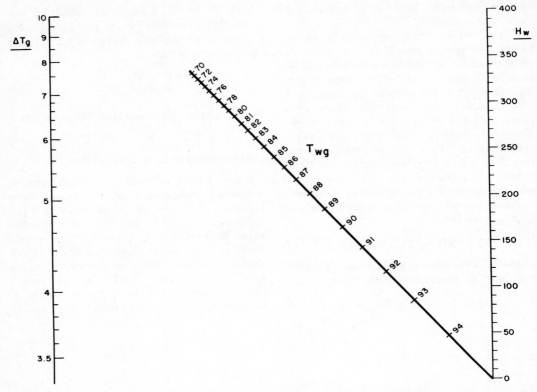

Fig. 2. Nomogram for estimating maximal heat dissipating capability of environment, including evaporative heat exchange with skin wet with sweat.

obtained. It turned out that the gray globe should have an absorption coefficient for sunlight of 0.6. With this color, the effects of convection, long-wave radiation and solar radiation can be combined as they affect man, using the single environmental temperature indicated by the globe.

Before proceeding to the effects of humidity, it is well to review the term environmental temperature. This might be defined as follows: The environmental temperature is the temperature to which an unheated object will come if placed in the environment. In sunlight, a black globe differs in temperature from a gray globe or an ordinary thermometer. Similarly, a thermometer with a wetted bulb comes to a temperature different from one which is dry. Thus, the environmental temperature as so defined depends not only on the environment but also on the object.

Man unfortunately is a varying object by this definition. If he is not sweating then the environmental temperature which applies is that of a dry gray globe thermometer. If, however, he is sweating, a heat loss is added which is equivalent to the latent heat of sweat evaporated. With sweating man, two rather distinct possibilities exist. The first is one in which he is evaporating all the sweat he secretes. In this case, his heat loss is that given by the equation above plus the latent heat of the sweat secreted. Sweat secretion can then be used by the man to adjust his heat loss to match heat production by metabolic processes so that he may maintain thermal equilibrium. That is, man and not his environment is controlling heat loss from the skin. The second possibility occurs when the man secretes more sweat than the environment can evaporate. Under such a condition, man's skin is wet and a further increase in sweat secretion provides no increase in heat loss. Thus, man can be considered as an object having a variable heat loss. The minimum occurs when he is not sweating and the maximum when his skin is wet with sweat. The environment can then be characterized only by the range of heat losses it allows.

For the maximum the equation is

$$H = A(T_s^4 - T_r^4) + B\sqrt{V}(t_s - t_a) + Y \\ + SB\sqrt{V}(P_s - P_a) \quad (11)$$

where

S = the hygrometric constant
P_s = the saturated vapor pressure of sweat at t_s, mm Hg
P_a = the vapor pressure of the air, mm Hg.

For a globe thermometer with a wet surface, the equation is

$$0 = A'(T_{wg}^4 - T_r^4) + B\sqrt{V}(t_{wg} - t_a) \\ + Y' + SB'\sqrt{V}(P_{wg} - P_a) \quad (12)$$

where the subscript wg refers to the wet-globe thermometer. Since $A/A' = B/B' = Y/Y'$

$$H = A(T_s^4 - T_{wg}^4) + B\sqrt{V}(t_s - t_{wg}) \\ + SB\sqrt{V}(P_s - P_{wg}) \quad (13)$$

In this equation, since P_{wg} is a function of t_{wg}, the temperature of the wetted globe characterizes the heat loss from man with a wet skin in the same way the temperature of the dry globe does for the man who is not sweating.

The heat exchange equation for the wet globe becomes similar to that for a wet-bulb thermometer as wind speed or V is increased. That is, the radiation terms $A'(T_{wg}^4 - T_r^4)$ and Y' remain constant while the convective and evaporative terms increase. Hence, the effects of radiation tend to become negligible and the equation approaches

$$0 = (t_{wg} - t_a) + S(P_{wg} - P_a) \quad (14)$$

Since wet-bulb lines on a graph of air vapor pressure plotted against temperature are approximately parallel straight lines, S is approximately a constant, 3.6°F/mm.

The equations for heat loss from man's skin cannot be solved unless the value of V is known. If two dry globe thermometers, one supplied with a known amount of heat, are

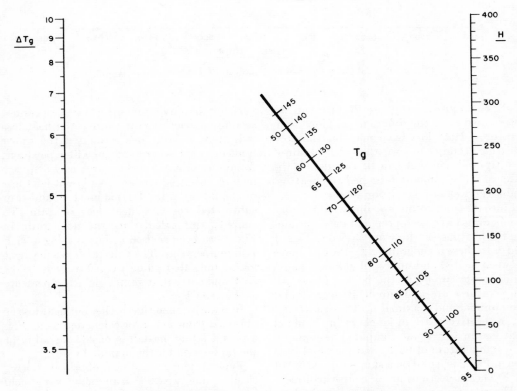

FIG. 3. Nomogram used with skin partially wetted to obtain non-evaporative component of heat loss. Add 333 kg-cal/m²hr to obtain maximal dissipation capability of environment.

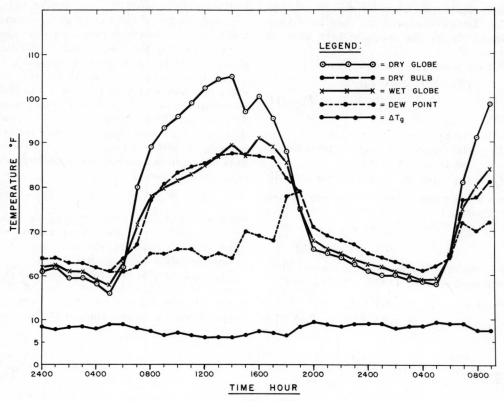

FIG. 4. Typical globe thermometer data during clear summer period.

used, the expression $(A + B\sqrt{V})$ can be determined from the difference in globe temperatures. Heat loss from man for the non-sweating condition can then be obtained directly and, since A can be calculated, the value of $B\sqrt{V}$ can be determined and heat loss under the wet skin condition found.

Since the calculations are somewhat tedious, nomograms have been prepared for determining the heat losses; these are shown in Figs. 1 and 2. In these nomograms ΔT_g, the difference between heated and unheated globes is based on a 4-watt supply to the heated globe. All temperatures are in Fahrenheit degrees and the minimal and maximal heat losses, H and H_w, respectively, are in kg-cal/m²hr. Minimal heat loss in Fig. 1 was computed assuming a skin temperature of 90°F, and maximal heat loss in Fig. 2 is based on a skin temperature of 95°F. These selections are of course arbitrary.

There is only one situation in which these limits on heat loss do not apply, namely in very hot dry environments where man cannot secrete sufficient sweat to give the heat loss indicated. Belding has estimated the upper limit of sweat secretion at one liter per hour. Assuming a man's surface area as 1.8 square meters, this is equivalent to a latent heat loss of 333 kg-cal/m²hr. To this must be added or subtracted the dry heat loss or gain. To simplify this calculation, the nomogram in Fig. 1 has been revised in Fig. 3 using a 95°F skin temperature. The value of H is a dry heat loss if unheated globe temperature is below 95°F and a dry heat gain if globe temperature is above 95°F.

In practice then the smaller net heat loss as obtained from Fig. 2, or calculated using Fig. 3 plus a latent heat loss of 333 kg-cal/m²hr should be used for the maximal value.

Typical globe readings obtained during clear summer weather in an uncultivated field in eastern Massachusetts are shown in Fig. 4. In this case, two dry globes supplied with 4 and

8 watts were used, and the true globe temperature was obtained by extrapolation. This was done to prevent dew formation during the night. These curves show the effect of an afternoon cloud at 1500 hours and the existence of radiational cooling at night.

It should be pointed out that this method of describing man's environment is different in that it suggests that because man can change his heat loss by secreting sweat, no single parameter of the environment will suffice to describe it. This concept of range in heat loss in any environment is too frequently overlooked, and it is hoped that the emphasis placed upon it here will help to correct this situation. The limits of heat loss are of course based on arbitrary choices of other parameters by the authors, but they seem reasonable. The other feature of the method which is not customary is that environment is defined in terms of its ability to absorb heat and not simply in terms of temperature, which is only one of the two fundamental variables in the equations. The other, air movement, is expressed as heat transfer coefficient $B\sqrt{V}$ rather than simply as a velocity since this is the way it affects man.

The complete system of measurement is undoubtedly complicated since it involves three globe thermometers, a heat supply, and a water source for the wetted globe. However, simplifications may be made in certain situations. For example, in a hot humid environment where wind is constant, it may need to be measured only once, and the use of the heated dry globe can be avoided. If simplification is desired, the analysis given above serves to indicate which factors will be over-emphasized or de-emphasized and the magnitude of error which is likely to result.

4. Production and Administration of Controlled Humidity in the Treatment of Obstructive Lung Disorders*

ROBERT DENTON, M.D.

Department of Pediatrics, School of Medicine, University of Pennsylvania

AND

JOSEPH M. ALLERDICE

E. I. duPont de Nemours & Company

This report describes one aspect of a biomedical engineering research project at the University of Pennsylvania in which engineers and physicians are working as a team to resolve some of the basic problems in the causative factors of human lung disorders. One important division of this project, which deals with treatment methods, offers an unusual challenge to engineers working in hygrometry. The problem is to produce a controlled atmosphere to be breathed by patients with obstructive lung disorders which will carry double the water content of room air at saturation. Loading room air or an air-oxygen mixture with such concentrations of water demands unusual and exacting applications of air conditioning. The rationale for the application of this specialized type of air conditioning is based on the peculiar internal architecture of the lungs and the physiological mechanisms for defense of the lungs which are active in protecting all of us from contamination by airborne infectious agents.

Protection of the lungs from such foreign materials is accomplished by series of barriers, starting at the nose, in the form of filters. Collection, transport and elimination of particulate matter both solid and liquid is the primary function of the film of mucus (Fig. 1) which covers the inner surface of the tubular conduction and distribution system, the respiratory tract. Continuous directional flow of the mucous blanket carries entangled bacteria, dust and other foreign material up from the smallest branching divisions centrally to the exit point at the entrance to the lungs, the larynx. Continuous regeneration of this moving filter is maintained by the secretion of mucus from millions of tiny glands in layers of the inner lining (Fig. 2). Flow of the mucous blanket at a rate of approximately 13 mm/min. results from the propulsive force of the rhythmic beating of countless millions of microscopic hairs, the cilia (Figs. 2 and 3) which protrude from the surface. The co-ordinated paddle-like motion of ciliary action maintains flow as a constant housecleaning which prevents contamination from the retention of a variety of infectious and toxic agents.

The great majority of lung diseases in both humans and animals are associated with interrupted flow of the mucous blanket and the resultant impaired drainage of the bronchial system. The retention of infectious or chemical agents forms sources of irritation

* Supported in part by Grant AM-03563 National Institute of Health, USPHS.

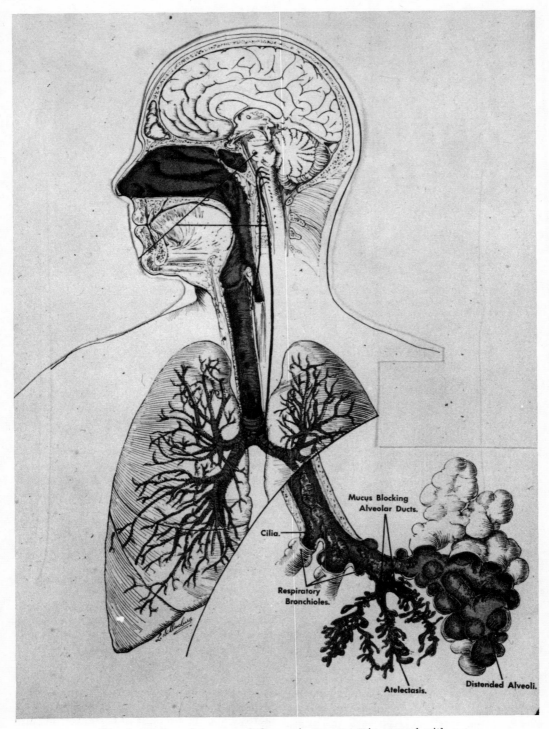

FIG. 1. Inner surface area of the respiratory tract is covered with a blanket of mucus.

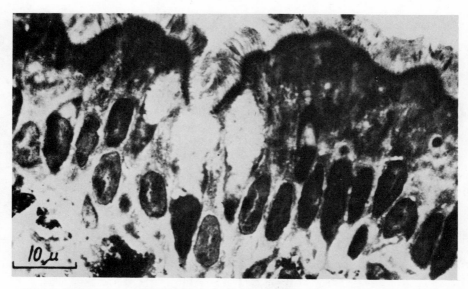

FIG. 2. Microscopic section of the inner lining of the respiratory tract. Note the three centrally located white areas, the goblet cells which secrete mucus and the hair-like cilia on the surface. (1110X)

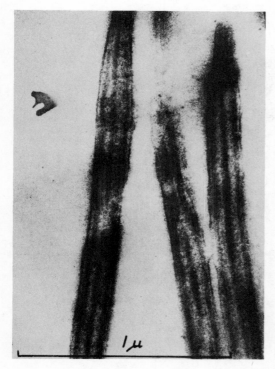

FIG. 3. Electron-microscopic study of individual cilia from lung of healthy rat. The paddle-like motion of cilia is the propulsive power to maintain the flow of mucus. (39,200X)

which cause increased production of mucus. In addition, this situation causes changes in the physical properties of mucus[2] in the direction of a greater flow resistance (Figs. 4 and 5). Progression of these changes in quality and quantity of mucus presents an overload for the propulsive force of ciliary action. Impaired drainage and accumulation of mucus narrows the caliber of the airways and reduces air flow (Fig. 6). Loss of water from mucus by absorption and evaporation again increases flow resistance and forms a cycle ending in complete obstruction of the smaller airways. Prevention of water loss can reverse this process and prevent alterations in the flow resistance of mucus.

Air entering the lungs can act as a vehicle to deliver moisture to the surface of the mucous blanket. Lung air contains 43.5 mg/l of water vapor at 37°C which corresponds to 99.4 per cent RH. For our purpose, the water content of inspired air should equal or exceed this value. There is the added problem of simultaneous introduction of various electrolytes, antibiotics and wetting agents in the aerosol solutions. The droplet size of the aerosol is of paramount importance to insure adequate penetration and deposition within the lungs. Maximum wetting of the inner

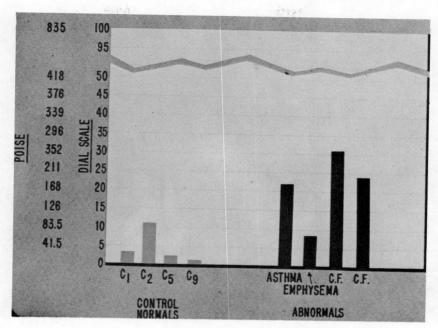

Fig. 4. Bar graph of resistance during flow of lung mucus measured on a rotational viscometer;[2] c = control subject, C.F. = cystic fibrosis, abnormal mucus.

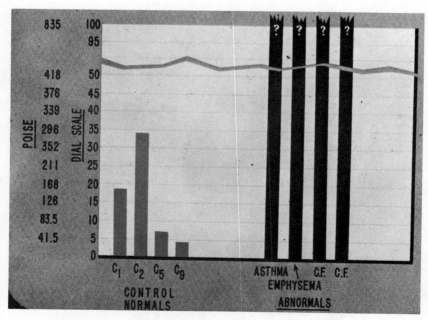

Fig. 5. Bar graph of initial viscosity (yield stress) of lung mucus measured on a rotational viscometer;[2] c = control subjects, C.F. = cystic fibrosis. The values for yield stress of the abnormal mucus exceeded the full dial scale area of the instrument.

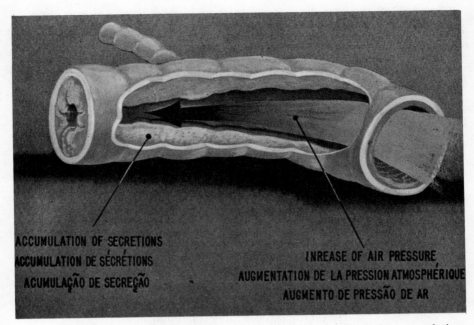

FIG. 6. Schematic of the narrowing of the lumen of the tubular airways by accumulations of mucus. The decrease in caliber of the air tube causes an increase in resistance to air flow.

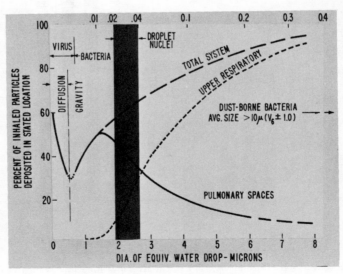

FIG. 7. Data from Hatch[3] on the relation of particle size to penetration in the respiratory tract.

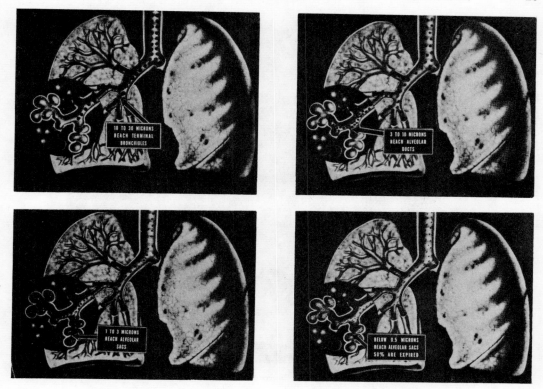

FIG. 8. Illustration of the droplet diameter to penetration relationship.

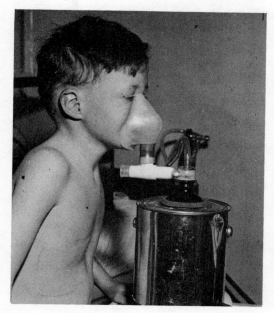

FIG. 9. Patient undergoing mask aerosol treatment.

surfaces is the goal of aerosol treatment. Accordingly, both penetration to the smallest divisions and maximum deposition in these areas are important as these are the locations of the first serious obstruction by accumulation of mucus. Figure 7 contains data from the work of Dr. Theodore F. Hatch of the University of Pittsburg, in which the diameter of water droplets in microns is related to the per cent deposited in the zones of the respiratory tract.[3] Droplets above 4 to 5 μ in diameter do not penetrate or deposit in the lower pulmonary spaces.

Figure 8 shows similar data to visually document this diameter-to-penetration deposition relationship. It is apparent that a sharp cut off of the droplets above 5-μ diameter is important.

Treatment to date has been with air or oxygen generated aerosols either by direct inhalation (Fig. 9) or by prolonged treatment during the sleeping hours (Fig. 10). For mist tent use, the nebulizer must be designed for

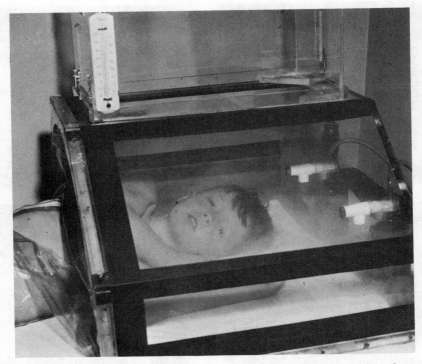

FIG. 10. Plastic enclosure forms "aerosol tent" for treatment during sleep.

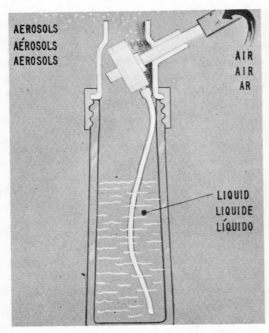

FIG. 11. Schematic of jet-type nebulizer which utilizes a baffle design to screen out droplets above 5 μ in diameter.

FIG. 12. Collection of water aerosol from the air jet nebulizer in Fig. 11 at time zero.

FIG. 13. Aerosol from air jet nebulizer at line +2 minutes showing rapid degeneration.

continuous operation over at least 10 to 12 hours on an air line pressure of 20 to 50 psi with a jet flow of 10 to 12 l/min. The fluid consumption rate should be something in excess

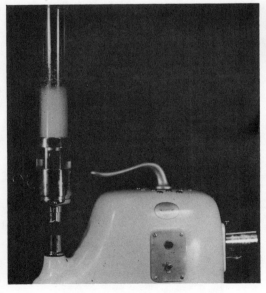

FIG. 14. Ultrasonic aerosol generator.

of 0.5 cc/min. Nebulizers currently available leave much to be desired both as to capacity and the particle size distribution of the generated aerosol. Figure 11 is a diagram of one of the best of the now available nebulizers. Figure 12 is an air-jet aerosol generated by a nebulizer in Fig. 11 photographed at time zero. Figure 13 is the same closed cylinder of aerosol at +2 minutes. The short life period of the aerosol is a gross indication of the widespread of the droplet size distribution. Figure 14 illustrates a more efficient aerosol generator which is powered by ultrasonic energy. The

FIG. 15. Cylinder of water aerosol from ultrasonic generator.

aerosol produced has a narrow distribution of droplet size, and the fluid consumption rate is above 1.4 cc/min. The result of these two factors of performance is a stable aerosol with prolonged life demonstrated by the appearance of the cylinders of aerosol produced by the ultrasonic generator in Figs. 15 and 16 with the same 2-minute time lapse between. Unfortunately, the ultrasonic generator is at present too expensive and too critical for practical application for hospital or home use.

The material presented illustrates the con-

FIG. 16. The same cylinder of water aerosol at +2 minutes.

tribution of a team approach to medical problems. In this instance, the technical knowledge of the physics of liquid aerosols to be found in the specialized fields of engineering offers an important approach to the much needed treatment to overcome impaired bronchial drainage. The development of these instruments and their eventual application to practical treatment problems will offer a more efficient control of obstructive pulmonary disorders. Future work to be accomplished is in the field of instrument development and eventual experimentation with the hospitalized patient.

References

1. Dalhamn, Tore, "Mucous Flow and Ciliary Activity in the Trachea of Healthy Rats and Rats Exposed to Irritant Gases," *Acta Physiol. Scand. Suppl.*, **36**, 123 (1956).
2. Denton, R., "Bronchial Obstruction in Cystic Fibrosis: Rheological Factors," *Pediatrics*, **25**, 611 (1960).
3. Hatch, T. F., "Distribution and Deposition of Inhaled Particles in the Respiratory Tract, *Bacteriol. Rev.*, **25**, 237 (1961).

5. The Measurement of Water Vapor Boundary Layers in Biological Systems with a Radio Refractometer

DAVID M. GATES

National Bureau of Standards, Boulder, Colorado

ABSTRACT

The thickness of water vapor boundary layers near surfaces is of particular importance in biological systems. A microwave refractometer with a capillary intake has been used to sample the moisture boundary layer near plant leaves, the human hand, and above an open water surface. The microwave refractometer can detect moisture changes of approximately 0.1 per cent RH at room temperature. The relatively fast response time, of the order of 30 seconds, of the refractometer makes it particularly suitable for observing transient phenomena in biological systems.

INTRODUCTION

Most organisms, plants and animals, are surrounded by a moisture boundary layer in still air. This boundary layer is the transition zone for the transport of moisture from the organism to the surrounding air. It also represents a transition zone for the exchange of heat to or from the organism and the air and for the diffusion of other gases such as carbon dioxide and oxygen. This boundary layer, as it exists in terms of air density changes near the surface of a plant or animal, can be photographed by the use of schlieren photography. Gates and Benedict[1] have applied this technique to living forms for studying free and forced convection near plant surfaces. In Fig. 1 the boundary layer near the forehead and face of two small girls can be seen as well as air

exhaled by them. In Fig. 2 the boundary layer near the surface of an oak leaf can be seen as well as the ascending warm air from the leaf surface since the leaf is warmed by irradiation with sunlight. The warm air near the leaf surface is more buoyant than the surrounding cooler ambient air and therefore rises. Also moist air is less dense than drier air and will ascend. Although these boundary layers as photographed here are changes in air density, they probably also represent changes in the moisture content of the air near the surfaces. The transport of heat and mass are generally considered to be of the same character.

Schlieren photography is a very sensitive

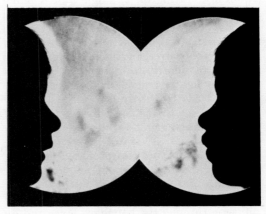

FIG. 1. Schlieren photograph of the boundary layers of warm air near the faces of two girls. The warm exhaled air from their mouths can also be seen as it mixes with the ambient air of the room.

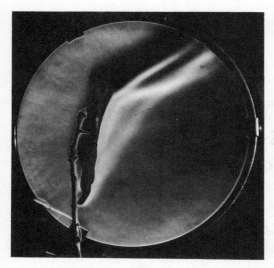

Fig. 2. Schlieren photograph of the free convection flow of air near an oak leaf (end on view) illuminated with light. Both dark and light areas represent the flow of warm air off the leaf.

optical arrangement for showing up very small deflections of light rays due to changes in refraction by the medium through which they pass. The amount of refraction or the degree of bending of a ray of light depends upon the density of the air, and a changing density will show up as a change in the bending of a light ray. The schlieren technique is a scheme for making this bending more apparent to photography or to the eye. A knife edge is placed at the focal point of a perfect mirror uniformly cutting off the light rays coming from a point source and focusing them as a point image. If there are no disturbances in the path, then all the rays will be cut off uniformly; however, any small changes due to varying air density will show up, either as darker or lighter regions in the field of view which is otherwise neutral.

In addition, this paper describes the use of a radio refractometer to measure extremely small amounts of water vapor in these boundary layers. Moisture profiles near leaves, near the human hand, and above a water surface are described.

Water vapor is lost from a surface by diffusion through the boundary layer and by free or forced convection beyond the boundary layer. The rate E_w in cm^{3}cm^{-2}sec^{-1} at which water vapor is lost from a surface by diffusion

depends upon the vapor pressure gradient in the following manner:

$$E_w = D_w \frac{e_s - e_a}{Pl} \qquad (1)$$

where D_w is the diffusion coefficient for water vapor in air, P the atmospheric pressure in mm of Hg or in millibars, $e_s - e_a$ the vapor pressure difference between the surface and the surroundings in mm of Hg or in millibars, and l the thickness of the boundary layer. The diffusion coefficient, D_w in cm^{2}sec^{-1}, for water vapor in air according to the International Critical Tables, is represented as follows:

$$D_w = (0.220/p)(T/273)^{1.75}$$

where p = pressure in atmospheres and T = absolute temperature in °K. For T = 300°K and p = 0.81 atmospheres (Boulder, Colorado), one gets $D_w = 0.32$ cm^{2}sec^{-1}. Therefore, in order to obtain the rate at which water vapor is lost from the surface, it is necessary to measure the vapor pressure gradient. The purpose of this paper is to report on one means for making this measurement.

REFRACTOMETER

The refractive index (n) at microwave frequencies of air is determined chiefly by the air temperature (T), the total pressure (P), and the partial pressure (e) of the water vapor present. In order to put the numerical value into simpler form without involving many digital places beyond the decimal point the index can be expressed as follows:

$$N \equiv (n - 1) \times 10^6 \qquad (2)$$

whose functional dependance on the atmospheric parameters is:

$$N = a \frac{P}{T} + b \frac{e}{T^2} \qquad (3)$$

The sensitivity of N to the various parameters is given by their partial derivatives, which for typical laboratory conditions have the following approximate values:

$$\frac{\partial N}{\partial T} = -1.2 \; N/°C, \quad \frac{\partial N}{\partial P} = 0.3 \; N/\text{mb},$$

$$\frac{\partial N}{\partial e} = 4 \; N/\text{mb} \qquad (4)$$

If the total pressure and the temperature remain constant during a series of measurements, it is then possible to measure directly changes in water vapor pressure to a high degree of accuracy. An instrument for measuring the value of the radio refractive index at microwave frequencies is known as a radio refractometer. Since refractometers have been developed with resolutions of the order of 0.1 N and accuracies of the order of 1 N, measurements of water vapor pressure can be made to corresponding values of 0.025 and 0.25 mb (approximately 0.1 and 1 per cent RH at a temperature of 20°C), if the pressure and temperature of the sample can be properly determined. Relative differences in vapor pressure can be measured easily and accurately since the air temperature and pressure of the samples will be nearly the same.

The application of a radio refractometer to the measurement of moisture boundary layers and to leaf transpiration has been described by Gates, Vetter, and Thompson.[2] Radio refractometers have been described by Birnbaum,[3] Crain and Deam,[4] Sargent,[5] and Vetter and Thompson.[6] These instruments operate by responding to changes which occur in the resonant frequency of a cavity resonator as the index of refraction of their contents changes. The instrument used for the experiments reported here operated at 9400 Mc/sec, X-band, and had a cavity in the form of a right circular cylinder 4.5 cm in diameter by 3.0 cm long. The resonant frequency of the sample cavity is compared with a hermetically sealed reference cavity containing dry argon. In the Vetter refractometer used here the reference cavity is tuned by a servo-operated probe which tracks the frequency changes of the sample cavity.

In order to probe the moisture content of a boundary layer and to produce the least possible disturbance of the layer, the air was drawn into the sample cavity through a hypodermic needle attached to the cavity with a flexible plastic tube. By selecting an appropriate orifice on the vacuum pump side of the sample cavity, a suitable compromise can be made between the sampling speed (response time) and the disturbance which the probe creates in the field to be measured. With the arrangement used here the time constant of the system was about 30 seconds; however, a

delay in response of about 5 seconds occurs because of the volume of the intake tubing.

All measurements were made within a rectangular chamber of 20″ × 20″ × 26″ in order that still air conditions could be realized. A potted plant was placed inside the chamber, and an attached leaf was suspended horizontally by means of a few very fine nylon threads which were stretched across an open aluminum frame. The hypodermic needle was mounted vertically on a rack and pinon in order that it could be moved toward or away from the leaf surface. An opening in the top of the box covered with acetate film permitted a floodlight to illuminate the interior. The flood lamp was run off a rheostat in order to select the desired level of illumination.

RESULTS

Examples of the moisture profiles near leaf surfaces are shown in Figs. 3, 4, and 6. It will be noticed that the measured profiles bend

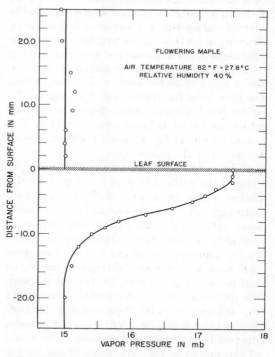

FIG. 3. The moisture boundary layer profile near the upper and lower surfaces of a flowering maple leaf when illuminated with approximately 400 foot-candles. The profile as measured is unnatural within about 4 mm of the leaf surface.

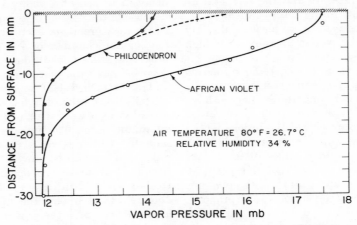

FIG. 4. The moisture boundary layer profiles near the under surface of a philodendron and an African violet leaf. The dashed line extending the profile for the philodendron leaf probably represents more correctly the actual character of the boundary layer within a few millimeters of the surface.

abruptly toward the surface within the last 2 or 3 mm from the surface. This would appear to be an unnatural situation which is probably introduced by the measurement technique of drawing in air through a constricted zone such that air of lower moisture content from further away from the surface is mixed with more moist air close to the surface. In other words, the flow lines for the air entering the needle probe bend outward away from the surface when the probe is close to the surface. The actual boundary layer should represent a continuation of the midsection slope toward the surface, with the gradient becoming steeper close to the surface as shown in Fig. 4 for the philodendron by means of the dashed line. Although the vapor pressure should reach some maximum value at the leaf surface, it probably does not reach the saturation valve at the temperature of the leaf surface since only within the intercellular spaces inside the leaf is the air saturated. On the other hand, the profile above a water surface must reach the saturation value close to the surface. Beyond the first 2 or 3 mm from the surface, the profile as measured is probably correct and of the proper shape. The slope of the profile throughout its entire midsection can be used to estimate the diffusion rate of water vapor transfer through this boundary layer. The shape of the profile at the outer extremity is influenced by convective motion, particularly for those profiles on the under side of the surface.

It would appear that the flowering maple of Fig. 3 was not transpiring from the upper surface, but only from the lower surface. The water vapor pressure was nearly constant at all heights above the leaf, and in fact appeared to have a slight maximum in vapor pressure in the vicinity of 12 cm above the leaf. This was probably due to the nature of the convective flow of air around the leaf in a manner similar to the flow shown in Fig. 2. Moist air is probably being carried up over the leaf from below, since the transpiration is taking place from the lower leaf surface. The drier upper surface of the leaf is indicated by the slightly reduced vapor pressure near the upper surface. Below the leaf, a definite, steady-state moisture-boundary layer formed approximately 16 mm thick. If one fits a straight line to the midsection of the boundary layer profile, calculates the vapor pressure gradient, and applies Eq. (1), one gets $E_w = 12.5 \times 10^{-4} \mathrm{cm^3 cm^{-2} sec^{-1}}$ or 10.7×10^{-9} g cm^{-2} sec^{-1} obtained by multiplying the volume rate of flow by the density of moist air.

The moisture profiles below the leaves of two other plants, a philodendron and an African violet, when illuminated with about 400 foot-candles of artificial incandescent light, are shown in Fig. 4. The boundary layer was 14 mm thick beneath the flat philodendron leaf and about 25 mm thick beneath the cup-shaped African violet leaf. However, about 10 mm of this was contained within the concave profile of the curved violet leaf. The shape of the water vapor profile beneath the philodendron leaf and beneath the African violet leaf are nearly the same between 12 and 13.7 mb vapor pressure. Furthermore the shapes are nearly identical near the surface of the two leaves. Calculations using Eq. (1) would indicate that both plants were transpiring from their lower leaf surfaces at about $18.9 \times 10^{-4} \text{cm}^3\text{cm}^{-1}\text{sec}^{-1}$ or 1.62×10^{-8} g cm^{-2}sec^{-1}. Much greater transpiration rates than these are often found in nature in still air. By contrast, the free water surface boundary layer in still air without illumination, reported by Gates, Vetter, and Thompson,[2] had an evaporation rate of $5.0 \times 10^{-4}\text{cm}^3\text{cm}^{-2}\text{sec}^{-1}$

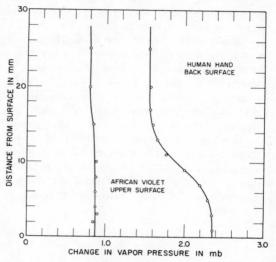

FIG. 6. The still air moisture profiles above an African violet leaf with about 400 foot-candle illumination and above the back side of a human hand in darkness.

or 4.24×10^{-9} g cm^{-2}sec^{-1}. The surface area of the water was approximately 12 cm^2 and was small compared to the area of the chamber in which the experiment was conducted.

The water vapor profiles above a much more extensive water surface of area 774 cm^2 are shown in Fig. 5. The rate of evaporation from the surface of the water decreased as the water vapor pressure of the free air within the chamber increased. This effect is clearly seen in Fig. 5. During the initial conditions the water surface was evaporating at 3.82×10^{-4} cm^{3}cm^{-2}sec^{-1} or 3.28×10^{-9} g cm^{-2}sec^{-1}, and twenty-five minutes later the evaporation rate was $2.87 \times 10^{-4}\text{cm}^3\text{cm}^{-2}\text{sec}^{-1}$ or 2.48×10^{-9} g cm^{-2}sec^{-1} and fifty minutes after the start of the experiment the rate was $1.52 \times 10^{-4}\text{cm}^3$ cm^{-2}sec^{-1} or 1.30×10^{-9} g cm^{-2}sec^{-1}.

Upper surface boundary layers are shown in Fig. 6 for the African violet with 400 foot-candle illumination and the human hand without illumination. The upper surface of the African violet was not transpiring any significant amount, and the water vapor pressure profile was nearly constant with height. The hand was losing moisture at the rate $3.83 \times 10^{-4}\text{cm}^3\text{cm}^{-2}\text{sec}^{-1}$ or 3.30×10^{-9} g cm^{-2}sec^{-1}.

Although it would be more desirable to use

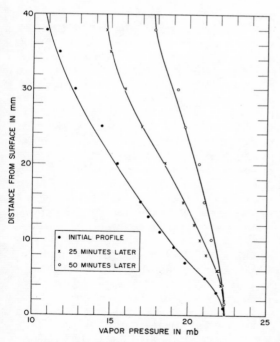

FIG. 5. The moisture profiles above a water surface which was located within a closed chamber. The changing profile shape with time shows how air within the chamber came closer to saturation. The curvature of the profile within 4 mm of the surface is probably unnatural because of the measuring technique.

a completely passive system for the measurement of moisture boundary layers, the method reported here appears to sample the air with relatively little disturbance of the boundary layer. By reducing the size of the microwave cavity (for example, K-band rather than X-band), it should be possible to reduce the response time by about one order of magnitude and increase the sensitivity. Although the method has more sensitivity than most techniques for the measurement of water vapor pressure and is extremely accurate when sampling free air, it would be desirable to check it against other methods, particularly passive ones, for the measurement of moisture boundary layers.

References

1. Gates, D. M., and Benedict, C. M., "Convection Phenomena from Plants in Still Air, *Am. J. Botany* (July 1963).
2. Gates, D. M., Vetter, M. J., and Thompson, M. C., "Measurement of Moisture Boundary Layers and Leaf Transpiration with a Microwave Refractometer," *Nature*, **197**, 1070–1072 (1963).
3. Birnbaum, G., "A Recording Microwave Refractometer," *Rev. Sci. Instr.*, **21**, 169–176 (1950).
4. Crain, C. M., and Deam, A. P., "An Airborne Microwave Refractometer," *Rev. Sci. Instr.*, **23**, 149–151 (1952).
5. Sargent, J. A., "Recording Microwave Hygrometer," *Rev. Sci. Instr.*, **30**, 348–355 (1959).
6. Vetter, M. J., and Thompson, M. C., "Absolute Microwave Refractometer," *Rev. Sci. Instr.*, **33**, 656–660 (1962).

6. Internal Surface - Intercellular Space Relationships and the Dynamics of Humidity Maintenance in Leaves

F. M. TURRELL

Department of Biochemistry, University of California, Riverside, California

ABSTRACT

An optical method is described for determining the volume (V_i) of the intercellular space of leaves. Results obtained on a wide variety of structural types are related to the leaf internal surface area (I) of the same leaves. The absolute values for these parameters and the ratios I/V_i per unit external leaf surface are shown to vary with age, exposure, habitat, phylla, genus, species and variety. Sun leaves of one variety give reproducible values over a period of years.

A linear relation is shown to exist between the internal-external surface ratio (R) and leaf thickness, or palisade thickness. Shorter methods for determining I and R from the above parameters are suggested.

Transfer of mass by leaves under optimum humidity, water supply and controlled illumination is shown to be proportional to I or R. Increasing lengths in the dimensions of V_i are shown to lower the intercellular space vapor pressure gradient and decrease the thickness of the vapor boundary layer.

INTRODUCTION

Land constitutes about 25 per cent of the earth's surface. It is largely covered by plants which maintain the relative humidity of the air near it. The magnitude of the plant influence can be visualized when the water loss of a small isolated catalpa tree[43] on an Iowa summer day is considered. With air temperatures of 90°F, a 30-ft tree can raise the relative humidity of 100^3 cu ft of air from 40 to 80 per cent, with a loss of 98 gallons of water.

Beginning with Stephen Hales in 1727,[33] more than 2000 papers had dealt with transpiration by 1920,[10, 11] and likely there have been as many published since then. The variables treated are far too lengthy to list. Some papers have been excellent as, for example, the classic works of Briggs and Shantz,[4-9] yet it is impossible to use the results of but a few in an equation of transfer of mass because one or more factors were not measured in the experimental regimen. Curtis[13] showed one such factor to be leaf temperature, and Martin[26] showed another to be leaf dimension. A third and equally fundamental parameter is the internal leaf surface and intercellular space ratio which will be treated in this paper. The presence and basic function of the leaf internal surface-intercellular space system and its importance to photosynthetic and transpiration efficiency were known in the latter part of the last century and early in the present one.[2, 3, 10, 12, 18, 21, 38] However, as far as the author is aware, only one paper[39] has included this factor in calculating transpiration rate. It is proposed in this paper (1) to describe optical methods for determining such surfaces and volumes (2) to present results of the application of these methods as bases for quicker and less laborious methods, and (3) to show the necessity of the internal surface - intercellular space system to kinetic equations for transfer of mass.

METHODS

An optical method was suggested by Turrell[44] for measuring internal leaf surface. Doi,[14] Nius,[28] Takenouchi,[40] and Schröder[35] used infiltration methods to measure the volume of intercellular space, and their results have been presented by Turrell, elsewhere[37]. No optical method has been published. As the values obtained by infiltration methods are not related to internal surface, they are not at present useful for studies of transfer of mass. To meet these deficiencies, an optical method is described and applied to the same material from which internal surface values were previously obtained.[44-46]

Volume of Intercellular Space (Mesomorphic Leaves)

Measurements of palisade depth were made directly on permanently prepared microscope slides. Camera lucida drawings of the other leaf tissues were used for chartometer and planimeter measurements of the volume of intercellular space, V_i, of leaves having both palisade and spongy mesophyll as was done for internal surface. V_i may be calculated by substituting the values obtained by these measurements in the equation

$$V_i = l_p (K^2 - A_p) + d_s (K^2 - A_s) \quad (1)$$

The percentage volume of intercellular space

$$V_\% = \frac{[l_p (K^2 - A_p) + d_s (K^2 - A_s)]}{T_B K^2} \times 100 \quad (2)$$

when the measurements are in μ, μ^2, or μ^3 as outlined below.

Palisade. The average length of the upper layer of palisade cells was determined by direct microscopic measurement of transverse leaf sections with 90 or 91X objective and 10X ocular fitted with a micrometer, and equals l_p (Fig. 1). In cases where several palisade layers were present, each layer was measured separately. Values were obtained for the first palisade layer (l_{p_1}), and the second palisade layer (l_{p_2}), (Fig. 1), etc., then

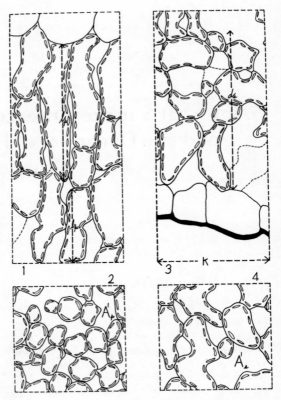

FIG. 1. Camera lucida drawings of microscopic internal structure of a leaf of *Medicago sativa* showing measurements made in determining V_i: (1) in palisade tissue from transverse section of leaf; (2) in palisade tissue from tangential section of leaf; (3) in sponge tissue from transverse section; (4) in sponge tissue from tangential section.

$$l_p = \Sigma l_{p_1}, l_{p_2} \ldots l_{p_n} \quad (3)$$

Ten to twenty cellular measurements were made in each layer; l_p is expressed in μ.

Areas were selected from the tangential leaf section, showing the intercellular spaces between palisade cells in cross section and a camera lucida drawing which was a 1600-diameter enlargement, made of the cells of each sample. One to five sample areas were used in each case for each layer of the palisade. The total cellular area (A_p) for each sample was measured with a planimeter. The area of the intercellular space (A_p') in μ^2 was found by subtracting A_p from the sample area (K^2), i.e.,

$$A_p' = K^2 - A_p \quad (4)$$

(Fig. 1). The volume of intercellular space in the palisade layer (V_{i_p}) is then

$$V_{i_p} = l \, (K^2 - A_p) \qquad (5)$$

Spongy Mesophyll. Ten to twenty measurements of the depth of sponge were made on camera lucida drawings of transverse leaf sections through the sponge with a Paragon chain scale, with 500-μ divisions. These measurements in microns were averaged (d_s). The drawings were made generally with 90X objective and 10X ocular; but for extremely thick leaves, lower powered optics were necessary.

Camera lucida drawings of the cells in the spongy mesophyll as seen in the tangential section (Fig. 1) were measured with a planimeter, and the total cellular area per sample was obtained. The mean of cellular areas of five samples is equal to A_s, and the area of the intercellular space, A'_s, is

$$A'_s = K^2 - A_s \qquad (6)$$

The volume of intercellular space (V_{i_s}) in the sponge is:

$$V_{i_s} = d_s \, (K^2 - A_s) \qquad (7)$$

External Surface. A sample area measured on the external surface of the leaf was equal to $K^2 (= 3600 \ \mu^2)$. The sample area was a square, the side of which was 60 μ $(6 \times 10^{-3}$ cm) on the microscopic slide, or 9.6 cm on paper, when a 10X ocular and a 90X objective were used in making the camera lucida drawings. This "sample area" limited the size of the drawings to a standard area. Since the external leaf surface, E, includes both dorsal and ventral leaf surfaces,

$$E = 2K^2 \qquad (8)$$

Percentage Volume of Intercellular Space

If V is the total volume of leaf tissue (space + cellular material) per unit external leaf area, then

$$V = T_B \, K^2 \qquad (9)$$

where T_B (average of ten to thirty measurements) is the thickness of the leaf blade. The percentage volume of intercellular space then can be expressed as

$$V_\% = \frac{V_i}{V} \times 100 \qquad (10)$$

where V_i is the volume of intercellular space in μ^3 per unit external leaf area (E_1) as determined from Eq. (1).

Xeromorphic Leaves. The volume of intercellular space of leaves which were composed of palisade tissue only can be obtained from the equation

$$V_i = \Sigma l_p \, (K^2 - A_p) \qquad (11)$$

Succulent Leaves. Where the leaf was composed entirely of sponge tissue, the equation for the volume of intercellular space is

$$V_i = d_s \, (K^2 - A_s) \qquad (12)$$

Internal Surface. Internal surface measurements (I) in μ^2 and the calculations of the internal-external surface ratio R were carried out according to methods of Turrell[44] for leaves of *Abutilon, Catalpa* (small) *Ginkgo, Pyrus, Syringa* (Turrell collection, mature sun), *Syringa* (immature), and *Zea.* Values of the internal surface (I) of the other leaves have been obtained from other work.[44-46]

Pickett and Birkeland[30] in studies on apple leaves found a high correlation ($r = +0.88$) between palisade depth (l_{p_m}) and R. The regression equation

$$R = 0.1122 \, l_{p_m} + 1.33 \qquad (13)$$

greatly reduced the work of computing R, but it involved leaf sections to obtain l_{p_m}. The values of I computed for R by several investigators[29, 30, 39, 44-46] are plotted against leaf thickness in Fig. 2. The curve is linear and shows that I in μ^2 can be determined from leaf thickness (T_B) in microns by a regression equation

$$I = 12.74 + 0.4147 \, T_B \qquad (14)$$

While the regression coefficient is highly significant, the leaf type must be known to conform to xeromorphic or mesomorphic leaf patterns. This is indicated by the very large deviation of the succulent from the regression line, lower right in Fig. 2.

The deviation from a linear regression within a species such as alfalfa (*Medicago sativa*) is quite small (Fig. 3). This correlation together with the use of a machinist's micrometer, which may be readily employed for determining leaf thickness in stiff xeromorphic leaves, should speed up the measurement of internal

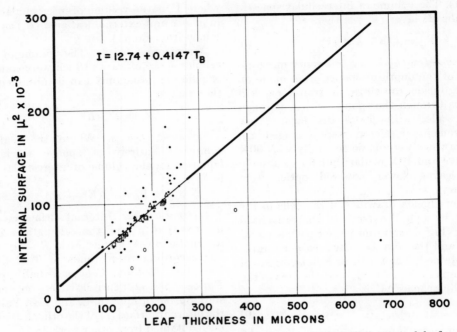

FIG. 2. Regression of internal leaf surface area per $3.6 \times 10^3 \ \mu^2$ external leaf area (upper surface) on leaf thickness in μ. From Turrell[44-46] ●; Swanson[39] ○; Pickett[29] △; Pickett and Birlande[30] □. $I = 12.74 + 0.4147 \ T_B$.

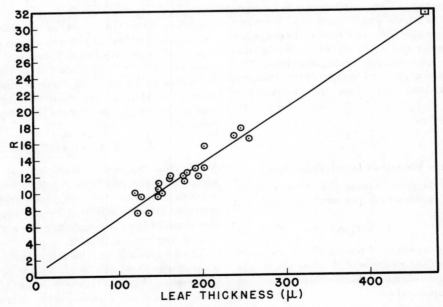

FIG. 3. Regression of internal-external surface ratio R on leaf thickness of alfalfa leaves, $r = +0.929$ and is highly significant. The regression equation is $R = 3.97 + 0.04 \ T_B$ and the standard error of estimate is 1.0. *Eucalyptus globulus* appears at the top of the curve for comparison.

TABLE 1. LEAF INTERNAL SURFACE (I) AND INTERCELLULAR SPACE VOLUME (V_i)
RELATIONSHIPS FOR $7.2 \times 10^3 \mu^2$ SAMPLE AREAS

Plant Name	T_B (μ)	I ($\mu^2 \times 10^{-3}$)	V_i ($\mu^3 \times 10^{-3}$)	I/V_i (μ^2/μ^3)
Woody, Ancient, Xeromorphic, Sun (Gymnosperm)				
Ginkgo biloba	242	32	359	0.089
Herbaceous, Medieval, Xeromorphic, Sun (Monocotyledon)				
Zea mays	170	44	168	0.262
Woody, Modern, Xeromorphic, Sun (Dicotyledon)				
Citrus grandis	237	124	197	0.629
Citrus limonia	237	160	230	0.695
Eucalyptus globulus	469	226	412	0.550
Mean	314	170	280	0.625
Woody, Modern, Mesomorphic, Sun (Dicotyledon)				
Catalpa speciosa (large leaf)	253	138	290	0.476
Cercis canadensis	143	112	166	0.674
Pyrus malus (Delicious)	280	192	352	0.545
Pyrus malus (Liveland)	229	182	281	0.647
Rhus glabra	181	117	209	0.559
Syringa vulgaris (Turrell)	199	96	180	0.533
Syringa vulgaris (Wylie)	227	95	168	0.565
Syringa vulgaris (small leaf)	153	75	165	0.455
Vitis vulpina	163	83	149	0.557
Mean	203	121	218	0.557
Woody, Modern, Xeromorphic, Shade (Dicotyledon)				
Berberis nervosa	253	71	330	0.215
Gaultheria shallon	229	59	279	0.211
				0.211
Mean	241	65	305	0.213
Woody, Modern, Mesomorphic, Shade (Dicotyledon)				
Catalpa speciosa (small leaf)	140	67	154	0.435
Catalpa speciosa (medium leaf)	178	277	103	0.372
Syringa vulgaris (medium leaf)	133	49	113	0.434
Mean	150	131	123	0.414
Herbaceous, Modern, Mesomorphic, Sun (Dicotyledon)				
Abutilon Theophrasti	116	81	136	0.595
Ricinus communis	152	92	184	0.500
Medicago sativa (early primary)	223	106	241	0.553
Medicago sativa (late primary)	206	103	198	0.536
Mean	174	96	190	0.546
Succulent, Modern, Sun (Dicotyledon)				
Bryophyllum calicynum	675	57	423	0.134

surface. For soft mesomorphic leaves, a radioisotope thickness gauge could facilitate rapid determination of the latter parameter.

Development of rapid physicochemical methods for the determination of I, based on the optical method presented here, are under study at our laboratory. The infiltration methods for determining V_i appear to be adequate. Use of an infiltration solution with a radioactive-isotope-labeled dye that can be adsorbed to the cell wall may yield a very rapid method for finding both I and V_i in one operation. Mature sun leaves make an excellent standard as they are representative of maximum development and can be duplicated annually. The *Syringa* sun leaf collected by Wylie has the same parameters as that collected by Turrell several years later (Table 1).

RESULTS

Internal Surface and Intercellular Space

The volume of intercellular space (V_i), internal surface (I) and leaf thicknesses (T_B) of a structurally heterogeneous group of leaves are given in Table 1. These form eight more or less homogeneous families having I/V_i ratios

averaging 0.089 for (1) woody, ancient, xeromorphic sun leaves of the gymnosperm *Ginkgo*; 0.262 for (2) herbaceous, medieval, xeromorphic, sun leaves of the monocotyledon, *Zea*; 0.625 for (3) woody modern, xeromorphic, sun, dicotyledon, leaves of *Citrus g*, and *l*, and *Eucalyptus*. In the modern dicotyledon leaves of the remaining five groups I/V_i averaged 0.557 for (4) woody, mesomorphic sun leaves of *Catalpa, Cercis, Pyrus, Rhus, Syringa*, and *Vitis*; 0.213 for (5) woody, xeromorphic leaves of naturally shaded forest undershrubs, *Berberis* and *Gaultheria*; 0.414 for (6) woody, mesomorphic, shade leaves of *Catalpa* and *Syringa*; 0.546 for (7) herbaceous, meso-morphic, sun, leaves of *Abutilon, Ricinus* and *Medicago*; 0.134 for (8) the sun leaf of the succulent, *Bryophyllum*. The internal surface of the leaves in this ordered series increases regularly (Fig. 4) but I/V_i varies erratically (Fig. 5.)

In a homogeneous structural group of leaves (within a species or variety such as the apple) R varies with little dispersion from a linear regression with palisade depth[30] or with T_B, V_i, I or I/V_i, as for *Medicago sativa* (Table 2).

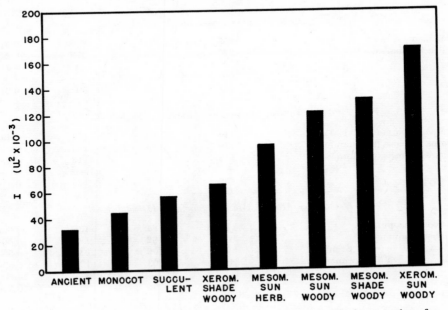

Fɪɢ. 4. Comparison of the internal surface areas per $7.2 \times 10^3 \mu^2$ external surface (upper + lower) for structurally heterogeneous groups of leaves from different kinds of habitats.

TABLE 2. VOLUME OF INTERCELLULAR SPACE (V_i), PERCENTAGE V_i, AND RATIO OF INTERNAL SURFACE (I) TO VOLUME OF INTERCELLULAR SPACE (V_i) OF LEAVES OF DIFFERENT SIZES FROM ALFALFA (*Medicago sativa*) PLANTS GROWN UNDER FIELD CONDITIONS IN SALT LAKE CITY, UTAH FOR $7.2 \times 10^3\ \mu^2$ SAMPLE AREAS

Leaf Number	Leaf Type	T_B (μ)	V_i ($\mu^3 \times 10^{-3}$)	V_i (%)	I ($\mu^2 \times 10^{-3}$)	I/V_i (μ^2/μ^3)
1	Early primary	196	227	32.2	85.9	0.378
6	,, ,,	256	312	33.8	118.5	0.380
11	,, ,,	192	129	18.6	93.0	0.721
16	,, ,,	247	294	33.0	127.2	0.433
Mean		222.8	241	29.4	106.2	0.553
2	Late primary	177	153	24.1	86.6	0.566
7	,, ,,	239	268	31.1	121.1	0.452
12	,, ,,	203	149	20.4	92.7	0.622
17	,, ,,	203	221	30.3	111.4	0.504
Mean		205.5	198	26.5	102.9	0.536
3	Secondary	147	157	29.7	74.2	0.472
8	,,	182	167	25.5	89.1	0.533
13	,,	147	136	25.7	67.7	0.498
18	,,	161	156	26.8	84.2	0.540
Mean		159.3	154	26.9	78.8	0.511
4	Tertiary	162	114	22.9	86.8	0.762
9	,,	136	130	26.6	61.5	0.473
14	,,	127	93	20.4	67.9	0.730
19	,,	179	146	22.7	81.2	0.556
Mean		151.0	120	23.1	74.4	0.630
5	Quarternary	152	116	21.2	71.3	0.614
10	,,	122	86	19.5	61.5	0.715
15	,,	120	77	17.7	71.9	0.934
20	,,	148	114	21.3	80.0	0.702
Mean		135.5	98	19.9	71.2	0.741

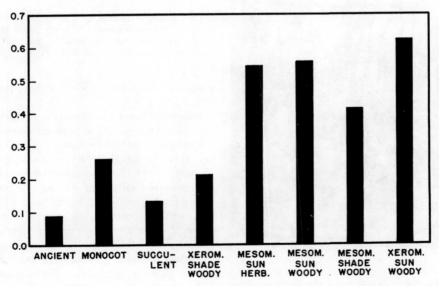

FIG. 5. Comparison of I/V_i for structurally heterogeneous groups of leaves from different habitats.

In randomly selected leaves even from the same plant, T_B varies quantitively as shown in Fig. 6 and 7, with concomitant variations in V_i and I which suggest that unit external surface is a dubious standard for expressing transpiration rates.

Transfer of Mass and Internal Surface - Intercellular Space

McGinnis and McDougall[27] compared the relative transpiration rates of corn with several weeds by the cobalt chloride method. These weeds are generally eradicated from corn fields because of their competition with corn growth. All of them have higher trans-

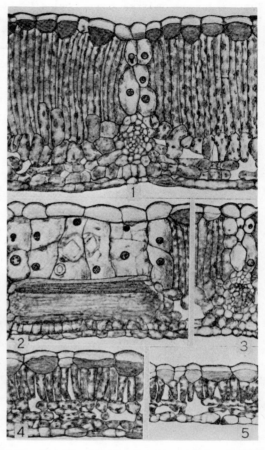

FIG. 7. Photomicrographs of leaves from various locations in the crown of a Norway maple tree at the same magnification. An outside sun leaf (1); an inside shade leaf (5). From R. B. Wylie[49].

FIG. 6. Photomicrographs of transverse sections of *Medicago sativa* leaves from the same plant at the same magnification. A quarternary leaf, upper; a late primary leaf, lower.

piration rates and larger R values than corn (Fig. 8).*

Swanson[39] and Turrell[46] tested the hypothesis that transpiration rate measured under the same microclimatic conditions was proportional to the internal surface, as suggested by Turrell[44] on the basis of the correspondence of his measured values of R, and the published transpiration rates of lemon and grapefruit leaves.[17] The transpiration rate m and the internal-external surface ratio R published by the above authors are compared in Fig. 9. Swanson measured transpiration rates on widely different structural types of plants at

* I was determined from leaf thickness values of Turrell and Turrell[47] and Eq. (14).

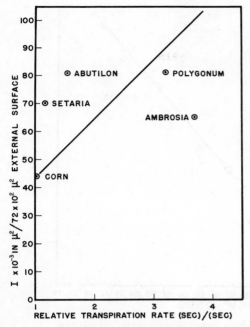

FIG. 8. The transpiration rates of certain weeds compared with transpiration rate of corn from McGinnis and McDougall[27] plotted against internal leaf surface determined from leaf thickness.[47]

which the plants were grown (curve A, Fig. 10). A higher correlation ($r = +0.852$) was found when m was corrected by the difference in evaporation from free water surfaces under the respective light sources (curve B, Fig. 10); then, when m was measured in these same plants, with all the plants under low intensity (Exp. II) and subsequently with all under high light intensity (Exp. III), the correlation was respectively higher ($r_{low} = +0.893$ and $r_{high} = +0.890$). Each r is highly significant (Fig. 11). Values of T_B, V_i, I and I/V_i for the plants used in the three experiments are given in Table 3.

Transpiration Equation

No equation has come to the author's attention in which the transpiration rate of one species of broad-leaved dicotyledon, if measured under known conditions, could be used to predict the transpiration rates of other species. The climatological factors were recorded for the duration of Experiment III. The mean air relative humidity was 61.2 per cent ($p_{air} = 21.000$ mm Hg), temperature =

different times of day and for different periods. Despite the extraordinary conditions imposed, the following comparisons could be made by use of tobacco leaf thickness[1] and transpiration rate[19]

$$\frac{R_{holly}/R_{tobacco}}{R_{holly}/R_{coleus}} = \frac{1.82}{2.3} = 0.79$$

and

$$\frac{m_{holly}/m_{tobacco}}{m_{holly}/m_{coleus}} = \frac{1.08}{1.16} = 0.93$$

Compared in this way they show only a 15 per cent discrepancy. This appears to be largely a result of values of R far below any obtained by us for mature dicotyledon leaves. A re-estimation of R from substitution of our leaf thicknesses[47] in Eq. (14), reduced this discrepancy (Fig. 9).

Turrell[46] found a high and significant correlation ($r = +0.781$) between transpiration rate and R for oleander (*nerium oleander*) and periwinkle (*Vinca rosea*) plants grown under two different intensities of artificial light when the transfer of mass was measured under the respective intensities of light (Exp. 1) in

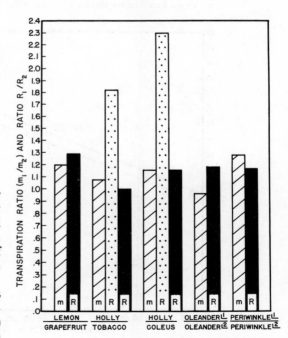

FIG. 9. Comparison of the ratios of transfer of mass m of species or varieties of leaves by pairs, striped bars; with R determined by the author, solid bars; and by Swanson[39], dotted bars.

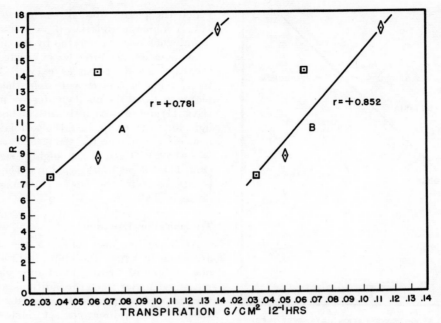

FIG. 10. Transfer of mass plotted against R for mesomorphic periwinkle plants and xeromorphic oleander plants grown under two different intensities of artificial light, 76.8 and 175 foot candles, with m measured simultaneously under these intensities. Curve A, uncorrected, $r = +0.781$; curve B, m corrected for evaporation of free water surfaces respectively, $r = +0.852$.

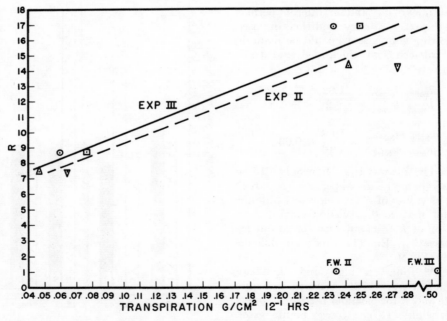

FIG. 11. Transfer of mass plotted against R for the same periwinkle and oleander plants shown in Fig. 10. Experiment II, lower curve, m of all plants and free water surface *FW II* measured under 76.8 foot candles, and Experiment III, m for all plants and *FW III* measured under 175 foot candles light intensity.

TABLE 3. VOLUME OF INTERCELLULAR SPACE (V_i), PERCENTAGE V_i, AND RATIO OF INTERNAL SURFACE (I) TO VOLUME OF INTERCELLULAR SPACE (V_i) OF LEAVES OF PERIWINKLE (*Vinca rosea*) AND OLEANDER (*Nerium Oleander*) PLANTS GROWN UNDER TWO DIFFERENT INTENSITIES OF ARTIFICIAL LIGHT, FOR $7.2 \times 10^3 \ \mu^2$ SAMPLE AREAS

Genus and Leaf Position	Plant Number	T_B (μ)	V_i ($\mu^3 \times 10^{-3}$)	V_i (%)	I ($\mu^2 \times 10^{-3}$)	I/V_i (μ^2/μ^3)
76.8 foot-candles						
Nerium Oleander						
Top	6	234	200	23.7	112.7	0.563
Bottom	6	154	233	42.1	79.3	0.340
Top	8	242	259	29.7	107.8	0.416
Bottom	8	181	270	41.5	109.3	0.405
Mean		203	241	34.3	102.3	0.431
Vinca rosea						
Top	2	108	117	30.0	68.3	0.584
Bottom	2	118	171	40.3	55.4	0.324
Top	4	65	58	24.9	34.4	0.593
Bottom	4	140	158	31.4	53.0	0.335
Mean		108	126	31.7	52.8	0.459
175 foot-candles						
Nerium Oleander						
Top	5	224	263	32.6	82.9	0.315
Bottom	5	232	285	34.1	132.1	0.464
Top	7	238	262	28.0	130.0	0.496
Bottom	7	260	299	34.9	142.0	0.475
Mean		239	277	32.4	121.8	0.438
Vinca rosea						
Top	1	131	103	21.8	67.2	0.652
Bottom	1	154	228	41.1	60.5	0.266
Top	3	94	97	28.6	55.8	0.576
Bottom	3	141	210	41.3	67.9	0.323
Mean		130	160	33.2	62.9	0.454

32.14°C, and barometric pressure (b_1) = 748.0 mm Hg, standard pressure = b_2. And m^p, the mass of water transpired in g/cm², was 0.00888 gram for the periwinkles, θ = the duration of the transpiration period in hours, p_{leaf} = the water vapor pressure of the transpiring leaf in mm Hg at leaf temperature. Leaf temperatures of the oleanders were the same as air temperature, i.e., within the experimental error ($\pm$ 0.11°C) of measuring leaf temperatures with thermocouples. The periwinkle leaves, however, averaged 0.80°C below air temperature. The constant D in g/cm²/hr can be calculated from the above data by Eq. (15). By using this constant in Eq. (16) and correcting D by the internal-external surface ratios, R_1 for oleanders *vs* R_2 for periwinkles, m can be calculated for the oleanders.

$$m^p = D^p \left(p_{\text{leaf}} - p_{\text{air}}\right) \frac{b_2}{b_1} \cdot \theta \qquad (15)$$

$$D = \frac{m}{\left(p_{\text{leaf}} - p_{\text{air}}\right) 760/748 \cdot 1}$$

$$D = \frac{0.00888}{(34.277 - 23.797) \cdot 1.0160 \cdot 1}$$
$$= 0.0008339$$

where θ is the time in hours.

$$m^0 = 0.0008339(35.947$$
$$- 23.797) \frac{760}{748} \cdot \theta \cdot \frac{R_1}{R_2} \qquad (16)$$

$$m^0 = 0.01027 \cdot \frac{15.55}{8.09} = 0.01974$$

This checks very well with 0.01984 gram, the mean mass transpired per cm² by the oleander plants.

DISCUSSION

Equations (15) and (16) contain the principal parameters shown to be effective for transpiration rates. They are leaf temperatures as shown in Fig. 12,[13, 50] relative humidity of the air,[41] leaf size and shape,[26] time, and true evaporation surface area as presented here. These equations do not differ from the old Dalton equation for evaporation from a free water surface, in any significant aspect. However, Eqs. (15) and (16) are not rigorous for the transfer of mass in the leaf.

Several factors are needed to make the analysis rigorous. Gates[16] has shown that the thickness of the vapor boundary layer is a function of the size and shape of the leaf. The boundary layer resistance is inherent in m^p as calculated for periwinkles in Eq. (15) but is not inherent for oleanders [Eq. (16)]. Further, the application of Fick's first law of diffusion,[20] where D' is the diffusion coefficient in cm² sec⁻¹,

$$J = -D' \partial c / \partial x \qquad (17)$$

cannot be made at present, for the assumption that D' is a constant, which I have made for periwinkle and oleander leaves, is untenable for the internal surfaces of different kinds of leaves. The differences in degree of external cutinization are well known, and they probably are as characteristic to the internal leaf surface as well. Scott, Schroeder and Turrell[36] showed by dissolution methods that the internal surface of the leaf was cutinized. Lewis[25] by adsorption (staining) and surface tension (infiltration) methods, also showed that internal leaf surfaces were cutinized. Verduin[48] calculated that diffusion from stomata may approach diffusion from free water surfaces, but Raschke[32] has shown that stomatal resistance to diffusion varies with the kind of plant. It seems probable that stomatal resistance will have to be considered as a factor in any rigorously designed transpiration equation.* A cellular resistance which is variable throughout the day was demonstrated

* Since the presentation of this paper, R. Lee and D. M. Gates have treated this subject quantitatively in a paper entitled, "Diffusion Resistance in Leaves as Related to Their Stomatal Anatomy and Microstructure," Am. J. Botan. 51, 1964.

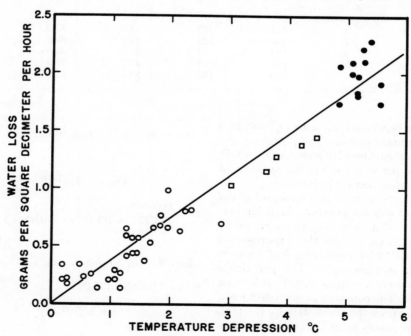

FIG. 12. Correlation between transfer of mass and temperature depression of wet muslin ●, and for leaf surfaces of pear, rose, peach, cucumber ○, and Bordeaux sprayed bean ☐.[50]

SURFACE-VOLUME COMPARISONS

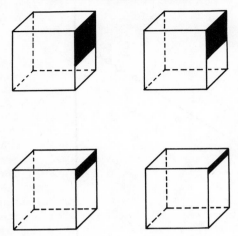

DIMENSIONS = 1μ × 1μ × 1μ

Fig. 13. Diagrammatic representations of the area of internal leaf surface bordering a unit volume of intercellular space. For woody, modern, xeromorphic, sun leaves $I/V_i = 0.6 \; \mu^2/1\mu^3 = 0.6$, upper left; for woody, modern, mesomorphic, sun leaves $I/V_i = 0.5\mu^2/1\mu^3 = 0.5$, upper right; for woody, modern, xeromorphic, shade leaves $I/V_i = 0.2\mu^2/1\mu^3 = 0.2$ lower left; for woody, ancient, shade leaves, and succulents $I/V_i = 0.1\mu^2/1\mu^3 = 0.1$, lower right.

by Ehlig and Gardner[15] who used a highly sensitive thermocouple,[34] and this will also have to be considered. For example, the change in this resistance reflected at the cell wall surfaces may be responsible for the change of slope in Thut's transpiration curves at low humidities, rather than stomatal closure as Thut[41, 42] suggested. But in any event, the resistance at the cell wall surface is the resultant of a catenary of potentials and resistances to water flow from the soil or root to the internal leaf surface. Kramer[22] has made it clear we cannot assume that transpiration of plants under field conditions is unaffected by these potentials and resistances.

If the three stages in the evaporation process, discussed by Langmuir and Schaefer[23] act the same for the leaf internal surface walls of different species the I/V_i ratio would be a critical factor in the diffusion of water vapor from leaf intercellular spaces, as can be seen from Fig. 13. It is clear that high air temperatures and low humidities might be optimum for xerophytes but would place a heavy strain on *Ginkgo*, a living fossil plant.

Factors in the kinetics of water diffusion of thick leaves, characteristic of xerophytic plants adapted to hot dry climates, are longer diffusion channels, lower diffusion gradients, and thinner vapor boundary layers. The effect of lengthened diffusion channels on lowering the diffusion gradient of a thick mesomorphic leaf such as sunflower, as compared with the thin bean leaf, is shown in Fig. 14. The relative humidity data are from Ehlig and Gardner[15] and Thut[42], and the vapor boundary layer thickness for dock is from Ramsay, Butler and Sang[31]. The effect of lowering the internal diffusion gradient within the leaf on boundary layer thickness can also be obtained by a comparison of the transpiration coefficient, D, of the mesomorphic periwinkle with xeromorphic oleander leaves by substitution in Eq. (18) for still air,[24] where K' is the value of the coefficient of diffusion of water vapor into air, in g cm^{-2} hr^{-1} for a vapor pressure gradient of 1 mm Hg cm^{-1}, obtained from Leighly's nomograph.

$$\tau = K' \frac{(p_{\text{leaf}} - p_{\text{air}})}{D} \quad (18)$$

The thickness τ of the boundary layer of the periwinkles is $1.42/2 = 0.745$ cm (stomata on upper and lower leaf surfaces) and that of the oleanders 0.39 cm, if it is assumed that the relative humidity is 99 per cent at their stomatal openings, in each case.

References

1. Avery, G. S., "Structural Responses to the Practice of Topping Tobacco Plants: A study of Cell Size, Cell Number, Leaf Size, and Veinage of Leaves at Different Levels on the Stalk," *Botan. Gaz.*, **96**, 314–329 (1934).
2. Blackman, F. F., "Experimental Researches on Vegetable Assimilation and Respiration; on the Paths of Gaseous Exchange Between Aerial Leaves and the Atmosphere," *Phil. Trans. Roy. Soc. London, Ser. B.*, **186**, 503–562 (1895).
3. Bower, F. O., "Size and Form in Plants," London, Macmillan & Co., 1930.
4. Briggs, L. J., and Shantz, H. L., "The Relative Water Requirement of Plants," *J. Agr. Res.*, **3**, 1–65 (1914).

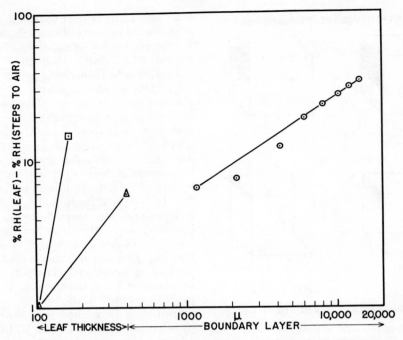

Fig. 14. The relative humidity gradient in the intercellular spaces of the thin leaf of the bean and the thick leaf of the sunflower. Relative humidity of the intercellular space from Ehlig and Gardener[15] △ and at stomatal openings from Thut, upper △ and ⊡ [41-42] lower two curves. The relative humidity gradient in the air boundary layer outside the leaf, lower surface facing up, of dock from data of Ramsay, Butler and Sang,[31] upper curve.

5. Briggs, L. J., and Shantz, H. L., "Influence of Hybridization and Cross-pollination on the Water Requirement of Plants," *J. Agr. Res.,* **4,** 391–403 (1915).

6. Briggs, L. J., and Shantz, H. L., "An Automatic Transpiration Scale of Large Capacity for Use with Freely Exposed Plants," *J. Agr. Res.,* **5,** 117–133 (1915).

7. Briggs, L. J., and Shantz, H. L., "Hourly Transpiration Rate on Clear Days as Determined by Cyclic Environmental Factors," *J. Agr. Res.,* **5,** 583–651 (1916).

8. Briggs, L. J., and Shantz, H. L., "Daily Transpiration During the Normal Growth Period and Its Correlation With the Weather," *J. Agr. Res.,* **7,** 155–213 (1916).

9. Briggs, L. J., and Shantz, H. L., "Comparison of the Hourly Evaporation Rate of Atometers and Free Water Surfaces With the Transpiration Rate of *Medicago sativa,*" *J. Agr. Res.,* **9,** 277–293 (1917).

10. Burgerstein, A., "Die Transpiration der Pflanzen," Part I, Jena, Gustav Fisher, 1904.

11. Burgerstein, A., "Die Transpiration der Pflanzen," Part II, Jena, Gustav Fisher, 1920.

12. Clements, Edith Schwartz, "The Relation of Leaf Structure to Physical Factors," *Trans. Am. Microscop. Soc.,* **26,** 1–102 (1905).

13. Curtis, O. F., "Comparative Effects of Altering Leaf Temperatures and Air Humidities on Vapor Pressure Gradients," *Plant Physiol.,* **11,** 595–603 (1936).

14. Doi, T., "On the Sun and Shade Leaves of Several Trees," *J. Coll. Sci. Imp. Univ. Tokyo,* **40,** 1–36 (1917).

15. Ehlig, C. F., and Gardner, W. R., "Relationship Between Transpiration and the Internal Water Relations of Plants," *Agron. J.* **56,** 127–130 (1964).

16. Gates, D. M., and Benedict, C. M., "Convection Phenomena from Plants in Still Air," *Am. J. Botany,* **50,** 563–573 (1963).

17. Haas, A. R. C., and Halma, F. F., "Relative Transpiration rates in *Citrus* Leaves," *Botan. Gaz.,* **93,** 466–473 (1932).

18. Haberlandt, G., "Physiological Plant Anatomy," p. 282, London, Macmillan & Co., 1928.

19. Hasselbring, H., "The Effect of Shading on the Transpiration and Assimilation of the Tobacco Plant in Cuba," *Botan. Gaz.,* **57,** 257–286 (1914).

20. Jost, W., "Diffusion in Solids, Liquids, Gases," New York, Academic Press, Inc., 1952.

21. Kemmerzell, A. "Beiträge zur Anatomie des Durchlüftungsystems," *Botan. Arch.,* **17,** 313–347 (1927).

22. Kramer, P. J., "Plant and Soil Water Relationships," New York, McGraw-Hill, Book Co. Inc., 1949.

23. Langmuir, I., and Schaefer, V. J., "Rates of Evaporation of Water Through Compressed Monolayers of Water," *J. Franklin Inst.*, **235**, 119–162 (1943).

24. Leighly, J. B., "A Note on Evaporation," *Ecology*, **18**, 180–198 (1937).

25. Lewis, F. J., "Water Movement in Leaves," *Discussions Faraday Soc.*, **3**, 159–162 (1948).

26. Martin, E., "Studies of Evaporation and Transpiration under Controlled Conditions," *Carnegie Inst. Wash.*, Pub. 550 (1943).

27. McGinnis, H. A., and McDougall, W. B., "A Comparison of the Transpiration Rates of Corn and Certain Common Weeds," *Trans. Ill. State Acad. Sci.*, **16**, 82–88 (1923).

28. Nius, E., "Untersuchungen über den Einfluss des Intercellular volumens und der Öffnungsweite der stomata auf die Luftwegigkeit der Laubblätter," *Jahrb. f. Wiss. Bot.*, **74**, 33–126 (1931).

29. Pickett, W. F., and Kenworthy, A. L., "The Relationship Between Structure, Chlorophyll Content, and Photosynthesis in Apple Leaves," *Proc. Am. Soc. Hort. Sci.*, **37**, 371–373 (1939).

30. Pickett, W. F., and Birkeland, C. J., "The Influence of Some Spray Materials on the Internal Structure and Chlorophyll Content of Apple Leaves," *Kansas Agr. Expt. Sta. Bull.*, **53**, 54 (1942).

31. Ramsay, J. A., Butler, C. G., and Sang, J. H., "The Relative Humidity Gradient at the Surface of a transpiring Leaf," *J. Expt. Biol.*, **15**, 255–265 (1938).

32. Raschke, K., "Uber den Einfluss der Diffusionwiderstande auf die Transpiration und die Temperatur eines Blattes," *Flora*, **146**, 546–578 (1958).

33. Reed, H. S., "A Short History of the Plant Sciences," Waltham, Mass., Chronica Botanica Co., 1942.

34. Richards, L. A., and Ogata, G., "Thermocouple for Vapor Pressure Measurement in Biological and Soil Systems at High Humidity," *Science*, **128**, 1089–1090 (1958).

35. Schröder, Johannes, "Über natürlische und Kunstliche Änderungen des Intercellular volumens bei Laubblättern," *Beitr. Biol. Pflanz.*, **25**, 75–124 (1937).

36. Scott, F. M., Schroeder, M. R., and Turrell, F. M., "Development, Cell Shape, Suberization of Internal Surface, and Abscission in the Leaf of the Valencia Orange, *Citrus sinensis*," *Botan. Gaz.*, **109**, 381–411 (1948).

37. Spector, W. S., "Handbook of Biological Data," Table 119, Philadelphia, W. B. Saunders Co., 1956.

38. Stahl, Ernst, "Einige Versuche über Transpiration und Assimilation," *Botan. Z.*, **52**, 117–145 (1894).

39. Swanson, C. A., "Transpiration in American Holly in Relation to Leaf Structure," *Ohio J. Sci.*, **43**, 43–46 (1943).

40. Takenouchi, M., "Investigations on the Relation Between Plants and Their Surrounding Conditions by the Quantative Method. V. Measuring the Dimensions of the Leaf-intercellular Spaces on Several Species of Plants and its Ecological Significance," *La Bul. Sci., Fak. Terkultura, Kyusa Imp. Univ.*, **5**, 254–263 (1933).

41. Thut, H. F., "Relative Humidity Variations Affecting Transpiration," *Am. J. Botan.*, **25**, 589–595 (1938).

42. Thut, H. F., "The Relative Humidity Gradient of Stomatal Transpiration," *Am. J. Botan.*, **26**, 315–319 (1939).

43. Turrell, F. M., "Leaf Surface of a Twenty-one-year-old Catalpa Tree," *Proc. Iowa Acad. Sci.*, **41**, 79–84 (1934).

44. Turrell, F. M., "The Area of the Internal Exposed Surface of Dicotyledon Leaves," *Am. J. Botan.*, **23**, 255–264 (1936).

45. Turrell, F. M., "A Quantitative Morphological Analysis of Large and Small Leaves of Alfalfa, with Special Reference to Internal Surface," *Am. J. Botan.*, **29**, 400–415 (1942).

46. Turrell, F. M., "Correlation Between Internal Surface and Transpiration Rate in Mesomorphic and Xeromorphic Leaves Grown Under Artificial Light," *Botan. Gaz.*, **105**, 413–425 (1944).

47. Turrell, F. M., and Turrell, Margaret E., "The Effect of the Great Drought of 1934 on the Leaf Structure of Certain Iowa Plants," *Proc. Iowa Acad. Sci.*, **50**, 185–194 (1943).

48. Verduin, J., "Diffusion Through Multiperforate Septa. Photosynthesis in Plants," pp. 95–112, Ames, Iowa, Iowa State University Press, 1949.

49. Wylie, R. B., "Differences in Foliar Organization Among Leaves From Four Locations in the Crown of a Single Tree (*Acer platanoides*)," *Proc. Iowa Acad. Sci.*, **56**, 189–198 (1949).

50. Yarwood, C. E., and Hazen, W. E., "The Relative Humidity at Leaf Surfaces," *Am. J. Botan.*, **31**, 129–135 (1944).

7. Use of Thermoelectric Method for Studying the Interrelations between Relative Humidity and Plant Transpiration*

M. E. BLOODWORTH, J. P. LAW, JR., AND J. R. MULKEY

The Texas A & M University, Department of Soil and Crop Sciences, College Station, Texas

ABSTRACT

A thermoelectric method has been developed and used successfully for determining the effect of relative humidity upon plant transpiration. The method is advantageous in that repeated measurements can be made on the same plant without injury to it.

Studies concerning the effect of relative humidity on water transfer rates in plant stems have been conducted under both laboratory and field conditions. The data show that relative humidity does play an important role in the transpiration rate of certain crop plants, as measured by the thermoelectric technique. Temperature has been observed in some cases to have a greater influence in controlling transpiration rates than relative humidity when the latter was below approximately 50 per cent. Furthermore, for cotton plants growing in soil, their transpiration rates were found to become lower when the air temperature was in excess of 100° F and the relative humidity was lowered to 20 per cent or below.

A study of recent data, which were obtained by use of the thermoelectric method, suggests that very low humidities and high air temperatures (arid conditions) can cause a reduction in the rate of plant transpiration in certain field crops such as cotton, even though soil moisture is ample. Apparently, an environment of this kind causes the desiccating power of the surrounding air to become so great that the absorption and transpiration of water by the plants cannot offset the moisture deficit of the air; therefore, the stomates close, water absorption is reduced, and transpiration rates are lowered.

The effects of relative humidity and air temperature upon the amount of water transpired by mature cotton plants grown in both nutrient solution (unlimited water supply) and clay soil are given. Although the total measured amount of water transpired by plants growing in nutrient solution were greater, the amount transpired per unit of leaf-surface area were almost the same for plants growing in the two media.

Additional data are presented which show that the thermoelectric method is well-suited to quantitative measurements of water transpired by cotton plants growing in soils of high moisture levels. A description of the equipment used also is discussed.

INTRODUCTION

The influence of soil water on plant growth is universally recognized, but the direct effect of the relative humidity of the air is sometimes questioned and often discarded as unimportant. However, there are data which have been brought together [2, 5, 6, 8, 9, 11, 13, 14] in recent years to indicate that relative humidity of the air strongly influences water use and fruit set by many plants. According to Hudson,[9] there are few recorded facts available for relating the direct effects of humidity on growth and water-use by plants, especially where humidity

* A contribution of The Texas A & M University, Texas Agricultural Experiment Station, College Station, Texas.

has been treated as an independent factor and separate from evaporation. Reviews by Crafts *et al.*[8] and Went[14] have stated that high humidity usually effects the lowering of transpiration* through the factors associated with it, and the most important one is considered to be temperature. Therefore, in considering the relationship between humidity and plant transpiration, it is always necessary to bring temperature into the overall picture because of its direct bearing on vapor pressure. Wind velocity also is a factor but will not be discussed in this paper.

Because evaporation** alone is a complex phenomenon and plant morphological characteristics add to the complexities, transpiration is an intricate and complicated process which presents many experimental difficulties within itself. Methods have been devised to determine transpirational water losses by plants under both greenhouse and field conditions. However, the researcher is often confronted with the difficult task of interpretation of the data, because of the numerous interrelated factors involved. Without some rigid means of control which can be exercised over all external factors during the course of a study, an explanation of the data may be difficult and in some cases even impossible. Numerous papers have been written to describe water evaporation from plants, soils and free-water surfaces, but relatively few, competent methods and formulas have been developed for expressing water transfer to the atmosphere in simple, absolute and measurable terms.

Some progress has been made at this laboratory in the development of methods for characterizing plant response to the changing soil and aerial environments. Such advancements have been brought about by the development of a controlled environment system[1, 4] which also has been used in conjunction with a thermoelectric method for studying the influence of the various environmental factors on the uptake and movement of water† in certain dicotyledonous-type plants. The

* Transpiration—loss of water from living plants in vapor form.
** Evaporation—process by which the precipitation reaching the surface of the earth is returned to the atmosphere as vapor. It also refers to the net rate at which liquid water is transferred to the atmosphere.
† The terms "water-flow" and "sap-flow" in the stem will be used interchangeably in this paper.

method employed has been used successfully for eight years with cotton, bean, and tomato plants and has not been found to cause injury in any way as a result of continuous measurements on an individual plant.[5, 6] The technique has been developed and used with the idea in mind that it will make available a quick, effective, and accurate method for using selected crop-plants as direct indicators of their environment. Furthermore, the technique provides a measurement or indication of plant response at the time when changes in environment occur, which is an all-important factor in soil-plant-water studies.

Limitations in measurement (instrumentation) methodology, or the inability to measure immediate plant response to the dynamic soil-water-climate system in exact and meaningful terms, are probably the greatest handicaps to the researcher today. Therefore, the main purpose of this paper is to report on several studies which have been concerned with the interrelations of relative humidity and plant transpiration as measured by the thermoelectric method. Although the method has been used primarily in a qualitative way at this laboratory, recent data are presented which indicate that quantitative measurements can be made successfully on cotton plants growing in soils that are maintained at relatively high moisture levels.

METHODS AND PROCEDURES

Thermoelectric Units

The thermoelectric method, as used in studies reported herein, has been described in detail in previous papers.[5, 6] However, a brief discussion will be presented in order to acquaint the reader with the technique and its various uses.

Two plastic-clip arrangements for stem mounting have been used successfully and are shown in Fig. 1. The procedure consists first of a brief application of moderate heat to the external stem area by the chromel-wire heating element, which is located on the lower part of the plastic-clip. Second, by using a small bead-type thermistor* which is in direct contact with the outside bark of the stem

* No. 32A12 thermistor as manufactured by Victory Engineering Company, Springfield Rd., Union, N.J.

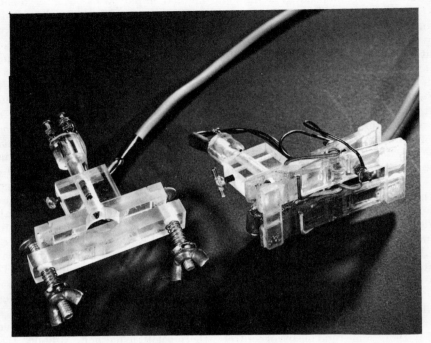

FIG. 1. Plastic-clip arrangements for stem mounting of the thermistor and heating element. Heating element is located on the lower part of each clip.

and permanently spaced 1.90 cm from the center of the heating element, the time required for the movement of the warmed-sap (water) up the stem can be measured. The thermistor forms one-arm of a Wheatstone bridge circuit, Rx, and a Sargent SR recorder* is used as a recording galvanometer of each deflection, as well as for recording the time required for maximum deflection to occur. Since the distance between the center of the heat-source and thermistor is fixed and the time required for a maximum deflection to occur can be measured, the sap (water) flow rate in centimeters per hour is easily calculated. Some difficulties in measurement may be encountered where extremely slow flow rates occur. The two most likely ones would be the transfer of heat due to conduction and convection. Recent papers by Closs,[7] Marshall,[10] and Swanson[12] have presented a modification of the thermoelectric method for measuring sap movement in woody plants.

* Model SR recorder as manufactured by E. H. Sargent & Company, Dallas, Texas.

Controlled Environment System

Environmental factors have been controlled individually and jointly by a test facility as shown in Fig. 2. Although bioclimatic chambers are available commercially, none are constructed in such a way that the aerial parts and root system of plants can be subjected to different climatic conditions at the same time.

The enclosure of the control unit illustrated in Fig. 2 is made of clear plastic and is 4 ft wide, 4 ft high, and 10 ft in length. Air temperature control ranges between 45 and 115°F ($\pm$ 1°F), and relative humidity can be controlled automatically between 15 and 90 per cent ($\pm$ 1 per cent). Wind velocities are available between 1 and 20 mph, and light is furnished to the growing plants through a quality-combination of 64-F96T12HO cool-white fluorescent tubes and eight 100-watt incandescent lamps. More detailed information concerning the controlled environment system has been presented elsewhere by Bloodworth[1, 2, 4].

Methods of Measuring Plant Transpiration Under Controlled Conditions

Cotton plants were grown in 3-gallon glazed-clay pots. The growing media consisted of a Miller clay loam soil and one-half strength standard Hoagland solution for the different plant series. Soil moisture was kept near field capacity in the clay soil, and a constant water-level was maintained (Fig. 3) in the nutrient solution studies.

The method for determining transpirational water losses by cotton plants growing in soil is illustrated in Fig. 2. The surface of each soil-filled pot was covered first with plastic sheeting to prevent water evaporation and then placed on a 20-kg scale for periodic weighing to determine the amount of water lost through transpiration.

A water flow-rate measurement was taken at each weighing and sometime between weighings. This was done for two purposes; first, the water rate measurement provided an indication as to the effect of treatment on transpiration or water absorption; second, the flow-rate was needed later for calculating Qc, which was the volume of water (grams) being transpired per unit of time (hours). Values for Qc were obtained by using the basic hydraulic formula $Q = av$, where a is the cross-section area of a pipe (stem of the plant in this case) and v is the flow rate in centimeters per hour Qm will be designated later (Table 4) as the volume of water (grams) transpired under conditions where all factors are known or can be measured.

In studying numerous problems concerning the interrelations of relative humidity, temperature, and plant transpiration, it was thought desirable to determine the maximum transpiration (potential) which might be expected where water was not a limiting factor. Plants were grown from seedling to two-thirds maturity in a nutrient solution which was contained also in 3-gallon glazed-clay pots. As shown in Fig. 3, the amount of water used and/or transpired was

FIG. 2. Environment control unit used for studying soil-plant-water-climate interrelations. Illustration shows the use of the thermoelectric method for determining transpiration rates of cotton. Water lost through transpiration is determined by weight difference as shown.

Fɪɢ. 3. Water absorption and flow rates are measured by use of the thermoelectric clip arrangement on the stem as illustrated. The amount of water used and transpired is determined by weight of water removed from the bottle shown in the background on the solution balance. Soil and nutrient solution temperature is controlled by circulating water of constant temperature around the insulated root-system container.

determined by the weight of water removed from the bottle shown in the background on the 20-kg scale. Water removed from the bottle was measured to the nearest gram. Nutrient solution temperature was controlled by circulating water of constant temperature (85°F) through coils which were located around the inside of the root-system container. The "potential" transpiration data, as influenced by relative humidity and temperature, are shown in Tables 1 and 2. Periodic water-flow measurements also were made with the thermoelectric unit.

Leaf Surface Areas

Previous studies have indicated that determining the transpiration of water in grams per square decimeter of leaf surface area probably offers the best solution for comparing individual plants. Therefore, this method was adopted and has been used successfully during the past two years in plant transpiration studies.

Upon completion of the cotton transpiration studies, leaves from each plant were removed immediately by clipping at the petiole and then placed on brown wrapping paper. Black paint was sprayed lightly over the entire mass. Upon drying, the leaf outlines were marked plainly by the paint and permitted immediate area determinations to be made with a planimeter. All leaf areas have been reported in square decimeters (dm^2).

RESULTS AND DISCUSSION

Water Flow Under Field Conditions

The effects of relative humidity, temperature, and wind velocity on water movement rates in the stem of three-fourths mature cotton plants growing under field conditions are presented in Fig. 4. The measured wind velocity at a height of 12 in. above the plant tops was 3.2 mph, and approximately 40 per cent of the available soil moisture had been exhausted when the field data were obtained. The data of Fig. 4 are typical of those obtained

TABLE 1. EXAMPLES OF THE DAILY TRANSPIRATIONAL CYCLE OF MATURE COTTON PLANTS GROWN IN NUTRIENT SOLUTION (I) AND A MILLER CLAY LOAM SOIL (II)

Treatment	Time of Day	Air Temp. (°F)	RH (%)	Rate of Water Absorption (cm/hr)	Water Transpired by Periods (g)	Total Water Transpired in 12 and 24 hours (g)	Water Transpired (g/dm² of leaf area*)
	8 a.m.	100	19	134	—		
	10 a.m.	102	17	143	580		
I	12 noon	102	18	162	920		
Nutrient	2 p.m.	103	16	162	1275		
solution	4 p.m.	102	16	140	940		
	8 p.m.	100	17	102	1785	5500 (12 hr)	21.7
	8 a.m.	—	—	—	585	6085	24.1
	8 a.m.	100	19	81	—		
II	12 noon	100	22	143	292		
Miller clay	4 p.m.	100	21	134	382		
loam soil**	8 p.m.	100	21	103	254	928 (12 hr)	23.9
	8 a.m.	—	—	—	100	1028	26.5

* Leaf area given in square decimeters (dm²). Cotton plant growing in nutrient solution had a leaf-surface area of 253.0 dm². Cotton plant growing in Miller clay loam soil had a leaf-surface area of 38.8 dm².
** Soil moisture content was maintained daily near field capacity.

TABLE 2. EFFECT OF RELATIVE HUMIDITY AND TEMPERATURE UPON THE AMOUNT OF WATER TRANSPIRED BY TWO-THIRDS MATURE COTTON PLANTS GROWING IN NUTRIENT SOLUTION*

Plant Series	Air Temp. (°F)	RH (%)	Maximum Rate of Absorption (cm/hr)	Water Transpired per Plant (g) 8 a.m.-8 p.m.	Water Transpired per Plant (g) 8 p.m.-8 a.m.	Total Water Transpired in 24 hours (g)	Water Transpired (g/dm² of leaf area**) 8 a.m.-8 p.m.
		22	108	2660	460	3120	11.6
A	75	50	76	2020	690	2710	8.9
		80	54	990	620	1610	4.3
		21	120	3960	870	4830	12.9
B	85	54	147	3993	854	4847	13.1
		85	93	2066	859	2925	6.8
		18	143	2683	555	3238	16.2
C	90	46	114	1680	763	2443	12.1
		81	93	1387	484	1871	8.4
		19	163	4633	679	5312	19.7
D	103	54	138	4844	634	5478	17.4
		81	114	3138	751	3889	11.3

* Temperature of the nutrient solution was maintained near 85°F during the period 8 a.m. to 8 p.m. daily Night temperature—70°F; relative humidity—about 80 per cent. Wind velocity was maintained at approximately 2.6 mph during the above period. Average height of cotton plants ranged between 48 and 52 in.
** Average leaf area for the four series were as follows: A—138.1 dm²; B—101.4 dm²; C—230.0 dm²; D—253.0 dm². Each series is an average of four selected plants of the same age and size.

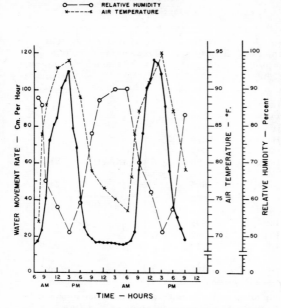

FIG. 4. Effect of daily environment in the field upon water flow rates in the stem of cotton plants as measured by the thermoelectric method.

under field conditions on a clear, sunny day; an intermittent to almost complete cloud cover will cause lower flow-rates to be measured. Furthermore, the response to intermittent cloud covers can be detected almost immediately. Relative humidity will show a rather sharp increase as a result of a decrease in temperature. Generally, the most rapid flow rates have been found to occur between 10 a.m. and 2 p.m. daily. Use of the thermoelectric method in other field studies has been reported previously by Bloodworth.[6]

Transpiration Studies Under Laboratory Conditions

Because of the rapid and numerous daily changes which occur in microclimate around plants, studies concerning the effect of the various climatic components which affect plant transpiration are difficult to conduct and almost impossible to study under field conditions. Therefore, a controlled environment system (Fig. 2) has been developed and used for the purpose of removing as much as possible the daily variations of climate. It must be realized that differences in climate between the field and the controlled environ-

ment system in the laboratory do exist, but eight years of experience in climate control research have shown conclusively that the two conditions can and must be worked together. Furthermore, controlled systems of environment are destined to play a much more important role in future soil-plant-water-nutrition research because many of the fundamental phases must be worked in the laboratory before being tested under field conditions. Much time and effort are often lost in field trials.

The interrelations of relative humidity and temperature upon the amount of water transpired by two-thirds mature cotton plants growing in both nutrient solution and Miller clay loam soil are shown in Tables 1, 2, and 3.

The data of Table 1 are presented to indicate that diurnal transpirational fluctuations occur and can be measured under controlled conditions in the laboratory as well as in the field (Fig. 4). Furthermore, water continues to be used and/or transpired during the night hours between 8 p.m. and 8 a.m., with the greatest amounts being removed by plants growing in the nutrient solution.

A second fact which was found to occur (Tables 1 and 2) concerned the large amounts of water which were transpired by plants growing in nutrient solution as compound to those growing in soil well-supplied with water. These data indicate again that cotton, as well as other crop plants, is an extravagant user of water if such is available, especially when the air temperature is about 100°F with a relative humidity below 50 per cent.

A comparison between plants grown in soil (Table 1 and 3) and those grown in the nutrient solution shows quite clearly that, although an ample supply of water was available for use and/or transpiration by the soil-grown plants, both the total amounts of water removed and those quantities transpired between 8 a.m. and 8 p.m. daily, were much less for the soil-grown cotton plants. This could be expected, perhaps, because of the larger-sized plants which were grown in the nutrient solution.

Total leaf-surface areas of the nutrient-grown plants were much greater; however, when placed on a basis of the amount of water transpired per unit of leaf-surface area (g/dm²), the values, as shown in Tables 1, 2, and 3, appear to have more meaning. The

TABLE 3. EFFECT OF RELATIVE HUMIDITY AND TEMPERATURE UPON THE AMOUNT OF WATER TRANSPIRED BY TWO-THIRDS GROWN COTTON PLANTS GROWING IN A MILLER CLAY LOAM SOIL*

Plant Series	Air Temp. (°F)	RH (%)	Rate of Water Absorption (cm/hr)			Water Transpired per Plant (g) 8 a.m.-8 p.m.	Water Transpired per Plant (g) 8 p.m.-8 a.m.	Total Water Transpired in 24 hours	Water Transpired (g/dm² of Leaf Area**) 8 a.m.-8 p.m.
			8 a.m.	12 noon	4 p.m.				
AB	70	30	124	95	70	601	85	686	12.1
		45	87	79	50	367	78	445	7.4
		70	68	72	55	366	78	444	7.4
CD	85	20	113	123	109	861	88	949	18.1
		45	106	116	97	777	110	887	16.3
		70	78	99	77	566	84	650	11.9
EF	100	20	114	142	115	972	92	1064	19.8
		45	99	152	105	918	79	997	18.7
		70	71	118	112	745	79	824	15.1

* Temperature of the soil ranged from 70°F at night to 85°F during the period 8 a.m. to 8 p.m. daily. Night temperature—70°F; relative humidity—about 80 per cent. Wind velocity was maintained at approximately 2.6 mph during the above period. Average height of cotton plants ranged between 34 and 37 in. Soil moisture was maintained daily near field capacity.

** Average leaf area for the three series were as follows: AB—49.5 dm²; CD—47.7 dm²; EF—49.2 dm². Each series is an average of six selected plants of the same age and size.

interrelated effects of relative humidity and temperatures also are evidenced in the tables by the water flow rates and water transpired per unit of leaf-surface area, regardless of whether plants were grown in soil or nutrient solution.

As evidenced from the data presented herein and other data which have been obtained from similar studies in the soil physics laboratory, the reporting of plant transpiration on a grams per square decimeter basis is valid and probably the best way to compare individual plants when considering transpirational water losses.

Further evidence concerning the interrelations of relative humidity and air temperature on water flow rates in the stem of cotton plants is well illustrated in Fig. 5. These data have been reported by Bloodworth[2] and follow closely those presented previously in Tables 2 and 3. It has been found in some cases, as shown in the top curve of Fig. 5, that water flow rates can be reduced with the occurrence of extremely low humidities (5 to 10 per cent) and high temperatures, such as those commonly found in many parts of the Southwest and West.

A flow reduction of this kind is brought about, perhaps, because the desiccating power of the atmosphere is so great that water absorption and transpiration are unable to off-set such an extreme drying condition; therefore, closure of the stomates apparently occurs which, in turn, causes a reduction in both water absorption and water flow rates as measured on the plant's stem. This effect has not been observed when lower air temperatures have prevailed; consequently, humidity must play an important role in the water economy of crop plants such as cotton and should not be minimized as a climatic component in soil-plant-water research.

Quantitative Measurements of Transpiration

As stated previously, the thermoelectric method for measuring water flow rates in the stem of plants has been used almost entirely as a qualitative indicator of environmental factors on transpiration. However, to make the method more practical and usable under both laboratory and field conditions, studies have been initiated for using the technique to measure quantitatively the amount of water transpired for any measured flow rate in the stem. As expected, many difficulties have been encountered but the possibility of success appears to be good. Data from some of the

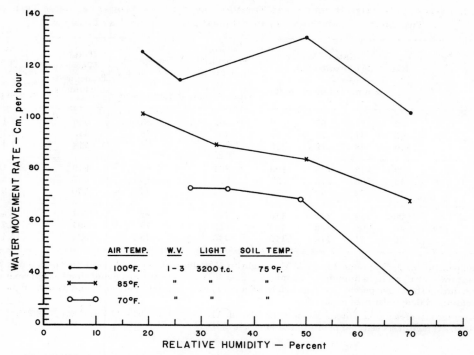

FIG. 5. Water flow rates *vs* relative humidity as affected by different air temperature levels. The environment control unit (Fig. 2) was used to obtain the above data.

preliminary studies are shown in Table 4. Qm indicates the actual measured amount of water transpired (grams by weight) for a given period, and Qc is the calculated amount for the same period and at a specific rate of flow for the same time interval.

Determination of Qm and Qc

The value for Qm, which was the quantity of water transpired for a given period of time, was determined by actual weighing as shown in Fig. 2. Evaporation of water from the soil surface was prevented by covering it with two thicknesses of plastic sheeting.

In determining the values for Qc, several methods were employed and none have been entirely satisfactory. However, Qc values presented in Table 4 were derived in the following way; the hydraulic formula, $Q = av$, where Q = quantity of water in cm³ or grams, a = cross-sectional area in cm², and v = velocity of flow in cm/hr was used in several modified forms. Initially, the value for a was determined by making thin sections and determining, by use of a microscope, the cross-

sectional area of the xylem in the stem of cotton plants which had been subjected to climatic control conditions. However, more recent studies have shown that use of the entire cross section of the stem for calculating a has provided a calculated value of Qc that was much closer to the measured value—Qm. Use of the xylem area has not given consistent results, whereas the total stem cross section has proven to be more useful. From the practical aspects, the total stem area is much more useful because it can be calculated quickly from a simple stem-diameter measurement.

The ratio of Qm/Qc, as shown in Table 4, is interrelated with air temperature and relative humidity, as well as the daily period in which flow rate measurements were taken. As shown in Table 4, only two periods are presented—8 a.m. to 12 noon and 12 noon to 4 p.m. However, more recent data have indicated that perhaps the 11 a.m. to 2 p.m. period would be more useful because this is the interval of time in which maximum transpiration of cotton has occurred in both the laboratory and field.

TABLE 4. EFFECT OF TEMPERATURE AND RELATIVE HUMIDITY ON TRANSPIRATION RATES OF TWO-THIRDS MATURE COTTON PLANTS GROWN IN MILLER CLAY LOAM SOIL

Plant Series	Air Temp. (°F)	RH (%)	Average Rate of Water Absorption (cm/hr)			Total Water Transpired (g) 8 a.m.-8 p.m.	Qm (av in g/hr) 8 a.m.-12 noon	Qc (av in g/hr) 8 a.m.-12 noon	Qm (av in g/hr) 12 noon-4 p.m.	Qc (av in g/hr) 12 noon-4 p.m.	$\dfrac{Qm}{Qc}$ 8 a.m.-12 noon	$\dfrac{Qm}{Qc}$ 12 noon-4 p.m.
			8 a.m.	12 noon	4 p.m.							
AB	70	30	124	95	70	601	62	58	56	46	1.06	1.21
		45	87	79	50	367	39	50	31	31	0.78	1.00
		70	68	72	55	366	41	46	30	34	0.89	0.88
CD	85	20	113	123	109	861	83	74	85	69	1.12	1.23
		45	106	116	97	777	78	74	72	62	1.05	1.16
		70	78	99	77	566	56	63	57	49	0.89	1.16
EF	100	20	114	142	115	972	90	91	101	73	0.99	1.38
		45	99	152	105	918	104	96	82	68	1.08	1.20
		70	71	118	112	745	66	76	71	71	0.87	1.00

Plans are now underway to explore further the 11 a.m. to 2 p.m. period to determine if a better relationship between Qm and Qc can be obtained.

An application of the findings can be made directly to irrigated conditions which concern problems of evapotranspiration. For example, if cotton plants are in the bloom and fruiting stage and are growing in 38-in. row widths with two plants per linear foot of row, the amount of water transpired between 8 a.m. and 8 p.m. (Table 3; Series EF at 20 per cent RH—972 grams) would amount to 0.26 in. The amount transpired for the 24-hour period (1064 grams) would be 0.28 in. Field evapo-transpiration rates for similar climatic conditions and about the same age cotton plants growing under conditions of medium to high moisture levels would range between 0.30 and 0.35 in. per day.[3]

The foregoing example illustrates two important aspects of soil-plant-water relations quite well: first, the greatest amount of water is lost through transpiration when the plants form an almost-complete canopy over the soil surface. This fact has been found to be correct in field experiments; second, the calculated value for transpiration—0.28 in. per day—is in line with actual values obtained in field irrigation studies[3] and shows convincingly that the methods and techniques presented herein are valid, even though added refinements are needed. Furthermore, the results show that the data obtained from soil-plant-water-climate studies under controlled environment conditions of the laboratory may be transferred to the field with a high degree of confidence in many cases.

Although the data presented, as well as the thermoelectric method and its uses, appear to offer much promise for direct application, it should be stressed that many problems remain apparent but there is a likelihood that they can be overcome as the limitations of instrumentation are mastered, Future studies will be pursued with these points in mind.

SUMMARY

A thermoelectric method for measuring water flow rates in selected agricultural crop plants has been used successfully for studying the interrelations between relative humidity and transpiration of cotton plants. Effectiveness of the method has been evaluated under both field and laboratory conditions. In the latter case, a test facility was used for controlling climatic factors of environment.

Application of the method consisted of a brief, local application of moderate heat to the stem of the plant and then detection of the rate at which the slightly warmed water moved in the stem. The technique was found to be advantageous in that repeated measurements could be taken on the same intact plant without injury. Furthermore, plant response to certain treatments could be studied at or during the time they occurred, which, in itself, is a significant improvement over methods which are presently available for soil-plant-water-studies.

The data indicate that for a given air temperature, relative humidities below about 50 per cent tend to cause high rates of transpiration as well as total water transpired. Air temperature was observed to be more effective in bringing about accelerated transpiration rates when it reached 85°F and proceeded to cause an increase of water transfer until 100 to 103°F were reached. Also, air temperatures were found to have a greater influence in controlling transpiration than relative humidity, especially when the latter was below 50 per cent.

Generally, previous use of the thermoelectric method has been confined to qualitative measurements; however, the data presented show that the technique, when properly calibrated, can be used as a quantitative measurement of water transpired by cotton plants. The amount of water transpired under controlled laboratory conditions was calculated to be 0.28 in. per day. Under similar field conditions, evapotranspiration values would range between 0.27 and 0.35 in. per day.

Although added refinements are needed, the reported data show that soil-plant-water-

climate studies conducted under controlled environment conditions of the laboratory may be transferred to the field with a high degree of confidence in many cases.

References

1. Bloodworth, M. E., "A Controlled Environment System for Studying Soil-plant-water Relationships," accepted for publication in *Agron. J.*
2. Bloodworth, M. E., "Effect of Soil Temperature on Water-use by Plants," *Trans. Intern. Congr. Soil Sci.*, **1**, 153–163 (1960).
3. Bloodworth, M. E., "Some Principles and Practices in the Irrigation of Texas Soils," *Texas Agr. Expt. Sta. Bull.*, 937 (1959).
4. Bloodworth, M. E., "The Use of Climatic Control for Determining Transpirational Water Losses by Plants," paper presented at Southwest Section Meeting, American Society of Agricultural Engineers, Texarkana, Texas, April, 1960.
5. Bloodworth, M. E., Page, J. B., and Cowley, W. R., "A Thermoelectric Method for Determining the Rate of Water Movement in Plants," *Soil Sci. Soc. Am. Proc.*, **19**, 411–414 (1955).
6. Bloodworth, M. E., Page, J. B., and Cowley, W. R., "Some Applications of the Thermoelectric Method for Measuring Water Flow Rates in Plants," *Agron. J.*, **48**, 222–228 (1956).
7. Closs, R. L., "The Heat-pulse Method for Measuring Sap Flow in a Plant," *New Zealand J. Sci.*, **1**, 281–288.
8. Crafts, A. S., Currier, H. B., and Stocking, C. R., "Water in the Physiology of Plants," Waltham, Mass., Chronica Botanica Co., 1949.
9. Hudson, J. P., "Control of the Plant Environment," New York, Academic Press, Inc., 1957.
10. Marshall, D. C., "Measurement of Sap Flow in Conifers by Heat Transport," *Plant Physiol.*, **33**, 385–396 (1958).
11. Steward, F. C., "Plant Physiology. III. Plants in Relation to Water and Solutes," New York, Academic Press, 1959.
12. Swanson, R. H., "An Instrument for Detecting Sap Movement in Woody Plants," Station Paper 60, Rocky Mt. Forest and Range Expt. Sta. Ft. Collins, Colo., 1962.
13. Thomas, M., "Plant Physiology," New York, Philosophical Library, Inc., 1956.
14. Went, F. W., "The Experimental Control of Plant Growth," Waltham, Mass., Chronica Botanica Co., 1957.

8. Programming Relative Humidity in Combination with Fluctuating Temperatures: The Influence of Relative Humidity on Development of Tropical Fruit Flies and Other Insects

N. E. FLITTERS

Entomology Research Division, Agricultural Research Service, U.S.D.A., Brownsville, Texas

ABSTRACT

Studies were conducted with the oriental fruit fly (Dacus dorsalis Hendel), melon fly (Dacus cucurbitae Coquillett), Mediterranean fruit fly [Ceratitus capitata (Wiedmann)], Mexican fruit fly [Anastrepha ludens (Loew)], German cockroach [Blatella germanica (L.)], brown soft scale (Coccus hesperidum L.), and other insects, in specially designed bioclimatic chambers wherein temperatures can be controlled from −5 to 125°F, ±1°F dry-bulb temperature, and relative humidity controlled concomitantly through a range of 6 to 100 per cent, ±3 per cent relative to dew point. Fluctuating patterns of temperature and relative humidity were simulated in the bioclimatic cabinets as they occurred naturally in selected agricultural sites in the United States; and the influence of these factors on the potential distribution, development, and reproduction of the insects was determined.

Areas having a dry climate with temperature patterns fluctuating within a range favorable for development were compared with humid areas having a similar pattern of temperature. Insect development and reproduction were shown to be affected by humidity values, especially in the near-critical temperature developmental zone.

The high relative humidities in the simulated site of Charleston, S. C., caused host fruits to decay rapidly, thus retarding fruit fly development and resulting in heavy larval mortalities.

Low relative humidities and high temperatures in the simulated El Centro, Calif., site caused desiccation of adult insects before they could attain sexual maturity. Cockroach activity was greater under conditions of high humidity, but low relative humidities aided the development of brown soft scale. High humidity increased the rate of reproduction in the fruit flies, and, to a lesser extent, in the cockroach.

Fundamental investigations of the influence of humidity and other climatic factors, singly, and in various combinations, on the development, abundance, and behavior of insects and mites, are in progress in both field and laboratory. Diapause, cold and heat tolerances, and microniche variations are currently receiving the greatest attention.

INTRODUCTION

To evaluate the relationship between climatic and biological processes, entomologists in the U.S. Department of Agriculture had equipment designed to simulate temperature and relative humidity patterns as they occur in nature.

The use of equipment to simulate climate was not a new idea, but the practical application of industrial equipment to control the exacting temperatures and relative humidities required for such research investigations was a milestone in the field of insect biometeorology.

The primary purpose of the bioclimatic-cabinet operation was to develop criteria for determining the ability of recently introduced insect pests, or those that potentially threaten us from foreign shores, to reproduce and develop to pest proportions in climates representative of important fruit-, vegetable-, and other crop-production areas in the United States.

Recently, these investigations were expanded to include studies on the influence of factors of climate individually and in various combinations on the life processes which affect development, seasonal occurrence, abundance, and distribution of insects and related arthropods; to develop concepts and criteria for predicting the occurrence or abundance of those species having agricultural importance; and to obtain microclimatological records essential for evaluating biological data.

The purpose of this brief paper is to review the results of studies in Honolulu, Hawaii, and Brownsville, Texas, on tropical fruit flies and other important insects.

Some of the early attempts to reproduce fluctuating temperatures and humidities have been carefully reviewed and summarized by Shelford[25] and Uvarov.[28] Significant entomological information has accrued from the use of rather simple equipment such as that designed by Headlee,[12] Stone,[26] Wishart,[29] and Munger.[19] Today, there are innumerable environmental chambers in a confusing price range; but they exemplify our progress in the field of ecology. No longer do we have to go to the field to study a specific problem—we bring records of the field conditions to the laboratory and simulate them with remarkable accuracy.

The bioclimatic cabinets used in our particular studies have been fully described in several publications.[5-9, 15-18] Thus a brief description should suffice at this time.

BIOCLIMATIC SIMULATION EQUIPMENT

The bioclimatic cabinets measure 10×12 ft and are 8 ft high (Fig. 1). Each is provided with two insulated doors, separated by a vestibule measuring $4 \times 4 \times 7$ ft. These doors provide entry into a stainless-steel

Fig. 1. A bioclimatic cabinet, showing (1) entrance door and vestibule, and (2) temperature and relative humidity transmitters and recorders.

working space measuring $6 \times 6 \times 7$ ft. Attached to the exterior walls of the cabinet are air-conditioning controls and instruments that permit the circulating air within the cabinet to be cooled, humidified, dried or heated as required by the cam transmitter. The major advantage provided by the equipment is that temperatures and humidities can be controlled in smoothly varying patterns such as occur naturally. Temperatures may be controlled to within plus or minus 1°F over the range −5 to +125°F. Humidities within this same temperature range may be controlled to within plus or minus 2 per cent over the range from 6 to 98 per cent. The unique feature is that relative humidity can be controlled at subfreezing temperatures.

In all cabinets temperature can be raised or lowered by 40°F and relative humidity lowered by 60 per cent, both in 60 minutes. Lamps designed to give a wide spectral band of visible light provide simulated daylight within the cabinets. These lights are automatically turned on and off by means of time-clocks, the settings of which are periodically varied to simulate natural photoperiods.

Studies were conducted with fruit flies in 12-in. diameter globular screen cages each having plastic-screen base fitted with a heavy zipper to facilitate introduction and removal of ovipositional substrates, food, water, and insects.

The cages were suspended from a bicycle-wheel assembly, the shaft of which passed through the ceiling of the chamber. The wheel, measuring 26 in. in diameter, permitted the suspension of four cages from its periphery. By means of suspension rods of varying lengths, the wheel could carry a maximum of 12 cages.

In order to minimize positional differences, cages were rotated at a speed of 1 rpm by means of a ⅓-hp electric motor connected to the bicycle wheel shaft through a gear-reduction box, pulleys, and belts. A slip clutch and bearing mounted on the shaft of the wheel allowed the cages to be stopped for observation or manipulation of biological material without interfering with operation of the gear train. So as to reduce further the positional effect, individual globular cages were also rotated intermittently, each on its own axis.

Cockroaches, houseflies (*Musca domestica* L.), and stable flies [*Stomoxys calcitrans* (L.)] were tested in standard 10×10-in. screen cages with removable glass fronts. Small citrus seedlings infested with brown soft scale (*Coccus hesperidum* L.) were held in 8-in. pots on the floor of the cabinet. All cages and plants were completely randomized.

METHODS

Insect studies, particularly those with fruit flies, were designed to demonstrate the effects of different patterns of fluctuating temperatures and relative humidities on the activity and development of the test insects during their complete life cycles. Testing involved detailed observations and measurements of preoviposition and sexual-development periods, mating, reproduction, rates of development, and dynamics of progeny buildup. Significant changes in behavior patterns and progeny climate tolerances were also carefully evaluated.

Reliability of biological results was evaluated by conducting a life-history study in an outdoor insectary and comparing the findings with those obtained by simulating the same climatic conditions in the bioclimatic cabinets.

In each cabinet one or more cages were maintained with mature adult insects from the insectary. Adequate food and water were readily available to the insects at all times. Fruit and oviposition substrate were exposed to infestation by these adults for 24 hours, 3 times weekly. After exposure, the substrate was placed within a specially constructed screen cage, given an identification number, dated, and held in the same cabinet.

A second group of caged insects, 1 to 3 days old, was maintained in each cabinet to study the effects of the simulated climate on the preoviposition or sexual maturity of the insect. Visual observations for copulatory action were made daily at sundown since the oriental, melon, and Mexican fruit flies are crepuscular in their mating habits. With fruit, house, and stable flies, oviposition indicated that females had matured and that mating had been consummated. With scales, the presence of nymphs indicated that sexual maturity had occurred; and with roaches, the presence of egg cases and nymphs indicated sexual maturity.

Adult progeny from infestations occurring in the different climates were collected daily as they emerged, counted by sexes, and caged according to generation.

In addition, studies to determine the effect of specific climate upon preimaginal stages of the insects were conducted weekly. The differences in growth rates of these stages, represented by eggs, larvae, and pupae, were correlated with the factors of climate then being simulated.

The bioclimatic-cabinet investigations have been in progress just in excess of 12 years during which time more than 30 climatological sites have been simulated. Certain of these sites were simulated initially in Hawaii and again during the bioclimatic studies in Texas. Following completion of the tropical fruit fly studies, the program was expanded to include a greater variety of insects. Our experimental design was directed toward obtaining basic information pertaining to the effects of specific factors of climate, singly and collectively, on insect activity, development, and perpetuation.

INSECT SENSITIVITY TO TEMPERATURE AND RELATIVE HUMIDITY

To a creature as small as an insect, the relationship of its surface to its volume places it at a tremendous disadvantage in combatting the two principles of climate—temperature and humidity.

Insects are very sensitive to changes in temperature and humidity. They become less active as the temperature falls and more active as it rises until a peak activity is reached at a specific value, beyond which they become negatively thermotropic. This behavior was evidenced in the study with tropical fruit flies. These flies, like most insects, do not have the mechanism for covering their body surfaces with moisture. As a consequence, they desiccate in extreme temperatures, particularly when accompanied by low relative humidity.

Each species has its optimal temperature and humidity range. When the macro-environment fails to offer the needed comfort level, the insect seeks a microenvironment, usually provided by vegetation. Certain in-

sects have the ability to go into a resting stage. Thus, they can persist in regions from which they might be eliminated by extremes of climate, or they can maintain a high population in an area which might otherwise be capable of supporting but a few individuals. Open, dry environments are populated predominantly by sucking insects which can compensate for moisture loss by constant intake of plant or animal juices.

Thus, even though insects are coldblooded animals, they have had to develop a high degree of sensitivity to the stimuli of temperature and humidity to exist.

RESULTS

The results of our tropical fruit fly studies have been well documented.[6, 7, 9, 15-18] Various criteria were used to determine the effect of temperature and humidity on these insects, including the specific season and its duration, the extent to which successful infestation in

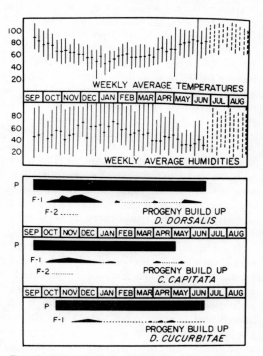

FIG. 2. Simulated site of El Centro, California, showing (1) weekly average temperature and relative humidity, and (2) progeny buildup of the oriental fruit fly (*Dacus dorsalis* Hendel), the melon fly (*Dacus cucurbitae* Coq.), and the Mediterranean fruit fly [*Ceratitus capitata* (Wied)].

fruits took place, and the generations of progeny produced in a single year plus population levels and reproductive capacity. The duration of individual stages of the fruit flies, as well as of the entire life cycle, was chiefly influenced by temperature. Soil moisture had a definite influence on the survival of the insect in its prepupal stage, and to a lesser degree on freshly formed pupae during the initial period of their existence. But again, temperature influenced the degree and extent of these effects.

Conditions optimum for development appeared to be associated with a certain range of temperature and humidity and not with specific, constant values. However, individual preimaginal processes had specific thermal preferendums within this optimal range. High temperatures, lethal to adults, had an accelerating effect on larval development in fruit and adult emergence from puparia in the soil. Both fruit and soil provided sufficient moisture to offset the desiccating effects of temperature.

Winter conditions typical of certain southern California sites depressed development, in one instance for periods up to 5 months in the simulated site of Riverside. Figures 2 and 3 illustrate the inhibiting effect

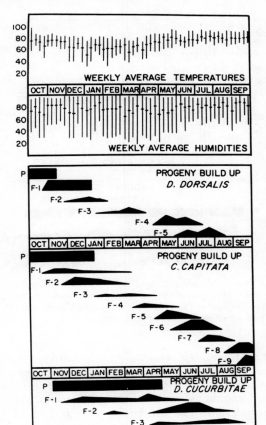

FIG. 4. Simulated site of Orlando, Florida, showing (1) weekly average temperature and relative humidity, and (2) progeny buildup of the oriental fruit fly (*Dacus dorsalis* Hendel), the melon fly (*Dacus cucurbitae* Coq.), and the Mediterranean fruit fly [*Ceratitus capitata* (Wied.)].

of winter temperatures simulated for El Centro, California, upon fruit fly reproduction and the lethal effect of high summer temperatures and concomitant low humidities on the adult population. Both extremes prohibited permanent establishment and perpetuation of the four fruit fly species studied. The upper section of each graph illustrates the weekly average temperatures and humidities (horizontal bars) and their weekly ranges (vertical bars). The progeny recovery and population density of the four species of fruit flies are illustrated by the silhouettes in the lower portion of the Figures.

In contrast to El Centro, the simulated Orlando, Florida, site (Figs. 4 and 5) provided

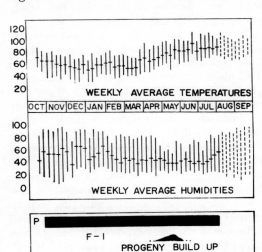

FIG. 3. Simulated site of El Centro, California, showing (1) weekly average temperature and relative humidity, and (2) progeny buildup of the Mexican fruit fly (*Anastrepha ludens* Loew).

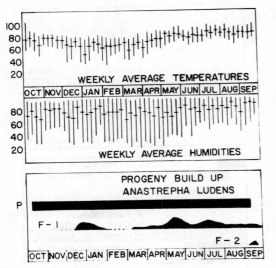

FIG. 5. Simulated site of Orlando, Florida, showing (1) weekly average temperature and relative humidity, and (2) progeny buildup of the Mexican fruit fly (*Anastrepha ludens* Loew).

year-round temperature and humidity patterns conducive to continued fruit fly perpetuation. The populations of all species were self-sustaining after reaching a strong F-1 population. The differences in numbers of generations were largely due to differences in length of a particular insect's life cycle, which is influenced by climate.

Although temperature conditions such as occur in Charleston, S. C., are within the fruit fly's preferendum for a greater part of the year, extreme humidity causes rapid decay of host fruits, killing off larval stages and creating conditions suitable for the development of disease.

Data from the bioclimatic-cabinet studies[5, 7, 15, 17, 18] show rather conclusively that self-sustaining infestations of all the four species of fruit flies investigated (oriental, Mediterranean, melon, and Mexican) could survive winter conditions in all areas of the United States where the average season provides no more than a 2-month period with the average temperature below 57°F. This favorable zone includes the lower Delta region in Louisiana; the lower Rio Grande Valley and a short coastal strip extending from Brownsville to approximately Galveston, Texas; the whole of southern Florida; the Imperial Valley of

California; and the Yuma and Lower Gila River areas in Arizona.

In another study of the German cockroach, conducted in a chamber in which the temperatures diurnally fluctuated from 95 to 72°F (mean 82°F) and relative humidities ranged from 20 to 40 and 85 to 95 per cent, the higher humidity range was much more conducive to insect activity and reproduction than the lower range. The German cockroaches were able to complete their cycle (egg to egg) in 72 days under the high humidity, whereas in the arid chamber, 102 days were required.

Citrus rust mite on naturally infested seedling citrus, subjected to the same extreme patterns of temperature and relative humidity, were deleteriously affected by the low humidity. Both egg hatch and adult survival were materially reduced.

Brown soft scales infesting citrus plants, introduced into these same climatic extremes, developed quicker under the drier atmospheric conditions. The scales thus demonstrated a low moisture tolerance.

Adult house flies could not tolerate the low humidity and high temperature, and mortality was very heavy. However, under the same conditions, the growth of egg, larval and pupal stages was somewhat accelerated since these stages are spent in moist media; but again, emerging adults did not live very long.

The effects of humidity on insect activity, abundance, reproduction, and longevity have been rather well documented. Bachmetjew in 1907 observed that the pupae of a sphinx moth (*Sphinx ligustri* L.) can lose up to 80 per cent of their weight through evaporation during the period of hibernation without serious deleterious effects. Eggs of grasshoppers can be so desiccated that they lose 51 per cent of their original weight without losing their viability.[20, 21] Published data on the influence of humidity on insect development are few and contradictory, and no exacting experimental data appear to exist on the actual influence of humidity on structural characters of insects. However, several authors[2, 3, 12, 13, 27] reported that the rate of reproduction in certain insects—bean weevil [*Acanthoscelides obtectus* (Say)], Colorado potato beetle [*Leptinotarsa decemlineata* (Say)], drosophila, fleas, the European cornborer [*Ostrinia nubilalis* (Hübner)], and the granary weevil [*Sitophilus granarius* (L.)]—is increased by higher percentages of humidity in the air.

The dependence of water balance in insects on water content of their food is unquestionably very important. Insects such as weevils, girdling beetles, and certain other borers, living and feeding upon dry materials, have a low water content, but the herbivorous-feeding insects—aphids, caterpillars, etc.—have obviously a very high water content. A very interesting series of estimations of body-water content for various insects was compiled by Robinson.[22]

Thus it can be concluded that because an insect is small it must balance the moisture between its external and internal structure to cope with the losses sustained from its proportionately large evaporating surface. This problem of moisture balance increases as the size of the insect decreases.

References

1. Bachmetjew, P., "Experimentelle entomologische Studien vom physikalisch-chemischen Standpunkte aus. Band II. Einfluss der äusseren Faktoren auf Insekten," Sophia, Staatdruckerei, 1907.

2. Bacot, A., "A Study of the Bionomics of the Common Rat Fleas and Other Species Associated with Human Habitations, with Special Reference to the Influence of Temperature and Humidity at Various Periods of the Life-history of the Insect," *J. Hyg.*, **3**, 447–654 (1914).

3. Breitenbrecher, J. K., "The Relation of Water to the Behaviour of the Potato Beetle in a Desert," *Carnegie Inst., Wash., Publ.*, **263**, 341–384 (1918).

4. Buxton, P. A., "Evaporation from the Mealworm and Atmospheric Humidity," *Proc. Roy. Soc. London Ser. B*, **106**, 560–577 (1930).

5. Flitters, N. E., and Messenger, P. S., "Bioclimatic Studies of the Oriental Fruit Fly in Hawaii," *J. Econ. Ent.*, **46**, 401–403 (1953).

6. Flitters, N. E., and Messenger, P. S., "Bioclimatic Studies of Three Species of Fruit Flies in Hawaii," *Jour. Econ. Entomol.*, **47**, 756–765 (1954).

7. Flitters, N. E., and Messenger, P. S., "Effect of Temperature and Humidity on Development and Distribution of Hawaiian and Mexican Fruit Flies," *J. Rio. Grande Valley Hort. Soc.*, **12**, 7–13 (1958).

8. Flitters, N. E., Messenger, P. S., and Husman, C. N., "Bioclimatic Cabinets Used in Studies on the Mexican Fruit Fly and the Pink Bollworm," *ARSJ.*, 33–33 (1956).

9. Flitters, N. E., "Application of Temperature and Relative Humidity Simulation Techniques to Insect Distribution Problems," *Proc. Intern. Soc. Climatology Biometeorology*, 1961, 523–530 (1962).

10. Hall, F. G., "The Vital Limit of Exsiccation of Certain Animals," *Biol. Bull.*, **42**, 31–51 (1922).

11. Headlee, T. J., Some Facts Relative to the Influence of Atmospheric Humidity on Insect Metabolism," *J. Econ. Entomol.*, **10**, 31–41 (1917).

12. Headler, T. J., "An Apparatus for the Study of Effects of Constant *vs.* Variable Temperatures on the Speed of Insect Metabolism," *J. N.Y. Entomol. Soc.*, **37**, 25–27 (1929).

13. Huber, L. L., Neiswander, C. R., and Salter, R. M., "The European Cornborer and its Environment," *Bull. Ohio Agric. Expt. Sta.*, **429**, 1–196 (1928).

14. Janisch, E., "Experimentelle Untersuchungen über die Wirkung der Umveltfaktoren auf Insekten. i. Die Massenvehrmehrung der Baumwolleneule *Prodenia littoralis* in Ägypten," *Z. Morph. Oekol. Tiere*, **17**, 339–416 (1930).

15. Messenger, P. S., and Flitters, N. E., "The Oriental Fruit Fly—Bioclimatic Cabinet Studies," California Joint Legislative Committee on Agriculture and Livestock Problems Bull., 1954.

16. Messenger, P. S., and Flitters, N. E., "Bioclimatic Studies of the Mexican Fruit Fly," California Avocado Society Bull., 1957.

17. Messenger, P. S., and Flitters, N. E., "Effect of Constant Temperature Environments on the Egg Stage of Three Species of Hawaiian Fruit Fly," *Ann. Entomol. Soc. Am.*, **51**, 109–119 (1958).

18. Messenger, P. S., and Flitters, N. E., "Effect of Variable Temperature Environments on Egg Development of Three Species of Fruit Flies," *Ann. Entomol. Soc. Am.*, **52**, 191–204 (1959).

19. Munger, Francis, "An Adaptation of a Thermograph to Relate Variable Temperature," *J. Econ. Entomol.*, **37**, 554–556 (1944).

20. Parker, J. R., "Some Effects of Temperature and Moisture upon the Activities of Grasshoppers and their Relation to Grasshopper Abundance and Control," *Trans. Intern. Congr. Entomol.*, *4th*, **2**, 322–332 (1929).

21. Parker, J. R., "Some Effect of Temperature and Moisture Upon *Melanoplus mexicanus*, Saussure, and *Camnula pellucida*, Scudder," *Bull. Univ. Montana Agric. Expt. Sta.*, **223**, 1–132 (1930).

22. Robinson, W., "Water Conservation in Insects," *J. Econ. Entomol.*, **21**, 897–902 (1928A).

23. Roubaud, E., "Recherches Biologiques sur les Conditions de Viviparité et de Vie Larvaire de *Glossina palpalis*," *R. Desv. C. R. Acad. Sci. Paris*, **148**, 195–197 (1909).

24. Schubert, W., "Biologische Untersuchungen über die Rübenblattwanze, *Piesma quadrata*, Fieb., im schlesischen Befallgebiet," *Z. Angew. Entomol.*, **13**, 129–155 (1928).

25. Shelford, V. E., "An Experimental Investigation of the Relations of the Codling Moth to Weather and Climate," *Ill. Nat. Hist. Surv. Bull.*, **16**, 307–440 (1927).

26. Stone, W. E., "An Instrument for the Reproduction, Regulation and Control of Variable Temperatures," *J. Wash. Acad. Sci.*, **29**, 410–415 (1939).

27. Strachov-Koltchin, A. I., "The Grain Weevil (*Calendra granaria* L.)," *Tr. Voronezhsk.*, **1**, 1–74 (1915).

28. Uvarov, B. P., "Insects and Climate," *Trans. Roy. Entomol. Soc. London*, **79**, 1–247 (1931).

29. Wishart, G., "An Adaptation of a Standard Bimetallic Thermoregulator to Control Variable Temperatures," *Can. Entomologist*, **72**, 78–81 (1940).

9. The Measurement of Water Stress in Plants

PAUL J. KRAMER

Department of Botany, Duke University, Durham, North Carolina

ABSTRACT

The most important aspect of plant water relations is the degree of water stress existing in the tissues of the plant. Plant water stress is best measured as diffusion pressure deficit or water potential because the water potential of the soil and the various parts of a plant can be expressed in the same terms, as ergs per gram or equivalent pressure in atmospheres or bars. Measurements of water stress are seldom made because of lack of a suitable method. However, it appears that two methods are available which are useful, at least for moderately high water stress. One method involves the use of a thermocouple hygrometer, the other method depends on measurement of change in density of the solution in which plant tissue is immersed. Our laboratory has made numerous measurements of plant water potential by both methods and finds that they give comparable results for moderate water stress. Both methods seem useful, but measurement of change in density is more suitable for field work than the electric hygrometer.

INTRODUCTION

Much attention has been given to measurement of soil and atmospheric water stress by agriculturists and ecologists. Soil and atmospheric water conditions are important because they affect the rates of absorption and transpiration, and the relative rates of these two processes control the internal water balance of plants. However, more attention ought to be given to measurement of plant water stress itself because this directly affects the physiological and biochemical processes which control the quantity and quality of plant growth, whereas the effects of soil and atmospheric moisture conditions are indirect.[7, 8]

The need for measurement of plant water stress has been appreciated by ecologists and physiologists for over half a century, but there has been no general acceptance of any of the many methods proposed for its measurement. Perhaps the variety of methods discouraged investigators, because of the difficulty in deciding which one to use. Attempts have been made to evaluate plant water stress in terms of water content, amount of water required to saturate plant tissue (water deficit of Stocker,[24] relative turgidity of Weatherley,[30]) stomatal aperture[1,17] and diffusion pressure deficit.[12, 13]

A satisfactory method of measuring plant water stress should have the following characteristics.

(1) There should be a good correlation between rates of physiological processes and the degree of water stress as measured by the method.

(2) A given degree of water stress as measured by the selected method should have similar physiological significance in a wide range of plant materials.

(3) The units employed to measure water stress and the method used to measure it should be applicable to a variety of plant materials and to soil.

(4) The method should be as simple and inexpensive as possible.

(5) It should require a minimum of plant tissue for a measurement.

Water movement into and through plants occurs along gradients of decreasing activity, free energy, or potential of the water. Furthermore, it seems likely that decrease in free energy must be responsible for the effects of water stress on enzyme-catalyzed processes such as carbohydrate and nitrogen metabolism. Thus the best measure of plant water stress probably is the free energy deficit of the water in the plant tissue as compared to pure, free water at the same temperature. This quantity has been termed suction force, suction tension, diffusion pressure deficit, and water potential by various writers. Although it is most widely known as diffusion pressure deficit,[12-14] this term has been criticized as theoretically unsound.[18] Slatyer and Taylor[22] proposed that it be replaced by the term "water potential," and this term will be used hereafter in this paper.

METHODS OF MEASURING WATER STRESS

The usefulness of the concept of water potential is widely appreciated, but it seldom is measured because of uncertainties concerning suitable methods. The principal methods which have been published are the volumetric, gravimetric, vapor equilibration, electric hygrometer, and density methods. These will be described, with special emphasis on those which seem most useful.

The volumetric method described by Ursprung and Blum[25,26] is based on the fact that strips of tissue composed principally of thin-walled parenchyma cells change in dimensions as the cells gain or lose water. If a number of strips of similar tissue of known length are immersed in a series of sucrose or mannitol solutions, the water potential is assumed to be equal to the osmotic pressure of the solution in which no change in length occurs. This method cannot be used on tissue containing thick walled cells because they show little or no change in dimensions with change in turgor and water potential.

The gravimetric method is used on tissue such as beet or potato from which a number of disks or cylinders can be cut. It assumes that the water potential of a tissue is equal to the osmotic pressure of a solution in which pieces of the tissue neither gain nor lose weight. Ashby and Wolf[2] discussed some of the errors which result from infiltration of water into intercellular spaces and from difficulty in drying pieces of tissue uniformly before weighing.

The vapor equilibration method described by Slatyer[21] eliminates errors caused by infiltration and has considerable advantages over the volumetric and gravimetric methods. Weighed samples of plant tissue are placed in closed jars over salt solutions of various osmotic pressures, and the jars are immersed in a water bath for about 24 hours. The samples are reweighed, and the water potential of the tissue is equal to the osmotic pressure of the solution over which no change in weight occurred. The chief disadvantages of this method are the relatively large amount of tissue required to provide samples and the fact that occasionally a series of measurements is unsuccessful because all of the solutions have osmotic pressures above or below the water potential of the tissue.

THE ELECTRIC HYGROMETER METHOD

The electric hygrometer or thermocouple method requires only one small sample of tissue. It also has the added advantage of permitting measurement of the osmotic pressure. Two methods are in use at the present time. We are using the modification of Spanner's method[23] described by Monteith and Owen.[15] It employs the Peltier effect caused by passage of a small current in the reverse direction through a thermocouple junction to cool it and cause condensation of water on it, so it functions as a wet junction in a dry and wet junction thermocouple. The cooling of the wet junction by evaporation, which is controlled by the vapor pressure of the surrounding air, is measured by a galvanometer. By this method, the water vapor pressure in equilibrium with plant material or soil in a closed container is measured. Brix[3] used this method to measure the effects of increasing plant water stress on photosynthesis and respiration of several species of plants.

We use weighing bottles 25×50 mm or 25×40 mm as containers, depending on the size of the sample. The container should be one-quarter to one-half full of the material, more material being needed if the water stress is high than if it is low. A sample of 3 ml of soil is sufficient, and 100 to 200 sq cm of leaf surface give reliable values. The containers are immersed in an inner bath which stands in a large outer bath which is kept a few degrees above the temperature of an air-conditioned room. The temperature of the outer bath is controlled to about 0.001°C by a large mercury thermoregulator, stirrer, and two light bulbs as heating units. Precise control of bath temperature is essential for accurate measurements. A period of 12 to 24 hours in the water bath is required for vapor equilibration. A current of 20 mA is passed through the thermocouple for 60 seconds to cool it and condense water on it. The thermocouple is then connected to the galvanometer, and the maximum deflection caused by cooling resulting from evaporation of the condensed water is recorded. The water potential is then read from a graph constructed from readings obtained with a series of sugar solutions of known osmotic pressures.

In the version of this method described by Richards and Ogata,[19] a droplet of water is placed on the wet junction rather than condensed by the Peltier effect. Apparently, equilibrium can be attained somewhat more rapidly with the Richards and Ogata method, and it also can be used at higher water stresses.[4] The Monteith and Owen method is not satisfactory at a water potential greater than 60 atm, but the Richards and Ogata method is usable at higher water stresses.

The electric hygrometer or thermocouple method has several advantages over all other methods.

(1) It can be used for a variety of tissues and for soil.

(2) Relatively small samples are required.

(3) No preliminary estimation of the water potential is required.

(4) There is little handling of material.

(5) Many samples can be handled in one water bath.

(6) The working time for a determination is very short after the tissue is equilibrated.

The disadvantages are:

(1) It can only be used in the laboratory.

(2) The cost of the equipment is relatively high.

(3) Considerable time is required to assemble, test, and calibrate the equipment.

THE SCHARDAKOW DYE METHOD

The need for a field method seems to be satisfied by the Schardakow dye method, described in Russia by Schardakow,[20] in Germany by Walter and Ellenberg,[29] and in France by Mouravieff.[16] This method has been tested in our laboratory by Brix[9] and more intensively by Knipling.[6]

A series of small test tubes (12 × 75 or 13 × 100 mm) are filled one-third full of sucrose solution of various osmotic pressures covering the range in water potential likely to be encountered in the tissue under study. The difference in osmotic pressure between tubes usually is 2 atm, but for measurement of very low water potentials, 1-atm increments are used. Steps of 5 atm are used where the water stress is unknown but probably high. Enough plant tissue is placed in each tube to fill it to the level of the liquid. A series of control solutions are set up which are identical except that they are lightly colored with methylene blue. After the tissue has been immersed in the test solutions for one or two hours, it is removed, and a drop of colored solution from the control tube is transferred to the corresponding test solution and injected into it by means of a medicine dropper. If the plant material has absorbed water from the test solution the latter will have become more concentrated and the colored drop of control solution will rise to the surface. If the plant material has lost water to the test solution, its concentration and density will have decreased and the colored drop of control solution will sink. The water potential is assumed to be intermediate between the osmotic pressure of the solution in which the drop of test solution rises and that in which it sinks.

Knipling[6] investigated the Schardakow dye method very carefully, using leaves of dogwood, sourwood, and tomato. He found it quite sensitive but subject to certain errors. The chief error seems to result from contamination of the test solutions by solutes escaping from the cut surfaces if the leaves are cut into small pieces to speed up equilibration. Enough solutes escape from the surfaces of uncut tomato leaves to contaminate the test solution. However, the error caused by this type of contamination can be corrected by a longer immersion time which permits enough water to escape from the leaves to compensate for the escape of solutes.

Experiments in which changes in concentration of the test solutions were measured by change in refractive index, as suggested by Ashby and Wolf[2] and Lemée and Laisné,[10] were less satisfactory than the dye method because the method is less sensitive.

DISCUSSION

The most useful measurement of plant water stress seems to be the diffusion pressure deficit or water potential because it can be used to evaluate the water stress of soil as well as of plants. The Schardakow dye method is particularly suitable for field measurements of water potential because it uses simple equipment which is transported easily. However, the electric hygrometer method has certain advantages where material can be transported to a laboratory. It requires only one sample of tissue per measurement, while the dye method requires several. It also is possible to measure the osmotic pressure of the sample used for measurement of water potential. The container is immersed in dry ice to kill the tissue and reequilibrated in a water bath, and the water potential of the dead material is then determined.[4] The electric hygrometer method also can be used for soil and other materials which cannot be measured by the dye method.

It would be desirable to make measurements of water stress on attached leaves, but no satisfactory method is available. Mederski[11] proposed use of a beta-radiation gauge, but this cannot be calibrated in any quantitative fashion. A qualitative estimate of water stress can be made for some species by measurement of stomatal aperture with the infiltration method.[1,17] Measurements of leaf water deficit or relative turgidity have some usefulness,[5] but they do not provide data for the comparison of different species. It appears that measurement of water potential provides the most useful information concerning plant water stress.

References

1. Alvim, P. de T., "Stomatal Opening as a Practical Indicator of Moisture Deficiency in Cacao," *Phyton*, **15**, 79–89 (1960).

2. Ashby, E., and Wolf, R., "A Critical Examination of the Gravimetric Method of Determining Suction Force," *Ann. Botany*, **11**, 261–268 (1947).

3. Brix, H., "The Effect of Water Stress on the Rates of Photosynthesis and Respiration in Tomato Plants and Loblolly Pine Seedlings," *Physiol. Plantarum*, **15**, 10–20 (1962).

4. Ehlig, C. F., "Measurement of Energy Status of Water in Plants with a Thermocouple Psychrometer," *Plant Physiol.*, **37**, 288–290 (1962).

5. Hewlett, J. D., and Kramer, P. J., "The Measurement of Water Deficits in Broadleaf Plants," *Protoplasma*, **56** (1963).

6. Knipling, E. B., "Investigation of the Schardakow Method for the Measurement of Diffusion Pressure Deficit," M.A. Thesis, Duke University, 1963.

7. Kramer, P. J., "The Role of Water in the Physiology of Plants," *Advan. Agron.*, **11**, 51–70 (1959).

8. Kramer, P. J., "Water Stress and Plant Growth," *Agronomy J.*, **55**, 31–35 (1963).

9. Kramer, P. J., and Brix, H., "Measurement of Water Deficits in Plants," International Symposium on Methodology of Plant Eco-Physiology, Montpellier, 1962.

10. Lemée, G., and Laisné, G., "La Méthode Réfractométrique de Mesure de la Succion," *Rev. Gen. Botan.*, **58**, 336–347 (1951).

11. Mederski, H. J., "Determination of Internal Water Status of Plants by Beta Ray Gauging," *Soil Sci.*, **92**, 143–146 (1961).

12. Meyer, B. S., "The Water Relations of Plant Cells," *Botan. Rev.*, **4**, 531–547 (1938).

13. Meyer, B. S., "A Critical Evaluation of the Terminology of Diffusion Phenomena," *Plant Physiol.*, **20**, 142–164 (1945).

14. Meyer, B. S., and Anderson, D. B., "Plant Physiology," 2nd ed., New York, D. Van Nostrand & Co., Inc., 1952.

15. Monteith, J. L., and Owen, P. C., "A Thermocouple Method for Measuring Relative Humidity in the Range 95–100%," *J. Sci. Instr.*, **35**, 443–446 (1958).

16. Mouravieff, I., "Tension de Succion et Déficit de Saturation Hydrique du Tapis Végétal des Pelouses Seches de la Region de Grasse (Alpes Maritimes)," *Bull. Soc. Botan. France*, **106**, 306–309 (1959).

17. Oppenheimer, H. R., and Elze, D. L., "Irrigation of Citrus Trees According to Physiological Indicators," *Palestine J. Botan.*, **R4**, 20–46 (1941).

18. Ray, P., "On the Theory of Osmotic Water Movement," *Plant Physiol.*, **35**, 783–795 (1960).

19. Richards, L. A., and Ogata, G., "Thermocouple for Vapor Pressure Measurement in Biological and Soil Systems at High Humidity," *Science*, **128**, 1089–1090 (1958).

20. Schardakow, W. S., "Wasserhaushalt der Baumwolle," *Arb. Akad. Wiss. Uzbek, SSR.*, cited from Walter and Ellenberg,[29] (1956).

21. Slatyer, R. O., "The Measurement of Diffusion Pressure Deficit in Plants by a Method of Vapor Equilibration," *Australian J. Biol. Sci.*, **11**, 349–365 (1958).

22. Slatyer, R. O., and Taylor, S. A., "Terminology in Plant and Soil-water Relations," *Nature*, **187**, 922 (1960).

23. Spanner, D. C., "The Peltier Effect and Its Use in the Measurement of Suction Pressure," *J. Expt. Botan.*, **2**, 145–168 (1951).

24. Stocker, O., "Das Wasserdefizit von Gefässpflanzen in verschiedenen Klimazonen," *Planta*, **7**, 382–387 (1929).

25. Ursprung, A., and Blum, G., "Zur Methode der Saugkraftmessung," *Ber. Deut. Botan. Ges.*, **34**, 525–539 (1916).

26. Ursprung, A., and Blum, G., "Zur Kenntnis der Saugkraft. VII. Eine neus vereinfochte Methode zur Messung der Saugkraft," *Ber. Deut. Botan. Ges.*, **41**, 338–343 (1923).

27. Walter, H., "Die Hydratur der Pflanze," Jena, G. Fischer, 1931.

28. Walter, H., "The Water Economy and the Hydrature of Plants," *Ann. Rev. Plant Physiol.*, **6**, 239–252 (1955).

29. Walter, H., and Ellenberg, H., "Ökologische Pflanzengeographie," *Fortschr. Botan.*, **20**, 100–117 (1958).

30. Weatherley, P. E., "Studies in the Water Relations of the Cotton Plant. I. The field Measurement of Water Deficits in the Leaves," *New Phytologist*, **49**, 81–97 (1950).

10. Water Vapor as a Critical Component in Sealed Cabins and Pressure Suits

PAUL WEBB

Webb Associates, Yellow Springs, Ohio

ABSTRACT

In the small closed space of a sealed cabin or full pressure suit, the human occupant(s) represents the dominant source of water vapor, and, unless an adequate sink is provided, the increase in water vapor pressure in the enclosure may quickly lead to loss of thermal equilibrium and body heat storage. A number of laboratory experiences and flight projects have borne out the need to deal precisely with the water vapor source and sink relationship. The rates of water vapor produced by man are quite variable, since both insensible and sensible water loss are influenced by a number of environmental conditions.

The relative humidity terminology in common use is a cumbersome and sometimes dangerous way of expressing humidity, since the apparently safe 50 per cent RH condition means far too much water vapor at temperatures above 80 or 90° F.

A rather narrow range of water vapor pressure is recommended for design purposes in pressure suits and sealed cabins. Our experience has resulted in our choosing a range of 5 to 10 mm Hg with a narrow temperature band, for a broad spectrum of activities, clothing, and external environments.

INTRODUCTION

The critical role of water vapor in maintaining human comfort and thermal balance in small sealed spaces has been defined by a variety of experiences in pressure suits, sealed cabins, and test chambers used in aerospace medical research. When water vapor is not carefully controlled but is allowed to build up in these small spaces, the results range from subjective discomfort to excessive storage of body heat. Problems of high humidity have plagued the early experimental work with sealed cabins and pressure suits, and they continue to arise even in some of the more sophisticated environmental designs of the aerospace age. In most cases, the trouble is a mismatch between the water vapor source and sink.

In this paper, the author will recount some troublesome experiences, then briefly describe the human as a source of water vapor, and conclude with a recommended control range for water vapor in these confining situations.

The underlying theme is that water vapor must be dealt with in a conscious and positive manner in confined spaces, as contrasted to our somewhat casual handling of humidity in ordinary situations in our earthly ocean of air. The atmosphere acts as an almost infinite diluent for the small amounts of water vapor produced by a man. That is, his contribution to the prevailing humidity is ordinarily negligible, but in a small space it can become dominant.

ILLUSTRATIVE CASES

The first example of a problem from accumulating water vapor in a small space comes from a rather routine experimental situation some years ago while the author was at the Air Force Aero Medical Laboratory at Wright Field. A series of experiments were being conducted in which four men dressed in flight clothing were observed for a period of 4 to 6 hours under the mild heat of 110°F air/wall temperature in an altitude chamber maintained at 18,000 ft (½ atm pressure). The first three experiments produced sweating and dehydration to the expected level, but the men were able to maintain thermal balance without much trouble. On the fourth experiment, under the same conditions, all subjects stored heat at a rapid rate and had to stop by the end of the second hour. Our puzzlement over this remarkable change in the results was resolved when it was discovered that a new chamber operator had been at the controls, one who had not been indoctrinated in the technique of "ventilating" the altitude chamber. To ventilate, the operator opens a valve to create a small leak from the laboratory room into the low pressure chamber, and balances the inward leak with a valve opening to the vacuum pump; in this way laboratory air is constantly drawn through the chamber and water vapor and odors are not allowed to build up. When ventilated, the chamber vapor pressure was approximately 10 mm Hg, and when the chamber was not ventilated and the four men were present, the vapor pressure built up to over 30 mm Hg.

A number of other examples may be drawn from published reports, several of which have been analyzed and the environmental conditions located on the chart in Fig. 1. These examples are quite varied, both in environments and in the type of clothing and the activity levels of the subjects. Starting in the upper section of Fig. 1, there are four data points shown to illustrate time-limited heat exposure for lightly clothed men who are engaged in light activity. The limit is set by storage of body heat and a condition of incipient heat stroke. The short 0.7 hour limit was established by Blockley et al,[2] and the 2- to 4-hour limits were established by Kaufman.[8]

It is difficult to see in Fig. 1 the specific effect of the water vapor pressure on the time limits at temperatures higher than normally encountered, but for milder climatic exposures a good deal more data exists. The water vapor effect is illustrated in Fig. 1 by the sloping line labeled "limit of regulation." This represents an approximate limit for maintaining thermal balance for a clothed man with higher than

normal body temperature, actively sweating, at sea level. It is clear that the higher the vapor pressure, the lower must be the ambient temperature be if the man is to be able to maintain physiological thermoregulation.

A man without clothing, drinking salted water to replace his sweat losses, can maintain thermal balance for 32 hours at a point somewhat above this line, as shown by the data point at 110°F and 25 mm Hg.[5]

By contrast, thermal balance was definitely not maintained at a point below the line for a man clothed in a partly impermeable suit in a sealed balloon gondola, shown by the data point at 95°F and 24 mm Hg. This rather heroic experience is described in the flight report of the Air Force balloon project entitled Manhigh III.[7] In this case, a well-sealed, tiny gondola heated up from the design point of 70°F to approximately 95°F, so that the pilot could lose little or no body heat by convection or conduction. His production of body sweat represented a sizable source in a small space, and the water vapor sink was insufficient for the amount of water vapor being produced. The vapor pressure rose from an initial level of approximately 8 mm Hg to a final value of 24 to 25 mm Hg. This high vapor pressure, an ambient temperature nearly equal to skin temperature, and the presence of partly impermeable clothing meant there was virtually no heat exchange between the man and his environment. His metabolic heat was stored, as shown by a rising body temperature. After five hours of flight, the rectal temperature had risen to 106°F. The flight was terminated successfully only because the pilot was able to resist delirium and control the descent and landing.

Other data below the sloping line represent environmental conditions in projects where thermal balance was maintained but comfort was not always achieved. In the case of Navy Stratolab balloon flights, Commander Ross[14] reported that he was uncomfortable even with the low vapor pressure of 9 mm and temperatures ranging from below 70 to 90°F. The discomfort was correctly ascribed to the partial pressure suits worn, suits which cover about half the body surface with impermeable rubberized cloth. Comfort was achieved in these Stratolab flights when the suit was opened up as much as possible by undoing

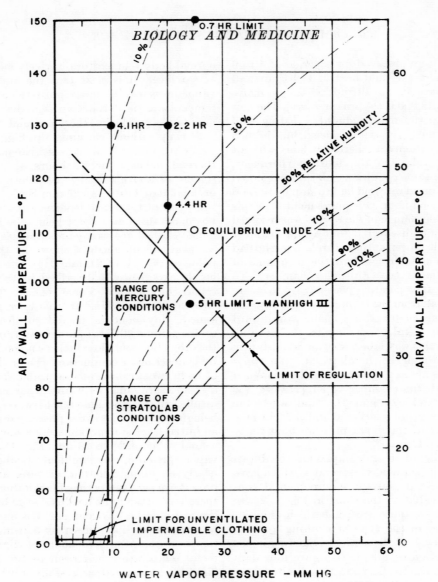

Fig. 1. A variety of experimental and flight experiences in which there were problems in maintaining human thermal balance. The humidity expressed in vapor pressure combined with the ambient temperature is a meaningful way to locate the data, whereas the relative humidity lines alone (e.g., 50 per cent RH) would be of no use in predicting the effect of exposure. The four solid dots above 110°F represent experimentally established time limits which are set by body heat storage, for clothed, mildly active men.[2,8] The open dot represents probably a maximum condition for nude men maintaining thermal equilibrium with a body temperature above normal, lying still.[5] The straight sloping line represents a composite of many studies which established the upper level of heat and humidity in which clothed active men maintain thermoregulation. Just below the line, another solid dot locates the conditions in the Manhigh III balloon flight,[7] in which extreme body heat storage caused the flight to terminate at 5 hours. The vertical bars represent the capsule conditions for the Project Mercury manned orbital flights[10,11] and the Navy Stratolab balloon flights[14]—conditions which are uncomfortable if the occupants were active and unable to open up their impermeable clothing. The horizontal bar at the bottom of the chart represents conditions tolerable in impermeable anti-exposure suits and full pressure suits when no ventilating air is introduced under the impermeable shell. The air motion in all these situations was less than 50 fpm.

zippers, removing gloves, opening helmets, etc. In neither the Stratolab flights nor the Man-high III flight was a ventilating system available for relieving the problem of limited evaporation from impermeable layers.

The environmental conditions in Project Mercury[10, 11] are also shown in Fig. 1. Here the temperature range was from the low 90's to just above 100°F, and the vapor pressure was kept at about 9 mm. The astronauts were clothed in full pressure suits, which are totally impermeable, but a ventilating gas stream was passed through the suit. Nevertheless, the main subjective complaint of the astronauts was the discomfort, overheating, and over-production of sweat in response to the exertion or excitement of the flight. The environmental control system in Project Mercury apparently was unable to cope with the highest rate of sweat production, and there was accumulation of moisture in the clothing, much of which may have occurred during the last portion of the flight when full cooling power was not available. The point is that the precise balance between source and sink of water vapor was not maintained.

There is one special comment to be made about several of the flight experiences. The transmitted data usually took the form of relative humidity, and the ground monitors were always reassured that water vapor control was correct when the relative humidity read 50 per cent. However, as is apparent on the chart, a 50 per cent RH at temperatures above 80°F becomes increasingly serious in terms of the absolute water vapor content of the environment. It is the absolute humidity which controls man's ability to lose heat, not the "relative humidity." A sizable vapor pressure gradient from skin to environment is essential for evaporation. Skin temperatures of clothed men in warm conditions are 95°F or above, at which the corresponding saturation vapor pressure is 42 mm Hg. To insure a gradient of 30 mm Hg for evaporation from the skin in spite of partially impermeable clothing or heavy clothing, humidity of the ambient air should not exceed 12 mm Hg.

Perhaps the most extreme example of the water vapor problem in a confined space is that of a man dressed in a completely impermeable garment, such as anti-exposure suits used by the military services for protection against water immersion, and full pressure suits used for very high altitude flying and space flights. In Fig. 1 is shown a recommended temperature for the use of such clothing if ventilation is not employed, this 50°F level being a rule of thumb developed some years ago at the Air Force Aero Medical Laboratory. Notice that the ambient vapor pressure in this situation is a matter of no importance since the impermeability of the suit means that only the internal vapor pressure has a bearing on what happens to the moisture the man produces.

The obvious solution, and one that has been the subject of a good deal of technological development, is to introduce controlled and conditioned air into the clothing. Such ventilated clothing has been used in a number of very high-temperature situations, either with open loop systems where air is brought from a source, sent through the clothing, and allowed to pass off into the surrounding space,[20] or in a closed circuit[16] where the air is constantly reprocessed and water vapor and extra heat removed. In a great many environmental conditions, if water vapor is kept to 5 to 10 mm Hg in the ventilating air and it is supplied in adequate quantity (usually above 10 cfm), then all the water produced by the man is effectively evaporated, thereby allowing him to maintain thermal balance despite the confined enclosure of an impermeable garment.

SOURCE OF WATER VAPOR

We have seen that in a small sealed space or pressure suit the balance between source and sink for water vapor is critical. It is appropriate, then, to examine man as the source.

Man is an inconstant source for water vapor, since his basic or minimum rate of water loss will increase in response to heat and the need for heat dissipation. In Table 1, values for water production are given for a number of environmental conditions.

Notice that a distinction is made between involuntary or insensible water loss and sweating. Insensible water loss results from a diffusion of water through the skin, this being a small quantity which is nevertheless a variable, depending on the vapor pressure gradient between skin surface and environment.[4, 17] The diffusion loss also is known to

TABLE 1. SOURCES OF WATER VAPOR*

Insensible water loss	g/hr
a. Diffusion through skin at 1 atm pressure	15–25
Diffusion through skin at ⅓ atm pressure	30–60
b. Respiratory water loss breathing dry air at rest (respiratory ventilation 8 1pm)	20
in strenuous exertion (respiratory ventilation 80 1pm)	165

Sweating	
a. Psychogenic or nonthermal	80–220
b. Thermal	
seated, nude, warm to hot environment	100–350
walking, lightly clothed, warm environment	250–400
moderate work (2.5 met) nude, warm environment	300–750
lying or sitting in desert sunlight at 100°F	600–750
walking clothed in desert sunlight at 100°F	(average) 950
walking nude in desert sunlight at 100°F	(average) 1160
highest values reported	above 2300

* See text for sources of data.

increase with a lowering of the atmospheric pressure.[6, 15, 18] Water lost from the respiratory tract is counted as insensible also; this quantity varies with the humidity of the inspired air and the amount of air moved in and out of the respiratory tract per unit time. The Table gives values for respiratory loss for the resting condition and for strenuous exertion in dry air, based on some of the author's data [19, 21] and that of Brebbia *et al.*[3]

Active water production by the sweat glands is much greater in amount than insensible loss. Two categories are shown, of which one is a nonthermal variety, or psychogenic sweating due to anxiety. The estimated value given in the Table is based largely on the data of Brebner *et al.*[4] The large range of sweat production in response to thermal load is shown in the final section of the Table, where the specified environments and activities account for the increasing levels of sweat production. The higher values shown are averages rather than ranges. This data is based upon the work of Adolph,[1] Randall,[12] Robinson *et al.*,[13] and Taylor and Buettner.[15]

The importance of small changes in rate of water loss from the man becomes apparent when considering people exposed for many days continuously in sealed cabins. For example, the reports from the Air Force School of Aviation Medicine space cabin simulator by Welch *et al.*[22] show an unexplained dehydration during a series of exposures to 1/3 atm pressure and pure oxygen for 17 days and for 30 days. The weight loss reported could easily be explained by the increase in insensible or diffusional loss due to low atmospheric pressure. However, this does not explain why the subjects failed to sense the increased water loss and make up for it by drinking when thirsty.

The dominant nature of water vapor as the element to be controlled in a space suit is evident from the data of Fig. 2. This illustrates the problem faced by engineers in designing a full pressure suit with backpack life support system (oxygen source, carbon dioxide remover, and temperature control via a ventilating, reconditioning gas circuit) for a man who is meant to be quite active while wearing it.

The example in Fig. 2 assumes an active man with a metabolic rate of 400 kcal/hr (1600 Btu/hr) who is sealed in a full pressure suit and who is, in effect, isolated thermally

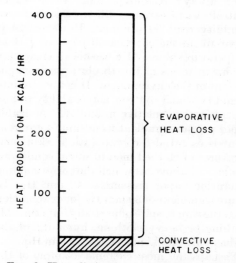

FIG. 2. Heat dissipation in a pressure suit. The conditions are: a man with a metabolic rate of 400 kcal/hr, thermal isolation of the suit from the environment, and ventilation with 0.3 lb/min. of air at 50°F.

from his surroundings, so that there is no heat exchange between the man-suit system and the environment. The backpack conditioning unit provides 0.3 lb/min. of cooling air at approximately $\frac{1}{3}$ atm pressure, the air having a minimum temperature of 50°F. In this situation, almost all of the heat produced by the man must be removed by evaporation, the convective fraction of heat removal via the cooling air being capable of removing only 25 kcal/hr, or $\frac{1}{16}$ of the total heat production. The remaining heat must be removed by evaporation of 650 grams of water from the man, which means that he will have to produce 800 to 1000 g/hr of sweat. This overproduction is a common observation in physiological research. A subject often produces about the right amount of sweat to maintain thermal balance, but not all of it evaporates and heat storage occurs.

There has been one report of an unexpectedly high water loss in a full pressure suit pressurized to $\frac{1}{3}$ atm in a vacuum chamber,[9] but it was not possible to distinguish the cause among several, such as increased insensible water loss and increased metabolic rate from a pressurized suit, exertion of the task, and anxiety on the part of the subject.

Sinks for water vapor in sealed cabins and in pressure suits are properly an engineering topic; the point is that sinks must be sized to match the rates of production encountered physiologically in order that the man may maintain thermal balance.

A RECOMMENDED RANGE FOR WATER VAPOR PRESSURE

In view of the experiences and research findings recounted in the previous two sections, a rather low water vapor pressure is recommended for pressure suits and sealed cabins. Figure 3 shows graphically a conservative, recommended control range for water vapor pressure from 5 to 10 mm Hg and a temperature spread of 65 to 80°F. If humidity and temperature are controlled to this range, most varieties of protective clothing with which we have any experience can be worn for extended periods without serious discomfort. Impermeable clothing must be ventilated with air having a temperature and humidity in the same range. A lower humidity would not be

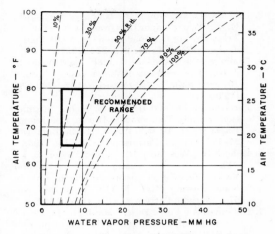

FIG. 3. A range of temperatures and vapor pressures recommended for design purposes in sealed cabins and pressure suits, assuming that activities may vary widely, occupancy is prolonged, pressure is between 1/3 and 1 atm, and air motion is between 50 and 200 fpm.

apt to cause any harm. A time limited period of exposure to 15 mm of vapor pressure would be permissible if the activity level were low and if high air motion or low atmospheric pressure prevailed.

Notice that in Fig. 3 the curved relative humidity line, representing 50 per cent of the saturation vapor pressure (50 per cent RH), traverses only a very small part of the recommended range. Experimental work in environmental physiology has caused many workers to rebel at the use of relative humidity as a means of defining moisture in the atmosphere. Almost any term for absolute moisture is useful, and the one preferred by the author is vapor pressure expressed in mm Hg, since this is the terminology used for expressing the partial pressures of oxygen, nitrogen, carbon dioxide and other gases common in closed spaces.

References

1. Adolph, E. F., and Associates, "Physiology of Man in the Desert," New York, Interscience Publishers, Inc., 1947.
2. Blockley, W. V., McCutchan, J. W., and Taylor, C. L., "Prediction of Human Tolerance for Heat in Aircraft: a Design Guide," WADC Tech. Rep. No. 53–346, Wright-Patterson AFB, Ohio, 1954.

3. Brebbia, D. R., Goldman, R. F., and Buskirk, E. R., "Water Vapor Loss from the Respiratory Tract During Outdoor Exercise in the Cold," *J. Appl. Physiol.*, **11**: 219–222 (1957).

4. Brebner, D. F., Kerslake, D.McK., and Waddell, J. L., "The Diffusion of Water Vapor Through Human Skin," *J. Physiol.*, **132**, 225–231 (1956).

5. Ferguson, I. D., and Hertzman, A. B., "Regulation of Body Temperature During Continuous Exposure to Heat," WADC Tech. Rep. No. 57–727, Wright-Patterson AFB, Ohio, 1958.

6. Hale, F. C., Westland, R. A., and Taylor, C. L., "The Influence of Barometric Pressure and Vapor Pressure on Insensible Weight Loss in Nude Resting Man," WADC Tech. Rep. No. 57–9, Wright-Patterson AFB, Ohio, 1957.

7. Holloman Air Force Base, "Manhigh III, USAF Manned Balloon Flight into the Stratosphere," AFMDC TR-60-16, April 1961.

8. Kaufman, William C., "Human Tolerance Limits for Some Thermal Environments of Aerospace," *Aerospace Med.*, **34**, 889–896 (1963).

9. Miller, Sherwin U., "Increased Human Body Water Loss at Reduced Ambient Pressure," *Aerospace Med.*, **33**, 689–691 (1962).

10. National Aeronautics and Space Administration (no author), "Results of the First United States Manned Orbital Space Flight," Washington, D.C., U.S. Government Printing Office, 1962.

11. National Aeronautics and Space Administration, "Results of the Second United States Manned Orbital Space Flight," NASA SP 6, Washington, D.C., U.S. Government Printing Office, 1962.

12. Randall, Walter C., "Effect of Heat, Exercise, and Chemical Substances on Composition of Sweat: Man," p. 469 in Altman, Philip L., "Blood and Other Body Fluids," ASD Tech. Rep. No. 61–199, Wright-Patterson AFB, Ohio, 1961.

13. Robinson, S., Turrell, E. S., and Gerking, S. D., "Physiologically Equivalent Conditions of Air Temperature and Humidity," *Am. J. Physiol.*, **143**, 21–32 (1945).

14. Ross, Malcolm, "A Comparison of Artificial Environments Used in Sealed Cabins During Flights into the Stratosphere," *Advances in Astronautical Sciences*, **4**, 432–437 (1959).

15. Taylor, C. L., and Buettner, K. J. K., "The Evaporative Effect on Human Perspiration," WADC Tech. Rep. No. 53–345, Wright-Patterson AFB, Ohio, 1953.

16. Webb, Paul, "Closed Breathing-Ventilating Systems Using Recirculated Oxygen," *J. Av. Med.*, **30**, 273–279 (1959).

17. Webb, Paul, Garlington, L. N., and Schwarz, M. J., "Insensible Weight Loss at High Skin Temperatures," *J. Appl. Physiol.*, **11**, 41–44 (1957).

18. Webb, Paul, Garlington, L. N., and Schwarz, M. J., "The Influence of Low Barometric Pressure and High Skin Temperature on Insensible Weight Loss," Proceedings of the XXI International Physiological Congress, Brussels, Belgium, 1956.

19. Webb, Paul, "Heat Loss from the Respiratory Tract in Cold," Report No. 3, Project No. 7-7951, Arctic Aeromedical Laboratory, Ladd AFB, Alaska, 1955.

20. Webb, Paul, and Klemm, F. K., "Design of Ventilated Clothing," WADC Tech. Rep. No. 58–608, Wright-Patterson AFB, Ohio, 1959.

21. Webb, Paul, and Neugebauer, M. Kenith, "Recording Dielectric Hygrometer for Expired Air," *Rev. Sci. Instr.*, **25**, 1212–1217 (1954).

22. Welch, B. E., Morgan, T. E., Jr., and Ulvedal, F., "Observations in the SAM Two-man Space Cabin Simulator. I. Logistics aspects," *Aerospace Med.*, **32**, 583–590 (1961).

SECTION II

AGRICULTURE

II. Problems of Humidity and Moisture in Agriculture

CARL W. HALL

Department of Agricultural Engineering, Michigan State University, East Lansing, Michigan

ABSTRACT

Humidity and moisture sensing elements and systems are used to direct energy in agriculture for providing the optimum environmental conditions for growth of plants and animals, for maintenance of structures and products, and for environment for humans.

Excessive condensation and freezing of moisture may occur on some structures housing livestock or other moisture producing items. The moisture may lead to excessive damage to the structure, affect its appearance, and provide an unacceptable environment for livestock, products, or humans. Negative radiation—cooling of the surface to as much as 14°F below ambient temperature—with some structual materials, is particularly troublesome.

Recent research indicates that the acceptable comfort index of 75 for people is satisfactory for certain breeds of lactating dairy cattle. Little research has been done with relative humidity as a controlled variable. In general, livestock production decreases rapidly for relative humidities above 90 per cent, particularly at high temperatures.

Hygroscopic products change in moisture content as the relative humidity changes at a constant temperature. These changes are approximately linear in the 20 to 60 per cent RH range. In the 0 to 20 and 60 to 100 per cent RH ranges, control of moisture by relative humidity is more difficult, because small changes in relative humidity cause large changes in moisture content. Practically all of the error in the control of moisture content by humidity and temperature is due to humidity variations.

Improper relative humidity control can mean loss through spoilage of a product if the relative humidity is too high or loss of money to the seller if the relative humidity is too low. Definite equilibrium relationships have been established for many agricultural products. These relationships are useful in predicting the response of products to various environments as identified by temperature and relative humidity.

It is important that the control system components be analyzed and designed to provide maximum reliability at an economical price. A classification of relative humidity instruments is needed to assist the designer in economical selection.

INTRODUCTION

In the book "Micrographia" by Robert Hooke is described ". . . an indicating hygrometer which measured the moisture in the atmosphere by the beard of a wild oat whose natural twist varies with the dampness of the air." (From "Lives in Science," New York, Simon and Schuster, Inc., 1959.)

Many of the problems in agriculture involve the relationships between humidity and moisture. Being hygroscopic, agricultural products change in moisture content with a change in the relative humidity and temperature of the environment. In agricultural applications, the relative humidity sensing devices and controls must often operate in high relative humidity conditions and dusty environments.

The importance of instrumentation in agriculture is often overlooked. Agriculture is the largest single industry in the United States.

Including the production, processing and marketing phases, agriculture involves 90 billion dollars per year. The agricultural industries are proceeding with automation as rapidly as other industries. There is a considerable potential market for accurate relative humidity instrumentation.

Environmental control in structures involves maintaining a desirable relative humidity and temperature level for the livestock, the structure, the products of plants and animals, and the workers.

Agricultural products must be harvested, handled, processed, packaged and transported. Quality and quantity must be maintained from harvest to consumption. Moisture control is essential for both quantity and quality control. Excessive moisture in grain causes storage losses; too little moisture causes the seller to lose money; and improper removal of moisture results in loss of quality or viability. The biological materials with which we work involve changes in many other factors than moisture—chemical, microbiological, respiration, surface and internal temperatures of thin or small particles, and organoleptic.

STRUCTURES

The flow of water vapor through structural materials and insulation is an important consideration in agriculture. If the vapor moves through the wall without condensation, the problem is minimized. When the temperature at some location in the wall is at or below the dew point of the environment air, moisture well be deposited. If this temperature is below freezing, water will change to ice.

The condensation of moisture and freezing at temperatures of 32°F and below is a serious problem in some sections of the country, especially for metal buildings housing livestock. Insufficient ventilation in many uninsulated structures can be attributed to the lack of information resulting in improper construction or operation. Dripping of moisture causing undesirable animal environment, saturation of bedding, and damage to the structure can occur from melting of ice from the inside of the roof or walls of the building. To avoid condensation, an adequate airflow must be provided through the structure. To avoid condensation, more airflow is required as the relative humidity of the outside air is increased or as the outside air temperature is decreased (Fig. 1).[5]

Conditions favoring frost accumulation on and dripping from the inside surface of buildings are as follows:

(1) Outside air temperatures below freezing during the night;

(2) Clear skies at night, causing large radiation losses;

(3) Wind velocities of 6 mph or less,

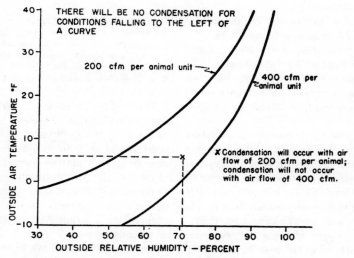

FIG. 1. Condensation on uninsulated steel structures with different air flow rates and various environments.

resulting in low air movement through naturally ventilated buildings;

(4) During the morning following freezing of moisture, outside air temperatures above freezing, usually with a clear day.

During clear nights in northern climates, the negative radiation from the structure is sufficient to lower the temperature of the surface considerably below the atmospheric temperature. The greater this difference in temperature, the more condensation will occur on the surface. For a new galvanised surface, the temperature may be 2°F below the ambient temperature, for aluminum paint, 6°F, and for oxide paints (color not important), 12 to 14°F.

A vapor barrier can be installed to impede the flow of vapor. To prevent vapor from entering the wall, the vapor barrier should be placed on the high vapor pressure side which is usually the warm side. The vapor pressure would be higher on the low-temperature side if a much higher relative humidity existed there than on the warm side. For example, the vapor pressure is lower at 60°F and 30 per cent RH than for any relative humidity above 62 per cent with a temperature below 40°F.

In some structures such as fruit and vegetable storages, the warm side is the inside in the winter and the outside of the storage in the summer. The question arises: Where should the vapor barrier be placed? Some people recommend that a vapor barrier be placed on both sides. (This is theoretically correct but in practice many failures have been experienced.) If the vapor moves through a wall crack or opening, the moisture may be trapped and the insulation may become soaked, decreasing the insulation effect. Therefore, it is usually desirable to let one wall breathe and cover the other wall with the vapor barrier. The vapor barrier should be placed on the side which has the highest vapor pressure for the longest time. The vapor barrier should also be placed where the interception of the moisture will prevent condensation and freezing in the wall.

Vapor barrier materials may be metal-steel, aluminum, aluminum foil; plastic sheets or films; asphalt-covered or impregnated materials; paints or surface coatings of vapor barriers such as some aluminum paints, asphalt paint and enamels. On the other hand, breather paints are available which permit a flow of vapor through the wall. It is difficult to seal a wall against vapor flow. An installation may originally be well sealed, but with time the wall may develop cracks and damage the vapor barrier.

Theories presented by Babbitt[2] illustrate that high pressures are necessary to separate paint from wood. These high pressures are caused by condensed vapor which is sealed under the paint and are due to temperature differences. The relationship of flow of vapor and the periodic effects of temperature fluctuations as related to the movement of moisture through walls and peeling of paint need to be investigated. The problem has been analyzed on steady-state conditions, but most practical applications in agriculture involve cycling or periodic temperature and humidity changes. Daily and yearly temperature and humidity changes are involved.

HYGROSCOPIC PRODUCTS

The moisture content of a hygroscopic product can be controlled by maintaining a certain relative humidity at a specific temperature. It is a common practice in agriculture to control the moisture content of the product by controlling relative humidity. The moisture content of a hygroscopic product at equilibrium is reduced as the relative humidity is reduced and/or the temperature is increased. The relationships are not linear. An isotherm of a hygroscopic material is characteristically an S-shaped or sigmoid curve, with the relative humidity on the abscissa and the moisture content on the ordinate (Fig. 2). Whether the isotherm passes through the origin depends on the method of moisture determination. As the temperature is reduced, the isotherm has a higher moisture content at a given relative humidity. The moisture content isotherm is often linear between 20 and 60 per cent RH (Fig. 3). When moisture content is being controlled by relative humidity, the same degree of accuracy of control can be obtained in this range. However, between 0 and 20 per cent and 60 and 100 per cent RH, each change of 1 per cent RH gives a larger change in moisture content than in the 20 to 60 per cent RH range. It is more difficult to maintain a certain moisture content through relative

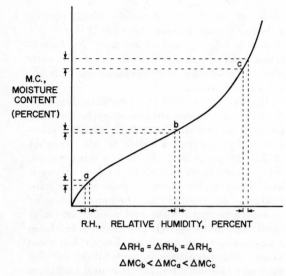

$$\Delta RH_a = \Delta RH_b = \Delta RH_c$$
$$\Delta MC_b < \Delta MC_a < \Delta MC_c$$

Fig. 2. Change in moisture content of product at different locations on an equilibrium isotherm for equal changes in relative humidity.

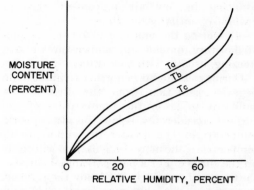

Fig. 3. Isotherms at various temperatures.

humidity control with a given accuracy at the low and high relative humidities.

The moisture content of a product at a constant relative humidity does not change inversely with the temperature, although for temperatures below 100°F, changes are often assumed to do so. Furthermore, the equilibrium moisture content values vary for different products. The changes in slope of the isotherm (change in moisture content per change in relative humidity) at various temperatures for several products and at different humidities are presented in Table 1. The difficulty of controlling the moisture content by relative humidity over a range of values is illustrated by the variation in values and a lack of consistent trends. It would be difficult to obtain the same high degree of accuracy for control over a wide range of humidities.

Another variable is that a product will not adsorb moisture to the same extent that it will desorb moisture. The difference in moisture content at a particular relative humidity between adsorption and desorption is known as the hysteresis effect. The moisture content depends upon the history of the product; that is, whether the equilibrium conditions were

TABLE 1. Change in Moisture Content, W.B., for a Change of 1 Per Cent RH from Desorption Data, for Different Temperature, Products and Humidities

| Product | Temperature (°F) | Relative Humidity (%) | | | | Source |
		10	50	75	90	
Shelled corn	60	0.35	0.10	0.23	0.68	Hall and Rodriguez[12]
	80	0.28	0.13	0.24	0.55	
Alfalfa hay (mature)	60	0.25	0.20	0.90	1.90	Bakker-Arkema, Hall, Benne[3]
	80	0.27	0.13	0.40	0.60	
Wheat	77	0.25	0.13	0.24	0.50	Becker, Sallans[4]
	122	0.28	0.14	0.26	0.65	
Rice, rough	80	0.28	0.13	0.18	0.30	Hogan, Karm[21]
	111		0.13	0.19		
Cacao beans	60	0.34	0.04	0.10	0.33	Hall[13]
	80	0.22	0.03	0.08	0.20	
Sugar beet seeds	60		0.11	0.20	0.64	Hall[11]
	80		0.11	0.15	0.54	
Dry milk (low-heat, nonfat)	60	0.31	0.15	0.61	1.33	Heldman[17]
	86	0.30	0.20	0.70	1.36	

obtained by wetting or drying (Fig. 4).

Relative humidity may be used as a means of measuring as well as controlling moisture content of a product. As a method of moisture measurement in the usual range at harvest, the relative humidity will give a more accurate measure of the moisture content for grain than for hay. Hay at high moisture contents will have an equilibrium relative humidity that will approach 100 per cent, making it difficult to accurately measure the relative humidity to determine the moisture content.

As a product adsorbs moisture, its volume is increased. The increase in volume might damage the storage structure.

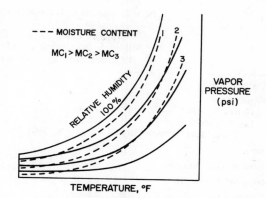

FIG. 5. Constant moisture content lines plotted on psychrometric chart.

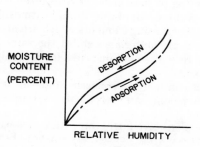

FIG. 4. Hysteresis effect on isotherms.

The moisture content—relative humidity—temperature data can be plotted on a psychrometric chart. At a particular temperature, a linear relationship exists between the relative humidity and pressure of vapor in air. At 80°F, the pressure of the vapor at 100 per cent RH is 5 psi, at 50 per cent, 2.5, and at 10 per cent, 0.5 psi. Although the constant moisture content curves, plotted on the psychrometric chart move in the same direction as the relative humidity line, they do not parallel each other (Fig. 5).

The degrees dew-point depression may be used to measure the moisture content. The dew-point depression is claimed to give an accuracy of ½°F depression which would provide a moisture content reading within 0.25 per cent of the actual product moisture content.[23]

It is desirable to know the relative humidity in the interstices of a product—grain in storage, hay in the mow, or insulation in a structure. The relative humidity of the interstices is often a better indication of safe

storage than moisture content. It is difficult to move air over a sensing device in the interstices for measuring the relative humidity such as can be done in a refrigerated storage, open room, or in the atmosphere. A device is needed which can determine the relative humidity in these interstices without adding heat to the air and without greatly disturbing the environmental conditions of the air. A relative humidity probe for sampling air in a hay mow was described by Hedlin.[16] A sample of air was withdrawn from the product and passed over a membrane-type humidity meter. The temperature of the air was determined in the mow and at the relative humidity meter. Hukill[22] reported on use of a pipe cleaner with cotton fibers for the determination of the relative humidity for obtaining the moisture content of a product in storage within 1 to 2 per cent. This is a simple and inexpensive approach to solving a difficult problem.

ANIMAL ENVIRONMENT

The temperature comfort zone for most farm livestock is from 35 to 80°F. The relative humidity becomes an important factor when the temperature goes above 80 or 90°F, depending on the animal. The maximum relative humidity under these high temperature conditions is from 80 to 90 per cent (Table 2).

The effect of relative humidity on productivity of animals has not been investigated as widely as the effect of temperature. A recent

TABLE 2. RELATIVE HUMIDITY RECOMMENDATIONS FOR LIVESTOCK

	Comfort Zone, Minimum-Maximum Temperature (°F)	Maximum RH at Minimum Temperature (%)	Maximum RH at Maximum Temperature (%)	Reference
Dairy cows	40–75		80–90	Stewart[30]
Poultry				
Heavy breeds	35–85	80	70	Longhouse[26]
Light breeds	35–90	80	70	
(Keep litter between 20 and 40%, w.b., MC)				
Swine	35–90		90 at 80°F	Hazen[15]
Beef cattle—Europe	20–60			Kelly[24]
Beef cattle—India	50–80			
Egg storage	32–60		80	

study established the discomfort index as a basis of evaluation. The discomfort index of 75, as used for air conditioning, applied to lactating Holstein dairy cattle as well. A discomfort index of 75 would include the range from 77°F to 80 per cent RH to 95°F at 0 per cent RH. At this discomfort index, the total heat dissipation was 2730 Btu/hr/1000 lb of body weight with 1.9 lb/hr of moisture produced.[8] Higher humidities at a given temperature impair total heat and vapor dissipation resulting in discomfort for the animals.

FRUIT AND VEGETABLE ENVIRONMENT

A higher relative humidity is desired for storing fresh fruits and vegetables and florist stocks than for cereal grains. Leafy vegetables are normally stored slightly above freezing at 90 to 95 per cent RH; bulb plants, like onions, garlic, and gladioli at 70 to 75 per cent; and fruits at 85 to 90 per cent RH.[31] (See Table 3). A wide variety of conditions must be met depending upon the product.

SENSING ELEMENTS FOR AGRICULTURE

The humidity sensing devices now on the market are far from satisfactory for agricultural operations. These are some of the problems. Reproducible response is not obtained. A wide range of humidities cannot be sensed with a single element with accuracy. High humidities are especially difficult to sense. Many instruments will not withstand the vibrations of equipment and buildings.

Recording or indicating devices often do not have a long life in a humid atmosphere. Humidity sensing elements which are made of hygroscopic materials exhibit the same non-linear responses enumerated for agricultural products.

The commercial concerns and the farmer whose income and profit depend upon the

TABLE 3. RELATIVE HUMIDITY RECOMMENDATIONS FOR STORAGE OF FRUITS, VEGETABLES, FLORISTS PLANTS[31]

	Relative Humidity (%)
Fresh fruits	
Apples	85–90
Cherries	85–90
Coconuts	80–85
Grapefruit	85–90
Grapes	85–90
Mangoes	85–90
Pears (Bartlett)	90–95
Pineapple	85–90
Nuts	65–75
Fresh vegetables	
Artichoke	90–95
Asparagus	85–90
Beets	90–95
Broccoli	90–95
Brussel sprouts	90–95
Cabbage	90–95
Carrots	90–95
Celery	90–95
Lettuce	90–95
Melon	85–90
Onions	70–75
Pumpkins	70–75
Vegetable seeds	50–65
Cut flowers	80
Florist greens	90

moisture content of his stored grain products needs relative humidity control to within 1 to 2 per cent. The cost of the instrument is a factor but not a limiting one. Agricultural producers and processers are willing to buy expensive instruments which meet their needs. The equipment and controls for ventilation of buildings for livestock may operate over a wider range of values, perhaps from plus or minus 5 to 10 per cent RH. Less expensive instruments and controls which will not meet the needs previously mentioned can be used for these applications.

Many farm applications require only that the humidity be indicated for the information of an operator. The relative humidity measurement may be transmitted to a fan, humidifier, dehumidifier or heater, so that the desired response is obtained. In some applications, a high-low humidity reading, similar to a maximum-minimum thermometer, would be useful.

The needs of processing plants differ in that a record might be desirable or required. The record may be printed or punched continuously or periodically on hourly, daily, weekly or monthly charts. The instrument and control needs of the agricultural researcher are similar to the needs of other engineers and scientists.

SUMMARY

Instruments and controls for humidity and moisture are essential for providing optimum environment for production and processing of agricultural products. Plants and animals and their products and humans require accurate humidity control for moisture control and thermal comfort. Condensation and freezing of moisture on structural surfaces may occur with thawing and dripping of moisture from the surface on the following day from solar heating. Migration of moisture through walls and insulation materials causing blistering of paint and discoloration can be partially prevented by proper vapor barrier selection and installation.

References

1. Agnor, D. C., and Von Bargen, Kenneth, "Controlled Temperature and Humidity System for Moisture Transfer Studies," *ASAE paper* 61-313, Iowa State University (June 25–28, 1961).

2. Babbitt, J. D., "Osmotic Pressure, Semipermeable Membranes and the Blistering of Paint," *Can. J. Technol.*, **32**, 49 (1954).

3. Bakker-Arkema, Fred, Hall, C. W., and Benne, E. J., "Equilibrium Moisture Content of Alfalfa," *Mich. State Univ. Agr. Exp. Sta. Quart. Bull.*, **44**, 492–496 (1962).

4. Becker, H. A., and Sallans, H. R., "A Study of the Desorption Isotherms of Wheat," *Cereal Chem.*, **33**, 79–91 (March 1956).

5. Birth, Gerald S., and Hall, Carl W., "Ventilation of Uninsulated Steel Structures Housing Livestock," *Mich. State Univ. Agr. Expt. Sta. Quart. Bull.*, **42** 251–261 (August 1959).

6. Bruhn, H. D., "How to Maintain a Thermocouple at Wet Bulb Temperature," *Agr. Eng.*, **31**, 348 (1950).

7. Campbell, L. E., "Temperature Measurement," *ASAE paper* 61-812, Chicago, Illinois (1961).

8. Cargill, B. F. J., "Effect of Humidity on Heat and Vapor Dissipation of Holstein Cows at 65, 80, and 90°F," Ph.D. Thesis, University of Missouri, 1960.

9. Dorsey, N. E., "Properties of Ordinary Water—Substances," New York, Reinhold Publishing Corp., 1940.

10. Flanigan, F. M., "Comparison of the Accuracy of Humidity Measuring Instruments," *ASHRAE J.* **2**, 56–59 (December 1960).

11. Hall, Carl W., "Drying Temperatures and Storage Problems of Sugar Beet Seeds," *J. Am. Soc. Sugar Beet Technologists*, **9**, 161–166 (1956).

12. Hall, Carl W., and Rodriguez-Arias, J. H., "Equilibrium Moisture Content of Shelled Corn," *Agr. Eng.*, **39**, 466–470 (1958).

13. Hall, Carl W., "Equilibrium Moisture Content of Cacao Beans," *Acta Agron.*, **10**, 53—56 (1960).

14. Haynes, B. C., Jr., and Smith, L. L., "Psychrometric Equipment for Recording Potentiometers," *Agr. Eng.*, **36**, 192 (March 1955).

15. Hazen, T. E., and Mangold, D. W., "Functional and Basic Requirements of Swine Housing," *Agr. Eng.*, **41**, 585–590 (1960).

16. Hedlin, C. P., "A Relative Humidity Probe Sample Air in Hay Mow," *Agr. Eng.*, **35**, 505 (1954).

17. Heldman, D., Hall, C. W., and Hedrick, T. I., "Equilibrium Moisture Content of Dry Milk," in "Humidity and Moisture," Vol. 2, New York, Reinhold Publishing Corp., 1964.

18. Henderson, S. M., "Negative Radiation—Its Relation to New Building Design," *Agr. Eng.*, **28**, 137–140 (1947).

19. Henderson, S. M., "A Constant Feed All Temperature Wet Bulb," *Agr. Eng.*, **33**, 644 (1952).

20. Henderson, S. M., "Moisture Content Determinations," *Agr. Eng.*, **34**, 108, 110 (February 1953).

21. Hogan, J. T., Karm, Melvin, "Hygroscopic Equilibrium of Rough Rice at Elevated Temperatures," *Agr. Food Chem.*, **3**, 855–861 (1955).

22. Hukill, W. V., "Grain Moisture Indicator," *Agr. Eng.*, **38**, 808 (1957).

23. Ives, Norton C., "A Dewpoint Moisture Indicator," *Agr. Eng.*, **33**, 85–87 (1952).
24. Kelly, C. F., "Effects of Thermal Environment on Beef Cattle," *Agr. Eng.*, **41**, 613–614 (1960).
25. Kliever, Waldo, "Instrumentation in A.E. Research," *Agr. Eng.*, **33**, 366, 368 (June 1952).
26. Longhouse, A. D., Ota, Hajirne, and Ashby, Wallace, "Heat and Moisture Design Data for Poultry Housing," *Agr. Eng.*, **41**, 567–571 (1960).
27. Norman, David A., "Diffusion Through Vapor Barrier Gaps in House Walls," MS Thesis, Michigan State University, 1959.
28. Richey, C. B., Jacobson, P., and Hall, C. W., "Agricultural Engineers' Handbook," New York, McGraw-Hill Book Co., Inc., 1961.
29. Saul, Robert A., "Continuous-recording Wet-bulb Apparatus," *Agr. Eng.*, **37**, 488 (July 1956).
30. Stewart, Robert E., "Physical Environment and Confinement Housing for Dairy Cows," *Agr. Eng.*, **41**, 596–598 (1960).
31. Wright, R. C., Rose, D. H., Whiteman, T. M., "The Commercial Storage of Fruits, Vegetables, and Florist and Nursing Stocks," *U.S. Dept. Agr.*, *Agr.* Handbook, **66** (September 1954).

12. Atmospheric Humidity and the Energy Budget of Plant Canopies*†

Wayne L. Decker

University of Missouri, Columbia, Missouri

ABSTRACT

Plant canopies are interacting agents in the hydrologic cycle. A part of the activity of plants is the supply of atmospheric moisture through evapotranspiration. The use of the theory of turbulence provides relationships by which evapotranspiration from plant canopies and evaporation from water surfaces can be estimated. These relationships are based on the gradient of water vapor in the atmosphere and on the wind shear. To utilize these functional relationships it is necessary to measure wind shears better than 0.1 mph and dew-point temperature gradients to the nearest 0.01°C.

The energy budget of plant or water surfaces have been suggested to estimate evapotranspiration and evaporation. The independent evaluation of the components of the energy budget also involves the precise determination of wind shear, water vapor gradients, and/or temperature gradients in the lower atmosphere.

Experimental evidence is presented that indicates that the net radiation of a surface is more readily used as latent heat than as sensible heat when abundant water is present at the surface. This fact permits the use of relationships based on net radiation for estimating the amount of evapotranspiration from a plant canopy or evaporation from a water surface.

Under conditions when latent heat is using a high portion of the net radiation, the equations requiring precise instrumentation need not be used.

* Contribution from the Missouri Agricultural Experiment Station. Journal Series Number 26020 Approved: Elmer R. Kiehl.

† Partial support for this research was granted by the U.S. Weather Bureau.

THE WATER BALANCE OF A VEGETATIVE COVER

Land surfaces are covered by canopies of plants in some stage of growth or dormancy, except in regions of the world with extreme climates, such as deserts and ice caps. These plants are interacting agents in the hydrologic cycle which is the cycle of water moving from the surface of the earth to become atmospheric moisture and returning to the surface as a result of cloud and rain-producing mechanisms. In the hydrologic cycle, the mantle of plants dissipates the energy of the rain which is intercepted. The surfaces of the plants receive small amounts of water as dew condensed from the atmospheric moisture and become the source of atmospheric moisture through transpiration from the stomata of the leaf surfaces.

Although plants serve as a source of atmospheric moisture, it is common knowledge that water is required for plant growth. When present in insufficient amounts growth is retarded, and when absent, death or dormancy result. Even in humid and sub-humid regions of the world, the plant canopy often does not receive sufficient water to care for its needs. For example, in Southeast Missouri where an average of 46 in. of rain per year occurs, deficiencies in water are usually felt by plants during the warm season of the year. The accumulative water available after runoff, as noted by McQuigg and Decker,[8] for this region of Missouri is shown in Fig. 1. Over a period of time only 28 in. of water are available for use by the plants each year, and this is 4 in. less than the amount required by plants in this region. Even in humid Southeast Missouri, a deficiency of water is the usual or normal occurrence. The vegetative cover adjusts to this deficiency by reduced water use which may be presumed to lower the yield of grain and/or stover.

The uncertainty of water supply and the normal inadequacy of rain in the humid areas of the world has stimulated the practice of supplemental irrigation during periods of dry weather. It has become a profitable practice to supplement the normal rainfall with irrigation in areas where high-priced crops are produced. It has been estimated by Stauber, Decker and Miller[11] for Southeast Missouri that in three years out of four, more than four applications of irrigation water could be profitably used by a summer grown crop. Indeed, six or more applications could be utilized on one out of four years with seven applications on one out of ten years.

The availability of water for use by a plant cover is determined by the relative size of the components of water balance. The water balance of the earth's surface is shown in Eq. (1).

$$P - RO - \Delta S - E = 0 \qquad (1)$$

where

$P =$ the water added by precipitation and irrigation
$RO =$ the runoff
$\Delta S =$ the change in soil moisture storage
$E =$ the evapotranspiration.

The availability of water in the soil for use by the plant canopy is determined by the relative size of the several components of the water balance.

The amount of water received as precipitation and lost as runoff may be measured. In the case of precipitation, many observing points are available, while runoff measurements are obtained at the gauging stations on streams, watersheds or experimental areas. In Fig. 1 the difference $P - RO$ is shown for Southeast Missouri.

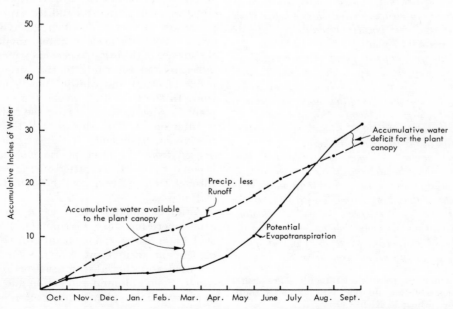

FIG. 1. The accumulative water balance of the Little River Drainage District of Southeast Missouri.

It is often assumed that the change in the storage of water in the soil profile, ΔS, is zero over a period of time. This is probably true when one is considering the definition of a climate of an area based on 30 to 50 years of record. Recent work by McQuigg and Decker[8] indicates for humid Southeast Missouri that great changes in the soil moisture term occurred for periods of two years duration. During the unusually wet period from 1956 through 1958, the upper and lower horizons of the soil gained over 20 in. of water, while during the extremely dry period of 1952-53, a similar amount of water was lost from the surface and subsurface soil layers. In considering the availability of water for the plant canopy to transpire to the atmosphere, it is necessary to account for changes in the storage term within the soil.

The evaporation and transpiration from the plant canopy is also an unknown quantity in most instances. To be sure, Thornthwaite[13] and Blaney and Criddle[1] presented simplified methods for estimating evapotranspiration. But the rate of evapotranspiration is determined by availability of water in the soil, the gradient of atmospheric moisture present and the rate of mixing in the lower atmosphere occurring as the result of the shear created by air movement above the canopy.

THE RATE OF EVAPOTRANSPIRATION AND ATMOSPHERIC MOISTURE

It has been recognized for a long time that the rate of evaporation from a surface is dependent essentially on two factors. The first of these involves the availability of water at the surface for evaporation, while the second is related to the ability of the atmosphere to transport water vapor away from the surface. This latter factor involves not only the change of vapor pressure with height, but also the amount of mixing which may occur in the atmosphere.

Much of the early work dealing with the relationship between evaporation and atmospheric moisture was empirical. Some of these studies involved the evaporation from a free water surface as related to the change of vapor content with height. A mathematical model was developed relating the amount of evaporation to the gradient of vapor pressure as measured between the vapor pressure of the air in contact with the surface and the vapor pressure in the air at the height of the instrument shelter. In these equations, it was not uncommon to use a simple relationship for the vapor pressure gradient involving the difference between the saturated vapor pressure at the mean air temperature and the mean vapor pressure as measured through psychrometry.

To account for the mixing which was favorable for enhancing evaporation, a function of the wind velocity was often inserted. A very well known relationship is that of Rahrer,[10] which the reader will recognize as shown in Eq. (2).

$$E = .40(e_s - e_d)(1 + .27 u_0) \qquad (2)$$

where

$E =$ the evaporation (mm/day)

$e_s =$ the saturated vapor pressure at the air temperature (mm of Hg)

$e_d =$ the saturated vapor pressure at the dew-point temperature (mm of Hg)

$u_0 =$ the surface wind speed (miles/day).

The relationship shown in Eq. (2), along with similar results from other studies, is quite useful in exploring the relationship between atmospheric moisture and evaporation. However, the use of such a relationship is limited by its empirical nature. Such a treatment includes none of the physical refinements in the theory of turbulent flow, nor does it involve the contribution of buoyancy of air heated near the surface. Fortunately, many of the considerations dealing with the flux of water vapor under turbulent and buoyant conditions have been studied. One such relationship is that of Halstead,[6] which was subjected to test at the O'Neill, Nebraska, Experiment in 1953 and is reproduced in Eq. (3). A discussion of the assumptions of this and other models has been presented by Lettau.[7]

$$E = .00142 (u_{2z} - u_z)(e_{2z} - e_z) \qquad (3)$$

where

$E =$ the evaporation in cm depth per hour

u_{2z} and $u_z =$ the wind velocities at $2z$ and z cm above the roughness height

e_{2z} and $e_z =$ the vapor pressures at these heights.

This relationship indicates that evaporation from a surface is related not only to the gradient of vapor pressure but also to the change of wind speed with height. This presents the hydrologist, climatologist and biologist with a definite instrumentation objective in obtaining micrometeorological measurements for estimating evaporation and transpiration from the plant canopy or water surface. To be sure, the assumptions of the physical theory on which the model is based should be kept in mind, and it is further assumed that the surface supplies an unlimited amount of moisture.

Prior to the adoption of the method proposed in Eq. (3) or a similar model for estimating evapotranspiration, it would be informative to examine the evapotranspiration associated with changing wind velocity at a constant atmospheric moisture gradient, and to similarly examine the evapotranspiration resulting from changes in vapor content at constant wind shear. Using the Halstead relationship, Fig. 2 and 3 demonstrate these functional relationships. From Fig. 2 there is found a sharp increase in evaporation with increasing wind shear, particularly at the high

levels of atmospheric moisture gradients. A similar conclusion is drawn from Fig. 3, where the gradient of atmospheric moisture has a correspondingly large influence on evaporation, particularly at the high wind shears.

Having selected a relationship for estimating evaporation or evapotranspiration from wind shears and the gradients of atmospheric moisture, the investigator immediately inquires concerning type of measuring equipment or instruments required to make these evaluations. Normally, the micrometeorologist attempts to measure the velocity differences in wind to the nearest centimeter per second, or with an accuracy equivalent to .0224 mph. Less precise measurements will result in appreciable errors in the evaluation of evaporation, particularly at the low wind speeds. With a wind velocity differences of .5 mph, an error of .1 mph in the measurement of the difference in wind speed will result in a 20 per cent error in the estimation of evaporation. At wind gradients of 1 mph an error of .1 mph in measurement will result in a 10 per cent error in the estimated evaporation.

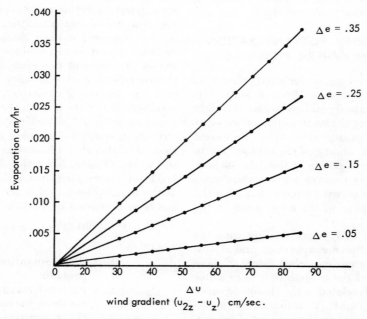

Fig. 2. The relationship between wind gradient and evaporation for different levels of vapor pressure gradient.

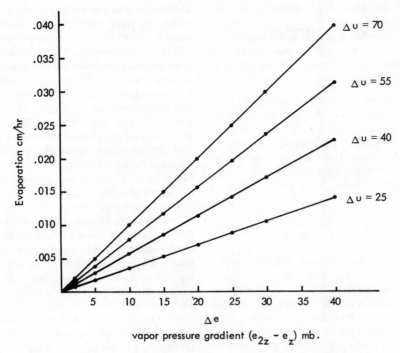

FIG. 3. The relationship between vapor pressure gradient and evaporation for different levels of wind gradient.

Moisture gradients must also be measured extremely accurately in order to evaluate the evaporation using Eq. (3). It is the normal practice to estimate vapor pressures to the mearest .01 mb or, when expressed in terms of the dew-point temperature, to estimate the quantity to the nearest .01°C. Vapor pressures vary with temperature so, for purposes of an example, dew-point temperatures of 20°C were used in determining the error of measurement. A measurement error of .01°C in dew-point temperature gradient will result in a 25 per cent error in the estimated evaporation when the gradient is about .05°C. For dew-point gradients of .15°C, the error per .01°C is about 5 per cent.

The investigator who desires to employ an estimate of evaporation based on the turbulent transfer theory is faced with a problem of securing precision instrumentation. Anemometers capable of measuring wind speed differences of less than a .1 mph are required, and pyschrometric measurements will be needed that are capable of producing observations of dew-point temperature gradients in the order of .01°C. For this reason, the evaluation of the relationship of Eq. (3) should not be undertaken casually.

THE ENERGY BUDGET OF THE CROP CANOPY AS RELATED TO EVAPOTRANSPIRATION

In order to overcome some of the instrumentation problems presented in the discussion of Eq. (3), the energy budget of the crop canopy is often employed for relating evapotranspiration to environmental factors. This relationship is based on Eq. (4) which yields an expression for the complete energy budget of the surface.

$$LE = R_n - Q - S - P \qquad (4)$$

where

L = the heat of vaporization
E = the evaporation in cm for the time interval of the period of investigation
R_n = the net radiation

$Q =$ the sensible heat transfer to the atmosphere

$S =$ the sensible heat transfer to the soil

$P =$ the energy used in photosynthesis which is normally neglected (see Ref. 3).

Results from such evaluations have been presented in many of the recent journals. These include the work by Penman,[9] Suomi and Tanner,[12] Gerber and Decker,[5] and others.

Lettau[7] discusses the assumptions of an energy budget relationship which he attributes to Suomi and others. This relationship is presented as Eq. (5).

$$LE = \frac{(R_n - S)}{1 + B} \qquad (5)$$

In this relationship, B is the ratio described by Bowen,[2] and is the ratio of the vertical flux of sensible heat to the vertical flux of latent heat. Strictly speaking, to evaluate this ratio it is necessary to determine, with a high precision, the gradient of vapor pressure and the gradient of temperature. The former may be determined with great difficulty while the latter may be precisely measured with considerably more ease.

To summarize, Eqs. (4) and (5) make possible, through the science of micrometeorology, the estimation of either the transfer of sensible heat or the transfer of water vapor to the atmosphere. Precise measurement of temperature gradient, atmospheric moisture gradient, and/or wind shear in the layer of the atmosphere near the surface is required. For this reason, it is impossible to evaluate the components of the energy budget or the turbulent transfer relationship without rather precise and expensive instrumentation.

The average energy budget of corn grown at high moisture levels in a Missouri experiment is shown in Table 1. During the early September period, corn does not utilize its energy in the same manner as during the midsummer periods. These differences in energy utilization are believed to be associated with morphological changes in the corn plant and not due to desiccation by maturity. Through the September period, the corn remained green without apparent change in turgor.

Investigations reported in the literature reveal that surfaces at high levels of moisture (i.e., vegetative covers grown under conditions of abundant rainfall or irrigation, and ponds or lakes) use a high portion of the net radiation in the latent heat process or in evapotranspiration and evaporation. Studies by Suomi and Tanner[12] and Decker[4] indicate that the use of the energy from net radiation for evapotranspiration takes precedence over its use in the transfer of sensible heat to the atmosphere. In Table 2 are shown the Bowen ratios, as well as the average fraction of net radiation used by each component of the energy budget, by semi-monthly periods for corn in Missouri. During the period of rapid corn development, from three to five times as much energy is used in the latent heat process as in the transfer of sensible heat to the atmosphere. With Eq. (5), it is possible to compute the percentage of energy to be used in the evapotranspiration for varying values of Bowen's ratio. These percentages are shown in Table 3 for Bowen

TABLE 1. THE AVERAGE ENERGY BUDGET OF IRRIGATED CORN AND EVAPOTRANSPIRATION BY SEMI-MONTHLY PERIODS

Growth Period	Heat Budget (cal/cm²/day)				Evapo-transpiration* (in./day)
	Net Radiation	Latent Heat	Sensible Air	Heat Soil	
July 1–15	473	332	92	48	.22
July 16–31	354	280	58	17	.19
Aug. 1–15	367	277	89	1	.18
Aug. 16–31	342	233	109	0	.16
Sept. 1–15	288	157	171	−40	.10

* Latent Heat/1500 = Evapotranspiration.

TABLE 2. RATIOS OF ENERGY FOR IRRIGATED CORN BY SEMI-MONTHLY PERIODS

| Growing Period | Fraction of Net Radiation Used in | | | Bowen's Ratio, Q/LE |
	Evapotranspiration	Warming Atmosphere	Warming Soil	
July 1–15	.70	.20	.10	.28
July 16–31	.79	.16	.05	.21
Aug. 1–15	.75	.25	*	.32
Aug. 16–31	.68	.32	*	.47
Sept. 1–15	.54	.60	−.14	1.09

* Less than .01.

ratios of the magnitudes noted for corn under high levels of irrigation in Missouri (see Table 2).

Since the energy available through net radiation tends to be used in the latent process (evapotranspiration) during periods of rapid growth and at high levels of moisture, it is possible to use the net radiation as an indicator of evapotranspiration. Relationships for estimating evapotranspiration from net radiation should be valid when the latent heat transfer is much greater, say from three to five times, than the transfer to sensible heat. Capitalizing on the fact that the magnitude of the net radiation term determines the amount of evapotranspiration, Penman[9] and others have developed relationships which depend upon the measurement or estimation of net radiation. These relationships are quite successfully employed for plant canopies during periods with high levels of soil moisture or for water surface. It would not be expected that the theoretical relationships of Eqs. (4) and (5) would provide a significantly better

estimate of evapotranspiration than those employing empirical relationships based on net radiation.

The agronomist, biologist, or hydrologist intending to utilize estimates of evaporation from a soil surface or plant canopies which are not supplied with an abundance of water will find that it is necessary to employ the more exacting relationships of Eqs. (4) and (5). This will necessitate measuring the wind, temperature and/or atmospheric moisture profiles in order to estimate evapotranspiration. Table 3 indicates that if Bowen's ratio is unity or greater (a Bowen ratio of one would indicate that as much heat goes into the atmosphere as sensible heat as is used for latent heat), relationships for estimating evaporation or transpiration by net radiation will lose their advantage.

TABLE 3. PERCENTAGE OF AVAILABLE ENERGY $(R_n - S)$ EXPECTED TO BE USED BY LATENT HEAT TRANSFER (EVAPOTRANSPIRATION, LE, AND SENSIBLE HEAT TRANSFER, Q)

| Bowen Ratio | Fraction of Heat Used as | |
	Latent Heat	Sensible Heat
.20	.833	.167
.25	.800	.200
.30	.770	.230
.35	.742	.258
.40	.714	.285
.50	.667	.333

References

1. Blaney, H. F., and Criddle, W. D., "Determining Water Requirements in Irrigated Areas from Climatological and Irrigation Data," *U.S. Dept Agr. Soil Conservation Service T. P.* 96 (1950).
2. Bowen, S. I., "The Ratio of Heat Losses by Conduction and Evaporation from any Water Surface," *Phys. Rev.*, **27**, 779–787 (1927).
3. Decker, W. L., "The Role of Environmental Factors in Evaporation and Transpiration in a Corn Field," Proceedings of the Sixteenth Annual Hybrid Corn Industry Research Conference, pp. 75–83, 1961.
4. Decker, W. L., "The Total Energy Budget of Corn in Missouri," *Missouri Agr. Expt. Sta. Res. Bull.* (1963).
5. Gerber, J. F., and Decker, W. L., "Evapotranspiration and Heat Budget of a Corn Field," *Agron. J.* **53**, 259–261 (1961).

6. Halstead, M. H., "The Fluxes of Momentum, Heat and Water Vapor in Micrometeorology," in "Publications in Climatology," Vol. 7, No. 2, pp. 326–358, New Jersey, Seabrook, 1954.

7. Lettau, H. H., "Computation of Heat Budget Constituents of the Earth-Air Interface," in "Exploring the Atmosphere's First Mile," pp. 305–327, New York, Pergamon Press, 1957.

8. McQuigg, J. D., and Decker, W. L., "The Hydrologic Balance of the Lowlands of Southeast Missouri," Unpublished note, 1962.

9. Penman, H. L., "Natural Evaporation from Open Water," *Proc. Roy. Soc. London Ser. A.*, **193**, 120–145 (1948).

10. Rahrer, C. "Evaporation from Free Water Surfaces," *U.S. Dept. Agr. Tech. Bull.*, **271** (1931).

11. Stauber, S., Decker, W. L., and Miller, F., "Incidence of Drought Conditions in Southeastern Missouri," *Missouri Agr. Expt. Sta. Res. Bull.*, (1963).

12. Suomi, V. E., and Tanner, C. B., "Evapotranspiration Estimates from Heat Budget Measurements over a Field Crop," *Trans. Am. Geophys. Union*, **39**, 298–304 (1958).

13. Thornthwaite, C. W., "A Rational Approach Toward Classification of Climate," *Geo. Rev.*, **38**, 55–94 (1948).

13. Defoliation—Controlled Relative Humidity in Cotton Fields

O. H. NEWTON

U.S. Weather Bureau, Stoneville, Mississippi

J. A. RILEY

U.S. Weather Bureau, Memphis, Tennessee

and

F. B. WILLIAMSON

Agricultural Research Service, U.S.D.A., Stoneville, Mississippi

ABSTRACT

Examples of weather's control over crop development are many. Examples of man's influence over these controlling weather factors are few. Cotton field defoliation (the application of a chemical to insure leaf drop at a predetermined time) prior to harvest is one example of man's ability to achieve a desirable change in weather conditions in a field crop.

The moisture content of seed cotton holds the key to the quality of the harvested product. Wet cotton before harvest promotes fungal boll rot. If the moisture percentage at harvest time is above a critical level, bacterial action is accelerated and a number of other factors combine to cause a loss of value in the harvested crop. A relative humidity of 50 per cent or less is equivalent to "safe" harvesting conditions.

Defoliation reduces obstruction of wind and light penetration into the plant zone. Experiments have shown twice as much sunlight within defoliated fields as compared with heavily leafed fields. Wind in the leafed field totaled only 25 per cent of the wind in the defoliated field. Evaporation averaged twice as much in the defoliated field. As a result of the complex of weather variables, relative humidity averaged 8 to 10 per cent lower in the defoliated field. This added an additional hour of safe picking time in the defoliated field.

Humidity and the way we adjust to its influences can have a profound effect on the way we live. As a specific example, we refer to a cotton farmer in a relatively humid area of the Cotton Belt. His margin of profit and thus his living standard may depend on his strict attention to the humidity level at critical stages during harvest time.

Cotton is widely grown under both semiarid and humid conditions as a herbaceous annual. It is planted in the spring after the soil has warmed to 65 degrees or higher. About four months are required for the plant to reach maturity, and a high per cent of the growth is confined to the last two months. Although the cotton plant is not a heavy user of moisture in the early stages of growth, moisture is one of the factors most critically affecting its growth. In order to maintain a continuous good growth, the soil should contain 50 per cent or more of available moisture. The moisture-use curve is similar to the growth curve and both reach a peak during the maximum growing and fruiting stage. Although as little as 12 in. of water will produce a good crop in humid areas, the moisture requirements go up to as high as 30 in. in very dry areas.

A cotton plant developing at a normal rate will reach a height of 6 to 12 in. during the first 30 to 40 days after emergence. It will gain another foot or more during the next 10 to 15 days and will spread laterally to a width almost equal its height. The dense foliage that is characteristic of the plant as it nears maturity blocks out a high per cent of the sunlight and seriously restricts the movement of air through the plant zone. A mature plant, if grown under excellent conditions, will often reach a height of 5 to 6 ft.

The cotton starts fruiting some 6 to 8 weeks after emergence and continues until harvest time. This means the fruit that is set early will reach maturity while the remainder is still in various stages of development. High humidity and other high moisture conditions which may occur in the form of dew or rain are usually beneficial during the growing period. However, when the first cotton bolls begin to open, the high humidity may adversely affect the crop.

For example, fungi and bacteria develop rapidly in warm and humid conditions and they can cause considerable damage to unopened or partially opened bolls. The term "boll rot" is used to describe the damaging effects of the fungi and bacteria. Losses from boll rot often range from 7 to 15 per cent of a cotton crop in the more humid sections of the Cotton Belt.

The control of humidity and/or the control of fungi and bacteria are obvious solutions to the boll-rot problem. So far, the application of fungicides and other chemicals to the plants has not proved to be a practical solution.

Defoliation, or the removal of the leaves of the cotton plant prior to harvest, is an example of man's ability to achieve a desirable change in the weather conditions in a field crop. Defoliation, either partial or total, reduces the obstruction to air movement and light penetration into the plant zone and results in a highly desirable climatic change.

If total defoliation is applied too early, many of the immature bolls will not develop because they no longer have a source of food. However, if one-third or even one-half of the leaves are removed, a high per cent of the young bolls will reach maturity. Defoliants and application

techniques have been developed to the extent that it is possible to defoliate the bottom one-third or one-half of the plants before the late-set bolls are mature.

This partial defoliation is not as effective as total defoliation, but it does permit increased light penetration and ventilation in the lower plant zone. As much as 50 per cent more light reaches the bottom areas of partially defoliated plants and results in higher temperature and lower average relative humidity.

Wind-flow measurements indicated that defoliation of the lower one-third of the plants has very little effect on the horizontal wind flow. Accumulation curves for a 13-day period in undefoliated and bottom-defoliated fields were almost identical, while the curve for a completely defoliated field showed an increase of about 100 per cent.

Precision anemometers were exposed at 12 in. above the ground in the plant zone. The total air movement during the 13 days in bottom-defoliated cotton was only 46 miles, while the total for undefoliated was 54 miles and in completely defoliated cotton the movement was 106 miles. The difference between the wind flow in the bottom-defoliated and undefoliated fields was not considered significant and was probably the result of the location of the instruments. The vertical profile of wind movement in and above the plant zone indicates the wind resistance offered by the plants. The flow at 12 in. above the ground surface is only 2 per cent of that at 40 ft. above the surface. The air movement only 1 ft. below the average surface of the plant zone, is 12 per cent of that at 40 ft.

Complete defoliation is more effective than bottom defoliation; however, when the practice is used it indicates that the crop is mature and ready for harvest. Mature bolls will open rapidly and a rather drastic change takes place in the microclimate. Research at the Delta Branch Experiment Station, Stoneville, Mississippi, has shown that there is a significant increase in solar radiation and air movement in the plant zone as well as a decrease in the duration of high humidity.

Quality control is an important economic consideration to the cotton grower. As indicated in this report, harvest time is a good time for the farmer to increase his net profit. Research has shown that if cotton is harvested when the moisture content is high (above 12 per cent), it will lose quality before it reaches the gin. The cost of the ginning process will also be increased because of the additional drying required.

Defoliation increases the number of optimum-moisture picking hours since drying will be more rapid in a leaf-free field after sunrise. The seed cotton moisture will also remain within the safe limit longer during the afternoon or evening. A picking guide based on relative humidity conditions, has been developed for cotton farmers in the Mississippi River Delta areas. This guide is designed to give the farmer an early morning estimate of when his cotton will be dry enough to harvest. Weather factors that are a basis for this guide include wind, dew, humidity, cloud cover and rain. The farmer, after listening to forecasts and observing existing conditions, can determine the best time to begin picking and can also plan his harvesting operations several hours ahead.

Since the cotton stalk is not killed during the defoliation process, new growth will develop if periods of rain interrupt the harvesting. As a result, the obstruction offered by the new leaves creates a condition similar to the original environment, even though the new growth is rarely as heavy as the original growth. These new leaves do not react to a defoliant but may be desiccated with a different type of chemical. In this case they remain on the stalk and are mixed with the cotton when it is harvested. Trash is one

source of moisture and adds to the total moisture content. Sources of moisture that compose the total moisture content of the harvested seed cotton include moisture applied to the spindles of the picker and moisture in the lint, seed and trash. Defoliation has an important effect on the per cent of moisture collected from most of these sources.

Cotton may be harvested from defoliated or undefoliated plants, but in either case the field moisture conditions are critical following nights of high humidity and moderate or heavy dews. The farmer that starts harvesting too early in the day may fall into the moisture trap and lose many dollars. It is a normal procedure to haul the cotton to the gin in trailers that hold four or five bales, Cotton that is harvested during the early morning is loaded first, and although seed cotton in the field may dry to an acceptable level, the average for the four or five bales is still too high. If the ginner tries to dry this cotton to an acceptable level, a part of the trailer load will be over-dried while other parts may still have too much moisture.

The final quality of the cotton that goes into the bale determines the price that the farmer will get. Many factors will have a strong influence on quality, but both the indirect and direct effects of humidity and moisture will be associated with most of them.

Defoliation of the cotton field at the right time has proved to be a cultural practice that will minimize the losses caused by high humidity and moisture.

14. Use of the Nuclear Probe in Studies of the Soil Moisture Regimen on Lysimeters and Small Watersheds*

F. R. DREIBELBIS

Soil and Water Conservation Research Division, ARS, USDA, Coshocton, Ohio

ABSTRACT

Resistance blocks and neutron scattering equipment were used to obtain soil moisture data on watersheds 0.5 to 0.9 hectare and on monolith lysimeters 8.09 square meters in area. Measurements were made in 1.8-meter profiles of two soil types under corn, wheat, meadow, and woodland covers. The reliability of the probe and blocks was confirmed by comparing data obtained from these with data from the weighing lysimeter. Likewise, ET as determined from weight changes checked closely with ET data obtained from the probe and blocks.

Soil type showed little influence in the 0-18 cm layer, the zone of major hydrologic activity, but exerted considerable influence in the lower soil layers. Agronomic practice influenced the moisture regimen more than did soil type. The contrast between different crops also had a marked effect.

The possibility of extrapolating these small-area results to the field of watershed management is discussed.

INTRODUCTION

Soil moisture measurements are a necessary phase of studies in watershed hydrology. With the introduction of the nuclear soil moisture probe, greater refinements in measuring soil moisture have been attained, particularly in the lower depths of soil. This refinement has enabled soil scientists and hydrologists to evaluate more accurately the role that soil moisture plays in watershed hydrology. The hydrologic installations at the Coshocton Station, together with the nuclear soil moisture probe, provide a unique opportunity for conducting water budget studies.

This paper presents soil moisture data with particular reference to the effects of land use and soil type on the moisture regimen on small watersheds, 0.5, to 0.9 hectare in area. It also deals with water budget studies conducted on lysimeters for three successive years showing effects of agronomic practice and soil type under meadow, corn, and wheat covers.

EXPERIMENTAL PROCEDURE

Soil Moisture

The neutron method of determining soil moisture was used to evaluate the moisture content for the complete soil profile except in the upper 18 cm. The electrical resistance method using "Fiberglas" gypsum blocks was used in this layer where the nuclear depth probe is not satisfactory because of the indeterminate extension of its zone of influence into the atmosphere. Although a surface probe has been designed to measure the moisture content of the surface soil, it has not been used at Coshocton because of the uncertainty of the depth of application of the reading. Furthermore, the preparation of the soil surface for its use requires the destruction of vegetation. The electrical resistance block, when properly

* Contribution in cooperation with the Ohio Agricultural Experiment Station, Wooster, Ohio.

replicated and operated, has given reasonably accurate results in this layer. Six blocks were placed at each depth of 0 to 2.5, 2.5 to 10.2 and 10.2 to 17.8 cm on the lysimeter, and three were placed at these same depths near each access tube on the watershed. Construction features and other pertinent information about these blocks were previously reported.[7]

The neutron equipment used was a Model P-19 depth probe and the Model 2800 scaler manufactured by the Nuclear Chicago Corporation.* The access tubing was a thin-walled, galvanised iron, electrical conduit having an inside diameter of 4.09 cm. One of these tubes was driven into the parent material (1.6 to 1.8 meters) on each of the lysimeters reported in this study. After installation, the bottoms of the tubes were sealed with a rubber stopper and hydraulic cement. One access tube on each watershed extended to a depth of 2.4 to

* Trade names and company names are included for the benefit of the reader and do not imply any endorsement or preferential treatment of the product listed by the U.S. Department of Agriculture.

2.7 meters. Other access tubes on each of the watersheds extended to a 1.22-meter depth. The areal distribution of the tubes was so planned that the entire watershed area (0.51 to 0.89 hectare) was fairly well represented. The number of access tubes on each watershed is given in Table 1.

A field calibration curve was developed by relating bulk density and gravimetric moisture determinations taken in a meadow soil with concurrent neutron meter counts taken at the same depth. After the initial calibration, a set of five 208-liter drums, each containing specified ammonium alum and alum-sand mixtures, were assembled to provide a set of "standards" for checking the calibration without laborious and time-consuming field calibrations. Calibration curves for both the neutron method and the "Fiberglas" gypsum blocks were developed to express moisture in per cent by volume. This facilitated conversion to either centimeters or inches of water, whichever system was used.

Further details of the nuclear equipment

TABLE 1. DESCRIPTIVE INFORMATION OF LYSIMETERS AND WATERSHEDS, COSHOCTON, OHIO*

Lysimeter No.	Y101D	Y102C	Y103A, Y103C**	None
Adjacent watershed No.	102	109	123	131
Soil type	Muskingum silt loam (sandstone origin)	Muskingum silt loam (shale origin)	Keene silt loam (shale origin)	Muskingum loam (sandstone and shale origin)
Slope, %	20	13	6	22
Rotation	Permanent grassland	4-year rotation, corn, wheat, meadow, meadow	4-year rotation, corn, wheat, meadow, meadow	Permanent woodland
Cover in 1960–61–62	Birdsfoot trefoil	Alfalfa, red clover, timothy, 1960. Corn to wheat 1961. Wheat 1962.	Alfalfa, red clover, timothy, 1960. Corn to wheat 1961. Wheat 1962.	Hardwoods
Date cover established	1957	1958	1958	Permanent woodland
Area of lysimeters, hectares	0.0008	0.0008	0.0008	None
Area of Adjacent watershed, hectares	0.51	0.68	0.55	0.89
Number of access tubes on lysimeter	1	1	1	None
Number of access tubes on watershed	5	6	7	6

* All watersheds and lysimeters Y102C, Y103A in improved practice. Treatment: 180 lb/acre 5-20-20, 10 tons manure on corn; 180 lb/acre 5-20-20 on wheat, limed to pH 6.8.

** Y103C in prevailing practice. Red clover, alsike, timothy, 1960. Corn 1961, wheat to meadow, 1962. Treatment: 50 lb/acre 5-20-20, 7.5 tons manure on corn. 100 lb/acre 5-20-20, on wheat, limed to pH 5.4.

used, field calibrations, number and dimensions of access tubes, and other pertinent information were presented in a previous publication.[5]

Soil moisture changes in one of the Coshocton lysimeters as determined by the nuclear soil moisture probe, together with blocks in the 0 to 18-cm layer, were compared with those determined from changes in the lysimeter weights.

Determinations of soil moisture were made on the lysimeters and watersheds about once a week during the growing season and from two to four times monthly during the dormant season.

Lysimeters

The lysimeters are of the monolith type, a rectangle 4.27 meters long, 1.9 meters wide on the contour or 8.09 square meters in surface area, with a profile depth of 2.44 meters. Data for three sites are given, each representing a different soil type as described in Table 1. Each lysimeter is equipped to record rates and amounts of runoff and percolation. Weight records on lysimeters Y102C and Y103A, adjusted for runoff and percolation, provide data on changes in soil moisture storage. Brief descriptions of the vegetative cover on lysimeters and watersheds appear in Table 1. More detailed descriptions of the lysimeters, of the soil types and of the recording and processing of the data, appear in U.S.D.A. Technical Bulletin No. 1179.[3]

Watersheds

Three watersheds in this study were located on Muskingum soils approximately 600 meters apart; a fourth was on Keene silt loam. These soil types were previously described.[1, 3] A description of the watersheds is given in Table 1 and in a recent publication.[6]

Although three of the watersheds were located on Muskingum soils, this should not imply that they were uniform in all respects. In addition to the minor differences previously mentioned,[1, 3, 6] Watershed 109 is underlain by silty and sandy shales; Watershed 102 by sandstone with a small amount of shale and with a watertable averaging 3 meters below the runoff gauge; and Watershed 131 by sandstone and shale with a watertable averaging 8 meters below the runoff gauge. Soil moisture

tension curves indicated only slight differences between the hydrologic characteristics of the upper 36 cm of soil in these watersheds. This is the zone of major hydrologic activity.[2] Although these hydrologic differences of the profile at the three sites become wider with increasing depth below the 36-cm level, they still remain relatively small.

RESULTS

Probe Reliability

Soil moisture changes in the 0- to 1.83-meter profile as determined by the nuclear probe and moisture blocks are shown in Fig. 1, together with moisture changes in the same part of the profile as inferred from data from the weighing lysimeter covering the entire 0- to 2.44-meter profile. At the start of the season, the 0- to 2.44-meter profile contained 63.8 cm of water (obtained from lysimeter weights). The moisture content of the 0- to 1.83-meter profile as determined by the nuclear probe and from moisture blocks was 50 cm. The moisture

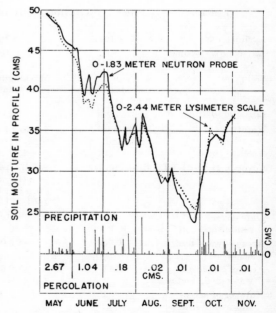

Fig. 1. Moisture content of 0- to 1.83-meter profile during the growing season for birdsfoot trefoil as determined from nuclear probe and moisture block measurements and as inferred from lysimeter weights covering the entire 2.44-meter depth of the lysimeter. Rainfall and percolation for the period are shown at the bottom.

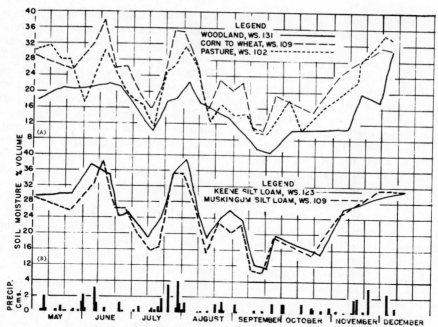

FIG. 2. Soil moisture fluctuations in 0- to 18-cm layer: (A) Land use effects; (B) soil type effects.

content of the 1.83- to 2.44-meter profile was, by inference, 13.8 cm. This value was used throughout the season although there was some evidence that it did not remain constant. Despite this, the two curves shown in Fig. 1 are reasonably close throughout the season. Data on precipitation and percolation for the same season are also shown. The crop on the lysimeter was birdsfoot trefoil.

Annual Soil Moisture Fluctuations

The zone of major hydrologic activity in the Coshocton soils lies in the upper 30 cm and particularly in the 0- to 18-cm layer.[2] Since infiltration as well as most of the depletion by evapotranspiration and percolation occur in this layer, soil moisture fluctuations were also greatest in this part of the profile. Soil moisture fluctuations in the 0- to 18-cm layer appear in Fig. 2. Data from watersheds in corn, pasture and woodland, all on Muskingum soils, are given for the growing season of 1961. During most of this season, there was less moisture in the woodland watershed soil than in that of either the corn or pasture watersheds. Interception of rainfall by the tree canopy, as well as by the dense vegetative understory and leaf

litter, resulted in a lower amount of water absorbed in woodland soils during the growing season. During May, the moisture curve representing the pasture showed the greatest drop, the slope of the depletion curve being much greater than those for the other areas. In May, transpiration was highest in pasture because legumes and grasses completely covered the soil surface and potential transpiration rates were reached. Little transpiration occurred in either corn or woodland at this time, because corn plants were very small and tree foliage was not fully developed. During the first part of August, depletion rates on corn were about the same as on pasture as indicated by the slope of the curves.

Accretion of moisture in the profile during the dormant season normally begins in October and ends in April. In 1961, this accretion was especially pronounced during November.

Soil Type Effects. Soil type effects on the moisture regimen in the 0- to 18-cm layer are illustrated in B of Fig. 2 in which data for the Keene silt loam are compared with those of the Muskingum silt loam. Both watersheds are in the same 4-year rotation of corn, wheat, meadow, meadow. Both receive the same fertility and cultural treatment. That the physical properties of these soils in the 0- to 18-cm layer are similar,[1] is reflected by the similarity in amount of soil moisture.

In the subsoils, however, a marked contrast in physical properties appears, and this is indicated by the contrast in amounts of moisture for 1961 in each of six different layers at depths of from 30 to 152 cm (Fig. 3). The moisture content of the Keene subsoil is consistently higher at each of the depths indicated. The upper subsoil of this profile is a heavy silt loam grading into a silty clay loam at the 50-cm depth, and into a heavy silty clay at the 70- to 90-cm depth. The silty clay layer, high in colloids, swells when wet, making the profile almost impermeable. This serves as a deterrent to root penetration. In the Muskingum profile, the subsoil becomes lighter in texture with depth, is unmottled, and there are no impeding layers present, therefore the profile is quite permeable. Thus, root penetration is deeper in Muskingum soils, thereby partly accounting for the lower moisture content in the lower parts of the profile.

The contrast in moisture curves between the two soil types is very evident at the 30-, 53-, 71-, and 91-cm depths. Prior to corn planting, the two curves are nearly parallel. During the July-August period, the curves separate, the curve representing the Muskingum soil dropping much more than that representing the Keene at the 53-, 71- and 91-cm depth. At the 30-cm point, the drop of the curve representing the Muskingum soil is evident during the August-September period.

The recharge period during the November-December period is also noteworthy. In the upper 3 subsoil layers, the curve representing the Muskingum soil rises farther than that of the Keene, indicating the more rapid drainage characteristics of the Muskingum soil. The lighter texture of the Muskingum subsoils also indicates a lesser retention of moisture than the heavier Keene subsoil.[4] Similar data for 1960 and 1962 indicated that the contrast between the two soil types was consistent.

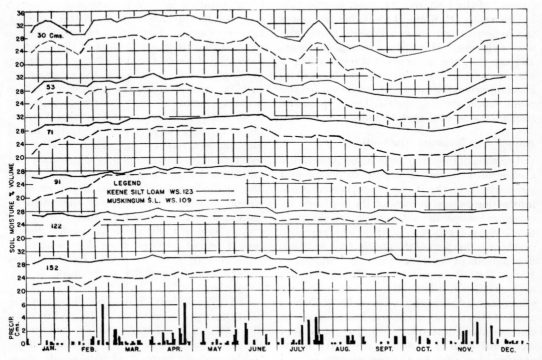

FIG. 3. Annual soil moisture fluctuations at various points in profiles of Keene silt loam and Muskingum silt loam, 1961.

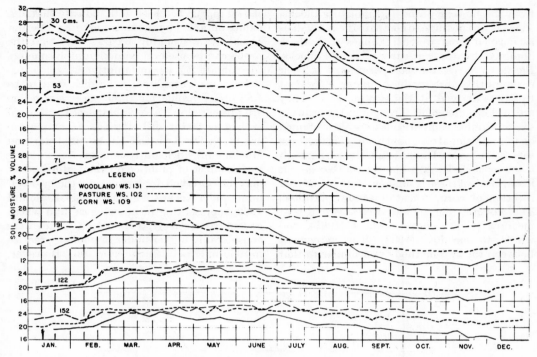

Fɪɢ. 4. Land use effects upon the soil moisture regimen in Muskingum soil profiles, 1961.

Land Use Effects. Land use effects on the moisture regimen in the 0- to 18-cm profile were presented before (Fig. 2). Similar effects on the moisture regimen below the 18-cm level are given in Fig. 4. Here data from corn, pasture and woodland watersheds are compared. During the latter part of the growing season, the moisture curve for each profile depth in the woodland area is lower than for either the corn or pasture areas. The slope of the depletion curve is especially pronounced in the four upper layers of the woodland soils. The slope of the curves for pasture in May shows a sharp contrast with both that for corn and woodland as explained above for the 0- to 18-cm layer.

At the 30-cm depth, the slope of the moisture depletion curve for the month of August is steep for both the corn and woodland watersheds. This reflects the large amount of transpiration taking place on these areas. The solar energy is high, and there was plenty of moisture available in the 30-cm profile. Appreciable rates of depletion in August are also evident at the 53.0- and 71.0-cm points in the profile. Even though minor differences

among the Muskingum soil watersheds prevail, as stated above, these influences are relatively small, and the contrast in soil moisture is essentially, although not entirely, due to land use effects.

Water Budget Studies

In a previous paper,[2] it was pointed out that water budget studies on lysimeters were conducted with a reasonable degree of accuracy by use of the equation.

$$ET = P - G - Q \pm \Delta M \qquad (1)$$

where

ET = evapotranspiration
P = precipitation
G = percolation
Q = surface runoff
ΔM = change in soil moisture.

All factors on the right side of the equation are determined directly on the lysimeters. On the weighing lysimeters ΔM was determined by weight. On each lysimeter where an access tube and moisture blocks (0 to 18 cm) were installed, the change in moisture was determined by data from the nuclear probe and moisture blocks. Thus, it was possible to compare the ET values as derived from weight changes with those obtained by the nuclear probe and blocks. Figure 5 gives the comparison of ET or consumptive use values under birdsfoot trefoil as derived by the two methods. They are in close agreement throughout the growing season. Similar comparisons were also obtained on two additional weighing lysimeters for three successive years. One was on Muskingum silt loam over shale, and one on the Keene silt loam. Both of these lysimeters were in a 4-year rotation of corn, wheat, meadow, meadow. The covers represented were second-year meadow (1960), corn to wheat (1961), and wheat to meadow (1962). The agreement between the two methods was similar to that

shown in Fig. 5. These data indicate that ET values obtained by the soil moisture probe and blocks are reasonably accurate and that the probe can be used on nonweighing lysimeters to evaluate ET or consumptive use.

Data on water budget studies in a 0- to 1.83-meter profile for three successive years are presented in Table 2. Numerical values of each of the factors on both sides of the equation are given for both the Keene silt loam and Muskingum silt loam lysimeters.

The effect of practice on the water budget may be observed by comparing the two columns under Keene silt loam for 1960, 1961, and 1962, representing meadow, corn, and wheat covers, respectively. Percolation values were considerably higher under prevailing practice in 1960 and to a lesser extent in 1961. However,

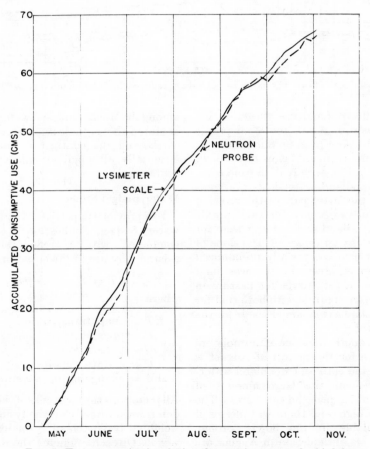

FIG. 5. Evapotranspiration during the growing season for birdsfoot trefoil as inferred from the water budget equation and profile moisture contents shown in Fig. 1.

TABLE 2. WATER BUDGET STUDIES ON LYSIMETERS, 1960–62

	Keene Silt Loam		Muskingum Silt Loam
	Prevailing*	Improved*	Improved
Period:	*April 12 to August 2,* 1960		*April 15 to August 1,* 1960
Land use	Meadow (centimeters)	Meadow (centimeters)	Meadow (centimeters)
Precipitation	40.03	40.03	37.74
Percolation	5.99	.61	.94
Runoff	.51	.23	.48
Δ Moisture**	−3.05	−9.22	−12.88
Evapotranspiration	36.58	48.41	49.20
Average daily *ET*	.328	.432	.455
Period:	*May 24 to Sept. 26,* 1961		*May 23 to Sept. 25,* 1961
Land use	Corn	Corn	Corn
Precipitation	36.02	36.02	33.83
Percolation	1.90	.56	1.65
Runoff	.86	1.22	2.87
Δ Moisture**	−12.22	−16.08	−17.86
Evapotranspiration	45.48	50.32	47.17
Average daily *ET*	.363	.401	.378
Period:	*April 19 to July 11,* 1962		*April 19 to July 10,* 1962
Land use	Wheat	Wheat	Wheat
Precipitation	16.15	16.15	14.86
Percolation	.81	.76	1.65
Runoff	.03	.03	.05
Δ Moisture**	−12.67	−20.04	−17.81
Evapotranspiration	27.98	35.40	30.97
Average daily *ET*	.338	.427	.378

* See Table 1 for description of practice.
** Data represent a 1.83-meter profile.

for the 83-day period in 1962, during which there was an extreme lack of rainfall, there was only 0.05-cm difference. The amount of percolation for each growing season is influenced considerably by the amount and distribution of rainfall. Runoff values for each of the three years were relatively small and showed no consistent relationship with practice.

There was a sharp contrast in soil moisture relationships with practice. (See Table 1 for description of practice.) During the meadow growing season, soil moisture storage under improved practice declined 9.22 cm as compared to 3.05 cm under prevailing practice. Similar declines were obtained for the corn and wheat seasons in 1961 and 1962, respectively. The greater reduction in soil moisture under improved practice was caused by the greater moisture removal by evapotranspiration (*ET*). *ET* values were consistently higher under improved practice for each of the three crops.

The effect of soil type on the water budget was observed by comparing values for the Keene silt loam under improved practice with those for the Muskingum silt loam. Soil type effects were considerably less than those of practice.

Percolation values were higher on the Muskingum silt loam in each of the three years because this soil is better drained and has no impeding layers in the profile. Runoff values which are higher on the Muskingum, did not show as great a contrast as the other depletion factors. Moreover, surface runoff values from lysimeters are not as reliable indicators of land use and soil type effects on runoff as are data obtained from small 0.8-hectare watersheds.

DISCUSSION

The use of the nuclear soil moisture probe together with "Fiberglas" gypsum blocks placed in the 0- to 18-cm layer have provided useful information pertaining to watershed hydrology.

The large soil moisture fluctuations that characterize the 0- to 18-cm layer indicate the enormous water storage opportunity in this zone under certain conditions. This favors more rapid infiltration and percolation with their resultant effects on watershed hydrology.

The slope of the moisture depletion curves in different parts of the soil profile indicates the relative effect of the various types of land use on the soil moisture regimen. They have important hydrologic implications as do those also showing soil type effects.

The influence of agronomic practice on the water budget as determined from lysimeter records may have implications in the field of watershed management. Under improved agronomic practices, the infiltration potential of an area tends to increase and the percolation potential to decrease,[4] thereby reducing surface runoff and groundwater recharge with a corresponding reduction in base flow.

However, in regions where land use practices are similar to those of Coshocton, the improvement in agronomic practices would alter the hydrology of only a part of the large watershed area. At least 60 per cent of the watershed areas around the Coshocton Station consists of forest, pasture and permanent grass, leaving less than 40 per cent subject to improved agronomic practices with their resultant effect on base flow. Thus in some years, the effect of practice on watershed flow might scarcely be discernible. The extrapolation of data from small areas such as lysimeters to large watersheds by use of an area factor is questionable. Blind extrapolation of such data is not warranted.

The results of water budget studies on lysimeters may serve to set maximum ET values for corn, wheat and meadow covers in larger watershed areas where conditions simulate those of the Coshocton area. Previous data[2] indicated that the lysimeters have slightly higher ET values than adjacent 0.6-hectare watersheds. Thus, the lysimeter ET values, although precise for Coshocton conditions, must be considered as approximations when applied to other situations.

SUMMARY

The nuclear soil moisture probe, together with "Fiberglas" gypsum blocks were used to obtain soil moisture data on watersheds 0.5 to 0.9 hectare in area and on monolith lysimeters 8.09 square meters in area. Soil moisture changes as determined by data from the weighing lysimeters confirmed the reliability of data from the nuclear probe and blocks. Likewise, ET as determined from weight changes checked closely with ET data from the probe and blocks.

The data obtained illustrate the variability in soil moisture fluctuations at various depths in 1.83-meter profiles on corn, pasture and woodland watersheds. They emphasise the importance of the nuclear probe in hydrologic studies. Some of the findings obtained indicate:

(1) The soil moisture fluctuations are greatest in the 0- to 18-cm layer which shows this is the zone of major hydrologic activity.

(2) Soil type exerts little influence in the 0- to 18-cm layer but has a considerable influence in the various subsoil layers which reflects the marked differences in the hydrologic characteristics of these subsoils.

(3) Changes in the slope of the soil moisture depletion curves reflect changes in transpiration as affected by crop. The slope of these curves is especially pronounced in the woodland watershed. The contrast with other land use areas is greater in the deeper subsoil layers.

(4) Water budget studies conducted on lysimeters showed that soil type affected moisture depletion less than did agronomic practice. The average daily ET for meadow, corn and wheat crops was much greater on improved practice than under prevailing practice. The average daily ET values for the growing season were within the range of 0.327 to 0.456 cm, both on meadow. Average daily values for the corn and wheat crops were within this range.

Acknowledgment. Grateful acknowledgment is made to R. E. Youker, D. B. Wall and William W. Bentz for their assistance in the collection and tabulation of the basic data.

References

1. Dreibelbis, F. R., and Bender, W. K., "A Study of Some Characteristics of Keene Silt Loam and Muskingum Silt Loam," *J. Soil Water Conserv.*, **8**, 263–266 (1953).
2. Dreibelbis, F. R., "Some Aspects of Watershed Hydrology as Determined from Soil Moisture Data," *J. Geophys. Res.*, **67**, 3425–3435 (1962).
3. Harrold, L. L., and Dreibelbis, F. R., "Evaluation of Agricultural Hydrology by Monolith Lysimeters," *U.S. Dept. Agr. Tech. Bull.*, **1179** (1958).
4. Harrold, L. L., Brakensiek, D. L., McGuinness, J. L., Amerman, C. R., and Dreibelbis, F. R., "Influence of Land Use and Treatment on the Hydrology of Small Watersheds at Coshocton, Ohio, 1938–1957," *U.S. Dept. Agr. Tech. Bull.*, **1256** (1962).
5. McGuinness, J. L., Dreibelbis, F. R., and Harrold, L. L., "Soil Moisture Measurements with the Neutron Method Supplement Weighing Lysimeters," *Soil Sci. Soc. Am. Proc.*, **25**, 339–342 (1961).
6. U.S. Dept. of Agriculture. ARS, "Monthly Precipitation and Runoff for Small Agricultural Watersheds in the United States," 1959.
7. Youker, R. E., and Dreibelbis, F. R., "An Improved Soil-moisture Measuring Unit for Hydrologic Studies," *Trans. Am. Geophys. Union*, **32**, 447–449 (1951).

15. Moisture in Grain*

W. V. HUKILL

Harvesting and Farm Processing Research Branch, AERD, ARS, USDA, Ames, Iowa

ABSTRACT

All plant seeds, including grain, have certain similarities in their moisture relation properties. Being hygroscopic, the vapor pressure of the constituent water depends not only upon the temperature but also upon the quantity of the water held. Grain continually tends to approach moisture equilibrium with the ambient atmosphere by absorbing or releasing water depending on whether its moisture content is above or below the equilibrium moisture content.

The physical and biological responses to variable quantities of water held in grain are closely associated with kernel temperature. The length of time a kernel retains its capacity to germinate, the rate of development of rancidity, and the resistance to attack by mold or other microorganisms or by insects, all are largely dependent on the moisture content and temperature. Grain is most suitable for livestock feed, human food, or for various industrial processes within limited ranges of moisture content.

The United States Department of Agriculture has specified certain procedures in measuring moisture for the official grain standards of the United States. Slightly different procedures are described as standard by the Association of Official Agricultural Chemists. Other methods are used and calibrated against these standards. A standard method for a given grain is to heat it in an oven at a specified temperature for a specified period. It is assumed that after such exposure all the water has been driven off and that the mass of constituents other than water has not

been changed. The question of the validity of these assumptions has never been resolved, even though such standard procedures serve as a satisfactory practical basis for defining moisture content.

The rate at which moisture enters or leaves seeds under given conditions has been studied extensively, but there is yet no generally acceptable explanation of the pattern of such movement. One theory currently used by some investigators to explain observed rates of moisture loss is that the rate of flow is a function of the "dynamic equilibrium moisture content," a changing base to which the moisture content of the grain is continually approaching at a predictable rate. Other studies are interpreted to show that the rate of flow is proportional to the square of a potential whose base is the static equilibrium moisture content.

All plant seeds. including grains, have certain similarities in their responses to moisture. It is an oversimplification, but perhaps a useful one, to consider physical responses on the one hand and biological responses on the other, even though what might be considered purely physical relations, such as water sorption, are modified by the living character of the seed, and the biological responses to moisture must depend on physical processes such as capillarity for example. With this in mind, it is useful to consider the physical relations of grain with water and vapor, such as hygroscopicity, rates of moisture exchange, and definition and measurement of moisture content.

All grains are hygroscopic, that is, when a seed is exposed to an atmosphere, there is a continuous exchange of moisture between the

* Journal Paper No. J-4581 of the Iowa Agricultural and Home Economics Experiment Station, Ames, Iowa. Project No. 1296 (USDA cooperating).

seed and the atmosphere. When the seed moisture content is high and the atmospheric humidity is low, there is a net loss of moisture from the grain and an increase to the air. When conditions are reversed, the net movement is in the other direction. For any given level of moisture content in the seed, there is a corresponding level of atmospheric humidity at which the net moisture exchange would be zero and moisture equilibrium would exist. The equilibrium relation is conveniently represented by a plot of grain moisture content against relative humidity at some given temperature. Since changes in temperature change the location of the curve, such plots are sometimes called sorption isotherms. Typical equilibrium moisture curves or desorption isotherms at three different temperatures are shown in Fig. 1. These curves are for grain sorghum as presented by Fenton.[2] Curves for other grains would fall close to those for sorghum, the grains with high oil contents tending to fall further to the right.

It has been observed that the equilibrium moisture curve is influenced by the direction from which the grain approaches equilibrium. Grain approaching equilibrium from a lower moisture content will not reach as high a moisture level as when it approaches from a higher moisture. This effect, called hysteresis, is illustrated in Fig. 2 which shows adsorption and desorption curves for corn according to Hubbard *et al.*[4]

Changes in the sorption curve with temper-

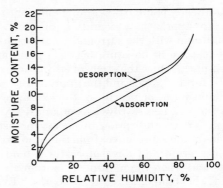

FIG. 2. Adsorption and desorption curves for corn illustrating hysteresis.

ature are related to the heat of wetting. Energy is released when water is absorbed by the grain. Upon evaporating, this energy must be replaced and shows up in a heat of vaporization greater than that of free water. The relation among these effects is covered by the Classius equation which states:

$$H_{fg} = V_{fg} \, T(DP/dT) \qquad (1)$$

where

H_{fg} = heat of vaporization
V_{fg} = specific volume of vapor
T = absolute temperature
P = vapor pressure, all in consistent units.

Shedd and Thompson[6] made estimates of the heat of vaporization of the water in grain from this relationship by using experimental observations on equilibrium moisture content.

Henderson[3] has suggested a general form for the equilibrium relation among moisture content, relative humidity, and temperature. He finds that observed values of equilibrium moisture fit the equation

$$1 - RH = e^{-cT(M_E)n} \qquad (2)$$

where

RH = equilibrium in relative humidity, a decimal
M_E = equilibrium moisture content, per cent dry basis
T = temperature, degrees Rankine
c and n = constants depending on the properties of the grain.

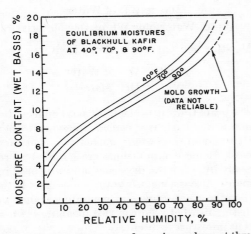

FIG. 1. Sorption curves for grain sorghum at three temperatures.

He gives values of c and n for certain grains and other hygroscopic materials.

As already pointed out, grain tends continually to approach a condition of moisture equilibrium with the surrounding atmosphere by exchange of moisture between grain and atmosphere. Since the atmospheric moisture is in the form of vapor and the grain moisture is in liquid form, or nearly so, the exchange in moisture is necessarily accompanied by a release or an absorption of energy or heat. When the moisture moves from the grain to the air, the grain and air temperatures tend to drop, and when the movement is from air to grain, the temperatures tend to rise. Even though the moisture movement is in the direction that will ultimately result in equilibrium if maintained long enough, the rate of exchange may be so slow that equilibrium is achieved only after long periods of exposure. For practical purposes, the rate of approach to equilibrium is of great importance.

Many experimenters have attempted to express a general relationship between time and grain moisture content from observations of successive grain weights during prolonged exposure of grains to constant atmospheric conditions. There is not very good agreement among the various interpretations of such observations. Perhaps the simplest and most readily tested hypothesis is that the rate of change of grain moisture content is proportional to the amount by which the moisture is out of equilibrium with the air, that is:

$$dM/dT = K\,(M_E - M) \qquad (3)$$

where

M = moisture content, dry basis, at any time

M_E = moisture content at equilibrium

T = time of exposure

K = a proportionality constant which is a function of temperature and air velocity.

Failure of this hypothesis to conform to observed moisture changes has led to proposed modifications such as the concept of "dynamic equilibrium" in which M_E of Eq. (3) is replaced by M_D, a moisture level intermediate between M_E and M which recedes stepwise toward M_E as the value of M changes. This permits the same value of K to be applied in each successive step.

Hukill and Schmidt[5] have suggested the hypotheses that as grain dries from a condition of uniform moisture content throughout the kernel in a constant atmospheric condition, the entire drying period consists of two aspects, the first occurs while the moisture gradient within the kernel is advancing toward the center, and the second occurs after the center has started to dry and the moisture content is dropping in all parts of the kernel. During the second or final aspect, the rate of moisture movement is proportional to the square of the difference between the vapor pressure of the kernel and the vapor pressure at equilibrium. None of these hypotheses has general acceptance, and it remains to describe the rate of moisture transfer in a generally acceptable manner consistent with observed weight changes in grain under controlled conditions.

The flow of moisture from grain is accompanied by loss of the energy of evaporation, and, therefore, both moisture and heat are flowing in response to a potential difference. The potential causing the flow, as pointed out above, is sometimes assumed to be a moisture concentration difference and sometimes a vapor pressure difference. Babbitt,[1] by manipulating the temperature gradient, showed that when the moisture concentration gradient is in one direction and the vapor pressure gradient is in the opposite direction, the moisture flow is from the region of high vapor pressure to that of low vapor pressure.

Moisture content of grains is usually expressed as a per cent. Moisture content, per cent wet basis, is

$$\frac{100 \times \text{Wt. of Water}}{\text{Wt. of Water plus Wt. of Dry Material}}$$

Moisture content, per cent dry basis, is

$$\frac{100 \times \text{Wt. of Water}}{\text{Wt. of Dry Material}}$$

The grain trade uses the wet basis and usually, unless dry basis is specified, reference to per cent moisture content means per cent wet basis. Some computations are handled more easily by using the dry basis, and it is used in many discussions of grain moisture. It is therefore necessary in communication, to distinguish between the two meanings of per cent moisture content.

To have a quantitative definition of per

cent moisture content, it is necessary to visualize the fact that in a quantity of grain having a given moisture content, there is a definite quantity of "dry material" on the one hand and a definite quantity of "water" on the other. This is perhaps an oversimplification. Some of the molecules are so arranged that only by arbitrary definition can they be classed as part of the "water" or part of the "dry material." In specifying percentage moisture content, certain arbitrary procedures have been chosen whereby removable moisture is measured and the remaining mass is classed as dry material. One set of standard procedures is defined for various grains by the United States Department of Agriculture.[7] Many methods are used for measuring moisture content of grain samples. Among the most common are electrical measurements (conductance and capacitance). In practice, such electric readings are translated by previous calibration of equivalent moisture content as measured by a standard method.

The usual methods of removing moisture for moisture content measurement are by exposure to low vapor pressure and high temperature either at atmospheric pressure or under vacuum. Chemical methods of moisture absorption have also been used. The rate at which the last moisture leaves the grain is extremely slow, and the time of exposure is important. Procedures of drying to constant weight are deceptive because weight changes are so slow. The weight may appear to be constant while there is still a significant amount of water not driven off. If the rate of moisture loss decreases as the square of the vapor pressure difference, as suggested by Hukill and Schmidt,[5] it is obvious that changes in weight become increasingly hard to detect as the condition of no remaining moisture is approached. This suggests that extrapolation of a "rate of drying" curve might be used to estimate the weight that would be achieved after an infinite time of drying. Extrapolation of the drying curve when the atmospheric vapor pressure is zero would provide another experimental means of establishing the dry weight of a sample. This could be done at low temperatures to avoid the possibility of oxidizing some of the constituents or driving off some of the more volatile parts other than water. This procedure has not been reduced to

practice but is mentioned here because it appears that it might avoid some of the difficulties that accompany high-temperature desiccation.

Grain drying in practice is accomplished by moving relatively dry air through a "deep bed" of grain. The actual depth of the grain bed varies from a few inches in the case of high-temperature drying to several feet in the case of drying with unheated air. Other methods such as vacuum drying, drying by dielectric heating and use of infrared heat sources have been tried experimentally. The heat pump has been used for reducing the moisture content of the drying air, and some experimental models of dryers in which the moisture is removed from the air by chemicals have been tested. In another method the kernels are suspended in a moving air stream at very high temperatures, 600 to 1000°F, for a short period of exposure.

Nevertheless, most of the present day dryers depend upon adiabatic saturation of air moving through a grain bed. This process is characterized by a moisture gradient moving through the grain bed in the direction of air flow, the grain being dryest where the air enters. As the air moves through the grain, its humidity increases, and its temperature drops. The change in humidity and temperature, as represented on a psychrometric chart, follows a line of constant wet bulb very closely. The heat for evaporating the water is supplied by the change in sensible heat of the air. The air may or may not become saturated before it has passed completely through the grain bed, depending on its rate of flow and the depth of grain. If it does, all the drying capacity of the air will be used in evaporating moisture, but the layer of grain where the air leaves will not be dried at all. If the air does not become saturated by the time it has passed through the grain, some drying will occur at all levels in the grain bed, but the full drying capacity of the air will not have been utilized. In this sense, in a batch dryer, high efficiency can be achieved only by lack of uniformity in grain moisture.

In drying with unheated air, as might be done in a storage bin having a perforated floor, the air usually becomes saturated long before it leaves the grain. As a result, only the lower layers dry at first. This leaves a rather well-defined level, sometimes called the drying front, above which the grain has not dried at all and below which the grain is drying or already dry. The drying front moves upward in the direction of air flow, and, when it reaches the upper surface, drying is completed. This is a somewhat oversimplified picture, but for practical purposes, in the usual range of air volumes and bin sizes, it describes approximately what takes place. When greater volumes of air are used, as is frequently done in heated-air drying, the air may leave the grain unsaturated, and all the grain dries from the start, although at a faster rate where the air enters than where it leaves.

Consider a particle of air starting with a given humidity and temperature as it passes through a bed of damp grain. As it moves forward, it picks up moisture. Its humidity at any time depends almost completely on how long it has been in the grain and on the moisture content of the grain it has passed through. The time it takes air to move from where it enters the grain mass to a point within the mass is sometimes called the "traverse time" to that point. It is useful to recognize that points of equal traverse time in a bin of drying grain are also points of equal air condition and equal grain moisture content. The drying front is a surface containing all the points in the bin having the same traverse time. When the air flow is linear and all the flow lines are parallel, the drying front is a flat plane. For various reasons, the air flow may not be linear, as, for example, when the air is introduced through spaced ducts instead of through a continuous perforated floor. In nonlinear air flow, the drying front will be a nonlinear plane, all points in which have equal traverse times.

The biological and chemical responses of grain to moisture are closely related to responses to temperature. Live seeds germinate only within limited ranges of both temperature and moisture content. The capacity to germinate tends to disappear as the seed ages. The aging process is fast when the moisture content and temperature are high and may be slowed down by drying or cooling. There is no evidence that it can be stopped, but it may become extremely slow. It appears that the length of life of a seed is exponentially related to both the moisture and temperature at which it is held. One estimate of this relation

for some seeds is that the life is doubled by a decrease of 1 per cent moisture content or by a decrease of 10°F. This relation may apply through limited ranges of moisture and temperature. It is known that seeds can be killed forthwith by freezing if the moisture content is high or by exposure to high temperatures. The lethal temperature is higher when the moisture content is low.

In this discussion, we have been considering the presence or absence of life. There are two other aspects of germination that we will have to dismiss with only a brief mention. Vigor of germination is related to moisture content as well as to temperature and other internal and external conditions. Dormancy is the property of a seed to refrain from germination even though it is still alive. Many seeds may be induced into or out of a dormant condition by the action of moisture, temperature, or light. Numerous examples are known of responses of specific seeds to specific sequences of treatment, and more are continually being discovered. In the vast area of unique biologic responses, generalizations about vigor and dormancy, even if limited to grains, may not apply to all varieties.

The life span of a seed is related to, if not controlled by, the disappearance of its constituent parts by respiration. Respiration is the process, common to all living organisms, by which organic nutrients including carbohydrates are continually oxidized with the release of energy, carbon dioxide, and other products. In grains, respiration of the seed itself is invariably accompanied by respiration of microorganisms which utilize the materials of the seed in their growth. Each of the species of microorganisms, of which there are an unknown number, has its own tolerances and optimums of temperature and moisture level.

Since most of the grain crop is used for food or livestock feed, the relation of moisture content to its preservation or utilization for feeding is of interest. Both the moisture content at the time of feeding or processing and the moisture history of the grain modify its usefulness. Animals differ in the ways they utilize food, but extremely dry grain is brittle and hard to chew. It may pass through the digestive system without being assimilated. Or animals may refuse to eat much of it. On the other hand, the moisture may be unusually high without affecting feed utility.

Sometimes high moisture grain is stored with no attempt to reduce the moisture content if the grain is intended for livestock feed. This is done in "sealed storage". By excluding atmospheric oxygen, even though the moisture is permitted to remain high and the temperature is not controlled, the aerobic microorganisms are exterminated. Anaerobic organisms dominate the biologic activity, and the resulting fermentation does not result in reduced palatability or nutritive value for some animals. This is similar to the process of ensiling forages. Under some circumstances, it is the most economical way of handling and utilizing a grain crop.

The various milling or other processing treatments, such as flour making, extraction of starch, feed mixing, etc., each have their own requirements and tolerances for grain moisture content at the time of processing.

The moisture and temperature history of grain up to the time of utilization may be of even more significance than its moisture when it is used. Obviously, if the seed is to be planted, it is valueless after having been held at too high moisture or temperature for too long a time. The same grain may or may not have lost its usefulness for other purposes. The tolerances for changes in quality or aging vary among the different uses to be made of the grain. Rice, for example, practically all of which is intended as human food, may lose most of its value by slight discoloration, whether or not the nutritive value has been impaired. In the manufacture of alcohol, much greater changes are acceptable without greatly affecting the value of the grain as a raw product. The moisture-temperature history is largely responsible for changes in quality of grain. Aging, which eventually results in the death of the germ, is a continuous process. The appearance of visible mold on grain is one of the symptoms of advanced deterioration.

Reduction of moisture content to a suitable level is depended upon to slow down the changes in bulk stored grain. Moisture contents of from 10 to 14 per cent, wet basis, depending on temperature, length of storage period, and other factors, are required for keeping grain in good condition during storage.

Changes in moisture content during storage may occur from several causes. Exchange of moisture with the atmosphere does occur, but this can be controlled if necessary by tight construction. One might assume that, if the grain were put in storage with a satisfactory average moisture content and no water or vapor were permitted to enter, no problems relative to moisture content would be encountered. This is not necessarily so. The movement of moisture by diffusion alone is extremely slow in such a mass of grain. A relatively small quantity of higher moisture grain in one part of the bin will lose its moisture to the surrounding grain only very slowly. Meanwhile, having a relatively high moisture content, it will respire at a faster rate. One of the products of respiration is heat. Since the surrounding grain acts as a thermal insulator, the heat cannot escape readily, and the local temperature increases, further speeding up the rate of respiration in a self-accelerating cycle. A small amount of moisture is generated in the respiration process, and this is added to the moisture already there. This process may result in excessive temperature and excessive molding in the affected area. Spoilage may be stimulated further by insects. They too thrive under favorable moisture and temperature conditions. Active insects respire at a greater rate than do grains and molds. They, therefore, contribute to the cycle of increasing temperature and moisture.

Frequently, even in winter, "hot spots" will be found in a grain bin, resulting from small local quantities of grain that were put into the bin at too high a moisture content. It is typical of such hot spots to reach temperatures between 100 and 110°F, at which level there seems to be a depressing effect on the respiration of the organisms involved, and further temperature rise does not occur. However, under these conditions, the respiration is at such a level that spoilage occurs quickly even though the temperature may not advance much higher.

One other effect may result in local increases in grain moisture, either in the presence or absence of insect infestation. This is described as "moisture migration." Since grain is a good thermal insulator, the temperature of grain in the center of a bin responds very slowly to seasonal temperature changes. As a result, the grain in the interior may be 40 degrees or more warmer during the winter than grain near the walls. The air in the space between kernels is warmer and lighter at the center than at the walls. The difference in air density sets up a slow convection current which moves upward through the bin center. The warm air comes to moisture and temperature equilibrium with the grain in the center. It moves upward, and, when it reaches the upper surface, it is chilled by contact with the cold grain there. Moisture is condensed on the cold grain when the air is cooled to its dew-point. Even before air reaches the dew-point, hygroscopic absorption will occur. In either case, the grain near the surface increases in moisture content. Surface moisture content as high as 25 to 30 per cent, wet basis, has been observed from this cause in bins in which the initial moisture content was uniformly between 13 and 14 per cent.

Moisture migration can be controlled by "aeration". Aeration is forced movement of low volumes of air through bulk stored grains. Its effect is to tend to equalize the temperature in all parts of the bin so that the potential for moisture migration is eliminated. Ordinarily, the volume rate of air flow in aeration is 0.1 cfm or less for each bushel of grain. At this rate, the traverse time for the air to pass completely through the grain is about five minutes or more. The air comes to approximate temperature equilibrium with the grain long before it has passed all the way through the grain. This results in a rather sharp "cooling front" which passes through the grain like a drying front. At the rate mentioned, 0.1 cfm per bushel, the grain in a bin can be cooled to approximately atmospheric temperature in about 100 hours. The cooling time is modified by any exchange of moisture between air and grain. Usually when the grain is initially warmer than the air, there will be some evaporation and the resultant evaporative cooling will speed up the cooling.

There is a substantial amount of information on the interrelation between moisture content, temperature, chemical and biological effects, and time of exposure. But many questions of immediate practical interest remain to be answered.

References

1. Babbitt, J. D., "Observations on the Permeability of Hygroscopic Materials to Water Vapor," *Can. J. Res.*, **18A**, 105–121 (1940).
2. Fenton, F. C., "Storage of Grain Sorghums," *Agr. Eng.*, **22**, 185–188 (May 1941).
3. Henderson, S. M., "A Basic Concept of Equilibrium Moisture," *Agr. Eng.*, **33**, 29–32 (1952).
4. Hubbard, J. E., Earle, F. R., and Senti, F. R., "Moisture Relations in Wheat and Corn," Cereal Chem., **34** (6), 422–433 (Nov. 1957).
5. Hukill, W. V., and Schmidt, J. L., "Drying Rate of Fully Exposed Grain Kernels," *ASAE Trans.*, **3**, 71–80 (1960).
6. Thompson, H. J., and Shedd, C. K., "Equilibrium Moisture and Heat of Vaporization of Shelled Corn and Wheat," *Agr. Eng.*, **35**, 786–788 (Nov. 1954).
7. USDA Service and Regulatory Announcements No. 147 (1959 Revision), Agricultural Marketing Service, U.S. Dept. of Agriculture.

16. Problems Associated with Moisture Determination in Grain and Related Crops

W. Haward Hunt

Grain Division, AMS, USDA, Agricultural Research Center, Beltsville, Maryland

ABSTRACT

This paper is primarily designed to acquaint farmers, elevator operators, inspectors and others concerned with the moisture content of grain with the problems associated with moisture determination in such organic material.

Inaccuracies in moisture content in initial farm-to-market movement are associated with poor sampling technique and with large, inherent variations in moisture content from one part of a field to another. Studies made by the grain division, AMS, USDA, at local elevators, have shown that there is as much as a 10 per cent difference in moisture content between successive loads of corn from the same field. Studies in the field on pure variety test plots have shown that there can be more than 1 per cent difference in moisture content between the ends of 50-ft rows of corn.

Even with grain samples that are uniform in moisture content, inaccuracies may occur because of the complex combination of water in the molecular structure of the grain. The so-called bound water has entirely different electrical properties from "free" water. These terms are defined in the paper, and their influence on moisture determination is evaluated extensively. In substance, the accuracy of electric moisture meters depends upon the "bound" water remaining constant at all times. Unfortunately, due to various causes, it frequently does not remain constant, and errors are then introduced into the measurement.

The two basic types of moisture meters are described, and their relative accuracy is compared.

The measurement of moisture in grain is a marketing matter of utmost importance. Some of the work in the Agricultural Marketing Service is in the area of marketing research, some the administration of food distribution programs. Much of the work is in the marketing service field—tying together the reporting of markets, the measuring of the quality of foods and fiber, and the protecting of free markets by prevention of unfair trade practices.

Through all this AMS work, there is strong concern for the quality of the product. This is especially true in the marketing of grain, where particular attention is given to quality. And, in grain, moisture content is one of the most important factors affecting quality.

It is a common practice for country elevators to base the price they pay a farmer for grain upon the moisture content of the grain and on other quality factors. Also, a farmer may "shop around" with a sample of his crop for the elevator which will show the lowest moisture value on the sample, and then deliver his crop to that elevator. However, when his wagon-load or truckload is delivered to the elevator, he may be greatly disturbed when the load shows a moisture value that is a per cent or more different from the sample which was tested. If the moisture value is shown to be higher, it may lead to a dispute and to charges of dishonesty. Actually, no matter how honest and conscientious the elevator operator is and no matter how accurate his moisture meter is, these differences in moisture content may occur for several reasons, which will be discussed in this article.

Corn is most likely to create difficulty in this

respect. Kernels of corn taken from different parts of the same ear may vary considerably in moisture content, particularly if the crop has been dampened by rain just prior to harvest and the tops of the ears have been partially dried by the sun by harvest time. The moisture content variance from ear to ear is likely to be even greater. Naturally then, when a few ears are taken from one elevator to another for moisture testing, each elevator may well record different values.

This problem was pointed up when, as a part of the USDA program of testing moisture meters, several makes of moisture meters were used at a number of elevators. As each load of corn arrived at the elevator, a sample was drawn and tested immediately on the meters and later by the official oven method. It was observed that successive loads from the same field differed by as much as 10 per cent in moisture content.

In studies on pure varieties of corn at the Agricultural Research Center in Beltsville, Md., it was found that differences in soil composition from one end of a 50-ft row to another or between parallel rows was often sufficient to produce moisture differences of more than 1 per cent.

The variations in moisture content within a lot of grain or among lots of grain is only one of the difficulties in accurately determining moisture content. These variations could be overcome by proper blending and then storing an aliquot for testing in an airtight container until equilibrium is reached. This will require approximately 12 hours.

The U.S. Department of Agriculture has tested many moisture-measuring devices manufactured in this country and abroad for possible use in grain inspection. Unfortunately, there is no moisture-measuring device on the market today which can be depended upon to give accurate results *at all times*, and some are almost worthless in this respect. The methods prescribed for determining moisture in grain under the Official Grain Standards of the United States are oven methods or any method or device which gives equivalent results. Although the oven methods prescribed in the standards are empirical, they are designed to give results that are as close as possible to what is believed to be the true moisture content. That they do meet this requirement has been confirmed by comparison with results obtained by the Karl Fischer (chemical titration) method.

Offhand it would seem that the determination of moisture content in grain would simply entail the heating of a sample of 100°C and maintaining it at this temperature until all the water is driven off. Unfortunately, it is far from being so simple as this. Some of the water is so tightly bound up in the molecular structure of the grain that it is difficult, if not impossible, to drive it out by heating without breaking down some of the organic matter to form carbon dioxide and water, thereby giving rise to water which was not originally present as such. In addition, the heating liberates small amounts of nonaqueous, volatile substances which are measured as water when the loss in weight is determined.

Moisture is believed to exist in several forms in organic matter such as grain. The two forms we are concerned with are "free" water and "bound" water. "Free" water is best defined as water that is capable of acting as a solvent and is found in the capillaries and other interstitial spaces of the grain structure. "Bound" water is electrically bound into the complex structure of the larger molecules and is mechanically, although not chemically, a part of the structure. Since the bound water does not act as a solvent for mineral salts, it cannot conduct electricity and is, therefore, not measured by conductance-type moisture meters.

Electric moisture meters are essentially of two types. One type imposes a controlled voltage between two electrodes. When grain is placed between these electrodes (usually under pressure) electricity will flow through the grain from one electrode to the other, and the current is measured. The conductivity of the grain depends almost entirely upon the amount of "free" water present. Therefore, it becomes essential that the "bound" water remain absolutely constant in all samples at all times if this type of electric moisture meter is always to give dependable results.

The second type of electric moisture meter sends a high-frequency radio wave through the grain, which is contained in a condenser-type cell. Some of these waves, as they pass through the grain, are absorbed by the spinning hydrogen atom of the water molecule. A measurement of the strength of this absorbtion, in a suitable instrument, is related to the moisture content. This is a highly simplified explanation of a measurement known as "dielectric constant." Pure water has a dielectric constant of 80. Therefore, the "free" water in the grain will have a dielectric constant close to this figure. However, there is evidence which shows that very tightly "bound" water has a dielectric constant of 4, which is very close to that of the starch or protein molecule with which it is associated.[1] Therefore, any variance in the amount of "bound" water will also influence moisture determinations by "dielectric" moisture meters.

In our laboratory, many samples of grain have been sealed in airtight containers and tested at intervals from 24 hours up to several weeks by the official oven method and by various moisture meters. It was found that some samples would show as much as one per cent *apparent* moisture change within 24 hours by some of the moisture meters, although the oven result remained constant. Over a period of weeks, a given sample on a given meter might show a constantly increasing deviation from the oven, while on another meter it might show little or no change. Further, the moisture values of samples of one type of grain sent into the laboratory from one part of the country might show excellent agreement when the determination is made with a particular meter and when it is made using the oven method; yet samples of the same grain from another part of the country might give results on the same meter that average a per cent or more higher or lower than the oven method value.

From two to four thousand representative samples of all the different grains from all growing areas are tested in our laboratory each year. The data from these tests are used to keep the moisture conversion charts for the meters used in grain inspection as up-to-date as possible. Data are also used to evaluate other moisture meters in the ever-constant search for the best possible meter for grain inspection purposes. From these tests made over many years on many types of moisture meters, we have come to the conclusion, as stated earlier, that there is no moisture-measuring device on the market today, outside of the official oven method and the Karl Fischer method, which can be depended upon to give accurate moisture results at all times. The oven and Karl Fischer methods require precision equipment and trained personnel and are too time-consuming for practical use in grain inspection.

Although research is underway on entirely new techniques which may eventually produce a moisture meter which will measure accurately all the moisture in grain regardless of whether it is free or bound, we have to limit ourselves at present to the search for a meter which, overall, shows the least error due to abnormal variances in electrical properties of grain. Such a meter, the Motomco Moisture Meter* was adopted in 1960 for moisture determination in rice inspection and also last year for the inspection for moisture content of corn and soybeans. Effective May 1 of this year it became an official device for the inspection of all grains, dry peas, split peas, beans, and lentils.

References

1. Oehme, F., "Dielektrisch Messmethoden," Monographie Nr. 70 zu, "Angewandte Chemie" und "Chemie-Ingenieur-Technik," Verlag Chemie, GMBH, Weinheim/Bergstr., 1958.

* The mention of firm names or trade products does not imply that they are endorsed by or recommended by the U.S. Department of Agriculture over other firms or similar products not mentioned. We have simply designated that the Motomco Moisture Meter be used by all licensed inspectors and our grain inspection supervisors. We recognize that there are other moisture meters on the market which are capable of estimating moisture content within the tolerances required for most farm or elevator purposes.

17. Humidity and Moisture Considerations in the Mechanical Curing of Peanuts*

E. O. BEASLEY

Department of Agricultural Engineering, N.C. State College, Raleigh, North Carolina

ABSTRACT

Mechanization of peanut harvesting has necessitated the introduction of bulk curing techniques to supplant traditional practices of curing entirely in the field. Poor or undesirable flavor results when temperatures above 95° F are used in the curing process, and excessive splitting and skinning of kernels is incurred in the subsequent shelling process if the rate of water removal has been too rapid.

Extensive research has established the limitations which must be imposed on the curing atmosphere to insure good flavor and milling quality in peanuts. Facilities in current use do not provide the close control of curing environment which is desirable for optimum quality, but only approximate these conditions on the average by adding a fixed quantity of heat when the ambient relative humidity exceeds 65 or 70 per cent.

Saturation minus actual vapor pressure in the curing air, which is dependent on both temperature and relative humidity, is a more positive measure of drying potential than relative humidity alone.

Preliminary tests indicate that a peanut dryer which continuously recirculates the air, condensing and removing the water by means of a refrigerated coil, provides an improved curing environment for peanuts. Economic and other aspects of this system are receiving further study.

* Contribution from the Agricultural Engineering Department, North Carolina Agricultural Experiment Station, Raleigh, North Carolina. Published with the approval of the Director of Research as Paper No. 1617 of the Journal Series.

INTRODUCTION

The curing of peanuts, like many agricultural commodities, has traditionally been accomplished by a natural process over which little control was possible. Natural conditions, however, are generally quite favorable for this curing process and, except for an occasional extended period of rain and dampness, might be considered ideal.

Recently, however, the peanut grower has been turning to mechanization of harvesting to reduce his dependence on a steadily declining and increasingly expensive labor supply. Mechanical curing is an integral part of this mechanized harvesting process. Since the curing environment in the mechanized system can be manipulated by the peanut grower, it is necessary that he exercise caution to see that proper conditions are maintained. The fact that peanut quality can be drastically affected by the curing process has become a matter of considerable concern to the peanut industry.

Two important manifestations of improperly or inadequately controlled mechanical curing are (1) poor to bad flavor[2] and (2) poor shelling characteristics of the cured peanuts.[3,5] Deficiencies in flavor usually occur when curing-air temperatures exceed 95°F for any appreciable length of time, and distinctly bad flavor frequently results if the temperature goes to 110°F or higher. The amount of flavor damage inflicted by a given temperature is greater for peanuts which are not fully matured when harvested.

Rapid drying and excessive drying, even at

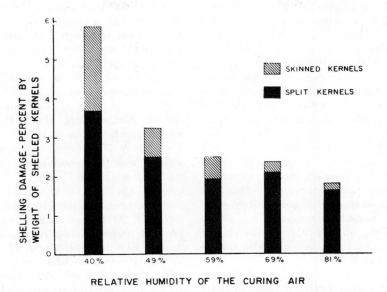

Fig. 1. Shelling damage of peanuts cured at 90°F as a function of the relative humidity of the curing air.

moderate temperatures, cause peanut kernels to split apart easily and lose their skins during the shelling operation. This fragility is undesirable and costly to the sheller, who performs the intermediate process of removing the hulls from peanuts which he buys from the grower and sells to the manufacturer of finished peanut products. Kernels which have been split apart command a much lower price than intact kernels. Skinned kernels are undesirable but are not penalized in price since they are difficult to separate from the unskinned kernels.

Figure 1 shows typical variations in splitting and skinning during shelling which were brought about by differences in the drying rate. The peanuts on which these data were obtained were treated identically in every respect except for the relative humidity of the drying air. Figure 2 illustrates the increase in shelling damage caused by drying peanuts below an optimum 9 or 10 per cent moisture, and shows that restoring the moisture content corrected most of the deficiency in milling quality. The peanuts in this test were all dried under the same conditions.

The sheller used for these milling quality evaluations is one which was developed by the Agricultural Marketing Service, USDA, for use in determining the official grade of peanuts at the time of sale by the grower.[3] It was designed to shell the peanuts with a minimum of mechanical injury, and therefore the percentage of split and skinned kernels in these tests

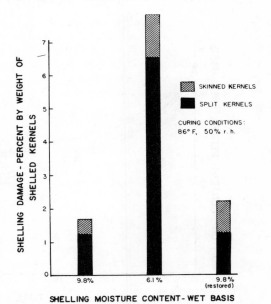

Fig. 2. Shelling damage of peanuts as a function of the moisture content when shelled.

is abnormally low. The average commercial sheller could be expected to produce 3 or 4 times as much mechanical injury to the same peanuts, with about the same relative differences between the various treatments. The increase in split kernels caused by rapid drying and/or overdrying may therefore amount to as much as 12 to 15 per cent of the shelled kernel weight, when shelled in a commercial mill.

Limiting the curing-air temperature to 95°F is an effective method of protecting the flavor of peanuts. The greatest need at present appears to be a simple, economical, yet positive system for close control of both the rate and amount of moisture removal to assure desirable milling quality. Flavor may also be improved by a moderate rate of drying during the curing process.

EQUIPMENT AND METHODS IN CURRENT USE

Mechanical peanut curing is presently being done in metal grain bins, trailers, wagons, and frame structures, with provisions for forcing heated air through bulked peanuts. In many instances, the same facility is employed for peanuts and other commodities such as corn. Air flow requirements for peanuts are generally about 2 cfm/lb of water to be evaporated in reducing the moisture content from the initial level to about 9 or 10 per cent. To achieve this approximate air-water ratio with a more or less constant fan delivery, the depth of the curing layer is varied according to initial moisture content.

A fixed quantity of heat sufficient to raise the air temperature about 10°F is added whenever the ambient relative humidity is above 65 or 70 per cent. A thermostat downstream from the heater limits the maximum temperature to 95°F. This system does not provide very effective regulation of either temperature or relative humidity in the curing chamber. At best it insures that drying will proceed under all conditions, and that off-flavor will not be introduced by high temperature. Although the amount of heat which is supplied and the relative humidity level at which it is introduced are both selected to optimize the average curing conditions, a wide variation in both temperature and relative humidity is permitted, with no minimum limit on either.

Another major deficiency of this system is that no compensation is made for the effect of temperature on drying rate, which can be considerable. Studies under closely-controlled conditions have indicated that a better method

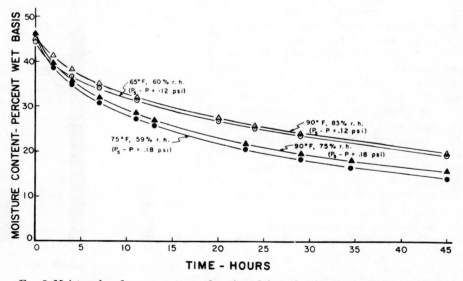

FIG. 3. Moisture loss from peanuts as a function of time, showing the dependence of drying rate on the difference between saturation and actual vapor pressure in the curing air.

would be to control the difference between the vapor pressure of the inlet air at a given temperature and the saturation vapor pressure at the same temperature. The typical moisture-loss curves of Fig. 3 illustrate the dependence of drying rate on P_s (saturation vapor pressure) minus P (actual vapor pressure).

Figure 4 shows the functional relationship which was observed between vapor pressure deficit and drying time. A deficit of about 0.20 psi appears to be desirable for peanuts from the standpoint of good milling quality and reasonable drying speed. A curing system like those currently in use would make no distinction between a situation in which it was adding heat at 60°F, 71 per cent RH to produce a 0.18-psi vapor pressure deficit, and one in which it was adding heat at 85°F, 71 per cent RH to produce a 0.40-psi vapor pressure deficit. The rate of water removal, of course, would be quite different under these two conditions.

The drying potential of ambient air sometimes becomes too great for peanuts, at least during midday. Relative humidities of 30 to 40 per cent with temperatures in the eighties are not uncommon in North Carolina during September and October. While these conditions probably do not normally prevail for a long enough period of time to cause extensive

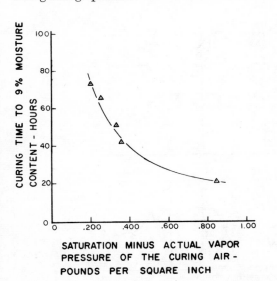

FIG. 4. Time required for drying peanuts which initially contained 35 per cent moisture as influenced by the difference between saturation and actual vapor pressure in the curing air.

damage, an ideal system would provide some means of controlling the minimum as well as the maximum relative humidity. Partial recirculation of the moisture-laden discharge air might be feasible for this purpose.

Experimental Heat Pump Drier

One system which was tested on a limited scale in 1962 used complete recirculation of the air, in conjunction with an electromechanical refrigeration unit or heat pump, to condense and remove the water.[1] Upon emerging from the layer of peanuts, the saturated air passed over the cold coil, where the temperature was lowered three or four degrees below the dew-point. Following this, the air passed successively across the fan motor, refrigerant compressor and motor, and the refrigerant condenser coil, each of which added heat and lowered the relative humidity. A humidistat, located near the point where the air reentered the peanuts, started and stopped the flow of refrigerant to the cold coil as needed to maintain the desired relative humidity. The compressor and fan ran continuously.

Figure 5 shows a plot of the average conditions inside and outside the chamber during a typical cure. Although no supplemental heat was provided, the waste heat of the two motors and compressor, plus the heat reclaimed from the refrigerant condenser, kept the entering-air temperature considerably above ambient. The relative humidity of the curing air was held fairly constant. The dashed portion of the curves covers a nine-hour period during which the temperature recording equipment was not operating.

Figure 6 is a comparison of the curing temperature and relative humidity in the heat pump drier with that which existed over the same period of time in a conventional heated-air unit with the humidistat set at 70 per cent RH. The temperature in the heat pump drier was at a somewhat higher level, and the relative humidity more stable, than in the conventional unit. Figure 7 compares the saturation minus actual vapor pressures in the two systems over the same drying period. The heat pump appeared to provide a little better control of this parameter. When computed at hourly intervals over the drying period, the mean value of $P_s - P$ for the heat pump was 0.218, with standard deviation

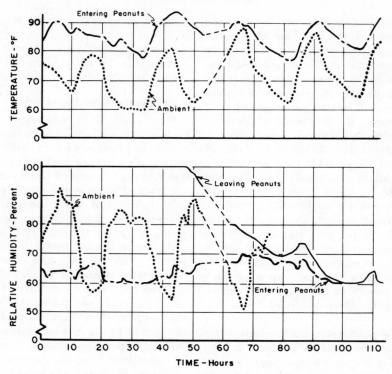

FIG. 5. Variation of relative humidity and temperature at strategic points inside an experimental refrigeration peanut dryer, compared with ambient conditions, over a complete curing cycle.

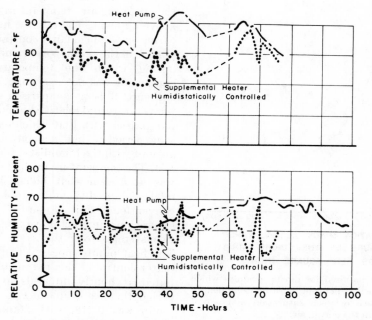

FIG. 6. Comparison of the relative humidity and temperature of the curing air in a conventional and an experimental peanut dryer, over the first three-fourths of a curing cycle.

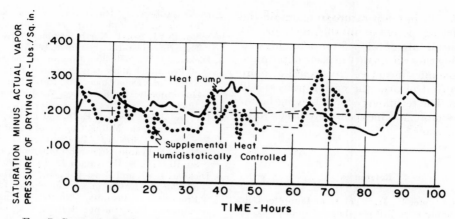

FIG. 7. Comparison of saturation minus actual vapor pressures of the curing air in a conventional and an experimental peanut dryer, over the first three-fourths of a curing cycle.

0.035; the mean for the conventional drier was 0.197, with standard deviation 0.045.

In spite of some procedural inefficiencies in the operation of this experimental equipment in the preliminary tests, operating costs were near those of conventional heated-air systems. Average fuel cost for three batches of peanuts cured with the conventional drier was 21 cents per hundred pounds, compared with an average cost of 25 cents per hundred pounds for electricity to operate the compressor in the heat pump drier. It is expected that modifications in the heat pump drier will reduce its operating costs to or below those of conventional systems. Initial costs will undoubtedly continue to be greater, however. Utilization of the heat pump in farm and commercial curing installations will be feasible provided (1) the total costs of ownership and operation can be brought in line with conventional systems or (2) the enhancement of peanut quality through better control of curing conditions is sufficient to justify a price differential which would compensate for some increase in curing costs.

SUMMARY AND CONCLUSIONS

Problems which are encountered when field-curing of peanuts is replaced by mechanical curing are: (1) off-flavor or lack of flavor due to exposure to temperatures over 95°F and (2) increased splitting and skinning of kernels during shelling due to accelerated water

removal. These problems are being met at present by limiting the temperature in the curing chamber to 95°F, and by adding supplemental heat to aid drying only when the ambient relative humidity exceeds 65 or 70 per cent.

Drying rate is related to the difference between saturation and actual vapor pressures in the inlet air, however, and the present systems do not effectively control this parameter. In addition, no provision is made to limit the minimum relative humidity which frequently drops below desirable levels. Recirculation of a portion of the discharge air, in conjunction with the appropriate controls, is proposed.

One recirculating system using a refrigeration unit to dehumidify the air was tested on a limited scale. It maintained a more stable relative humidity than the conventional system and permitted smaller fluctuations in the vapor pressure deficit of the drying air. Operating costs were about 20 per cent higher for the heat pump but probably can be substantially reduced.

Studies have shown that regulating the difference between the vapor pressure of the inlet air at a given temperature and the saturation vapor pressure at the same temperature is an effective means of controlling the drying rate of peanuts. Our ability to exercise close control over drying rates is somewhat limited by the lack of any sensing element which will vary relative humidity with changes in temperature to maintain the same drying potential in the inlet air. As better means are developed for detecting and measuring the true quality aspects of peanuts, the economic incentive to exercise more positive control over the curing process will increase. The technology for achieving better control simply and inexpensively needs to be developed now.

References

1. Davis, Chester P., Jr., "The Heat Pump for Conditioning Corn," Proceedings of Conference on Field Shelling and Drying of Corn, Section O, pp. 1–10, Chicago, Illinois, May 17 and 18, 1956.

2. Dickens, J. W., "Harvesting Bottleneck: Off-Flavor in Peanuts," Research and Farming, Vol. XVI, No. 1, North Carolina Agricultural Experiment Station, Summer, 1957.

3. Dickens, J. W., "Shelling Equipment for Samples of Peanuts," Marketing Research Report No. 528, U.S. Department of Agriculture, U.S. Government Printing Office, Washington, D.C. 1962.

4. Dickens, J. W., Beasley, E. O., and Turner, W. K., "Measuring the Milling Quality of Peanuts with a Sample Sheller," Proceedings of Second National Peanut Research Conference, pp. 72–80, Raleigh, N. C., August 13–15, 1962.

5. Dickens, J. W., and Beasley, E. O., "The Influence of Curing Environment on Some Physical Properties of Peanuts," North Carolina Agricultural Experiment Station, Agricultural Engineering Information Circular No. 16, March, 1963.

18. Rapid Measurement of Moisture in Flour by Hygrometry

F. J. Hughes, J. L. Vaala and R. B. Koch

Minneapolis-Honeywell Research Center, Hopkins, Minnesota

ABSTRACT

It is well known that foods and food components have characteristic variations of equilibrium relative humidity with moisture content. Use of the isotherm as a practical measure of moisture content in flour requires rapid equilibration and closely similar isotherms for various samples.

In using the Honeywell portable relative humidity instrument, placing of the sensing element in the flour rather than above it allowed rapid equilibration.

Flour samples of widely varying moisture and protein contents were found to conform rather closely to a single isotherm of relative humidity vs moisture content. Isotherms were obtained at different temperatures, and heats of vaporization were calculated for various amounts of water in flour.

INTRODUCTION

Historical Development

Briggs[1] appears to have been the first to obtain the now familiar S-shaped isotherms of moisture content *vs* relative humidity by determining the moisture content of proteins in different constant humidity environments. Bull[2] extended this work by obtaining isotherms for a number of pure proteins. He interpreted the three regions of moisture content to be: (1) a water monolayer adsorbed between crystal planes, (2) an additional layer between the planes spreading the side chains, and (3) water in large enough quantity to

begin to dissolve the protein. Later workers have applied these measurements to various foods and food products. Idealized isotherms of moisture *vs* equilibrium relative humidity are shown in Fig. 1.

Approach

Use of the equilibrium relative humidity-moisture isotherm as a practical measure of moisture content of flour requires rapid equilibrium and closely similar isotherms for various samples. Previous work on moisture-relative humidity isotherms on organic substances seems to indicate that the humidity determination of the system was made from position A in the air space as indicated in

GENERALIZED FOOD ISOTHERMS

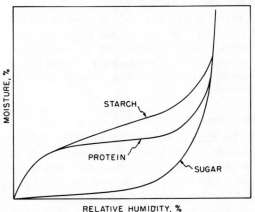

FIG. 1. Generalized food isotherms.

POSITION OF SENSING ELEMENT

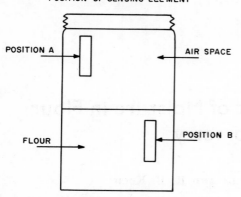

FIG. 2. Position of sensing element.

TABLE 1. ANALYSIS OF FLOUR SAMPLES

Sample	Oven Moisture, 1½ hours at 130°C (%)	Protein (%)
1	9.50	5.6
2	10.30	9.2
3	10.40	8.1
4	11.00	7.1
5	11.30	9.0
6	11.59	12.3
7	11.59	12.7
8	11.63	15.9
9	12.10	10.8
10	12.30	12.6
11	12.33	9.2
12	12.60	8.9
13	12.89	5.4
14	13.20	12.0
15	13.69	10.6
16	13.76	9.1
17	13.90	15.5

Fig. 2. Time to reach equilibrium varies considerably for different substances, undoubtedly because of the interruption of the mean free path of diffusing water molecules. If, on the other hand, the sensing element is placed in position B so that its surface is in intimate contact with flour particles, the diffusion of water from flour to sensor should be rapid. Previous workers probably refrained from this approach because hygrometers are delicate and must be kept away from dusts, powder and liquids which may impair the sensitive surface. Our measurements were made with the element in intimate contact with the flour without impairment of the sensor surface.

EXPERIMENTAL

Materials

Flour samples were obtained from the Pillsbury Company and are listed in Table 1 together with their moisture and protein contents. These samples are representative of various kinds of flour which Pillsbury processes.

Apparatus

The Honeywell W611A Portable Relative Humidity Readout Instrument with its variety of sensors for various humidity ranges was used to measure the relative humidities of the flour samples. This instrument is essentially a null-point resistance bridge with a temperature compensating rheostat shown

schematically in Fig. 3. The sensor is a Dunmore-type element containing lithium chloride.

Most readings were taken at room temperature, 74°F, but a regulated oven was used to obtain 95°F readings, and refrigerated units were used to obtain 45 and 56°F readings.

Procedure

For each reading, the element was thrust into the flour and allowed to reach equilibrium. After each reading, the element was blown clear of flour with compressed air filtered through glass wool and activated charcoal.

RESULTS AND DISCUSSION

Variation of equilibrium relative humidity with moisture content of various flour samples is shown in Fig. 4. Since these samples

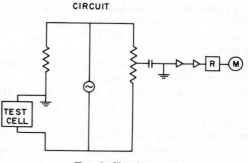

FIG. 3. Circuit.

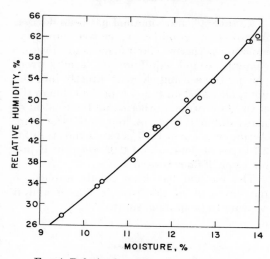

FIG. 4. Relative humidity *vs* moisture.

varied from 5 to 15 per cent in protein content, the fact that they lie so closely to a single line on the plot indicates that the isotherms for various flours are closely similar. The average deviation in moisture from the curve is 0.11 per cent whereas the standard deviation is 0.13 per cent. The maximum deviation is 0.2 per cent moisture. For a single flour, deviations would be expected to be less than a quarter of those above.

In the range of 9 to 14 per cent, which is that of most concern to commercial producers, the moisture appears to be mainly of the second type, delocalized adsorbed, perhaps the

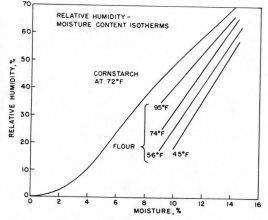

FIG. 5. Relative humidity-moisture content isotherms.

second and third layers after the monolayer. It has a steep slope of relative humidity with moisture which accounts for the good accuracy mentioned above.

Variation of equilibrium relative humidity-moisture isotherms with temperature is shown in Fig. 5. Isotherms for 45, 56, 74, and 95°F are plotted and compared with that of corn starch at 72°F. Since flour contains protein and since the physical structures of the flour and starch granules do differ, the difference in plots is not surprising. However, it would appear that the moisture measurement method should apply equally well to starch.

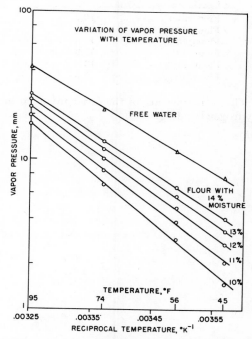

FIG. 6. Variation of vapor pressure with temperature.

The variations of relative humidity with temperature for a given moisture content are approximately 0.2 to 0.4 unit/°F.

From the curves in Fig. 5 a series of isotherms can be plotted for 5-degree temperature intervals. This series of standard curves can then be used to refer relative humidity readings to moisture at any temperature.

The measurement system actually involves an equilibrium at which the fugacities of the water in the flour, air and element are equal.

It would therefore be expected that a plot of logarithm of vapor pressure in the air in equilibrium with the flour *vs* reciprocal absolute temperature would give a straight line for each moisture content, the slope of which would be proportional to the heat of vaporization. The results of such a plot are shown in Fig. 6. As the moisture content of the flour increases, the slope of the line approaches that of free water.

Heats of vaporization calculated from the lines in Fig. 6 are as follows:

Type of Water	Heat of Vaporization (kcal/mole)
Free water	10.7
Flour, 14%	12.0
Flour, 13%	12.5
Flour, 12%	12.9
Flour, 11%	13.8
Flour, 10%	15.3

These energies are of the order involved in hydrogen bonding.

CONCLUSIONS

A rapid, accurate method has been devised for using the equilibrium relative humidity-moisture isotherm of flour to measure moisture content. Rapid equilibration results from placing the sensing element directly into the flour, and good accuracy is present due to the steep slope of the isotherm and the close fit of many different types of flour to the isotherm. Accuracy is about 0.15 per cent moisture for all types of flour, about 0.05 per cent if just one type of flour is used.

The method has been briefly applied to measurement of moisture in starch and it appears to be quite accurate.

References

1. Briggs, D. R., "Water Relationship in Colloids," *J. Phys. Chem.*, **35**, 2914–29 (1931).
2. Bull, H. B., "Adsorption of Water Vapor by Proteins," *J. Am. Chem. Soc.*, **66**, 1499–1507 (1944).

19. Moisture Measurements In Various Hygroscopic Materials using Nuclear Magnetic Resonance

WILLIAM L. ROLLWITZ

Southwest Research Institute, San Antonio, Texas

ABSTRACT

Measurements, using nuclear magnetic resonance signal from hydrogen, of moisture in various materials are shown to demonstrate some of the problems and successes involved. First is shown the ease with which moisture measurements are made when there are no environmental interactions with the hydrogen nuclei. Environmental interactions cause a nonlinear amplitude curve, a nonlinear linewidth curve, but a linear area curve as a function of moisture. Methods are discussed for separating the signals from two hydrogen containing materials so that measurements can be made of moisture in the presence of fat. The technique works very well on flowing materials and a series of results are shown to demonstrate this measurement. Nuclear magnetic resonance signals from hydrogen nuclei can give a quantitative measure of the moisture in liquids and solids. However, care must be taken to reduce to insignificance the environmental effects and the interference of other hydrogen signals. If environmental effects cannot be eliminated, the quantitative measurement can be made by the solution of two simultaneous equations. Moisture in a gas can be measured if the number of hydrogen nuclei have a concentration greater than $10^{14}/cm.^3$

INTRODUCTION

The phenomena associated with nuclear magnetic resonance and the ways in which the nuclear magnetic resonance signals can be measured are described in another paper in this book (Vol. IV, Paper 20), which also indicate that signals are influenced by their surroundings and what this influence might be. The present paper will give the results obtained from several nuclear magnetic resonance measurements on moisture in various hygroscopic materials in order to attempt to demonstrate the usefulness and the problems of the nuclear magnetic resonance measurement of moisture.

MOISTURE MEASUREMENTS ON SAMPLES

No Environmental Interaction

As is shown in Paper 20 of Vol. IV, if T_1 and T_2 are constant for all values of concentration, the amplitude of the absorption curve or the peak-to-peak amplitude of the first harmonic curve should be linearly proportional to the per cent moisture. This result is shown in Fig. 1, where an increasing concentration of hydrogen nuclei was obtained by adding methanol to carbon tetrachloride. The nuclei of the hydrogen in the methanol have a very nearly constant T_2 as a function of concentration and a straight line results. There will be a slight change because of viscosity changes with concentration.

This same result is also shown in Fig. 2 for moisture in sand. Here again, the sand does not sufficiently influence or change the value of the T_2 of the moisture to cause a noticeable nonlinearity in this curve.

The value of T_2, however, will change with temperature as shown in Fig. 3. The water signal is approximately 0.5×10^{-3} gauss wide

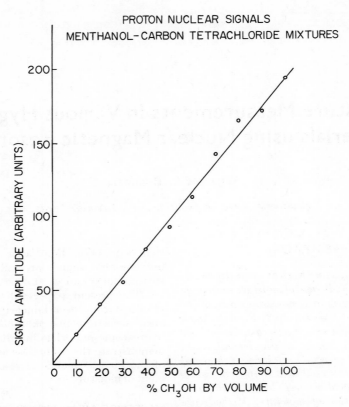

FIG. 1. The peak amplitude of the nuclear magnetic resonance absorption signal for a methanol-carbon tetrachloride mixture.

whereas the ice at −180°C is about 10 gauss wide, with the width at −10°C being 4 or 5 gauss. There is a rather rapid change in linewidth as the water freezes, and the nuclear magnetic resonance measurements are excellent indicators for a phase change in the molecule containing the nucleus being measured.

Environmental Interaction

If the water is present in a solid material which also contains hydrogen, such as starch, and if the total hydrogen signal is measured, two distinct nuclear magnetic resonance absorption curves may be obtained as shown in Fig. 4. The moisture concentration is 0.5 per cent. The broad curve is from the hydrogen in the starch molecules, and the narrow line is from the hydrogen in the water. Since the hydrogen in the two molecules do not rapidly, or perhaps even slowly, exchange, there are

two separate lines. When more water is added, say to about 10 per cent, the water hydrogen signal is now so large in amplitude that the broad line from the starch hydrogen is not seen as shown in Fig. 5. The water hydrogen signal in Fig. 4 is approximately 2 gauss wide, whereas that in Fig. 5 is approximately 250 milligauss wide. The broader 2-gauss and the narrower 250-milligauss curves are not separated in Fig. 5 because of two effects: (1) the rapid interchange between the hydrogen in the two conditions giving a single broadened curve and (2) the relative magnitudes of the two signals make the 2-gauss signal lost in the noise.

If the linewidth of the moisture signal is plotted as a function of the moisture level for water in starch, the curve of Fig. 6 is obtained. This decrease in linewidth means an increasing T_2 as the moisture levels increase. This is

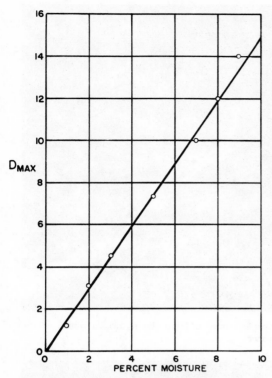

SIGNAL AMPLITUDE vs PER CENT MOISTURE
FOR SAND

Fig. 2. The peak amplitude of the first harmonic curve from moisture in sand.

amplitude and the absorption curve amplitude as shown in the curves for water in syrup in Fig. 10.

Oil-water Separations

When fat is present in unknown amounts, it can cause a wide spread in the data and no correlation as shown in Fig. 11. When the oil concentrations are subtracted, curves as expected from the water alone are obtained as shown in Fig. 12. Therefore, when oil is present in a material in which a moisture measurement is desired, special techniques must be used if it is desired to obtain a separate measurement of both moisture and oil.

The absorption component of the nuclear magnetic resonance signal is given by

$$S'' = \frac{K\omega_0 M_0 \gamma H_1 T_2}{1 + (\omega_0 - \omega)^2 T_2^2 + \gamma^2 H_1^2 T_1 T_2} \quad (1)$$

At the center of the resonance curve, its value is

$$S_0'' = \frac{k\omega_0 M_0 \gamma H_1 T_2}{1 + \gamma^2 H_1^2 T_1 T_2} \quad (2)$$

The peak value of S_0'' is obtained when

$$D = \gamma^2 H_1^2 T_1 T_2 = 1 \quad (3)$$

because at the lower levels, the water molecules are held more firmly by the starch, and there is less relative motion of the hydrogen nuclei resulting in a wider linewidth. The higher moisture levels are held less firmly giving more motion and a decrease linewidth. The linewidth reaches asymptotically the linewidth of the water alone.

This decreasing linewidth with increasing moisture would make the peak-to-peak first harmonic amplitude *vs* moisture curve be nonlinear as shown in Fig. 7 rather than a straight line. It was found, however, that a calibration curve could be obtained for the various starches that would permit a measurement of moisture to a 1 per cent accuracy (10 ± 0.1). Two representative calibration curves are shown in Figs. 8 and 9.

With some materials it may be advantageous to measure both the first harmonic

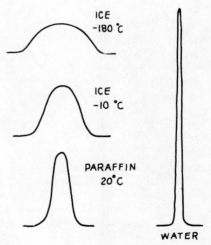

Fig. 3. The increase in line width shown by the decrease in the motion of one nucleus relative to its neighbor of the same species caused by the decrease in T_2 with decreasing temperature. There is also a change caused by the viscosity difference between water and paraffin.

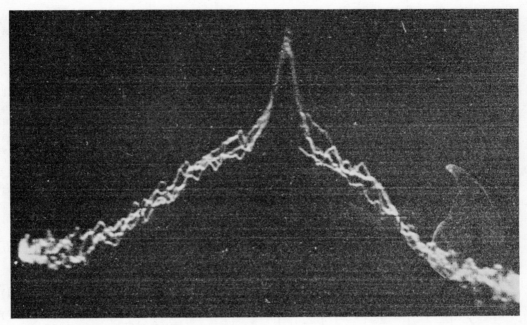

Fig. 4. Total hydrogen signal from starch. The broad curve is from the hydrogen nuclei of the starch molecule and the narrow curve is from the water.

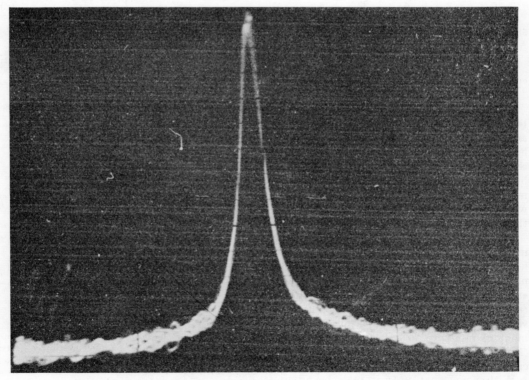

Fig. 5. The moisture hydrogen signal from 10 per cent moisture in starch at 10,000 gauss of magnetic field.

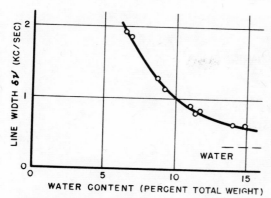

FIG. 6. The change in line width as a function of water content for starch.

The peak value with $D = 1$ is

$$(S_0'')_{D=1} = k\omega_0 M_0 \left(\frac{T_2}{T_1}\right)^{1/2} \tag{4}$$

If the water and oil are not interacting, then the peak of the absorption curve may be

$$(S_0'')_{\substack{\text{oil} \\ + \\ \text{water}}} = \left(\frac{k\omega_0 M_0 \gamma H_1 T_2}{1 + \gamma^2 H_1^2 T_1 T_2}\right)_{\text{water}} + \left(\frac{k\omega_0 M_0 \gamma H_1 T_2}{1 + \gamma^2 H_1^2 T_1 T_2}\right)_{\text{oil}} \tag{5}$$

where the values of M_0, T_1 and T_2 are the values for oil and water in the appropriate parenthesis. If the values of T_2 and therefore the product $T_1 T_2$ are very much different for the oil and for the water, then at a certain value of H_1, one will be saturated and the other not saturated so that one term in Eq. (5) will be small compared to the other. Therefore, by determining the various values of H_1, T_1 and T_2 in Eq. (3), (4) and (5), it may be possible to determine the values of M_0 for both water and oil

If the T_2 values are not widely different, they can be made so by freezing if their melting points are different. However, if this cannot be permitted, then one value of T_2 can be increased over the other if one can dissolve selectively a paramagnetic ion. In many cases, however, neither of these methods are possible, and it will be necessary to make a plot of Eq. (5) as a function of H_1. By a measurement of the linewidth, enough data can be obtained to calculate the two concentrations.

MOISTURE MEASUREMENTS ON FLOWING SAMPLES

When moisture measurements are required on flowing materials, techniques have been developed for passing the whole stream (see

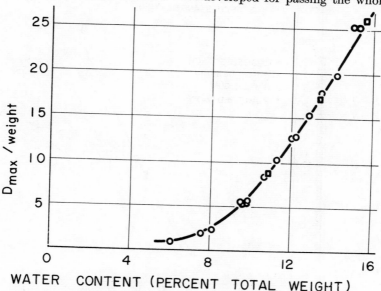

FIG. 7. The weight normalized peak amplitude of the first harmonic signal from a substance having the line width change of Fig. 6 plotted as function of the water content.

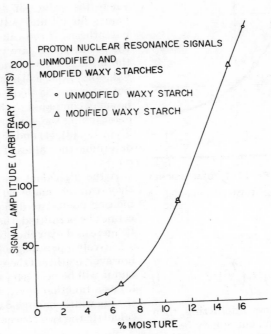

FIG. 8. The plot of the peak amplitude of the first harmonic
signal as a function of per cent moisture for unmodified and
modified waxy starches.

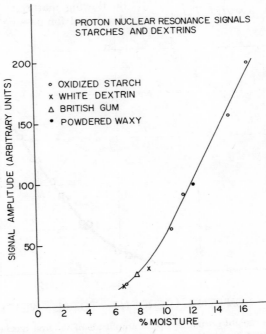

FIG. 9. The plot of the peak amplitude of the first harmonic
signal as a function of per cent moisture for starches and dextrins.

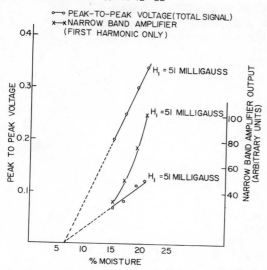

PROTON NUCLEAR RESONANCE SIGNALS
C.S.U. SYRUPS— 45° TO 42° BÉ

FIG. 10. Peak-to-peak total signal voltages and the first harmonic amplitude plotted as a function of moisture for syrup.

Fig. 13) through the radio-frequency coil and the magnet. If the system is completely stabilized, a continuous measure of moisture will be obtained as shown in the calibrating run, with samples, of Fig. 14. The continuous flow measurement run is shown in Fig. 15 and 16. The repeatability is shown in Fig. 17. As can be seen from Fig. 17, the density of the material in the sampled volume makes large deviations especially when the material first flows. The author holds a patent, assigned to Corn Industries Research Foundation, which uses the variation in linewidth with moisture level (Fig. 6) instead of the variation in amplitude. Therefore, the system does not require consistent packing or density, since it only requires sufficient signal to obtain a measure of linewidth. The system is fully automatic and has an accuracy of 1 per cent. It has been estimated from measurements that the accuracy can be maintained for filling factors of from 0.3 to 1.0. Therefore, large voids will not cause errors.

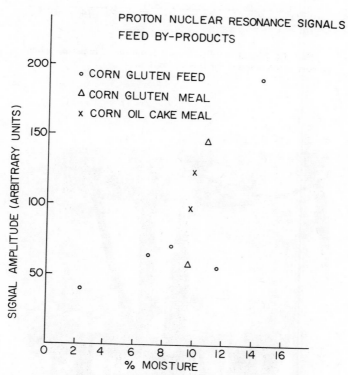

PROTON NUCLEAR RESONANCE SIGNALS
FEED BY-PRODUCTS

○ CORN GLUTEN FEED
△ CORN GLUTEN MEAL
× CORN OIL CAKE MEAL

FIG. 11. Nuclear magnetic resonance absorption first harmonic amplitude as a function of moisture percentage when various amounts of fats are present.

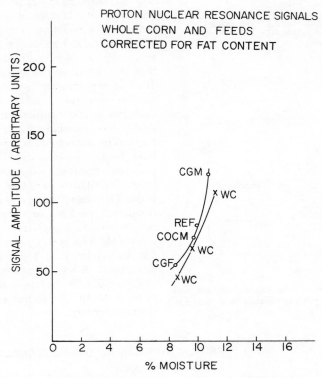

FIG. 12. Signal amplitude as a function of moisture when a correction is made for the fat content.

FIG. 13. The flowing process stream passing through the magnet gap and the radiofrequency coil. The pipe is a plastic material.

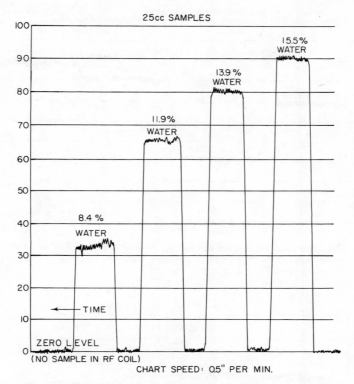

FIG. 14. Recording of the peak of the nuclear magnetic resonance absorption first harmonic curves as milo-maize of differing moisture levels was fed through the pipe of Fig. 13.

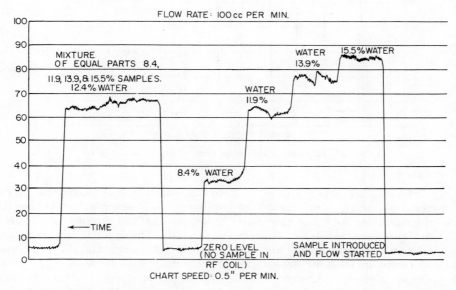

FIG. 15. Recorded signals for flowing milo-maize of four moisture levels and for a mixture of all four.

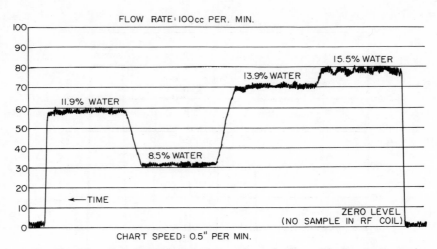

FIG. 16. Recorded signals for continuous flow of milo-maize wherein the grain of the various moisture levels was poured one on top of another in the hopper at the top of the pipe of Fig. 13.

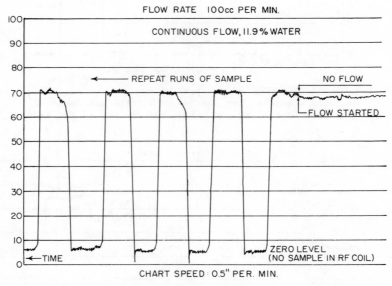

FIG. 17. Repeated continuous runs of the same sample.

CONCLUSIONS

This paper has shown some results of moisture measurements and has discussed some of the problems involved. Nuclear magnetic resonance measurements are not specific for the moisture itself but are specific for the hydrogen nucleus. Therefore, NMR measurements are a function of all of the hydrogen in the sample. If the hydrogen exists in two states, host molecules and water molecules such as starch and moisture, then the NMR signals from the two usually are easily separated. Thus NMR measurements of moisture in starch and like materials are readily made with accuracy over a wide range of moisture levels. At the very low moisture levels, however, the two signals may be difficult of separation.

Difficulty also exists for a material with two hydrogen containing liquids absorbed or adsorbed. The NMR signals from these two liquids, such as water and oil, may be difficult to separate if a rapid determination is desired. If a little time is allowed, the two quantities may be resolved by drying, freezing, or adding paramagnetic ions and then using the saturation phenomenon.

Quantitative measurements can be effectively performed on flowing materials providing that the previously discussed problems have been solved. If there is a useful curve of linewidth as a function of moisture, then measurements can be made which are independent of the filling factor. Therefore, the system is independent of density changes and voids.

Nuclear magnetic resonance measurements should not be considered to be a cure-all for all moisture measurements if only one piece of equipment is used. Each individual material or condition should be considered both experimentally and theoretically to determine values of the NMR parameters which will provide the measurement and accuracy. Then equipment should be set, modified or constructed to meet the requirements. However, with care and understanding, a single NMR moisture meter will provide a rapid, accurate and non-destructive measurement of the moisture in a wide variety of materials if a calibration system compatible with the materials is available.

20. Certain Dielectric and Physical Properties of Cured Tobacco Leaves*

W. H. HENSON, JR.

Department of Agricultural Engineering, University of Kentucky, Lexington, Kentucky

AND

F. J. HASSLER

Department of Agricultural Engineering, North Carolina State College, Raleigh, North Carolina

ABSTRACT

In recent years considerable interest has been shown with regard to the electrical properties of biological materials which are common to agricultural processing. Electrical measurements on these materials are of fundamental importance as related to the analysis of (a) quantity of absorbed water, (b) cell structure and electrolytic nature of the cytoplasm, and (c) dielectric heating characteristics.

Investigations of the dielectric behavior of tobacco leaves, i.e., the influence of moisture content, density, temperature, frequency and chemical composition on the dielectric constant, dielectric loss factor and conductivity were conducted in order to establish an objective criteria for evaluating intact leaves. In conducting such a study it was first necessary to develop methods of measurement under controlled laboratory conditions which would give results of sufficient precision to permit an attack on the general problem of deriving and testing theoretical relationships to explain the dielectric behavior of the tobacco leaf.

Electrical measurements were made on an AC capacitance bridge (1 kc to 1 MC) and a Q meter (5 kc to 50 MC). Leaf moisture contents ranged from 5 to 25 per cent, dry basis.

The dielectric properties of cured leaves showed marked dependence on leaf moisture content and frequency of the measuring voltage. The dielectric constants for leaves of a typical bright-leaf variety at 10 kc and 77° F were 2.02, 6.71 and 51.94 for leaf moisture contents of 9.47, 15.35 and 21.24 per cent, respectively. At 1 Mc the dielectric constants were lowered to 1.67, 2.29 and 7.46. The dielectric constant, dielectric loss factor and AC conductivity of cured tobacco leaves increased exponentially with both temperature and moisture content.

* Contribution from the Agricultural Engineering Department, North Carolina Agricultural Experiment Station, Raleigh, N.C. Published with the approval of the Director of Research as Paper No. 1663 of the Journal Series in cooperation with the Agricultural Engineering Research Division, ARS, USDA.

INTRODUCTION

Electrical properties of biological material of both animal and vegetable origin have been studied ever since suitable electrical techniques became available for this purpose. Earlier contributions did not help much toward an understanding of the factors responsible for the electrical properties of tissue. This was due to inadequate theory and techniques. A very active period followed between 1925 and 1940 when a number of biophysicists applied potential theory originally developed for dielectrics. About 1935, investigations began of electrical properties of protein molecules by application of the concept of polar molecules originated by Debye.[6] After 1940, techniques became available for investigation of electrical properties at ultrahigh and low frequencies. The frequency range so far explored extends from 5 cps up to 30,000 Mc, i.e., almost ten decades instead of the four decades (1 kc to 10 Mc) available before 1940.

In recent years considerable interest has been shown with regard to electrical properties of biological materials of interest in agricultural processing. Electrical measurements on these materials are of fundamental importance as related to the analysis of (a) quantity of absorbed water, (b) cell structure and electrolytic nature of the cytoplasm, and (c) dielectric heating characteristics.

It is a well-known fact that the electrical properties of a material, namely, dielectric constant and conductivity, are affected by the moisture content of the material. For instance, the dielectric constant of cellulosic material (a major component of most cereal and vegetable solids) is in the range of 7, whereas the value for water is about 80 at room temperature. These materials are hygroscopic in nature, and small quantities of adsorbed water may cause large changes in the elcetrical properties of the material. The change of electrical properties with change of moisture content of agricultural products is basic to the design of many commercial moisture-testing instruments.

Differences in the electrical constants of cell-wall membrane and cytoplasm make it possible to obtain the electrical properties of these membranes apart from the cytoplasm when ultrahigh frequencies are employed. Moreover, the electrolytic nature of the cytoplasm can be deduced from the variation of dielectric constant with frequency and moisture content. For example, dielectric constant values exceeding that of water could indicate an electrolytic effect, which in turn might furnish a key to the chemical nature of the material.

The dielectric heating characteristics of a material are of interest from the standpoint of product drying and differential heating effects. Though dielectric heating is less efficient than common heating methods, its use may be advantageous in special applications. The primary advantage of dielectric heating lies in the possibility of selective heating of materials, based on differences in AC conductivity. Thus, a knowledge of the dielectric properties of a material is necessary for the application of dielectric heating.

From these considerations, it seemed that an investigation of the dielectric behavior of tobacco leaves, i.e., the influence of moisture content, temperature, frequency and chemical composition on the dielectric constant, dielectric loss factor and conductivity, could contribute to the establishment of objective criteria for evaluating intact tobacco leaves. It was necessary, therefore, to develop methods of measurement under controlled laboratory conditions that would give results of sufficient precision to permit an attack on the general problem of deriving and testing theoretical relationships to explain the dielectric behavior of the tobacco leaf.

The first objective was to derive theoretical relationships to elucidate the dielectric behavior of biological materials similar in nature to the tobacco leaf. The formulation of such relationships will furnish a valuable research tool that may be applied in other similar investigations.

The second objective of this investigation was to measure those electrical properties of both uncured and cured tobacco leaves that were dependent on the material and not on its dimensions. The properties that meet these requirements are the dielectric constant, dielectric loss factor and specific conductivity. The experiment was designed to determine the influence of leaf density and moisture content on these electrical properties.

REVIEW OF LITERATURE

Theory of Dielectric Properties

The important dielectric properties include dielectric constant (or specific inductive capacity), dielectric loss factor, and AC conductivity. The term *dielectric behavior* usually refers to the variation of these properties with frequency, temperature and composition. Murphy and Morgan[11] outlined the physiochemical interpretation of the dielectric constant.

In the analysis of dielectric behavior, it has been assumed that no inductive reactances are present in biological material. This assumption follows from the fact that extensive experimentation has failed to show such inductance.[12] Hence, it is necessary to consider only combinations of resistance and capacitance for the equivalent electrical circuit of a biological material.

It is a familiar fact that the dielectric constants of many liquids and solids depend markedly on the frequency of the impressed voltage employed in the measurement. The dependence is in general found to be a decrease from the static value ϵ_0 at low frequencies to a smaller limiting value of ϵ_∞ at higher frequencies. The magnitudes of ϵ_0 and ϵ_∞, of course, vary from one material to another. In general, the dielectric constants of all biological materials exhibit this type of dependence on frequency. This feature which is known as anomalous dispersion of the dielectric constant has been discussed in detail by Murphy and Morgan.[11] These authors indicated that anomalous dispersion plays a very important part in the behavior of dielectrics in the electrical range of frequencies. In fact, it is seldom possible to interpret a set of measurements of dielectric constant without encountering some manifestation of anomalous dispersion.

The classical theory of the anomalous dispersion for polar liquids is due to Debye.[6] The theoretical analysis in this case leads to the equation

$$\epsilon^* - \epsilon_\infty = (\epsilon_0 - \epsilon_\infty)/(1 + j\omega T)$$
$$= (\epsilon' - \epsilon_\infty) - j\epsilon'' \quad (1)$$

which can be written

$$\epsilon' - \epsilon_\infty = (\epsilon_0 - \epsilon_\infty)/[1 + (\omega T)^2] \quad (2)$$

$$\epsilon'' = (\epsilon_0 - \epsilon_\infty)\omega T/[1 + (\omega T)^2] \quad (3)$$

where

$\omega T = f/f_m$
$\epsilon^* =$ complex dielectric constant
$\omega = 2\pi f$, where f is the frequency of the applied voltage.
$j = \sqrt{-1}$
$T =$ a characteristic constant which may be called the relaxation time
$f_m =$ the frequency at which the dielectric loss factor reaches a maximum
$\epsilon' =$ dielectric constant
$\epsilon'' =$ dielectric loss factor.

Theories of other types of dispersion phenomena also lead to equations of the same type or form. One might thus expect these relations to have a very general validity as a description of dispersion processes. However, according to Cole and Cole,[5] there is a considerable amount of experimental evidence to indicate that Eq. (2) and (3) are not a correct description of the observed frequency dependence in such processes. The observed behavior is rather generally found to consist of a considerably broader frequency range of dispersion and absorption together with a smaller maximum value of ϵ'' than predicted by Eq. (3). This is particularly true of liquid and solid dielectrics of complex chemical structure. Their analysis led to a general equation of the form

$$\epsilon^* = (\epsilon_0 - \epsilon_\infty)/(1 + j\omega T)^{1-\alpha}; 0 \leqslant \alpha \leqslant 1 \quad (4)$$

Expressions for dielectric constant and dielectric loss factor may be derived from Eq. (4). The expressions are identical with Eq. (2) and (3), respectively, for the particular case $\alpha = 0$.

The AC conductivity defined by Eq. (5) may be derived from basic electrical theory

$$\gamma = \omega\epsilon_r\epsilon''$$
$$= 0.556f\epsilon'' \cdot 10^{-12} \text{ ohm}^{-1} \text{ cm}^{-1} \quad (5)$$
$$(f \text{ in cycles per second})$$

where

$\epsilon_r =$ permittivity of free space
$= 0.855 \cdot 10^{-12}$ farads/meter.

Dielectric Properties of Specific Materials

The dielectric constant is related to the ability of a substance to enhance the capacity of a condenser in which the substance is the dielectric. Its magnitude varies from slightly more than one for gases to eighty for water at room temperature, and even higher values for certain mixtures.

Swenson[13] gave the dielectric constants of typical compounds at 20°C as shown in Table 1.

Since water has a high dielectric constant, the quantity of water in a material should be easy to estimate by measurement of the dielectric constant of the material. Moreover, water is an important constituent of all agricultural materials. Literally dozens of methods have been developed for assaying the quantity of water in these materials. Only one

TABLE 1. DIELECTRIC CONSTANTS OF TYPICAL ORGANIC COMPOUNDS AT 20°C

Air	1.00
Benzene	2.28
Carbon tetrachloride	2.30
Pentane	1.85
Hexane	1.89
Ethyl ether	4.40
Acetone	21.30
Ethyl alcohol	23.80
Methyl alcohol	34.00
Water (distilled)	80.00

of these, however, can claim distinct advantages of speed and nondestructiveness; that one is the so-called dielectric constant method.

The principal disadvantage of the dielectric constant method is the requirement of a calibration curve. Edlefsen[7] gave a comprehensive summary of dielectric methods for measuring moisture present in materials. Müller discussed nine methods of measuring the moisture content of tobacco. One of these methods is the dielectric method. Resultant accuracy and temperature effects were also noted by Müller.

Interest in the dielectric behavior of biological materials has increased with the advent of radio frequency heating techniques. Brown *et al*[4] discussed in detail the application of radio-frequency heating to good electrical conductors as well as poor electrical conductors. These authors measured the dielectric constant and power factor of poor electrical conductors such as wood, and good electrical conductors such as frozen foods, at several radio frequencies. The power factor increased slightly with frequency while the dielectric constant fell slowly.

There is little in the literature concerning dielectric constant measurements on tobacco. Some work has been done in Germany on electrical properties of cut and powdered tobacco. Tausz and Rumm[14] conducted a study of the dielectric constants of several hygroscopic materials including tobacco. They used a Wagner bridge for measuring dielectric constant and loss factor at relatively low frequencies of 435, 870 and 1740 cps. They found that the dielectric constant of shredded tobacco (from cigarettes) depended on density of packing, moisture content, temperature, and frequency. The dielectric constant showed a positive correlation with density, moisture content and temperature, and a negative correlation with frequency.

The authors' conclusions were that the temperature sensitivity of the dielectric constant was dependent upon the moisture content of the material. The frequency-dependence of the dielectric constant was also limited by the moisture content. For example, their results indicated only small variations of dielectric constant with frequency for low-moisture samples, whereas large variations of dielectric constant with frequency were indicated for high-moisture samples.

No explicit data for the AC conductivity of tobacco were found in the literature. However, Tausz and Rumm[14] gave values for resistance and loss tangent that permitted a rough estimate of the conductivity and dielectric loss factor of shredded tobacco. The value of conductivity was $0.0057 (10^{-6})$ ohm^{-1} cm^{-1} at 0.217 g/cc, 12.10 per cent moisture content, 18°C and 1.1 kc. Of course, the conductivity would be higher than this value for higher frequencies. The dielectric loss factor ϵ'', for these same conditions was 9.40, while the dielectric constant, ϵ', was 5.51.

EXPERIMENTAL EQUIPMENT AND PROCEDURE

Equipment for Measuring Dielectric Properties

Capacitance Bridge. The bridge employed for measuring the capacitance and dissipation factor of the tobacco samples was a type 716-C capacitance bridge, serial number 3439, manufactured by General Radio Company (GRC), West Concord, Massachusetts. A schematic diagram of the bridge circuit is shown in Fig. 1.

The following accessories were used with the capacitance bridge: a bridge oscillator was employed as the signal generator. The signal waveform from the oscillator was sinusoidal, and the voltage amplitude was variable from 0 to about 10 V (rms). A sensitive vacuum tube voltmeter was used as a null detector, and five GRC type 505 capacitors were employed as balancing capacitors when substitution measurements were made on the bridge. The capacitance bridge is shown in Fig. 2 with the voltmeter-type detector and bridge oscillator in the left foreground of the photograph. The capacitance bridge is in the center with the

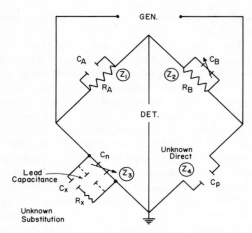

FIG. 1. Capacitance bridge circuit with sample C_x located for substitution measurements.

sample holder in place. A Q meter is at the right.

The estimated accuracy of measurements when using the substitution method with the capacitance bridge was $+$ 0.2 per cent or ± 2 $\mu\mu$f (whichever is the larger) for capacitance, and ± 2 per cent for dissipation factor.

Test Condenser. The accepted method of evaluating the dielectric constant and dissi-

pation factor of a solid dielectric material is to place the material between metallic electrodes and to measure the capacitance and dissipation factor of the resulting capacitor. If the configuration of the electrodes is such that the distribution of the electric field is accurately known, the constants of the material can be determined. One of the simplest electrode systems is a pair of circular parallel plates with one plate movable for plate-spacing adjustments.

The micrometer-capacitor type of sample holder has been recognized as the most satisfactory method of holding specimens of solid dielectric material for measurement at radio frequencies. Holders of this type are recognized in ASTM Specifications D-150[2] for use in the frequency range to about 100 mc. The excellent high-frequency performance is a result largely of the fact that the effect of lead inductance and resistance are substantially eliminated from the measurement. In addition, the use of this type of holder properly calibrated virtually eliminates the errors from fringing fields and stray capacitance.

Since the tobacco leaf may be considered a solid dielectric material, it seemed desirable to use the micrometer-capacitor type of sample

FIG. 2. Equipment for measuring the dielectric properties of tobacco.

holder for the dielectric measurements. A GRC type 1690-A dielectric sample holder was employed over the total frequency range of the bridge.

The sample holder is shown in Fig. 3. The main micrometer capacitor is formed by two electrodes of 2-in. diameter. The lower electrode is supported by insulators while the upper electrode is positioned by the micrometer-type screw, the spacing in mils being read directly on the drum and barrel. This electrode is designed so that as it comes in contact with the sample, the drive screw disengages from the plate, thus allowing a predetermined pressure to be exerted on the sample by means of spring tension. The force in pounds exerted by the upper plate at various plate spacing (d_s in mils) was determined for this particular sample holder to be

$$F_{lb} = 0.040 \, (d_s + 150) \qquad (6)$$

Thus the pressure on a 1-in. diameter sample at 25-mil plate spacing is

$$F_{psi} = F_{lb}/A = 7/\pi/4 = 8.92 \; lb/in.^2 \quad (7)$$

One problem that was encountered with the sample holder was the difficulty of balancing the bridge by decreasing the plate spacing

when C_x was large ($> 100 \; \mu\mu f$). That is, the maximum capacitance that could be measured with the sample holder by decreasing the plate spacing was about 100 $\mu\mu f$. This corresponded to a plate spacing (d_2) of about seven mils. Theoretically, it was possible to balance any capacitance by merely decreasing the plate spacing to a small enough value, but this was not practical since minute particles invisible to the naked eye could shunt the plates at the small spacings. Therefore, the test sample was selected, if possible, to yield a capacitance in the range from 20 to 100 $\mu\mu f$. However, since this was not always possible, it was convenient to use another method for calculating capacitance that was well adapted to the capacitance bridge circuit.[8]

The calibration provided for the micrometer electrodes includes the variation of edge capacitance with spacing. The calibration also takes into account any mechanical imperfections in the screw thread and any lack of parallelism of the electrodes.

Since capacitance differences only are used for measurements, the absolute level of the calibration is unimportant. As suggested in ASTM D-150, the correlation is arbitrarily taken as zero for the 100-mil setting. The actual nominal values of the geometric capacitance at any spacing d is given by:

$$C = 0.2249 \, A/d \; (\mu\mu f, in) \qquad (8)$$

where A is the area of the electrode.

For the 2-in. electrodes of the sample holder, this reduces to:

$$C = 706.4/d \; (\mu\mu f, mils) \qquad (9)$$

Further details on the use of the micrometer-electrode system described here may be found in the report by Henson[8].

Equipment for Temperature and Moisture Control

Room Conditions. The room conditions were maintained at 77°F (25°C) and 60 per cent RH during the tests. These conditions were selected because they are commonly used in tobacco laboratories in which physical and chemical properties of tobacco are determined. Temperature was controlled with a precision of $\pm\frac{1}{2}$°F and humidity was controlled with a precision of ±1 per cent RH. Close control of these variables was absolutely necessary because the dielectric behaviour of biological materials is greatly influenced by temperature and moisture content of the material.

Leaf Moisture Conditions. Cured samples were stored in the air-conditioned room at 77°F and 60 per cent RH for about three months before the electrical measurements were made on them. This period was, of course, more than adequate for equilibrium moisture content of the samples to be obtained. Artho[1] found that equilibrium moisture content could be approximately established for flue-cured tobacco in three days provided the leaves were loosely packed.

The moisture content of the samples was determined on the dry basis by drying samples at 80°C for 24 hours and weighing on sensitive laboratory balances that weighed to the nearest milligram.

The samples were brought to high moisture content by suspending them in a wire mesh basket over a saturated solution of NaCl in a closed container at 77°F. A similar procedure with a saturated solution of K_2CO_3 was used to bring the samples to low moisture content. The solution of NaCl was assumed to maintain 75 per cent RH, according to tests conducted by Artho.[1] However, the absolute value of the humidity was not important since the moisture content of the samples was determined at the time the electrical measurements were made.

Procedure

Selection of Tobacco Leaf Samples. The experimental material consisted of leaves from three varieties of flue-cured tobacco. The varieties—Coker's 139, Hicks and Dixie Bright 101—were selected to furnish a cross section of common varieties with different physical and chemical characteristics. Each variety was further classified by selections A and B. Selection A possessed typical characteristics of the variety, whereas selection B was different in certain characteristics, e.g., leaf size and color.

Fifty uniform plants were obtained from each of the six distinct selections. These plants were set in six adjacent rows on the Oxford Tobacco Research Station farm. Normal fertilization and cultural practices were used in growing the experimental plants in order to obtain representative material for the tests.

Obtaining and Measuring Leaf Samples. After the plants had fully developed, twenty of the sturdiest plants in each selection were marked for identification. As the bottom leaves matured, three leaves at a time were primed from each plant in the plot. Leaves from the tagged plants were marked with a code which identified the variety, selection, plant number and priming number.

The selected leaves were placed on sticks in the conventional manner along with leaves from the remaining plants. Each selection was cured in a separate curing compartment so that the curing schedule could be altered to suit each selection. The conventional curing schedule has been described in the literature (Bacon *et al*, 1951).

After the leaves had been cured and had regained sufficient moisture for handling, they were removed from the sticks and 2-in. diameter samples were taken from the marked leaves. The cured samples were then placed in coin envelopes and stored in the air-conditioned room until the electrical measurements were made.

A flat leaf surface insured better electrical contact between electrode and leaf web, thereby reducing the error in capacitance and dissipation factor measurements associated with contact impedances. For this reason, 1-in. diameter samples which were free of large lateral veins were cut from the 2-in. diameter field samples prior to measuring the electrical properties.

In order to set a limit on the number of samples, electrical properties of leaves from the third priming only (mid-stalk position) were measured. Duplicate samples (designated as *a* and *b*) from each selection were composed of one plug from each of five plants. The five 1-in. diameter plugs were then stacked in series like coins between the electrodes of the sample holder for the electrical measurements.

The experimental plan for determining the influence of moisture content on the dielectric properties was to make measurements on cured leaves which had been equilibrated at 77°F and 45 per cent RH, 77°F and 60 per cent RH, and 77°F and 75 per cent RH. The low moisture content of the samples equilibrated at 45 per cent RH represents the lower limit of moisture content at which leaves may be handled without excessive shattering, while the high moisture content of samples equilibrated at 75 per cent RH represents a condition of excessive moisture content for safe handling of flue-cured tobacco.

RESULTS AND DISCUSSION

Dielectric Constant, Conductivity and Dielectric Loss Factor of Cured Tobacco Leaves

Precision of Measurement of Dielectric Constant. Early in the experiment, error was noticed in making repeated measurements on the same sample plug of cured tobacco. An indication of reproducibility of measurements at various frequencies and sample thicknesses may be obtained from Table 2. The results indicated that measurements on thicker samples were more reproducible. Consequently, subsequent testing was conducted on plugs which were at least five leaves thick.

Application of General Relaxation Theory for Predicting Dielectric Behavior. The main advantage that is realized by using a model to describe the dielectric behavior of a material is that a relatively small number of measurements over a few decades of frequency (four decades in the case of the present investigation) enables one to predict the dielectric behavior outside the range of measurement. Also, this approach helps to determine the relation of such factors as sample moisture content, density, temperature and chemical composition to the dielectric properties.

The mathematical model for the dielectric behavior of intact tobacco leaves was taken as Eq. (4). The technique for calculating the parameters of the model was to plot an Argand diagram, using the real and imaginary parts of the complex dielectric constant

$$\epsilon^* = \epsilon' - j\epsilon'' \qquad (10)$$

where ϵ' and ϵ'' were measured experimentally. The parameters ϵ_0, ϵ_∞, α and f_m were then deduced from this diagram.

The dielectric behavior of intact tobacco leaves is illustrated in Fig. 4. Each point on the arc is characteristic of one frequency of measurement. The value of α was obtained by measuring the angle from the arc plot. The ratio, v/u, was measured graphically and was plotted against frequency on logarithmic paper to form a line with slope $1 - \alpha$. This follows from the fact that

$$v/u = (\omega T)^{1-\alpha} = (f/f_m)^{1-\alpha} \qquad (11)$$

The measured values of ϵ', ϵ'' and γ for the Hicks (A3a) variety are shown in Table 3 along with the calculated values which were obtained by Eqs. (4) and (5). The measured and calculated values are plotted against frequency in Fig. 5. Assuming the same dispersion characteristics, extrapolation of these data to 100 Mc was justified on the basis of the close agreement between the measured and calculated values of the dielectric properties for the frequency range 1 kc to 1 Mc. Generally, the dielectric constant showed dispersion over about five decades of frequency. This wide dispersion was evidence of a wide distribution of relaxation times for the intact leaf.

The dielectric constant at 10 Mc was approximately equal to the high-frequency dielectric constant ϵ_∞.

From the comparison of measured values

TABLE 2. FOUR CONSECUTIVE DETERMINATIONS OF DIELECTRIC CONSTANT OF CURED-LEAF PLUGS

Frequency (kc)	Test No.*				Average Thickness	Average ϵ' with 95% Confidence Interval
	1	2	3	4		
1	20.01	48.03	41.20	24.99	three	33.54 ± 24.29
10	8.73	20.38	12.60	8.78	leaves	12.62 ± 10.07
100	5.23	9.16	6.46	4.33	(13.8 mils)	6.30 ± 3.86
1000	4.23	6.72	5.08	3.24		4.84 ± 2.70
1	38.00	41.32	39.78	38.72	seven	39.46 ± 1.62
10	17.70	14.43	13.23	10.29	leaves	13.91 ± 5.64
100	8.54	7.02	6.84	5.24	(31.8 mils)	6.91 ± 2.48
1000	55.49	6.01	5.01	3.83		5.09 ± 1.71

* Test conditions: 77°F, 60% RH. Sample 139A-5—16.1% moisture content, 0.631 g/cc.

HA3a, 77°F/60%, 15.35% moisture content, Density 0.616 g/cc

f_m = 680 cycles
ϵ_0 = 57
ϵ_∞ = 2
α = 0.38

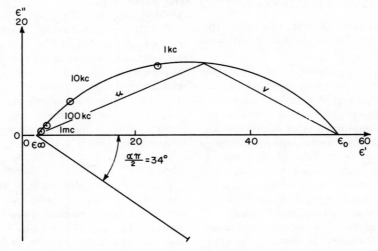

FIG. 4. Arc plot of a medium-moisture sample from a typical variety.

TABLE 3. EXPERIMENTAL VALUES AND CALCULATED VALUES OF ϵ', ϵ'', AND γ FOR HICKS (A3A) VARIETY AT VARIOUS FREQUENCIES AND MOISTURE CONTENTS AT 77°F

Frequency (kc)	Measured Values			Calculated Values		
	ϵ'	ϵ''	$\gamma(\Omega^{-1}\mathrm{cm}^{-1} \times 10^9)$	ϵ'†	ϵ''†	γ‡$(\Omega^{-1}\mathrm{cm}^{-1} \times 10^9)$
9.47% Moisture Content						
1	2.63	0.40	0.22	2.65	.42	.23
10	2.02	.23	1.28	2.06	.30	1.67
10^2	1.75	.13	7.23	1.74	.13	7.23
10^3	1.67	.07	38.92	1.67	.05	27.80
10^4	—	—	—	1.62	.02	111.20
10^5	—	—	—	1.60	.005	278.00
15.35% Moisture Content						
1	23.58	13.25	7	25.35	14.36	8
10	8.08	6.33	35	8.24	6.90	38
10^2	3.85	1.88	105	3.40	1.96	109
10^3	2.76	.45	250	2.33	.49	272
10^4	—	—	—	2.08	.12	667
10^5	—	—	—	2.00	.03	1668
21.24% Moisture Content						
1	116.00	35.03	19	133.11	20.34	11
10	83.77	31.58	176	83.65	38.86	216
10^2	31.99	27.83	1550	28.89	23.93	1,331
10^3	12.04	9.31	5180	10.59	7.32	4,070
10^4	—	—	—	6.25	1.82	10,119
10^5	—	—	—	5.29	.46	25,576

† Use Eq. (4) and values of ε_∞, ε_0, f_m and α from Fig. 4.
‡ Use Eq. (5) and calculated values of ε''.

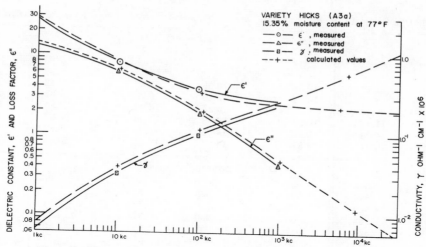

FIG. 5. Experimental values and calculated values for ε', ε'', and γ for a medium-moisture sample at 77°F.

and calculated values of ε', ε'' and γ, it appears that the application of the empirical relations of Cole and Cole[5] as depicted in Eq. (4) gives a reasonably close approximation of the dielectric behavior of the cured tobacco leaf.

Influence of Leaf Density and Moisture Content on Dielectric Properties. The moisture content of flue-cured tobacco at the time it ripens in the field is usually between 500 and 700 per cent (dry basis); at the end of the curing period the leaf is "bone-dry". Normally, the leaf will regain about 15 to 18 per cent moisture when left at temperature and humidity conditions of approximately 77°F and 60 per cent R.H. It has been observed that "trashy" leaf types will regain less moisture than the better grades of leaf. In addition, the leaf density is an important factor, especially in cigarette manufacturing. Therefore, from these considerations, it was important to determine the influence of these factors on the dielectric properties of the cured leaf.

The relation of density to dielectric constant has been described by Lichtenecker.[9] Thus, it has been observed that an increase in density will increase the dielectric constant of the material, other things being equal.

It was observed that the effective sample density, which was determined while the sample was clamped between the spring-loaded plates of the sample holder, increased out of proportion to increases in absorbed moisture. This disproportionate increase in density of high-moisture samples for a given electrode pressure was a consequence of sample compression. For example, Artho[1] found that leaf elasticity (i.e., compressibility) increased directly with absorbed moisture.

It was desirable to determine the effect of compression (increase in density) on the dielectric constant. This was best accomplished by varying the density of a sample at constant moisture content. The effect of compression upon the dielectric constant and dielectric loss factor of a medium-moisture sample is shown in Table 4.

TABLE 4. THE VARIATION OF DIELECTRIC CONSTANT AND DIELECTRIC LOSS FACTOR WITH LEAF DENSITY*

Dielectric Property	Leaf Density (gm/ml)	Frequency (kc)			
		1	10	10^2	10^3
ε'	0.712	49.71	11.48	5.14	3.81
	1.172	47.14	20.17	8.14	5.96
ε''	0.712	41.56	12.87	2.85	.68
	1.172	28.99	11.98	3.57	1.00

* Sample 139A 3b, 16.0% moisture, 77°F, 60% R.H.

The compression of the sample increased the dielectric constant almost uniformly for all frequencies. For frequencies above 10 kc, an increase in density by a factor of 1.65 caused an increase in dielectric constant by essentially the same factor.

TABLE 5. PER CENT MOISTURE CONTENT, DRY BASIS, AND DENSITY OF THE TOBACCO-LEAF SAMPLES

Sample	77°F—45% RH		77°F—60% RH		77°F—75% RH	
	a	b	a	b	a	b
Per Cent Moisture (dry basis)						
139 A3	11.27	10.68	16.55	15.87	23.43	23.30
B3	9.45	10.76	13.10	16.23	21.83	24.11
H A3	9.47	9.36	15.35	16.00	21.24	22.22
B3	11.44	10.89	16.00	15.56	20.32	21.85
101 A3	10.28	10.69	14.58	15.44	18.89	20.61
B3	10.71	9.87	14.63	13.46	20.68	20.05
Density—grams/cc at 8 psi						
139 A3	.580	.631	.670	.694	.963	1.018
B3	.575	.571	.633	.695	.882	.921
H A3	.509	.566	.616	.729	.817	.900
B3	.536	.600	.630	.616	.795	.864
101 A3	.523	.581	.608	.653	.832	.860
B3	.588	.625	.681	.612	.876	.832
Density Adjustment Factor = $\dfrac{\text{Density at Low Moisture Content}}{\text{Density at Actual Moisture Content}}$						
139 A3	1.00	1.00	.87	.91	.60	.62
B3	1.00	1.00	.91	.82	.65	.62
H A3	1.00	1.00	.83	.78	.62	.63
B3	1.00	1.00	.85	.97	.67	.69
101 A3	1.00	1.00	.86	.89	.63	.68
B3	1.00	1.00	.86	1.02	.67	.75

The dielectric constant was adjusted for density effects in order to determine the effect of moisture content alone. The measured dielectric constant at various moisture contents was multiplied by the factor shown in Table 5, which had the effect of adjusting the data to the density of the low-moisture content samples. Table 5 shows the per cent moisture content, density, and density adjustment factor of the cured-leaf samples which were measured in the experiment.

The influence of leaf density on the conductivity and loss factor was much less pronounced than the influence of density on dielectric constant. For frequencies above 10 kc, an increase in leaf density by a factor of 1.65 had a negligible effect on leaf conductivity and dielectric loss factor.

The moisture content of the leaf influenced the dielectric properties more than any other single variable. An increase in leaf moisture increased the dielectric constant, conductivity and dielectric loss factor for all frequencies. Table 3 shows the variation of these dielectric properties with changes in sample moisture content. These data were adjusted for differences in sample density as previously related.

When the dielectric constant was plotted against frequency for the low-, medium-, and high-moisture samples from a particular variety, an interesting family of curves resulted. In Fig. 6, the dielectric constant of Hicks (A3a) variety is shown for three values of moisture content. It is clear that the shape of the dielectric-constant curves is different for different sample moisture contents. The shape of these curves is related to the dielectric-relaxation characteristics of the samples.

The variation of AC conductivity and loss factor of cured tobacco with change in frequency at various moisture contents is shown in Table 3 for one variety. In the moisture content range of 10 to 20 per cent, the AC conductivity was increased 100-fold by doubling the moisture content. This is shown graphically in Fig. 7 for the Hicks (A3a) variety. These curves illustrate the fact that conductivity is extremely influenced by moisture content of the sample.

Generally, the dielectric properties of leaves from each variety were similarly influenced by variations in density, moisture content, frequency and temperature.

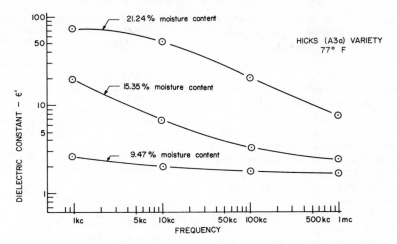

Fig. 6. Variation of the dielectric constant of cured tobacco with change in frequency at various moisture contents at 77°F.

SUMMARY AND CONCLUSIONS

Dielectric measurements of tobacco indicated a broad frequency range over which dispersion of the dielectric constant occurred. A mathematical model for the dielectric behavior of the intact tobacco leaf was taken as a modified Debye model. By using the modified Debye model for expressing the dielectric constant and loss factor as a function of frequency, it was possible to predict the dielectric behavior outside the range of measurement.

Measurements were made of the dielectric constant, dielectric loss factor, and specific conductivity as functions of frequency (1 kc to 1 Mc), leaf moisture content (9 to 24 per cent), and density (0.500 to 1.000 g/cc) at a constant temperature of 77°F. The measurements were made on three well-known flue-cured varieties.

An AC capacitance bridge was used for making the measurements in the range 1 kc to 1 Mc. The sample holder consisted of a micrometer-electrode system that was adequately shielded to reduce the effect of stray capacitance. This type of electrode system simplified the calculation of the capacity of the sample which normally consisted of five 1-in. diameter leaf plugs stacked like coins in series between the spring-loaded plates of the test condenser.

The relatively high values of dielectric constant obtained for high-moisture samples

indicated that the moist tobacco leaf was electrolytic in behavior. This was consistent with findings of other investigators.[14]

The experimental results showed that increases in leaf moisture content increased the dielectric constant and dielectric loss factor,

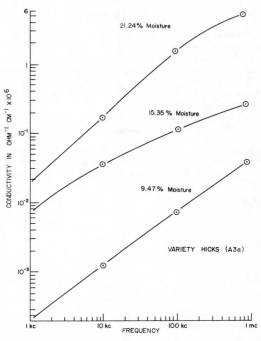

Fig. 7. Variation of AC conductivity of cured tobacco with change in frequency at various moisture contents at 77°F.

while frequency had the opposite effect. An increase in leaf density caused a proportionate increase in dielectric constant, but caused little change in the dielectric loss factor and AC conductivity.

The dieletric behavior of each of six selections of flue-cured tobacco was similar within the limits of the experiment.

The dielectric constants for cured leaves of a typical variety (Hicks A3a) at 10 kc and 77°F were 2.02, 6.71 and 51.94 for leaf moisture contents of 9.47, 15.35 and 21.24 per cent, respectively. The dielectric loss factors were 0.23, 6.33 and 31.58, and AC conductivity were $1.28 \cdot (10^{-9})$, $35.00 \cdot (10^{-9})$ and $176.00 \cdot (10^{-9})$ Ω^{-1} cm^{-1} for the same conditions. The values of the dielectric properties at 1 Mc were: 1.67, 2.29, and 7.46 for dielectric constants; 0.07, 0.45 and 9.31 for dielectric loss factors, and $38.92 \cdot (10^{-9})$, $250.00 \cdot (10^{-9})$ and $5180.00 \cdot (10^{-9})$ Ω^{-1} cm^{-1} for AC conductivities.

In conclusion, for future work of a similar nature, the arc plot of the real and imaginary components of the complex dielectric constant in an Argand diagram will enable one to make fewer measurements over a narrow band of frequencies in order to predict the dielectric parameters of biological materials.

Acknowledgment. The study reported herein was conducted under joint cooperation of the North Carolina Agricultural Experiment Station, Agricultural Engineering Department, and the Farm Electrification Research Branch, Agricultural Engineering Research Division (ARS), United States Department of Agriculture.

References

1. Artho, A. J., "Physical Properties of Cured Tobacco Leaves," *Naturforschende Gesselschaft Zurich, Vierteljarysschrift*, **100**, 87–113 (1955).

2. ASTM Standards, Part 9, "A.C. Capacitance, Dielectric Constant, and Loss Characteristics for Insulating Materials," D-150-54T:645-692, 1958.

3. Bacon, C. W., Wenger, R., and Bullock, J. F., "Biochemical Charges in Tobacco During Flue Curing," *U.S. Dept. Agr. Tech. Bull.*, **1032**, 1–37 (1951).

4. Brown, G. H., Hoyler, C. N., and Bierwirth, R. A., "Theory and Application of Radio-Frequency Heating," New York, D. Van Nostrand Co., Inc., 1947.

5. Cole, K. S., and Cole, R. H., "Dispersion and Absorption in Dielectrics," *J. Chem. Phys.*, **9**, 341–351 (1941).

6. Debye, P., "Polar Molecules," New York, Chemical Catalog Co., 1929.

7. Edlefsen, N. E., "A Review of Results of Dielectric Methods for Measuring Moisture Present in Materials," *Agr. Eng.* 14:243–244, 1933.

8. Henson, W. H., "Certain Dielectric Properties of Intact Tobacco Leaves," Unpublished Ph.D. Thesis, North Carolina State College, Raleigh, 1962.

9. Lichtenecker, K., "Die Dielekrizitätskonstante naturlicher und künstlicher Mischkorper," *Physikalische Z.*, **27**, 115, 833 (1926).

10. Müller, H., "Methods for Determining the Moisture in Tobacco," *Tabak-Technikum Hamberg, Tech. Sci. Series I*, Vol. No. 1–4 (1957).

11. Murphy, E. J., and Morgan, S. O., "The Dielectric Properties of Insulating Materials. I. Outline of the Physio-chemical Interpretation of the Dielectric Constant," *Bell System Tech. J.*, **16**, 493–512 (1937).

12. Stacy, R. W., Williams, D. T., Worden, R. E., and McMorris, R. O., "Essentials of Biological and Medical Physics," New York, McGraw-Hill Book Co., Inc., 1955.

13. Swensen, T. L., "Research on Agricultural Products," *Sci. Monthly*, **62**, 525–537 (1946).

14. Tausz, V. J., and Rumm, H., "Untersuchungen über die Dielektrizitätskonstanten wasserhaltiger Stoffe (Studies of the dielectric constant of substances containing water)," *Kolloid-beihefte*, **39**, 59–104 (1933).

21. Humidity and Moisture Measurements in Relation to Storage Stability of Dehydrated Foods*

John G. Kapsalis, Max Wolf, Margaret Driver and Albert S. Henick

Armed Forces Food and Container Institute, Chicago, Illinois

ABSTRACT

The stability of ground freeze-dehydrated raw beef, precooked freeze-dehydrated shrimp, and precooked freeze-dehydrated spinach was studied in relation to equilibrium relative humidity conditions upon storage at different temperatures. Deterioration was followed by gas chromatographic analysis in the headspace, by spectrophotometric reflectance measurements, and by free fatty acids determination. Beef samples stored at 100°F showed only slight stability differences between 0 and 11 per cent RH, in terms of oxygen uptake and meat pigment degradation. Formation of free fatty acids was appreciably higher in the 11.1 per cent than in the 0 RH samples. Deterioration as measured by all methods was greatest at 31.6 per cent RH. Shrimp stored at 100°F showed maximum stability at 0 RH, with relatively little deterioration at 11.1 per cent RH. At 20.4 per cent RH rapid oxygen uptake took place. Spinach stored at 120°F exhibited maximum stability at 1.5 per cent, the lowest relative humidity tested. The different types of degradation upon storage as determined by the methods of this study are discussed.

* This paper reports research conducted by the Armed Forces Food and Container Institute and has been assigned Nr. 2267 in the series of papers approved for publication. The views or conclusions contained in this report are those of the authors. They are not to be construed as necessarily reflecting the views or indorsement of the Department of Defense.

INTRODUCTION

In the past decade relative humidity has been increasingly recognized as an important parameter in the investigation of food stability problems. Rockland[7] observed that walnuts have an optimum moisture range with respect to stability. He suggested that the differential coefficient ($\Delta M/\Delta$ RH), which he reported for 45 foods, is related to stability. Hamm[1] treated the water binding properties of beef muscle proteins in terms of the moisture sorption isotherm. Recently, Taylor[13] has published isotherms for 12 foods together with a new method for determining the vapor pressure of foods. An automatic apparatus for determining moisture sorption was described by Hofer.[3] Salwin[8, 9] showed the importance of the level of relative humidity to the stability of dehydrated foods. He postulated that a certain amount of water in the form of a statistical monomolecular layer on active molecular sites is protective against oxidation in many foods. Practical application of these concepts and the interpretation of the deteriorative and protective mechanisms of water sorption necessitate more information on the effect of controlled humidity conditions on storage stability of dehydrated foods.

In the present study and as a first approach to the above problem, the storage stability of selected dehydrated foods was examined at controlled zero and higher relative humidity conditions. Work currently under way includes study of specific isothermic moisture values at, below and above the BET monomolecular layer of water in relation to stability.

MATERIALS AND METHODS

The dehydrated foods used in this study were ground freeze-dehydrated raw beef, precooked freeze-dehydrated shrimp and precooked freeze-dehydrated spinach. The spinach and beef were dehydrated in a pilot plant freeze dehydrator. The dehydrated

shrimp was obtained from a commercial source.

The experimental methods of this study required preparation of a series of samples of known relative humidity. Each sample was ground to a particle size suitable for quick equilibrium and for reflectance spectrophotometric measurements.

In the case of dehydrated beef and shrimp, grinding in a Waring Blendor to a sandy texture for the former and floury texture for the latter was satisfactory. For dehydrated spinach, sieving the ground material to a particle size within the 20- and 40-mesh sieve

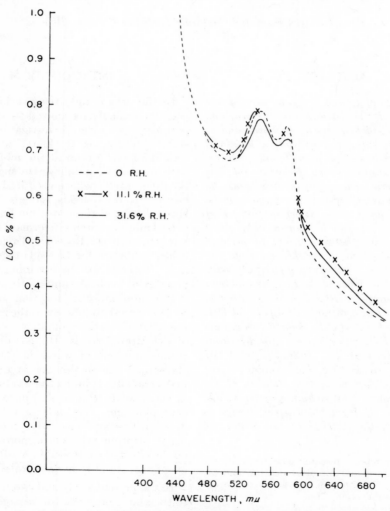

FIG. 1. Pigment degradation of ground freeze-dried raw beef stored at 100°F for 2 days under controlled relative humidity atmospheres.

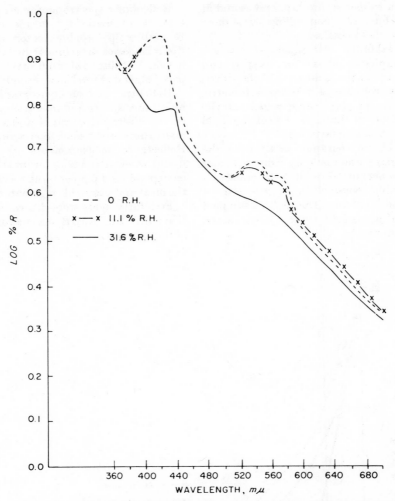

Fig. 2. Pigment degradation of ground freeze-dried raw beef stored at 100°F for 60 days under controlled relative humidity atmospheres.

sizes was necessary in order to produce a uniform color distribution. Grinding and sieving of spinach was best at moisture contents in the neighborhood of 6 per cent; at very low moisture levels grinding resulted in excessive pulverization of the dry material.

The beef and shrimp samples were stored at 100°F in 4-ounce prescription bottles, stoppered air tightly with a rubber serum cap (Fig. 2). Controlled humidity conditions were established by inserting into the bottle two small test tubes containing a humidity controlling substance. The flat side of the bottle was a suitable surface for successive reflectance spectrophotometric measurements during

storage; use of the rubber serum cap made possible periodic nondestructive gas sampling for chromatographic analysis. Humidity was controlled by means of dry magnesium perchlorate and solutions of lithium chloride, magnesium chloride, potassium acetate and sodium chloride. To expedite equilibration, the samples were preconditioned by exposing to atmospheres of higher or lower than desired moisture for 1 to 2 days before storing in the prescription bottles.

The spinach samples were preconditioned in the same manner as the beef and shrimp samples above. They were then placed in 2-ounce square bottles which were air-tightly fitted with a rubber serum cap, and stored at 120°F. No humidity controlling substances were used in these bottles.

Storage stability was followed by gas chromatographic analysis for oxygen and carbon dioxide in the headspace of the stored samples; by reflectance spectrophotometric measurements in the visible region of the spectrum; and, in the case of beef, by final determination of free fatty acids.

The gas chromatographic analysis of the headspace gases was made by using a Fisher Gas Partitioner fitted with a hexamethyl-phosphoramide column in series with a molecular sieve column. The gas was sampled by means of a gastight syringe through the rubber serum cap.[2]

Reflectance spectrophotometric determinations were made by means of the Cary Recording Spectrophotometer equipped with the reflectance attachment of type II illumination. Vitrolite calibrated against freshly prepared MgO was used as a secondary standard.

Both the gas chromatographic and the reflectance spectrophotometric measurements are nondestructive, rapid and can be made many times on the same food sample in storage. Reflectance measurements are particularly useful where storage deterioration results in changes of food pigments, as was the case with the meat and vegetable pigments of this study.

Free fatty acids were determined by titration with $0.01N$ NaOH of a chloroform extract of the sample.

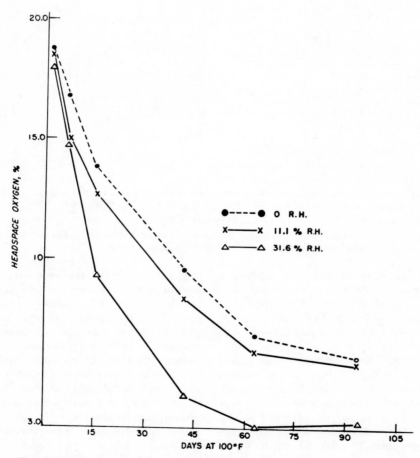

FIG. 3. Headspace oxygen, per cent of ground freeze-dried raw beef stored at 100°F under controlled relative humidity atmospheres.

RESULTS AND DISCUSSION

Ground Freeze-dehydrated Raw Beef

Results on meat pigment stability at 100°F are presented in the form of reflectance spectra characteristics, Figs. 1 and 2, and as a decrease in the prominence (i.e., decrease of the difference of Log Per Cent Reflectance between peak and valley) of the 578 mμ or "alpha" and 540 mμ or "beta" absorption bands, Table 1. Pigment degradation (Figs. 1

TABLE 1. CHANGES IN ABSORPTION BANDS OF THE REFLECTANCE SPECTRUM OF STORED GROUND FREEZE-DRIED RAW BEEF

Days at 100°F	Relative Humidity (%)					
	0.0		11.1		31.6	
	a*	b**	a	b	a	b
0	0.17	0.05	0.16	0.06	0.07	0.07
2	0.12	0.01	0.09	0.01	0.09	0.02
5	0.10	0.02	0.08	−0.02	0.08	0.02
19	0.04	0.02	0.04	−0.01	0.01	0.00
22	0.03	0.00	0.00	−0.02	0.00	−0.03
60	0.03	−0.03	0.02	−0.04	−0.02	−0.02
95	0.02	−0.03	0.01	−0.03	−0.03	−0.03

*a = alpha peak, log % R_{578} − log % R_{560}.
**b = beta peak, log % R_{540} − log % R_{510}. (Designation of "alpha" and "beta" peaks in this Table is arbitrary.)

and 2) was evident by a decrease in sharpness and final disappearance of the absorption maxima at about 578 and 540 mμ after 60 days. Stability was maximum at 0 RH (below the moisture monolayer value), and minimum at 31.6 per cent RH (above the moisture monolayer value). There was only slight difference between the samples at 11.1 per cent RH (close to the monolayer value) and the samples at 0 RH.*

* The moisture monolayer value of freeze-dried beef muscle at 41.0°F was given by Hamm as about 12 per cent RH or 4 per cent moisture.[1]

Absorption bands at approximately 570 and 550 mμ of the reflectance spectrum of meats are characteristic of hemochromes.* Oxidative conversion of the hemochromes to hemichromes results in substitution of a broad band at about 550 mμ for the above two bands.[10, 12]

Degradation upon storage as determined by gas analysis for oxygen and carbon dioxide in the headspace is shown in Table 2 and Fig. 3. Oxygen uptake was consistently lower for the 0 and 11.1 RH than for the 31.6 per cent RH. samples. Carbon dioxide evolution followed a similar trend. These data substantiate the results of reflectance spectrophotometric measurements. They indicate that increased oxidation at higher relative humidities is closely associated with meat pigment degradation, in addition to other changes which may occur.

Results on free fatty acid formation after 93 days are shown in Table 3. Stability was appreciably better at 0 than at 11.1 and 31.6

TABLE 3. FREE FATTY ACID FORMATION IN GROUND FREEZE-DRIED RAW BEEF STORED AT 100°F FOR 93 DAYS UNDER CONTROLLED RELATIVE HUMIDITY ATMOSPHERES

RH (%)	FFA* (%)
0.0	1.3
11.1	13.2
31.6	23.3

* Expressed as oleic acid on % extracted fat basis.

per cent RH. The results indicate that under the conditions of this experiment, hydrolytic in addition to oxidative changes may have taken place as relative humidity increased.

In terms of oxidative changes and of pigment degradation, dehydration of ground raw

* The pigment of freshly freeze-dried meat has been reported to be mostly oxymyoglobin.[4]

TABLE 2. OXYGEN AND CARBON DIOXIDE, %, IN THE HEADSPACE OF GROUND FREEZE-DRIED RAW BEEF STORED AT 100°F UNDER CONTROLLED RELATIVE HUMIDITY ATMOSPHERES

Relative Humidity (%)	Days at 100°F											
	2		7		15		42		62		93	
	O_2	CO_2	O_2	CO_2	O_2	CO_2	O_2	CO_2	O_2	CO_2	O_2	CO_2
0.0	18.8	0.0	16.8	0.4	13.8	0.4	9.6	0.7	6.9	0.8	5.8	0.8
11.1	18.5	0.2	14.9	1.0	12.6	1.2	8.4	1.7	6.2	1.7	5.7	1.6
31.6	18.0	0.3	14.7	1.0	9.3	2.0	4.3	3.5	2.9	3.5	3.3	3.1

TABLE 4. SPECTRAL REFLECTANCE CHANGES AT 400 AND 560 mμ OF FREEZE-DRIED SHRIMP STORED AT 100°F UNDER CONTROLLED RELATIVE HUMIDITY ATMOSPHERES

Relative Humidity (%)	Days at 100°F									
	0		3		42		78		105	
	Wavelength (mμ)									
	400	560	400	560	400	560	400	560	400	560
	log % R									
0.0	0.183	0.062	0.213	0.076	0.258	0.080	0.264	0.064	0.284	0.082
11.1	0.198	0.082	0.213	0.070	0.262	0.073	0.283	0.080	0.294	0.077
20.4	0.188	0.073	0.218	0.080	0.297	0.088	0.331	0.105	0.323	0.090

beef to the 4 per cent moisture of the mono-layer region seems to bring practically the same benefits as "bone" dehydration. Hydrolytic changes at 100°F, however, which result in free fatty acid formation, become progressively important as relative humidity increases from the 0 to 11.1 and 31.6 per cent relative humidity.

Precooked Freeze-dehydrated Shrimp

Results of spectral reflectance changes upon storage of the samples at different relative humidities are presented in Table 4 and Figs.

4 and 5. A slight but consistent "darkening" upon storage (increase in absorption) was observed, as relative humidity increased from zero to 11.1 and 20.4 per cent relative humidity. This was more evident at 400 than at 560 mμ. Visually, the change was apparent as a slight yellowish discoloration. Deterioration was more evident in terms of gas analysis for oxygen and carbon dioxide, Table 5 and Fig. 6. Maximum stability was obtained at 0 RH with a relatively small change at 11.1 per cent RH. At 20.4 per cent RH rapid oxygen uptake took place. The principal result of oxidative

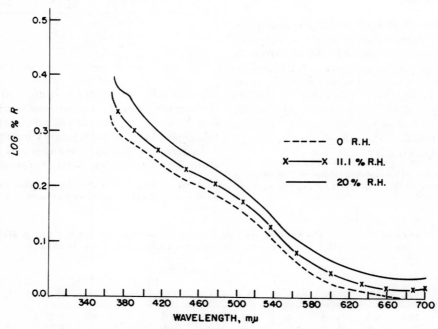

FIG. 4. Spectral reflectance changes of precooked freeze-dried shrimp stored at 100°F for 69 days under controlled relative humidity atmospheres.

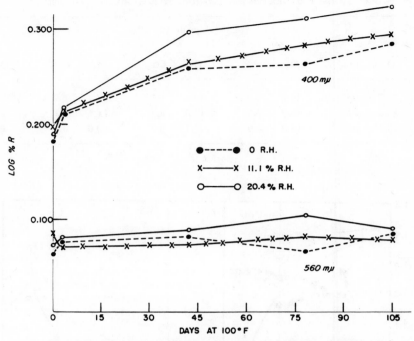

FIG. 5. Spectral reflectance changes at 400 and 560 mμ of precooked freeze-dried shrimp stored at 100°F under controlled relative humidity atmospheres.

deterioration in shrimp seems to be flavor rather than pigment degradation. This was also evident by simple sensory evaluation.

Precooked Freeze-dehydrated Spinach

Representative reflectance spectra of precooked freeze-dehydrated spinach stored at 120°F after preconditioning to different relative humidity levels are shown in Figs. 7, 8 and 9. Significant in this set of curves are the presence and prominence of characteristic absorption bands rather than the absolute position of the spectra along the absorbance scale. These bands characterize molecular absorbing species whereas position of the reflectance spectra may be also affected by particle size and other factors.

Degradation of chlorophyll (which has a maximum absorption band at about 660 to 670 mμ) is indicated by appearance of new bands at about 530 to 540 mμ and 610 to 620 mμ. Formation of pheophytin is responsible for the 530 to 540 mμ and probably also for the 610 to 620 mμ bands[11].

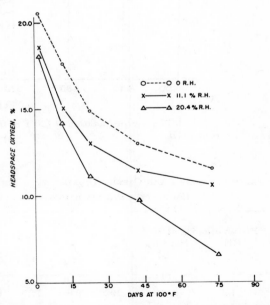

FIG. 6. Headspace oxygen, per cent, of precooked freeze-dried shrimp stored at 100°F under controlled relative humidity atmospheres.

TABLE 5. OXYGEN AND CARBON DIOXIDE, %, IN THE HEADSPACE OF PRECOOKED FREEZE-DRIED SHRIMP STORED AT 100°F UNDER CONTROLLED RELATIVE HUMIDITY ATMOSPHERES

Relative Humidity (%)	Days at 100°F									
	1		12		23 %		42		73	
	O_2	CO_2	O_2	CO_2	O_2	CO_2	O_2	CO_2	O_2	CO_2
0.0	20.5	0.0	17.6	0.0	14.9	0.3	13.1	0.0	11.5	0.0
11.1	18.6	0.3	15.0	0.3	13.0	0.4	11.4	0.3	10.6	0.0
20.4	18.1	0.3	14.2	0.0	11.1	0.5	9.0	0.5	6.6	0.0

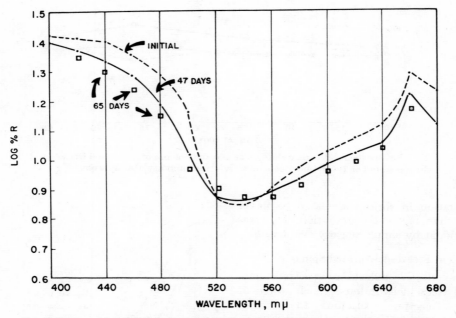

FIG. 7. Pigment degradation at 120°F of freeze-dried spinach preconditioned to 1.5 per cent ERH.

TABLE 6. OXYGEN AND CARBON DIOXIDE, %, IN THE HEADSPACE OF FREEZE-DRIED SPINACH STORED AT 120°F AFTER PRECONDITIONING TO DIFFERENT RELATIVE HUMIDITY LEVELS

Preconditioning at 80°F		Days at 120°F									
RH (%)	Moisture (%)	2		8		21 %		53		67	
		O_2	CO_2	O_2	CO_2	O_2	CO_2	O_2	CO_2	O_2	CO_2
1.5	0.50	19.3	0.0	17.9	0.3	17.4	0.4	16.7	0.5	13.5	2.3
12.2	3.53	18.9	0.4	16.8	1.8	14.5	0.2	13.0	1.8	9.1	5.7
30.0	5.65	18.8	1.0	15.6	2.5	12.7	2.4	12.6	2.1	7.9	5.8

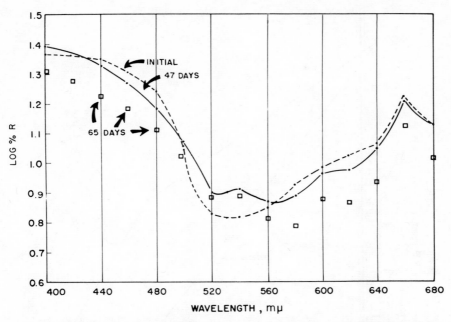

Fɪɢ. 8. Pigment degradation at 120°F of freeze-dried spinach preconditioned to 12.2 per cent ERH.

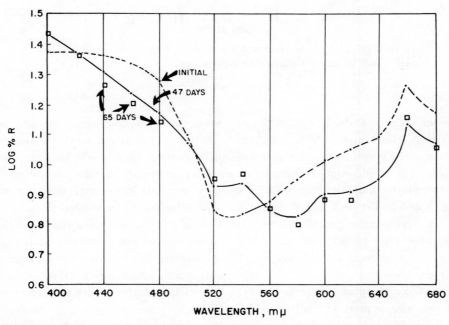

Fɪɢ. 9. Pigment degradation at 120°F of freeze-dried spinach preconditioned to 30 per cent ERH.

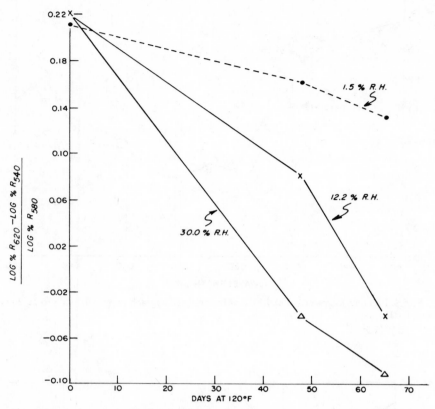

Fɪɢ. 10. Pigment degradation of freeze-dried spinach upon storage at 120°F after preconditioning to different relative humidity levels.

Maximum pigment stability at 120°F was obtained with the sample which was preconditioned to the lowest relative humidity of 1.5 per cent, Fig. 7. Chlorophyll degradation increased as relative humidity rose to 12.2 per cent, Fig. 8, and 30 per cent, Fig. 9. This can be more clearly seen in Fig. 10, where the (620–540): 580 mμ absorbance ratio was selected as index of green color deterioration upon storage.

In terms of oxygen uptake (Table 6, Fig. 11) stability was also appreciably better at 1.5 than at 12.2 and 30 per cent RH.

In stored foods different types of reactions may occur simultaneously or successively. Therefore the means used for determining deterioration, be it residual oxygen, peroxide values or spectrophotometric characteristic, may give an apparently different picture, depending on the particular change followed.

Food acceptance testing may be particularly useful in evaluating overall stability. Simple sensory examinations confirmed the results of this study, which indicate that deterioration is minimal at the lowest relative humidity. Spinach showed maximum green color stability at the lower moisture level. Chlorophyll degradation, which may be considered hydrolytic in nature is important in green vegetables. However, the protective effect of higher moisture levels in lessening the oxidative deterioration of carotene in carrots has been reported.[9] In selecting the moisture level for optimum stability, the effectiveness of low relative humidity for preventing nonenzymatic browning, and for depressing the formations of free fatty acids in meat, may far outweigh the importance of the higher peroxide values[9] reported at 0 RH. This, for example may be the case in freeze-dried beef where browning and direct protein oxidation seem to major deteriorative reactions. The attainment of the practical objective, that of defining the moisture levels for optimum stability, requires more information on the specific pathway of deterioration. The application of moisture sorption concepts promises to be a useful guide in research.

References

1. Hamm, R., "Biochemistry of Meat Hydration," *Advan. Food Res.*, **10**, 355–463 (1960).
2. Henick, A. S., and Bishov, S. J., "Fat Stability Testing with Gas Chromatography," *J. Am. Oil Chemists, Soc.* (in press).
3. Hofer, A. A. von, and Mahler, H., "Apparatus zur messung der Sorptionskinetik und eine Micromethode zue messung on Sorptionisothermen," *Helv. Chim. Acta*, **45**, 1415–1418 (1962).
4. Penny, I. F., "The Effect of Accelerated Freeze Drying on the Colour of Beef," *Food Processing and Packaging*, **29**, 363–366 (1960).
5. Regier, L. W., and Tappel, A. L., "Freeze-Dried Meat," III. "Non-Oxidatie Deterioration of

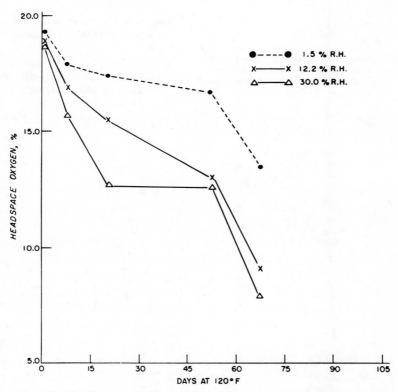

FIG. 11. Headspace oxygen, per cent, of precooked freeze-dried spinach stored at 120°F after preconditioning to different relative humidity levels.

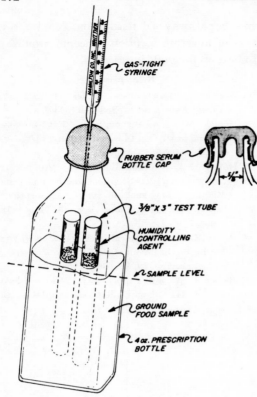

GAS-TIGHT
SYRINGE

RUBBER SERUM
BOTTLE CAP

3/8"X 3" TEST TUBE

HUMIDITY
CONTROLLING
AGENT

SAMPLE LEVEL

GROUND
FOOD SAMPLE

4 oz. PRESCRIPTION
BOTTLE

FIG. 12. Sample storage system for controlled relative humidity atmospheres, reflectance spectrophotometric measurements, and headspace gas analysis.

Freeze-Dried Beef," *Food Res.*, **21**, 630–639 (1956).

6. Regier, L. W., and Tappel, A. L., "Freeze-Dried Meat," IV. "Factors Affecting the Rate of Deterioration," *Food Res.*, **21**, 640–649 (1956).

7. Rockland, L. B., "A New Treatment of Hygroscopic Equilibria: Application to Walnuts and Other Foods," *Food Res.*, **22**, 604–628 (1957).

8. Salwin, H., "Defining Minimum Moisture Contents for Dehydrated Foods," *Food Technol.*, **13**, 594–595 (1959).

9. Salwin, H., "Moisture Levels Required for Stability in Dehydrated Foods," *Activities Report, Research and Development Associates, Food and Container Institute Inc.*, **13**, 191–199 (1961).

10. Sidwell, C. G., Salwin, H., Driver, M., and Koch, R. B., "Spectral Examination of Cured-meat Pigments During Frankfurter Processing," *J. Food Sci.*, **27**, 9–14 (1962).

11. Sweeny, J. P., and Martin, M., "Determination of Chlorophyll and Pheophytin in Broccoli Heated by Various Procedures," *Food Res.*, **23**, 635–647 (1958).

12. Tappel, A. L., "Spectral Studies of Pigments of Cooked Cured Meats," *Food Res.*, **22**, 479–482 (1957).

13. Taylor, A. A., "Determination of Moisture Equilibria in Dehydrated Foods," *Food Technol.*, **15**, 536–540 (1961).

22. Equilibrium Moisture Contents and Moisture Adsorption Rates of Dry Milks

D. R. Heldman, C. W. Hall and T. I. Hedrick

Departments of Agricultural Engineering and Food Science, Michigan State University, East Lansing, Michigan

ABSTRACT

The keeping quality of dry milk is directly dependent on the moisture content during storage. The moisture contents at which dry milks will come to equilibrium with given temperature and relative humidity conditions have been determined. In addition, relationships of equilibrium values and moisture adsorption rates with preheat treatment and fat level of dry milk have been investigated.

Equilibrium isotherms and hysteresis effects for dry milk are similar to those demonstrated for other hygroscopic materials. Equilibrium moisture contents at 100°F were about 2.5 per cent moisture content lower than values at 35°F. In general, moisture adsorption rates increased with an increase in relative humidity and storage temperature.

At 35°F storage, high-heat nonfat dry milk demonstrated an equilibrium moisture content as much as 2.1 per cent moisture content higher than low-heat non-fat dry milk. However, at 100°F storage, the low-heat nonfat dry milk had values about 1.0 per cent moisture content higher than the high-heat product at equilibrium. In addition, the same relationship between preheat treatment and storage temperature was demonstrated by the moisture adsorption rates. One possible explanation for this change at around 70°F is the browning reaction.

Dry milk with 26 per cent fat had equilibrium moisture contents as much as 3.1 per cent moisture lower than nonfat dry milks. However,

dry milk with fat demonstrated significantly faster moisture adsorption rates.

Latent heat ratios for dry milk increased from 1.04 at 20.0 per cent moisture content to 1.53 at 5.0 per cent moisture content. The latent heats of vaporization increased with an increase in preheat treatment.

INTRODUCTION

Dry milk, like other hygroscopic materials, gains or loses moisture at various rates depending on the environmental conditions. If a material of this type is exposed to a given environment for a sufficient time period it will attain an equilibrium moisture content. Since the keeping quality of dry milk depends directly on the moisture content during storage, the importance of equilibrium moisture values and moisture adsorption rates for establishing optimum storage conditions becomes obvious.

Equilibrium moisture data can be used to demonstrate other properties of dry milk, such as latent heats of vaporization. These properties, along with moisture adsorption rate, are useful in demonstrating various relationships with preheat treatments and fat contents of the dry milk.

The primary objective of this research was to establish equilibrium moisture contents and moisture adsorption rates of several dry milks at various relative humidity and temperature conditions. A secondary objective was to

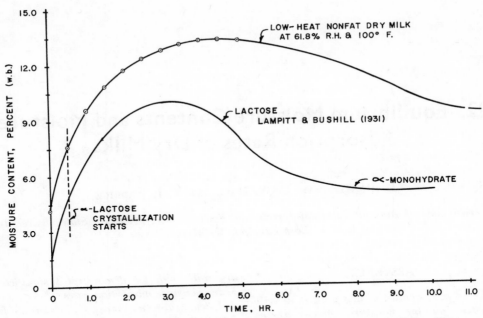

Fig. 1. Moisture adsorption curves for dry milk and lactose illustrating effects of lactose crystallization.

investigate the effects of preheat treatments and fat contents of dry milk on the equilibrium moisture values and moisture adsorption rates.

PROCEDURE

Equilibrium moisture contents and moisture adsorption rates of spray-dried milks were determined by exposing 3.0 ± 0.05g of the product to various relative humidity and temperature conditions. Dry milk samples included nonfat dry milk with three different preheat treatments: low-heat, 143°F for 30 minutes; medium-heat, 165°F for 25 minutes; and high-heat, 185°F for 20 minutes, and low-heat dry milk with three different fat levels: low-fat, 1.0 per cent BF; medium-fat, 13 per cent BF; and high-fat, 26 per cent BF. Equilibrium moisture values and moisture adsorption rates were determined at four relative humidities, 20, 40, 60 and 90 per cent at four different temperatures, 35 60, 86 and 100°F. Constant relative humidities were maintained in tightly sealed containers by saturated salt solutions. Three determinations were made at each condition.

The dry milk samples were allowed to attain

equilibrium by adsorption in a given humidity and temperature condition. Each sample was then transferred to a high humidity condition and allowed to gain excessive moisture. Finally, each sample was returned to the original environment where equilibrium was attained by desorption. The moisture content of each dry milk was determined initially by the Toluol Distillation Method as described in the M.I.F. Laboratory Manual[9] and again after completion of the experiment by the vacuum method recommended by A.O.A.C. Methods of Analysis.[1]

PRINCIPLES INVOLVED

Some of the physical and chemical changes which occur in dry milk when moisture is added will be reviewed to provide a background for understanding the results.

Lactose Changes

In spray-dried milk, lactose exists in a supersaturated solution of "glass" state, which cannot crystallize due to the lack of moisture. The existence of this situation gives spray-dried lactose and any material in which it is present very hygroscopic properties. Therefore, a major portion of the initial moisture adsorbed by spray-dried milk is taken up by the lactose solution. As soon as the lactose adsorbs sufficient moisture, crystalliz-ation begins and continues until all lactose is in the α-monohydrate crystalline state. The point at which this crystallization begins in dry milk is not clearly defined. Recent work by Heiss[4] indicates that it starts as low as 5.07 per cent moisture content. His work indicated further that the optimum conditions for the crystallization were between 5.4 and 8.5 per cent moisture content.

Due to the high hygroscopicity of lactose in the "glass" state, lactose tends to adsorb more moisture than the amount held in the mono-hydrate crystal. Therefore, a moisture adsorp-tion curve for spray-dried lactose would

appear as indicated in Fig. 1. This curve, as demonstrated by Lampitt and Bushill,[7] indicates that lactose adsorbs up to about 10 per cent moisture before crystallization is complete. However, when crystallization is completed, the α-monohydrate crystal holds only 5 per cent moisture content. Figure 1 reveals a similar curve for nonfat dry milk as demonstrated in this study. The curve indi-cates the effect of lactose on the moisture adsorption of dry milk, with the moisture attaining some "peak" value before reaching the equilibrium content.

Browning

The discoloration of concentrated and dried milk products is a chemical reaction between the casein and lactose components. Previous work on dry milk by Coulter *et al.*[2] Hollender

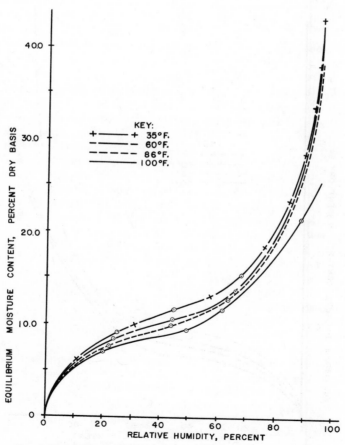

FIG. 2. Desorption equilibrium moisture content isotherms for non-fat dry milk at various storage temperatures.

and Tracy,[5] and Doob *et al.*[3] indicates that this reaction and the resulting browning is related to storage temperature, relative humidity during storage, preheat treatment of the milk before drying and moisture content of the product during storage. In general, previous results indicate that browning results from storage at temperatures above 68 to 70°F when the moisture content of the product is above 5.0 per cent. Usually, control of temperature below the stated range and storage in a relative humidity below 30 per cent will prevent any visible browning. Preheat treatment of the milk before drying affects the degree to which browning occurs. Higher preheat treatments accelerate and intensify the browning which will occur in the dried product.

RESULTS AND DISCUSSION

The data of this study will be presented on rectangular coordinates plotted as equilibrium moisture content *vs* relative humidity as illustrated in Fig. 2. The resulting sigmoid or S-shaped isotherms for dry milk are typical of curves obtained for most hygroscopic materials. These desorption isotherms (Fig. 2) indicate a rapid increase in equilibrium values at relative humidities up to 20 per cent, followed by a slight increase up to 55 to 60 per cent RH. Beyond 60 per cent RH humidity, the isotherms indicate a significant increase in which the equilibrium moisture content appears to go to infinity at high humidities, at least in lower storage temperatures.

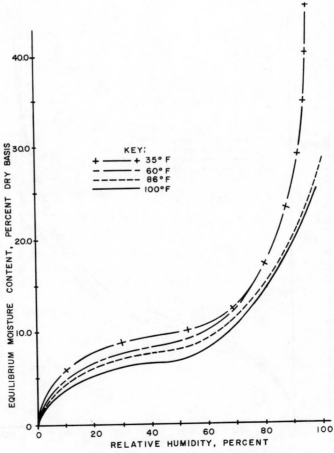

Fig. 3. Desorption equilibrium moisture content isotherms for dry milk with 26 per cent fat at various storage temperatures.

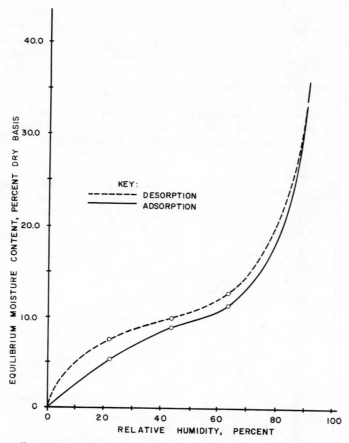

FIG. 4. Desorption and adsorption equilibrium moisture content isotherms for nonfat dry milk at 86°F, illustrating hysteresis.

Effect of Temperature

The effect of storage temperature on equilibrium moisture values and the resulting isotherms are revealed in Figs. 2 and 3. Results (Fig. 2) for low-heat nonfat dry milk reveal significant decreases in equilibrium values for a storage temperature of 100°F as compared to 35°F. The maximum difference of about 2.5 per cent moisture content appears to occur between 40 and 50 per cent RH. Figure 3 illustrates the effect of storage temperature on the equilibrium moisture values of a dry milk containing 26 per cent BF. Equilibrium values at 100°F are about 3.0 per cent moisture content lower than the values at 35°F for a rather wide humidity range between 25 and 50 per cent RH.

Hysteresis

The difference between equilibrium moisture contents obtained by desorption as compared to adsorption is called hysteresis (Fig. 4). These results illustrate that the desorption values are higher than the adsorption values, but to different degrees depending on relative humidity. The maximum difference between desorption and adsorption values of about 2.5 per cent moisture content occurs between 15 and 20 per cent RH. Troy and Sharp[10] proposed that part of the hysteresis in dry milk is due to the 5 per cent moisture content held by α-monohydrate lactose crystals. The results presented (Fig. 4) would tend to support this proposal. Since lactose crystallization does not start until the dry milk has over

5 per cent moisture content and the crystallization occurs at an optimum rate up to 8.5 per
cent, the lactose in dry milk at equilibrium
with relative humidities up to around 40 per
cent will remain in the "glass" state or, at
most, will be partially crystalline. However,
during the procedure used in obtaining
desorption equilibrium values, the dry milk
moisture content was increased well above
8.5 per cent providing ample moisture to allow
complete crystallization of all lactose present.

Therefore, it seems quite probable that part of
the hysteresis in dry milk is due to the 5 per
cent moisture content bound by the α-
monohydrate lactose crystal. This explanation
would hold in the low humidity range (0 to 40
per cent RH) where hysteresis was maximum.

Moisture Adsorption Rate

The moisture adsorption rates of the dry
milks were determined by exposure of a given
amount of sample $(3.0 \pm 0.05$ g) to a given

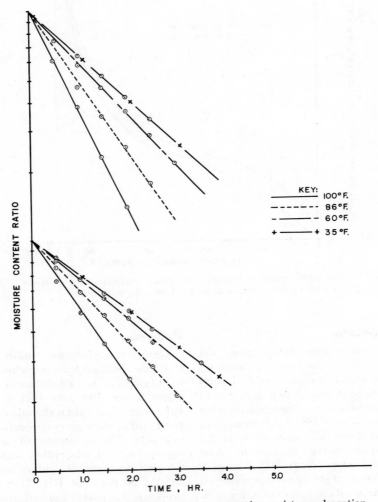

FIG. 5 (top). Adsorption rate curves comparing moisture adsorption
rates at different storage temperatures for dry milk with 26 per cent fat
(relative humidity range = 88.7 to 97.3 per cent).

FIG. 6 (bottom). Adsorption rate curves comparing moisture adsorption rates at different storage temperatures high-heat nonfat dry milk
(relative humidity range = 61.8 to 68.3 per cent).

temperature and humidity condition. The sample was weighed at ½-hour intervals for the first 5 hours of exposure to a given condition. The moisture content at each interval was calculated from the initial moisture content and weight gain.

The adsorption data were analyzed by using following equation derived from Newton's heating and cooling equation:

$$\frac{M - M_e}{M_0 - M_e} = e^{-k\theta} \qquad (1)$$

where

M = moisture content at any time, θ, % (dry basis)

M_e = equilibrium moisture content, % (dry basis)

M_0 = initial moisture content, % (dry basis)

k = adsorption rate constant, hour^{-1}

θ = time, hours

One modification made was to substitute the moisture content of the dry milk at 5 hours for the equilibrium moisture content. The value at 5 hours was usually the "peak" value on the adsorption curve, while the equilibrium value was much lower than many of the moisture contents on the adsorption curve, due to the effect of lactose crystallization. By plotting the moisture content ratio $(M - M_e)/(M_0 - M_e)$ vs time (θ) on semilogarithmic paper, a straight line with slope (k) is obtained.

Figures 5 and 6 illustrate typical adsorption rate curves obtained for nonfat dry milk and dry milk with fat at various temperatures. The adsorption rate constants (k) obtained from curves similar to those in Figs. 5 and 6 are presented in Table 1. In general, the results in Table 1 reveal that adsorption rate of dry milk increases with temperature and relative humidity.

Effect of Preheat Treatment

Desorption equilibrium moisture contents for nonfat dry milks with three different preheat treatments are plotted vs storage temperature in Fig. 7. In general, these results indicate a gradual decrease in equilibrium values with increasing storage temperature. Adsorption rate constants (k) for nonfat dry milks with three different preheat treatments are plotted vs storage temperature in Fig. 8. These results indicate a rather significant increase in adsorption rates with increasing storage temperature.

TABLE 1. ADSORPTION RATE CONSTANTS FOR VARIOUS DRY MILKS AT SEVERAL RELATIVE HUMIDITY AND TEMPERATURE CONDITIONS, 1/hr

RH (%)	High-heat Nonfat Dry Milk	Medium-heat Nonfat Dry Milk	Low-heat Nonfat Dry Milk	Low-heat Dry Milk with 13% Fat	Low-heat Dry Milk with 26% Fat
100°F					
88.7	0.722	0.768	0.862	0.903	0.961
61.8	0.728	0.742	0.817	0.856	0.875
49.0	0.712	0.751	0.800	0.826	0.868
86°F					
90.7	0.472	0.502	0.583	0.708	0.775
63.3	0.493	0.499	0.510	0.513	0.572
43.6	0.428	0.433	0.450	0.456	0.469
60°F					
94.1	0.409	0.388	0.385	0.481	0.507
66.0	0.392	0.392	0.324	0.425	0.480
44.0	0.422	0.403	0.327	0.382	0.554
35°F					
97.3	0.360	0.345	0.319	0.402	0.439
68.3	0.353	0.352	0.212	0.348	0.512
44.4	0.517	0.413	0.429	0.462	0.512

Both Figs. 7 and 8 indicate a rather unexpected relationship. At lower temperatures (35 and 60°F), the dry milk with high preheat treatment had higher equilibrium moisture contents and faster moisture adsorption rates. However, at higher temperature (86 and 100°F) the low preheat dry milk had higher equilibrium values and faster adsorption rates. In both Figs. 7 and 8, this reversal occurs between 65 and 75°F.

Since nonfat dry milks with high preheat treatments would be expected to adsorb more moisture at a faster rate, the results would tend to indicate that some reaction is occurring at the higher storage temperatures. One such reaction is browning, a chemical reaction between lactose and protein. Browning, as indicated earlier, becomes visible at storage temperatures above 68 to 70°F, in dry milks with moisture contents over 5.0 per cent. In addition, the reaction is accelerated by higher preheat treatments. Based on these observations, it seems possible that the browning reaction, occurring at accelerated rates in high-heat dry milk, may result in the high-heat dry milk having a lower equilibrium moisture content and slower moisture adsorption rates than low-heat dry milk. This reaction would occur at temperatures above 68 to 70°F, which corresponds to the storage temperatures where the unexpected behavior of the equilibrium moisture values and adsorption rates occurred.

Effect of Fat Content

Results (Fig. 9) reveal the significant effect of fat level in dry milk on the equilibrium moisture content. Dry milks with 13 per cent fat and 26 per cent fat were found to have significantly lower equilibrium values than nonfat dry milk at all humidities. The effect appears to be maximum between 20 and 50 per cent RH, with as much as 2.5 to 3 per cent moisture content difference between low and high fat levels. One proposal by Jenness and Patton[6] with respect to the effect of fat level

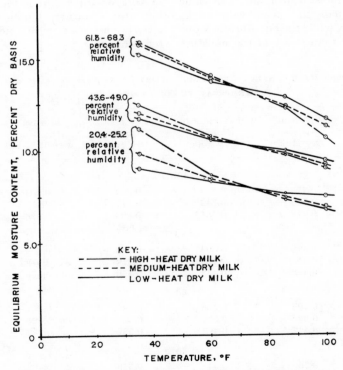

FIG. 7. Effect of storage temperature on desorption equilibrium moisture content of nonfat dry milks with different preheat treatments.

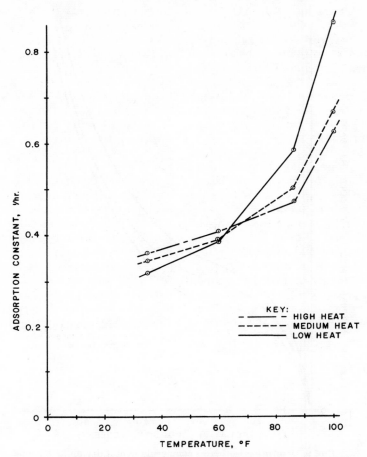

FIG. 8. Relationships between moisture adsorption rates and preheat treatments of nonfat dry milks as effected by storage temperature (relative humidity range = 88.7 to 97.3 per cent).

on equilibrium moisture content is that by calculation of the moisture content on a solids-not-fat basis, the same equilibrium values as indicated for nonfat dry milk in the same conditions are obtained.

In short, the fat in dry milk produces a "dilution" effect on the equilibrium moisture content. Results obtained in this study would tend to support this proposal.

Adsorption rate constants in Table 1 reveal the effect of fat level on moisture adsorption rate. In all conditions studied, increased fat level resulted in a significant increase in moisture adsorption rates. These results would indicate that although dry milks with fat have lower equilibrium moisture contents, they will adsorb moisture at significantly faster rates.

However, the increases in adsorption rates tend to become insignificant on a solids-not-fat basis.

Latent Heat Determinations

The method of Othmer[9] provides a direct method of calculating latent heats of vaporization for hygroscopic materials from equilibrium moisture data at various temperatures. The following expression derived from the Clapeyron equation, is used.

$$\log P = \frac{L}{L'} \log P' + C \qquad (2)$$

where

P = vapor pressure of reference (water)
P' = vapor pressure of material (dry milk)

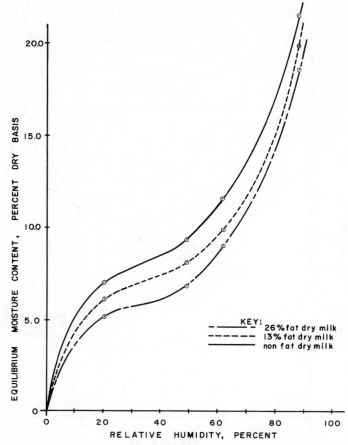

FIG. 9. Desorption isotherms comparing nonfat dry milk, dry milk with 13 per cent fat, and dry milk with 26 per cent fat at 100°F storage.

L = latent heat of reference
L' = latent heat of material
C = constant

By plotting the vapor pressure of dry milk at various moisture contents *vs* the vapor pressure of water on logarithmic coordinates, straight lines are obtained as indicated in Fig. 10. The slope of each of these lines is the ratio of the latent heat of the dry milk to the latent heat of water at a particular moisture content.

The latent heat ratios of the dry milks with various preheat treatments and fat levels at selected moisture contents are presented in Table 2. These results indicate obvious effects of preheat treatment and fat level. Higher preheat treatments result in an increase

in the latent heat ratio and therefore, in higher latent heats of vaporization of moisture from the product. Increases in fat level also result in increases of the latent heat ratio and latent heat of vaporization for the product at lower moisture contents (5.0 and 7.5 per cent). No particular relationships between fat level and latent heat ratios are indicated at higher moisture levels.

Of more significance is the effect of moisture content on the latent heat ratio. The results (Table 2) indicate a significant increase in the latent heat ratio for all dry milks as the moisture content decreases from 20.0 to 5 per cent. In each case, there is a moisture content interval in which the latent heat ratio makes a substantial increase. For nonfat dry milks this change occurred between 15 and 10 per cent

TABLE 2. LATENT HEAT RATIOS FOR VARIOUS DRY MILKS

Product	Moisture Content, Dry Basis (%)				
	5.0	7.5	10.0	15.0	20.0
High-heat nonfat	1.5329	1.4895	1.4241	1.0838	1.0367
Medium-heat nonfat	1.4082	1.3293	1.3141	1.0419	1.0262
Low-heat nonfat	1.2598	1.2378	1.2205	1.0315	1.0079
Low-heat 13% fat	1.3465	1.3386	1.1102	1.0551	1.0315
Low-heat 26% fat	1.3750	1.3648	1.0945	1.0315	1.0158

moisture content while for dry milks with fat, the change occurred between 10 and 7.5 per cent moisture. In any event, the latent heat ratios and resulting latent heats of vaporization increase by as much as 50 per cent as the moisture content level of 5 per cent is approached.

SUMMARY

The equilibrium moisture properties and moisture adsorption rates of dry milks with different preheat treatments and different fat levels have been investigated. These determinations have been conducted under various relative humidity and temperature conditions.

Dry milks demonstrate equilibrium isotherms and hysteresis effects which are typical for most hygroscopic materials. Higher storage temperatures resulted in lower equilibrium moisture contents in all cases.

Moisture adsorption rates of dry milks have been expressed in the form of adsorption rate constants. The adsorption rates increase with increasing relative humidity and storage temperature.

An interrelationship between preheat treatment of nonfat dry milk and storage temperature was demonstrated. At lower storage temperatures (below 65°F) high-heat nonfat dry milk had higher equilibrium moisture

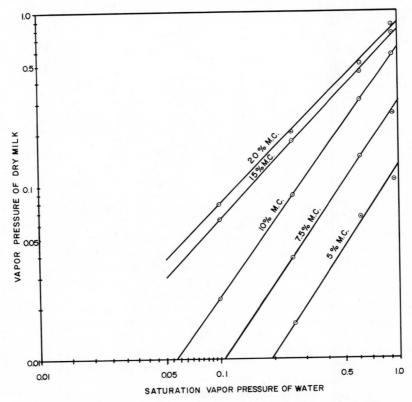

FIG. 10. Other plots of desorption data for high-heat nonfat dry milk at various moisture contents.

contents and faster moisture adsorption rates. At higher storage temperatures (above 75°F) the high-heat product had lower equilibrium values and slower adsorption rates. A possible relationship with the browning reaction is proposed.

Higher fat levels in dry milk resulted in lower equilibrium moisture contents. However, the higher fat levels increase the moisture adsorption rates.

Higher preheat treatment results in higher latent heat values whereas no consistent relationship with fat level was revealed. Significant increases in latent heats of vaporization have been demonstrated as moisture levels approach that of the dry product.

References

1. A.O.A.C. Methods of Analysis, "Vacuum Oven Moisture Determination," pp. 265, 1955.
2. Coulter, S. T., Jenness, R., and Crowe, L. K., "Some Changes in Dry Whole Milk During Storage," *J. Dairy Sci.*, **31**, 986 (1948).
3. Doob, H., Williman, A., and Sharp, P. F., "Influence of Moisture on Browning of Dried Whey and Milk," *Ind. Eng. Chem.*, **34**, 1460–8 (1942).
4. Heiss, R., "Chemical and Physical Changes in Dried Milk Products on Storage," *Deut. Lebensm. Rundschau*, **46**, 4–6 (1950), *Chem. Abs.* 7245g (1952).
5. Hollender, H. A., and Tracy, P. H., "The Keeping Quality of Powdered Whole Milk," *J. Dairy Sci.*, **25**, 249 (1942).
6. Jenness, R., and Patton, S., "Principles of Dairy Chemistry," New York, John Wiley & Sons, Inc., 1959.
7. Lampitt, L. H., and Bushill, J. H., "The Physicochemical Constitution of Milk Powder," *Analyst*, **56**, 178–94 (1931).
8. M.I.F. Laboratory Manual, "Moisture Determination by the Toluol Distillation Method," pp. 240–241 (1949).
9. Othmer, D. F., "Correlating Vapor Pressure and Latent Heat Data," *Ind. Eng. Chem.*, **32**, 841–46 (1940).
10. Troy, H. C., and Sharp, P. F., "α- and β-lactose in Some Milk Products," *J. Dairy Sci.*, **13**, 140–157 (1930).

23. The Distribution of Moisture in Butter

J. H. PRENTICE

National Institute for Research in Dairying, Shinfield, England

ABSTRACT

Butter is basically almost a perfect emulsion. About 15 per cent by volume is aqueous, dispersed phase; the remainder is a semisolid fatty phase. While nearly all the moisture is dispersed in small droplets, there also exist small undispersed inclusions or continuous channels. It has been shown that the incidence of these inclusions has considerable bearing on the keeping quality of the butter. The total moisture content is also important economically, particularly in view of legal requirements in many countries.

The two phases in butter have dissimilar electrical properties. This difference has been utilized in studying the moisture distribution. The conductivity of butter provides an assessment of the undispersed moisture, if certain precautions are taken in sampling and in making the measurements. Dielectric theory predicts a dependence of the permittivity of an emulsion on the volume fraction of the dispersed phase. With butter there is considerable divergence between theory and experiment. This divergence may be due to distortion of the droplets, or to an uneven distribution of electrolyte amongst the droplets. It is suggested that both causes may operate simultaneously.

Good butter, from the point of view of many of its physical properties, may be considered as an almost perfect emulsion. The continuous phase, which amounts to rather more than 80 per cent of the whole consists of the semisolid butterfat; the dispersed phase, about 15 per cent by volume, is water. The remaining constituents, some 3 or 4 per cent of the total are mainly salts, which are dissolved in the water, and proteins which also serve as emulsifying agents. As far as the overall physical picture is concerned, these lesser constituents are relatively unimportant.

There are two aspects of the moisture distribution which are of practical importance. It has already been mentioned that the emulsion is not quite perfect. Although almost all the water is dispersed as droplets, there is nearly always a very small quantity which exists in the form of minute continuous channels through the butter.[1, 2] Figure 1(a) shows in a diagrammatic form the structure of an ideal butter, a perfect dispersion, in which all the water droplets are discrete and randomly distributed, whilst Fig. 1(b) shows in an exaggerated manner the structure usually encountered in practice in which there exist some continuous channels through the butter and a tendency for the individual droplets to align themselves as a result of the mechanical working of the butter during manufacture or subsequently during printing. The extent of the defect, for the existence of these channels may be regarded as a defect in the emulsion, is of great practical importance from the point of view of the keeping quality of the butter.[3] Provided that the butter has been produced under hygienic conditions, and this is almost universally the case nowadays, one of the principal ways in which it may deteriorate during storage is by the growth of water-borne bacteria.[4, 5] Any bacteria can only grow while a supply of nutriment is available. The supply of nutriment in a small droplet is strictly limited, and if that droplet is completely isolated by an impervious wall of fat

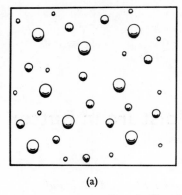
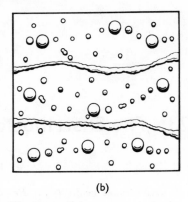

(a)   (b)

FIG. 1. Structure of butter (diagrammatic).

around it, no further nutriment may reach it, and the bacterial growth must be necessarily limited accordingly. It will be apparent then that a butter which is a perfect emulsion may be expected to be of good quality. In a defective part of the emulsion, however, a supply of nutriment may reach the bacteria by way of the continuous channels of moisture, and they will multiply continuously. Butter containing such continuous channels may thus be expected to deteriorate rapidly. It will follow that in any samples of butter which are slightly imperfect emulsions, the more gross the defect of the emulsion, by way of both the size and the frequency of these continuous channels the more rapidly the butter may be expected to deteriorate through bacterial action.

The conventional method for detecting the presence of these defects is by examining a freshly cut surface of butter visually. For example, the butter grader when grading bulk butter takes a boring from the block and examines both the clean surface of the boring and the back of the borer. The presence of small droplets of water on either surface indicates the existence of free moisture, as the continuous water channels are termed. Only the larger defects are shown up in this way. A somewhat more sensitive test may be made by the use of indicator papers.[6] The paper is pressed carefully upon a freshly cut surface of the butter, and spots appear wherever there is free moisture. From the size and abundance of the spots, a qualitative estimate of the defectiveness of the emulsion may be made. Bromophenol blue is commonly used as the indicator. It is golden yellow when prepared

from acid solution and turns to a deep blue when it comes into contact with water of any pH value likely to be encountered in butter.

While these subjective methods are generally adequate to serve as a rejection test for poorly made butter, they do not give more than a rough estimate at best of the extent of the imperfection, and fail entirely to distinguish those which have only small channels of free moisture. Fortunately there exists, in principle at least, a simple means of measuring even small traces of free moisture. The fats in butter, being mainly triglycerides of the fatty acids, are all fairly good electrical insulators, while the water, by reason of the salts dissolved in it, is a good electrolytic conductor. If, then, a sample of butter is placed in an electric field, since the continuous phase is an insulator no conduction will take place if the emulsion is perfect. On the other hand, any continuous channels of electrolyte will conduct, and the effect of parallel channels will be additive. It follows that the measurement of the conductivity of the butter is an indication of the extent of the free moisture present. If the conductivity of the water is known, either by calculation from the complete analysis of the butter or by direct measurement, a simple calculation converts the conductivity of the sample into an index of the defectiveness of the emulsion. Even with unsalted butter, the method is effective because although no salt has been added to the butter during the processes of manufacture, the serum of the original milk from which it was made would have contained sufficient salts to make it a conductor.

In practice there are a few precautions which

must be taken to ensure that the result is reliable. In the first place, it is very important that the butter suffers no mechanical damage during sampling. With a weak-bodied butter it is very easy to break some of the fat walls separating neighbouring globules, allowing them to coalesce and thereby to augment the number of continuous channels already existing. In order to minimize the probability of mechanical damage during sampling, a special cell has been developed.[7] Figure 2 shows this cell with the outer sleeve removed to enable the disposition of the electrodes and the butter sample to be seen. In this cell the electrodes are concentric cylinders; the outer one serves both as a borer to obtain the sample from the bulk or the butter print and as the sample holder, so that it is only necessary to take a boring before making a measurement. The risk of damage to the structure is greatest when removing the sample from the borer. When using this cell this takes place after the measurement has been made. The concentric cell has two other advantages apart from this. Any errors which might arise as a result of slight misalignment upon reassembling the

cell after demounting are kept to a minimum by this configuration; also a high value of cell constant is obtainable with a comparatively small quantity of sample.

The resistance of a centimeter cube of well-made butter may be of the order of hundreds of megohms or higher. Such a resistance is not easy to measure accurately, and here is seen the importance of having a measuring cell with a high constant. Strictly, it is the resistance to direct current which is required; however in practice, since the conduction is electrolytic, it is necessary to use alternating current methods. Even if butter were a perfect emulsion, without any free moisture, it would not be a perfect dielectric. There would still be a residual dielectric loss due to losses in the fats and the presence of other ingredients. At any particular frequency, the result of this dielectric loss will appear in the measurement as an equivalent resistance which will be in parallel with the true resistance to be measured causing the measured value to be artificially low. Since this effect varies with the frequency, it is evidently desirable to keep the frequency as low as possible. On the other hand, the lower the frequency, the greater is the risk of errors due to polarization at the electrodes and it is evident that some compromise is necessary. It has been found in practice that a reasonable compromise, coupled with simplicity in the design of the equipment, is to use alternating current of supply mains frequency (50 cps in the United Kingdom). The field strength, too, is important. If the sample is placed in too strong a field, dielectric breakdown may occur in some of the thinner fat layers separating the water droplets, causing them to rupture, allowing them to coalesce, and hence augmenting the continuous channels.

In a good sample of butter, the amount of moisture that exists as free moisture may well be less than 1 ppm; even in a poor sample of butter it is unlikely to be as much as one per cent. Table 1 gives the measured values obtained in one experiment, when two bulk butters, both of acceptable quality, were blended together. In this particular example it may be seen that both the original butters, though acceptable by normal standards, contained measurable quantities of free moisture. The insufficiently blended butter contained more free moisture, sufficient in fact to be

Fig. 2. Butter conductivity cell.

TABLE 1. FREE MOISTURE IN SOME BUTTERS

Butter	Resistivity (MΩ-cm)	Total Water (%)	Free Moisture (ppm)
Sweet cream	0.67	14.1	100
Ripened cream	1.07	13.3	140
Insufficiently blended	0.12	14.7	550
Fully blended	>100	15.2	<0.5

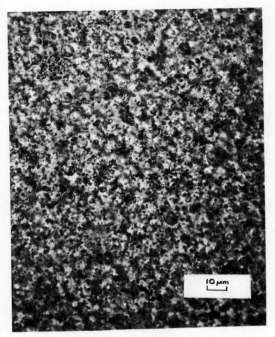

observed by the usual subjective tests. It was possible in this instance to continue the blending process, and hence the redistribution of the moisture, until such a good dispersion had been obtained that free moisture was undetectable even by the electrical technique. The relation between the electrical resistance, and hence the amount of free moisture in some butters, and the length of storage before their flavors became unacceptable to a panel of observers is shown in Fig. 3. In this experiment, one butter was still of acceptable quality when the experiment was abandoned at the end of ten weeks; this was a blended butter.[1]

It appears, then, that normally well over 99 per cent of the water in butter exists as discrete droplets of small size. These droplets are essentially spherical, and their size and size distri-

FIG. 4. Photomicrograph of butter.

bution may readily be seen by microscopic examination. A typical photomicrograph is shown in Fig. 4, where the water droplets are seen as spheres against a mottled background of the fat. Although the slide was prepared by pressing a smear of butter into a thin film between the slide and cover glass, the droplets have retained their spherical shape with very few exceptions, and in this particular instance no continuous channels can be seen. The size distribution varies with the type of butter and with the method of manufacture. In ordinary churned butter there is a more or less random distribution of sizes from a few microns up to about 30 μ. In some butter made by continuous process, such as the Alfa process, the distribution is more uniform and the droplet size is of the order of 5 μ.[8]

From the practical point of view, however, the size distribution of the droplets is relatively unimportant. More important is the total quantity of water present. An exact determination of this is necessary to comply with the legal requirements in many countries. The problem of determining the total moisture rapidly by means of a direct physical measurement has not yet been satisfactorily solved.

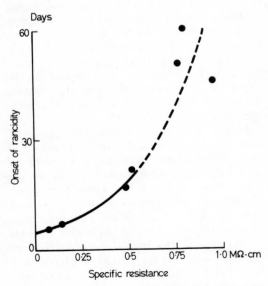

FIG. 3. Relation between keeping quality and specific resistance of butter.

The only method which is sufficiently accurate, at present, is the laborious method of heating to dryness.

Theoretically butter as an emulsion would be expected to show characteristic dielectric properties. According to dielectric theory,[9, 10] a dispersion of conducting spheres in a non-conducting medium should give rise to a single absorption peak, whose height depends only upon the volume fraction of conducting spheres present and whose frequency of maximum absorption depends upon the temperature and the conductivity of the material of the spheres. For a normal salted butter this peak should occur in the neighborhood of 2 to 3 Gc/sec at room temperature, and in the Mc/sec region for an unsalted butter. As a corollary, the dielectric constant measured at low frequency should exceed that measured at high frequency by an amount proportional to the moisture content. Another corollary of the Maxwell-Wagner theory[9] is that the equation connecting the real and imaginary components of the complex permittivity, obtained by eliminating the frequency, should be a semicircle with its center on the axis midway between the high- and low-frequency dielectric constants.[11] In practice, the curve obtained with butter is a shallow arc of a circle, showing that there is not a single relaxation frequency, but a distribution of them. This may arise as a result of absorption due to asphericity of the water globules[12] or as a result of a distribution of the conductivities of the droplets. It is not unlikely that both effects are simultaneously present. The presence of some elongated droplets or incomplete continuous channels is to be expected, and only a small incidence of these is required to increase the low-frequency absorption considerably. However, microscopic examination of butter shows very little evidence of appreciable departure from sphericity and insufficient incidence of elongated droplets to account for the observed broadening of the absorption band. There remains the possibility that the salt is not distributed uniformly among the individual water droplets. This has yet to be investigated.

References

1. Prentice, J. H., "A Note on the Electrical Resistance and the Keeping Quality of Butter," *J. Dairy Res.*, **20**, 327 (1953).
2. von Gavel, L., "Die Butterstruktur auf Grund von Beobachtungen an Mikrotomschnitten," *Z. Lebensm.-Untersuch Forsch.*, **104**, 1 (1956).
3. Prentice, J. H., "Some Observations on the Electrical Properties and Consumer Quality of Butter," *Intern. Dairy Congr. Proc.*, 13th, **2**, 727 (1953).
4. Long, H. F., and Hammer, B. W., "Effect of Moisture Dispersion in Butter on Growth of Bacteria," *Iowa Agr. Exp. Sta. Res. Bull.*, **246** (1938).
5. Hiscox, E., and House, A. G., "Bacteriological Aspects of the Reworking and Blending of Stored Butter," *J. Dairy. Res.*, **18**, 291 (1951).
6. Knudsen, S., and Sörensen, A., "Uber eine Methode zur Beurteilung der Grösse der Wassertröpfehen in Butter," *Fette Seifen* **45**, 669 (1938).
7. Prentice, J. H., "A Test Cell for the Measurement of the Conductivity of Butter and Margarine," *J. Sci. Instr.*, **31**, 29 (1954).
8. King, N., and Fritz, W., "Das Physikalische Bild der Butter," *Milchwissenschaft*, **3**, 102 (1948).
9. Wagner, K. W., "Erklärung der dielektrischen Nachwirkungsvorgänge auf Grund Maxwellscher Vorstellungen," *Arch. Elektrotech.*, **11**, 371 (1914).
10. Hanai, T., "Dielectric Theory on the Interfacial Polarization for Two-Phase Mixtures," *Bull. Inst. Chem. Res. Kyoto. Univ.*, **39**, 341 (1961).
11. Cole, K. S., and Cole, R. H., "Dispersion and Absorption in Dielectrics," *J. Chem. Phys.*, **9**, 341 (1941).
12. Sillars, R. W., "The Properties of a Dielectric Containing Semiconducting Particles of Various Shapes," *J. Inst. Elec. Engrs.*, **80**, 378 (1937).

24. Relation of Humidity to Lactation and Some Related Physiological Responses of Dairy Cattle

LeRoy Hahn

Agricultural Research Service, U.S. Department of Agriculture

AND

Milton D. Shanklin and H. D. Johnson

University of Missouri, Columbia, Missouri

ABSTRACT

The physiological reactions of dairy cattle to hot-dry and hot-humid conditions generally result in lower milk production and slower growth rates than in less severe climates. Constant-condition studies at the Climatic Laboratory (located at the University of Missouri) over the past 15 years have shown the degree to which adverse humidity and temperature conditions can affect lactating dairy cows.

At temperatures above 78° F, increased humidity resulted in decreased milk production. The level of humidity began to depress evaporative cooling, causing an increase in body temperature, at about 75° F in European cattle. Above 80° F, most temperature-humidity combinations caused significant decreases in TDN and water consumption. Other measured responses affected by the level of humidity at high temperatures were respiration rate, pulmonary ventilation rate, skin and hair surface temperatures, and outer-surface and respiratory vaporization. At temperatures of 65° F and below (to 12° F), the level of humidity had very little effect on milk production.

The degree of response of individual animals to humidity at temperatures above 75° F is conditioned by level of production or genetic potential and by heat tolerance. The low heat tolerance of cows in general is associated with their relatively high heat production and low moisture vaporization at temperature-humidity conditions above 75° F.

BACKGROUND

The physiological adjustments of dairy cattle to changes in environmental conditions are of major importance. The structures industry requires quantitative data on moisture vaporization and heat production of animals under various environmental conditions for use in designing ventilating and air-conditioning systems. Physiologists examine the data to obtain information on temperature-regulating mechanisms evolved in different species under different conditions. Dairymen need information on the selection of animals for different climatic regions based on heat or cold tolerance, and on the most desirable and economical hot- or cold-weather shelter.

Physiological adjustments due to the climatic environment reflect seasonal and diurnal changes in humidity, temperature, wind, thermal radiation, barometric pressure, and rainfall. Quantitative change in these factors is also important, as change itself stimulates (or depresses) the body, its' nerves, glands and involved temperature-regulating mechanisms. Because of the interactions of these environmental components, it is impossible under field conditions to evaluate the effects of change in a single component.

The Psychroenergetic Laboratory, commonly called the Climatic Laboratory, was constructed to house animals under controlled conditions of the primary climatic factors of

190

humidity, temperature, wind and radiation. Cooperative research is conducted by the Missouri Agricultural Experiment Station and the U.S. Department of Agriculture in this laboratory, located on the University of Missouri campus, Columbia, Missouri. The outside dimensions of the laboratory are 40' × 60'; inside are two independently controlled test rooms, each 26' × 18' × 9'. A mixture of fresh and recirculated air is moved through each chamber at about 45 fpm (½ mph). The air, interior walls, ceiling and floor have approximately the same temperature. Six cows can be housed in each room in 4-ft wide standard stalls, complete with stanchions, gutters and mangers. Cows are confined throughout each test. Feed consists of standard grain rations of the University of Missouri dairy herds, with ad-lib feeding of alfalfa hay. Machine milking is used.

Temperature and humidity inside the rooms are regulated by circulation of air passing through air-conditioning units located outside the chambers. For the entire period of operation, the control of humidity has been maintained by hygroscopic animal membrane elements. What is found wanting in this element in terms of sensitivity, response time and stability is more than compensated for by the rugged simplicity of its nonelectronic construction. Under steady-state conditions, a competent technician can hold a desired relative humidity to within ± 2 per cent with membrane element control—a degree of control thought satisfactory for the environmental studies made to date.

The hair element, in the form of recording hygrographs, has been used for auxilary humidity measurement in each test room continuously from the beginning. This was the principal measuring device at below-freezing temperatures, supplemented with frequent sling psychrometer readings. At the time the laboratory opened, the principal above-freezing humidity measuring element was an iron-constantan thermopile kept wet by a wick suspended in a constant-level water reservoir. As with all constant-feed wet-bulb elements, these proved to be inordinately troublesome, and in 1950 they were replaced with the Foxboro "Dewcel", an element measuring the dew point of a saturated lithium chloride solution. This equipment or, rather, its descendant is still in use today, not so much because it is perfect, but because it is as rugged and dependable as any equipment available today. When used continuously in a dirty air stream contaminated with various organic salts, the sensing elements do well to last a year, but their performance characteristics remain stable or virtually so, for the life of the element. Since the primary measurement made by the "Dewcel" is temperature, periodic calibrations may be made against a certified thermometer, and reliance on the sling psychrometer with all of its inherent error sources is unnecessary.

Aside from the measurement and control of humidity in the two test rooms, measurement of evaporative heat loss by the test animals has created additional problems in humidity measurement, the solutions of which have undergone evolutionary change since the laboratory first opened.

Respiratory vaporization data, a by-product of the open-circuit respiratory gas analysis method employed by Brody since 1928, initially was a gravimetric measure, depending upon the moisture in the exhaled air being absorbed by a hygroscopic drying agent, anhydrous calcium sulfate, which, over a period of time, gained weight according to the amount of water absorbed. This method required, of course, a twin system through which air moved at an identical rate, to account for ambient humidity. A comparison of the gravimetric method with wet- and dry-bulb, or psychrometric, techniques showed excellent agreement. Consequently, with the introduction of the lithium chloride dew-point technique of humidity measurement, the gravimetric system was abandoned in its favor and is still in use today.

The total insensible heat loss of an animal, i.e. respiratory vaporization plus surface vaporization, was also initially measured gravimetrically. In this case, the total weight loss of an animal over a period of time was measured by holding it on a platform scale modified to measure to the least 12.5 g and to record at fixed time intervals. From the total weight loss was subtracted the metabolic weight loss, or net gaseous exchange, leaving a balance assumed to be the moisture vaporized, or total insensible heat loss. The net gaseous exchange was determined while the animal was on the scale platform by open-circuit analysis. This circuitous method of measuring total insensible heat loss was, as might be expected, fraught with possible sources of error. A more direct approach was devised, based on the inclusion of the test animal in a plastic tent through which a measured flow of air collected the vaporized moisture as determined by "Dewcels" placed at inlet and outlet ports. This method, still in use, is described in detail in a succeeding paper on the program by its creator, Dr. Yeck, who also discusses other techniques of measuring vapor losses from farm livestock.

A total of 24 long-term tests have been completed in the laboratory during the 15 years it has been in operation. In each of these tests, engineers and physiologists have co-operated to obtain information needed for gaining insight into the facts and mechanisms relating climate to productivity and for over-coming environmental disadvantages to productivity where they exist.

Simply, dairy cows may be considered as converters of feed into milk. For high-producing cows, the efficiency of energy conversion of digestible nutrients into milk is on the order of 25 to 30 per cent. Most of the remaining nutrient energy is given off as waste heat. For body temperature to remain normal, this heat must be dissipated by evaporative (moisture vaporization) and non-evaporative (convection, radiation, conduction) cooling. At moderate temperatures, most of the heat dissipated is by nonevaporative cooling. When the environmental temperature equals or exceeds the surface temperature of the animal, body heat is dissipated almost exclusively by evaporative cooling, and thus, moisture vaporized from the respiratory tract and skin becomes the most important method of heat dissipation. The ability to withstand high temperatures is a function of heat production and of the ability to produce surface moisture for vaporization, which varies considerably among animals. Related factors involved in heat tolerance are body weight, body form, feed consumption, milk production, and acclimation. Tropically evolved cattle, for instance, have a greater surface area for heat dissipation and low productivity (with correspondingly low heat production).

Productivity is a function of many inter-related factors. The productive processes of homeotherms require a relatively fixed internal body temperature. The reactions of cattle to moderate climatic changes are generally of a compensatory nature tending to maintain or restore thermal balance. Increases of only a degree or two above normal body temperature tend to lower productivity, and persistent unfavorable climatic conditions which exceed the limits of physiological compensation may cause deterioration or death. The environmental temperature* required to produce these changes in body temperature depends on the thermoregulatory capacities of the individual animals and breeds.

How should the effects of climatic factors on cows be estimated? For man, the air-conditioning engineer has developed a "comfort zone," within which most humans are comfortable. This zone is related to the physiologists' zone of thermoneutrality at which heat production is lowest (where body temperature is maintained normal without resorting to the body's chemical thermo-regulative devices). For cows, then, the comfort zone might be estimated from heat production under various environmental conditions, as well as milk production, feed consumption, rectal temperature, respiration rate, pulse rate and thryoid activity.

Investigations into the effects of continuous exposures to controlled humidity and other primary climatic factors on milk production of dairy cows have been conducted almost exclusively at the Climatic Laboratory. For this reason, the ensuing discussion will be of results obtained during tests in the laboratory. Detailed references are omitted, as material was drawn from practically all the Environmental Physiology and Shelter Engineering series of bulletins reporting work from the laboratory. A complete listing of the bulletins is included in the References.

---

* The environmental "temperature" here referred to is actually the "physiologically-effective temperature," or the reaction of the animal body to a combination of all meteorological factors, as contrasted to the physical, or dry-bulb, temperature measured by a thermometer. This effective temperature concept has been used for years by air-conditioning engineers in providing environments within structures for human occupancy.

ORIENTATION

The theoretical effect of humidity* is that the rate of moisture vaporization from the body surface to the environment is proportional to the difference in vapor pressure (the lower the humidity of the environment, the lower is its vapor pressure and the greater is the vaporization rate from the animal). However, the physiological effects of humidity differ at

* Humidity refers to water vapor in the given air. Several forms of expressing humidity are commonly used: (1) absolute humidity—weight of water vapor per unit volume of air; (2) specific humidity—weight of water vapor per unit weight of dry air; (3) relative humidity—the percentage ratio of water vapor in the air compared to the amount at saturation for the given temperature and pressure; (4) vapor pressure of the moisture in the air; and (5) dew point —the temperature at which water vapor condenses. In this paper, relative humidity is normally used because of the uniformly wide range at low and high temperatures (not obtainable with absolute humidity or vapor pressure) and also because it is the most widely used and understood index of humidity. The use of relative humidity does not imply that physiological reactions can be related only to this measure of humidity.

high and low temperatures, for vapor pressure changes insignificantly at 0°F when the relative humidity changes by 100 per cent. At 100°F, a 100 per cent change in relative humidity changes vapor pressure by 0.94 lb/in.^{2} (1.91 in. Hg).

In man, the level of humidity in the air greatly affects the feeling of comfort in hot weather by depressing the vaporization rate of outer-surface moisture (sweat), and this effect increases with increasing temperature. In slightly sweating cattle, however, evaporative cooling appears to be limited more by lack of outer-surface moisture for vaporization than by an excessive level of humidity.

PROCEDURE AND RESULTS

Three overall series of tests were run involving humidity and temperature as primary factors. In the first series, humidity was held relatively constant (between 50 and 65 per cent), and temperatures were varied according to a selected schedule, while in the second series, humidity was varied at each of

TABLE 1. ENVIRONMENTAL SCHEDULES DURING TEMPERATURE-HUMIDITY AND HUMIDITY-TEMPERATURE TESTS ON DAIRY CATTLE, CLIMATIC LABORATORY

Test No.	Temperatures Used (°F)	Humidities Used (%)	Test Animals
1	50 to 105 (5–10° increments)	55–70	6 Jersey and 6 Holstein (all lactating except 2 Holstein)
2	5 to 95 (5–10° increments)	50–75	As in test 1
3	50 to 105 (5–10° increments)	60–75	4 Jersey, 4 Holstein, 4 Brahman (all lactating except 1 Brahman)
4	50 to 5 (10° increments)	55–70	As in test 3 (except both Brahman dry)
5	40 to 105 (5–10° increments)	50–75	3 lactating Brown Swiss, 3 dry Brahman
6	50 to 10 (10° increments)	High, medium and low*	6 Jersey, 6 Holstein (all lactating)
7	65 to 100 (5–10° increments)	High, medium and low*	3 Holstein, 4 Jersey, 3 Brown Swiss and 2 Brahman (all lactating except 2 Jersey and 2 Brahman)
17	65	50	20 lactating Holstein†
	80	30, 50, 80	
	90	20, 40, 50	
18	65	50	20 lactating Holstein
	75	90	
	85	50, 70	
	90, 95	25	

* The ranges of relative humidity covered by each classification were high, 75 to 90% (high at 100°F was 50 to 65%); medium, 55 to 70%; and low, 35 to 50% (low at 12 and 15°F was 60 to 65%).

† Twenty cows were involved due to the experimental design used to determine effects of stage of lactation. Only 12 cows were in the laboratory at a given time.

several constant-temperature levels. The third series was similar to the second, but it was designed to improve information concerning the effect of humidity at high temperatures. During each series, thermal radiation was held constant at a level of 5 Btu/hour-ft² and wind velocity was held constant at a rate of 45 fpm.

The general scheme of testing is outlined in Table 1. Experimental design during tests 1 to 4 involved comparing one group of animals exposed to the test environment to a similar group simultaneously exposed to a standard constant-environment of 50°F and 65 per cent R.H. In the remaining tests, each animal was used as its own control by measuring the change shown in each animal. Two-week test periods were generally used, except at extreme conditions which the cows were unable to withstand.

The zone of thermoneutrality as indicated by minimum levels of heat production* and pulse rate was between 40 and 60°F. These responses increased below and immediately above this range; above 70 or 80°F, they decreased. Total heat load† showed a like decrease as air temperatures increased from 65 to 90°F. The ratio of latent heat, or evaporative cooling, to total heat increases almost exponentially with increasing air temperature up to 85°F, regardless of breed, weight and level of production (Fig. 1). The rise in this

* Heat production rate by the animal was computed from the rate of oxygen consumption and carbon dioxide production as measured by an open-circuit mask method.

† Total heat load is the heat dissipated within the test room and picked up by the air-conditioning system (deductions were made for the heat added by lamps, equipment and personnel, and with deductions or additions for the heat gained and lost from the building).

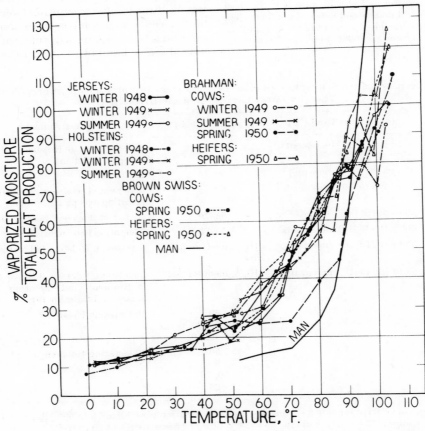

Fig. 1. Ratios of evaporative cooling to total heat production for cattle and man as a function of temperature.[14]

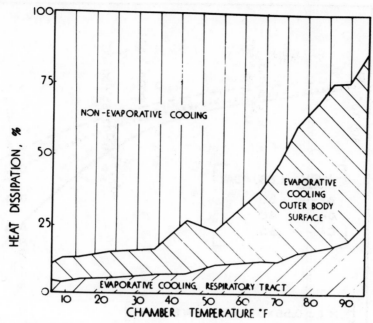

FIG. 2. Heat dissipation by three categories for Holstein and Jersey cows (averaged) as a function of temperature.[10]

ratio is somewhat different in man (a profusely sweating species) than in cattle (a slightly sweating species). Humidity apparently had no effect on total heat load at temperatures below 65°F. Increased humidity, within the range of 20 to 80 per cent, decreased total heat and vapor dissipation for a given temperature above 75°F. Using a regression line of pooled data from 12 lactating Holstein cows, total heat and vapor dissipation values as given in Table 2 were obtained.

TABLE 2. TOTAL HEAT AND VAPOR DISSIPATION WITHIN TEST ROOMS (CORRECTED FOR EXTRANEOUS HEAT AND VAPOR GAINED OR LOST FROM MECHANICAL EQUIPMENT, LAMPS AND PERSONNEL), AVERAGE FOR 12 LACTATING HOLSTEIN COWS

Room Environment	Total Heat Dissipation (Btu/hour/ 1000 lb. body wt)	Total Vapor Dissipation (lb/hour/ 1000 lb. body wt)
80°F; 30% RH	2980	2.33
50	2840	2.10
80	2629	1.74
90°F; 20% RH	2784	2.67
50	2624	2.57

Of the animal heat production, the proportion dissipated by respiratory vaporization ranged from 4 per cent at 5°F environmental temperature to 15 to 30 per cent at 95°F (Fig. 2). Skin surface vaporization accounted for 5 to 10 per cent at 5°F up to 40 to 70 per cent at 80 to 95°F temperature. Between 50 and 90°F, surface vaporization quadrupled, with a maximum of 400 cal/hour for Jerseys and 500 cal/hour for Holsteins. At the lowest temperatures, the weight of moisture vaporized was 60 to 65 per cent of the total insensible weight loss; at the higher temperatures, insensible weight loss was essentially identical to the weight of vaporized moisture (linear change). High levels of humidity (in the range of 75 to 90 per cent) depressed surface vaporization at temperatures between 75 and 100°F; respiratory vaporization rates were also depressed to a lesser extent. The effects of high humidity at 95° and 100°F on vaporization rates were less on Jerseys than on the larger and higher producing Brown Swiss and Holsteins. The European cattle appeared to have dissipated a smaller proportion of their total heat by evaporative cooling at high temperatures (and particularly at high relative

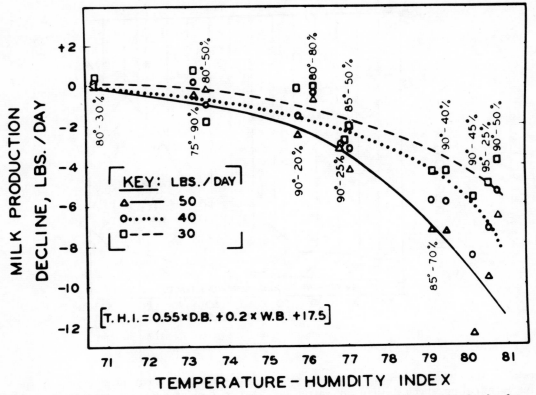

Fig. 3. Milk production decline as related to the temperature-humidity index for three levels of production.[59]

humidity levels) than tropically evolved Brahman cows.

Milk production of Holstein cows was decreased by all temperature and humidity conditions of 75°F and higher, although decreases at 75°F, 90 per cent RH and 90°F, 20 per cent RH were not significant. Production decline with increasing environmental temperature was more pronounced for Holstein than for Jersey cows. The recovery in production following return to a 65°F condition is quite marked. Temperature-humidity conditions combined on the basis of the U.S. Weather Bureau Temperature-Humidity-Index* (THI) were found to be suitable for predicting the decline in milk production from the normal level at 65°F (based on Holstein cows). Figure 3 shows average decline as a function of THI for 3 levels of milk production.

* THI = 0.55 (DB) + 0.2 (DP) + 17.5, where DB = dry-bulb temperature and DP = dew-point temperature for the given air.

Above THI values of about 74, averages for all cows indicated a decrease in milk production; significant declines occurred in most cows at all THI values above 79. The wet-bulb temperature was also an adequate measure of humidity for predicting production declines, as shown in Fig. 4 for two levels of production.

The environmental temperature above which rectal temperature increased was 70°F for Holstein cows, 75°F for the Jersey, 80°F for the Brown Swiss, and 95°F for the Brahman. Between 75 and 85°F, rectal temperature increased more at high than low humidity in all cows except the Brahmans. Substantial differences occurred in rectal temperatures of all cows between high and low humidity at 95 and 100°F. At moderate humidity (55 per cent), an environmental temperature of 105°F increased rectal temperatures of Jersey cows to 106.7°F and of Holstein cows to over 108°F. Figure 5 relates the departure of rectal

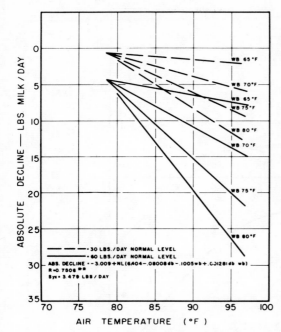

FIG. 4. Milk production decline as a function of dry-bulb temperature for four wet-bulb temperatures and two production levels.[71]

temperature from "normal" to the Temperature-Humidity Index for Holstein cows. A gradual increase begins at a THI value of about 73.

Significant decreases in TDN consumption by Holstein cows occurred above 80°F for all temperature-humidity combinations except 90°F, 20 per cent RH. Above a THI value of 77 (see Fig. 5), obvious decreases in TDN and water consumption began to occur. Feed consumption declines for Holsteins were sharper than for Jerseys, thus paralleling milk production declines. Also paralleling milk production is the rapid recovery to the normal level of feed consumption following return to a 65°F condition.

Skin and hair surface temperatures vary markedly with temperature; at 0°F ambient temperature, hair surface temperature is about 50°F and skin temperature about 75 to 80°F for Jerseys and Holsteins, while at 103°F ambient temperature, skin and hair temperatures are also 103°F. Skin and hair surface temperatures are lower at low humidity for air temperatures above 75°F.

Various other responses were affected by temperature and humidity conditions. Respiration rate at 100°F was 4 to 5 times more rapid than at 50°F. High humidity caused higher respiration rates than low humidity at 85 to 100°F for Jersey, Holstein and Brown Swiss cows, and from 95 to 100°F for Brahman cattle. The pulmonary ventilation rate increased 2 to 3 times during the ambient temperature change from 50 to 100°F. It was also greater at high than low humidity at temperatures from 85 to 100°F, although quite variable among cows. Pulse rate was little affected by changes in humidity at any temperature level. Blood composition was not significantly changed by temperatures between 0 and 65°F. Between 65 and 105°F, at moderate humidities, the creatinine level was doubled, and the carbon dioxide-combining capacity, ascorbic acid and cholesterol were halved. A respiratory alkalosis develops due to the decline in CO_2-combining capacity at ambient temperatures exceeding 85°F. Table 3 lists upper critical temperatures and the direction of change with changing temperatures of the physiological responses for the various breeds.

All the preceding results cover responses at constant conditions, which eliminated various complicating factors encountered under field conditions. However, as it is also important to interpret the results for application to naturally varying environments, two tests, each involving 6 Holstein and 6 Jersey lactating cows, were conducted using diurnal temperature combinations of 10 to 40°F, 40 to 70°F, 70 to 100°F, 40 to 110°F, 50 to 110°F and 60 to 110°F. Relative humidity varied as the temperature changed during the day, but it was normally within the limits of 40 to 70 per cent for all diurnal cycles.

The ratio of evaporative heat loss to metabolic heat production at any given temperature within a diurnal was approximately the same as previously measured under constant conditions. Vaporization rates rapidly changed with changing environmental temperatures within each diurnal cycle, indicating the cows rapidly adjusted evaporative heat dissipation rates.

Rectal temperature varied in a diurnal cycle, but lagged behind the ambient temperature.

Milk production and feed consumption as affected by a diurnal cycle were roughly

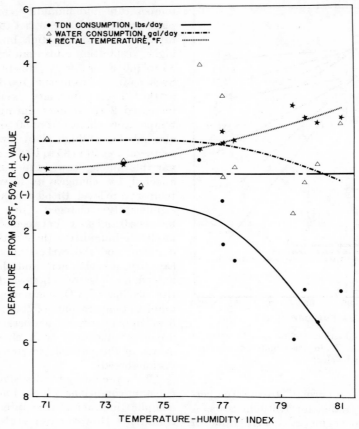

FIG. 5. Departure from normal of feed consumption, water consumption and rectal temperature for Holstein cows (each point is an average of 12 cows) with increasing temperature-humidity index values.[65-72]

equivalent to a constant temperature condition matching the average temperature of the diurnal cycle. For example, the diurnal 70 to 100°F, with an actual average temperature of 84°F, resulted in about 5 per cent decline in milk production for Jerseys and a slightly greater decline for Holsteins. This compares with an approximate decline of 6 and 17 per cent for the 2 breeds, respectively, under constant conditions.

DISCUSSION

An optimal temperature or comfort* zone for milk production, with regard to quantity

* Not identical with the zone of thermoneutrality. The latter is the temperature range which does not affect the heat production in animals under conditions of basal metabolism.

and efficiency, is indicated to exist between 30 and 75°F for all breeds. In this temperature range and below, relative humidity has no significant effect on production, since evaporative and nonevaporative cooling processes are sufficient to carry away excess body heat and maintain normal body temperatures. Above about 75°F in European-evolved cows (the critical temperature being dependent on breed), heat dissipation processes are no longer adequate. A resultant increase in rectal temperature occurs along with varied other physiological responses. The final result appears as a decline in feed consumption and milk production; the extent of the decline is dependent on the severity of the temperature-humidity condition to which the cow is exposed.

TABLE 3. THE CRITICAL TEMPERATURE* (°F) OF THE VARIOUS PHYSIOLOGICAL REACTIONS FOR BREED AVERAGES

Reaction	Lactating				Dry Brahman
	Jersey	Holstein	Brown Swiss	Brahman	
Feed consumption					
Decrease after	75	70	80	95	95
Milk production					
Decrease after	85	85	85	95	
Heat production					
Decrease after	85	75	70	95	70
Pulse rate					
Decrease after	80	80	85	95	85
Increase after	100	90	95	100	100
Body weight					
Decrease after	85	80	80	†	†
Butterfat, %					
Increase after	90	85	90	†	
Respiration rate					
Increase after	60	60	60	75	80
Decrease after	85	80	90		
Vaporized moisture					
Increase after	60	60	50	85	70
Decrease after	70	70	85	95	95
Respiratory vaporization					
Increase after	75	75	60	90	95
Decrease after	85	85	90	100	
Pulmonary ventilation rate					
Increase after	75	65	60	90	95
Decrease after	85	85	85	100	100
Creatinine					
Increase after	80	80	85	95	100
CO₂-combining capacity					
Decrease after	85	85	85	95	85
Ascorbic acid					
Decrease after	90	80	80	95	80
Rectal temperature					
Increase after	75	70	80	95	95

* Critical temperature refers to approximate environmental temperature above which marked changes occur to animals subjected to rising temperature 50 to 105°F.
† Indicates no change.

To say that the critical temperature occurs in a given breed at a particular temperature is, however, an extreme oversimplification. Individual animals within breeds vary considerably in responses to given environmental conditions, particularly with level of production and heat tolerance. Also, an individual's reactions are dependent on time factors—stage of lactation, gestation and acclimation.

As ambient temperatures increase above the critical temperature of the animal (about 75°F), heat dissipated by nonevaporative methods (conduction, convection and radiation) becomes less. The evaporative heat loss tends to be adjusted by homeothermic mechanisms to rid the body of this heat. Increasing humidity above 75°F affects the heat exchange of the animal body by depressing the rate of heat dissipation by skin and respiratory vaporization. The insignificant decline in production for ambient conditions of 90°F, 20 per cent RH indicates the beneficial aspects of low humidity at high temperatures.

At a point near 105°F, the only avenue of heat dissipation remaining for the animal is vaporization from the outer surface and the respiratory surface. Since the maximum evaporative cooling rate for sustained periods is about 80 cal/m²/hour* from the skin surface and 30 from the respiratory tract, an imbalance of about 40cal/m²/hour* exists (the heat production rate of lactating animals being about 150 cal/m²/hour) to hinder maintainance of thermal balance and maximum milk production. As body temperature rises, the homeothermic mechanisms further act to reduce heat production by reducing feed consumption, thyroid activity and milk production. This relation of heat production to feed intake and milk production may partially explain the low heat production of the more heat tolerant Brahman cows† as compared to Jersey cows of about the same weight for conditions of 50 to 85°F. The more heat tolerant Brahmans are also aided in dissipating heat by having 12 per cent more surface area per unit body weight than European-evolved cows of the same weight. (There are no results to indicate the Brahman cows sweat more profusely than European cows.)

The actual decline in milk production with increasing temperature depends to a large extent on normal level of production. A cow having the capacity due to genetic potential or stage of lactation to produce 60 pounds of milk per day in a 65°F environment will decline more in pounds of milk per day at higher temperature-humidity conditions than a cow whose potential is only 30 lb/day. However, the higher producing cow will still have the higher total production under most temperature-humidity conditions.

To attain maximal evaporative cooling, a cow must partially compensate for lack of sweating by panting to increase the rate of air flow over respiratory surfaces. The pulmonary ventilation rate of a cow is twice that of man, as indicated by measurements of the composition of expired air. However, the superior sweating ability of man is apparent, as both a 1000-pound cow and a 150-pound man evaporate about 2 pounds of moisture per hour at temperatures between 90 and 100°F. Evaporative cooling in sweating man is mainly limited by the vaporizing effect of the environment, while for sparsely sweating cows, the

* Based on outer surface area.

† It should be emphasized that *in general* the tropically evolved cows are more heat tolerant than the European-evolved cows. However, there were large individual variations in heat tolerance within the breeds of European cows of animals of the same body weight. This would suggest the importance of intrabreed selection for heat tolerance.

limiting factor is the moisture secretion rate of the body surfaces. The presence of high humidity in the environment does moderately depress heat dissipation by vaporization for cows, particularly the outer surface vaporization rate.

The indicated comparability of a constant environment and the average temperature of the diurnal cycles used are helpful in applications of results obtained from the laboratory. Such applications should be used with caution, however, as the stressing effects of high diurnal conditions are the results of the average, maximum and minimum conditions; the length of exposure to heating temperatures above 80°F and cooling temperatures below 70°F; and the rates of rise and decline in the diurnal cycles. Also, the present laboratory data do not account for thermal radiation and high air velocity effects, which can be important factors in the overall environment.

SUMMARY

Comfort is a function of several interrelated factors, among which are the climatic factors of humidity, temperature, thermal radiation, barometric pressure and rainfall. Humidity and temperature have been shown, from constant-condition results obtained in the Climatic Laboratory, to play a large role in the comfort of lactating dairy cows. Milk production of Holstein cows was adversely affected by humidity at dry-bulb temperatures of 75°F and higher. The level of humidity began to depress evaporative cooling, with a resultant increase in body temperature, at about 75°F in European cattle. Above 80°F, most temperature-humidity combinations caused significant decreases in TDN and water consumption. Other measured responses affected by the level of humidity at high temperatures were respiration rate, pulmonary ventilation rate, skin and hair surface temperatures, and outer-surface and respiratory vaporization. A measured variable not significantly affected was pulse rate. The degree of response of individual animals to humidity at temperatures above 75°F is conditioned by level of production or genetic potential and by heat tolerance. The low heat tolerance of cows in general is associated with their relatively high heat production and low moisture vaporization at temperature-humidity conditions of 75°F and above.

At temperatures of 65°F and below (to 12°F), the level of humidity had very little effect on milk production. Vaporization decreased only slightly when humidity was increased.

During diurnal cycle studies, cows rapidly changed evaporative heat dissipation rates within the limits of the individual animal's capacity. Milk production and feed consumption were indicated to be comparable for cows in a constant-temperature environment and in a diurnally cycling environment where the average temperature of the diurnal cycle and the constant temperature were equal.

References

Research Bulletins of the Missouri Agricultural Experiment Station in the "Environmental Physiology" Series

1. Brody, Samuel, "Physiological Backgrounds," Bulletin No. 423, Series No. I, 1948.
2. Ragsdale, A. C., Brody, Samuel, Thompson, H. J., and Worstell, D. M., "Influence of Temperature, 50 to 105 F, on Milk Production and Feed Consumption in Dairy Cattle," Bulletin No. 425, Series No. II, 1948.
3. Brody, Samuel, Burge, Gloria, Blincoe, Clifton, Barton, Jay, Tary, Robert, and Platner, Wesley, "Influence of Ambient Temperature 50 to 100 F. on the Blood Composition of Jersey and Holstein Cows," Bulletin No. 433, Series No. III, 1949.
4. Kibler, H. H., Brody, Samuel, and Worstell, D. M., "Influence of Temperature 50 to 105 F on Heat Production and Cardiorespiratory Activities in Dairy Cattle," Bulletin No. 435, Series No. IV, 1949.
5. Thompson, H. J., Worstell, D. M., and Brody, Samuel, "Influence of Temperature, 50° to 105°F, on Water Consumption in Dairy Cattle," Bulletin No. 436, Series No. V, 1949.
6. Ragsdale, A. C., Worstell, D. M., Thompson, H. J., and Brody, Samuel, "Influence of Temperature, 50° to 0°F and 50° to 95°F, on Milk Production, Feed and Water Consumption and Body Weight in Jersey and Holstein Cows," Bulletin No. 449, Series No. VI, 1949.
7. Kibler, H. H., and Brody, Samuel, "Influence of Temperature, 50 to 5°F and 50° to 95°F, on Heat Production and Cardiorespiratory Activities of Dairy Cattle," Bulletin No. 450, Series No. VII, 1949.
8. Thompson, H. J., McCroskey, R. M., and Brody, Samuel, "Influence of Ambient Temperature, 0° to 105°F, on Insensible Weight Loss and Moisture Vaporization in Holstein and Jersey Cattle," Bulletin No. 451, Series No. VIII, 1949.
9. Ragsdale, A. C., Thompson, H. J., Worstell, D. M., and Brody, Samuel, "Milk Production and Feed and Water Consumption Responses of Brahman, Jersey, and Holstein Cows to Changes in Temperature, 50° to 105°F and 50° to 8°F," Bulletin No. 460, Series No. IX, 1950.
10. Kibler, H. H., and Brody, Samuel, "Influence of Temperature, 5° to 95°F, on Evaporative Cooling from the Respiratory and Exterior Body Surfaces in Jersey and Holstein Cows," Bulletin No. 461, Series No. X, 1950.
11. Kibler, H. H., and Brody, Samuel, "Effects of Temperature, 50° to 105°F and 50° to 9°F, on Heat Production and Cardiorespiratory Activities in Brahman, Jersey, and Holstein Cows," Bulletin No. 464, Series No. XI 1950.
12. Ragsdale, A. C., Thompson, H. J., Worstell, D. M., and Brody, Samuel, "Influence of Increasing Temperature, 40° to 105°F, on Milk Production in Brown Swiss Cows, and on Feed and Water Consumption and Body Weight in Brown Swiss and Brahman Cows and Heifers," Bulletin No. 471, Series No. XII, 1951.
13. Kibler, H. H., and Brody, Samuel, "Influence of Increasing Temperature, 40° to 105°F, on Heat Production and Cardiorespiratory Activities in Brown Swiss and Brahman Cows and Heifers," Bulletin No. 473, Series No. XIII, 1951.
14. Thompson, H. J., McCroskey, R. M., and Brody, Samuel, "Influence of Temperature on Insensible Weight Loss and Moisture Vaporization in Brahman, Brown Swiss, Holstein, and Jersey Cattle," Bulletin No. 479, Series No. XIV, 1951.
15. Thompson, H. J., Worstell, D. M., and Brody, Samuel, "Influence of Environmental Temperature, 0° to 105°F, on Hair and Skin Temperatures and on the Partition of Heat Dissipation Between Evaporative and Non-Evaporative Cooling in Jersey and Holstein Cattle," Bulletin No. 481, Series No. XV, 1951.
16. Stewart, R. E., Pickett, E. E., and Brody, Samuel, "Effect of Increasing Temperature 65° to 95°F, on the Reflection of Visible Radiation from the Hair of Brown Swiss and Brahman Cows," Bulletin No. 484, Series No. XVI, 1951.
17. Blincoe, Clifton, and Brody, Samuel, in collaboration with Burge, Gloria, Turner, H. G., Worstell, D. M., and Elliott, J. R., "The Influence of Temperature on the Blood Composition of Cattle," Bulletin No. 488, Series No. XVII, 1951.
18. Thompson, H. J., Worstell, D. M., and Brody, Samuel, "Influence of Environmental Temperature, 0° to 105°F, on Hair and Skin Temperature of Holstein, Jersey, Brown Swiss, and Brahman Cattle with Notes on the Thermal Properties of Hair and Skin," Bulletin No. 489, Series No. XVIII, 1952.
19. Kibler, H. H., and Brody, Samuel, "Relative Efficiency of Surface Evaporative, Respiratory Evaporative, and Non-evaporative Cooling in

Relation to Heat Production in Jersey, Holstein, Brown Swiss, and Brahman Cattle, 5° to 105°F," Bulletin No. 497, Series No. XIX, 1952.

20. Worstell, D. M., and Brody, Samuel, "Comparative Physiological Reactions of European and Indian Cattle to Changing Temperature," Bulletin No. 515, Series No. XX, 1953.

21. Ragsdale, A. C., Thompson, R. J., Worstell, D. M., and Brody, Samuel, "The Effect of Humidity on Milk Production and Composition, Feed and Water Consumption, and Body Weight in Cattle," Bulletin No. 521, Series No. XXI, 1953.

22. Kibler, H. H., and Brody, Samuel, "Influence of Humidity on Heat Exchange and Body Temperature Regulation in Jersey, Holstein, Brahman, and Brown Swiss Cattle," Bulletin No. 522, Series No. XXII, 1953.

23. Thompson, H. J., Worstell, D. M., and Brody, Samuel, "The Effect of Humidity on Insensible Weight Loss, Total Vaporized Moisture, and Surface Temperature in Cattle," Bulletin No. 531, Series No. XXIII, 1953.

24. Thompson, H. J., "Effect of Temperature Upon Heat Exchanges in Dairy Barns" (a report on ventilation studies in the Psychroenergetic Laboratory), Bulletin No. 542, Series No. XXIV, 1954.

25. Brody, Samuel, Ragsdale, A. C., Thompson, H. J., and Worstell, D. M., "The Effect of Wind on Milk Production, Feed and Water Consumption and Body Weight in Dairy Cattle," Bulletin No. 545, Series No. XXV, 1954.

26. Thompson, H. J., Yeck, R. G., Worstell, D. M., and Brody, Samuel, "The Effect of Wind on Evaporative Cooling and Surface Temperature in Dairy Cattle," Bulletin No. 548, Series No. XXVI, 1954.

27. Kibler, H. H., and Brody, Samuel, "Influence of Wind on Heat Exchange and Body Temperature Regulation in Jersey, Holstein, Brown Swiss, and Brahman Cattle," Bulletin No. 552, Series No. XXVII, 1954.

28. Brody, Samuel, Ragsdale, A. C., Thompson, H. J., and Worstell, D. M., "The Thermal Effects of Radiation Intensity (Light) on Milk Production, Feed and Water Consumption, and Body Weight in Holstein, Jersey and Brahman Cows at Air Temperatures 45°, 70° and 80°F," Bulletin No. 556, Series No. XXVIII, 1954.

29. Stewart, R. E., and Brody, Samuel, "Effect of Radiation Intensity on Hair and Skin Temperatures and on Respiration Rate of Holstein, Jersey, and Brahman Cattle at Air Temperatures 45°, 70° and 80°F," Bulletin No. 561, Series No. XXIX, 1954.

30. Dale, H. E., and Brody, Samuel, "Thermal Stress and Acid-Base Balance in Dairy Cattle," Bulletin No. 562, Series No. XXX, 1954.

31. Kibler, H. H., and Brody, Samuel, "Influence of Radiation Intensity (Light) on Evaporative Cooling, Heat Production, and Cardio-

respiratory Activities in Jersey, Holstein, and Brahman Cows," Bulletin No. 574, Series No. XXXI, 1955.

32. Blincoe, Clifton, and Brody, Samuel, "The Influence of Ambient Temperature, Air Velocity, Radiation Intensity, and Starvation on Thyroid Activity and Iodide Metabolism in Cattle," Bulletin No. 576, Series No. XXXII, 1955.

33. Brody, Samuel, Ragsdale, A. C., Yeck, R. G., and Worstell, D. M., "Milk Production, Feed and Water Consumption, and Body Weight of Jersey and Holstein Cows in Relation to Several Diurnal Temperature Rhythms," Bulletin No. 578, Series No. XXXIII, 1955.

34. Blincoe, Clifton, and Brody, Samuel, "The Influence of Diurnally Variable Temperatures on the Thyroid Activity and Iodide Metabolism of Jersey and Holstein Cows," Bulletin No. 579, Series No. XXXIV, 1955.

35. Yeck, R. G., "Heat and Moisture Removed by a Dairy Stable Ventilation System During Diurnal Temperature Rhythms," Bulletin No. 595, Series No. XXXV, 1955.

36. Brody, Samuel, Dale, H. E., and Stewart, R. E., "Interrelations Between Temperatures of Rumen (At Various Depths), Rectum, Blood, and Environmental Air; and the Effects of an Antipyretic, Feed and Water Consumption," Bulletin No. 593, Series No. XXXVI, 1955.

37. Yeck, R. G., and Kibler, H. H., "Moisture Vaporization by Jersey and Holstein Cows during Diurnal Temperature Cycles as Measured with a Hygrometric Tent," Bulletin No. 600, Series No. XXXVII, 1956.

38. Kibler, H. H., and Brody, Samuel, "Influence of Diurnal Temperature Cycles on Heat Production and Cardiorespiratory Activities in Holstein and Jersey Cows," Bulletin No. 601, Series No. XXXVIII, 1956.

39. Dale, H. E., Burge, G. J., and Brody, Samuel, "Environmental Temperature and Blood Volume," Bulletin No. 608, Series No. XXXIX, 1956.

40. Blincoe, Clifton, "Design and Testing of a Hair Measurement Beta-Gauge," Bulletin No. 616, Series No. XL, 1956.

41. Thompson, H. J., "Influence of Humidity and Wind on Heat Loads within Dairy Barns," Bulletin No. 618, Series No. XLI, 1957.

42. Ragsdale, A. C., Cheng, Chu Shan, Johnson, H. D., "Effects of Constant Environmental Temperature of 50°F and 80°F on the Growth Responses of Brahman, Santa Gertrudis, and Shorthorn Calves," Bulletin No. 642, Series No. XLII, 1957.

43. Kibler, H. H., "Energy Metabolism and Cardiorespiratory Activities of Shorthorn, Santa Gertrudis, and Brahman Heifers during Growth at 50° and 80°F Temperature," Bulletin No. 643, Series No. XLIII, 1957.

44. Yeck, R. G., "Stable Heat and Moisture Dissipation with Beef Calves at Temperatures of 50° and 80°F," Bulletin No. 645, Series No. XLIV, 1957.

45. Johnson, H. D., Ragsdale, A. C., and Cheng, C. S., "Comparison of the Effect of Environmental Temperature on Rabbits and Cattle. Part I. Influence of Constant Environmental Temperatures (50° and 80°F) on the Growth Responses and Physiological Reactions of Rabbits and Cattle," Bulletin No. 646, Series No. XLV, 1957.

46. Johnson, H. D., Ragsdale, A. C., and Cheng, C. S., "Comparison of the Effect of Environmental Temperature on Rabbits and Cattle. Part II. Influence of Rising Environmental Temperature on the Physiological Reactions of Rabbits and Cattle," Bulletin No. 648, Series No. XLVI, 1958.

47. Blincoe, Clifton, "The Influence of Constant Ambient Temperature on the Thyroid Activity and Iodide Metabolism of Shorthorn, Santa Gertrudis, and Brahman Calves During Growth," Bulletin No. 649, Series No. XLVII, 1958.

48. Stewart, R. E., and Shanklin, M. D., "Effects of Growth and Environmental Temperature on Surface Temperature of Beef Calves," Bulletin No. 656, Series No. XLVIII, 1958.

49. Johnson, H. D., Ragsdale, A. C., and Yeck, R. G., "Effects of Constant Environmental Temperatures of 50° and 80°F on the Feed and Water Consumption of Brahman, Santa Gertrudis, and Shorthorn Calves During Growth," Bulletin No. 683, Series No. XLIX, 1958.

50. Kibler, H. H., and Yeck, R. G., "Vaporization Rates and Heat Tolerance in Growing Shorthorn, Brahman and Santa Gertrudis Calves Raised at Constant 50° and 80°F Temperatures," Bulletin No. 701, Series No. L, 1959.

51. Dale, Homer E., Ragsdale, A. C., and Cheng, C. S., with the technical assistance of Barrows, G. T., Grosse, C. W., McGinnis, J. P., and Nicoletti, P. L., "Effect of Constant Environmental Temperatures of 50° and 80°F on Ovarian Activity of Brahman, Santa Gertrudis, and Shorthorn Calves with a Note on Physical Activity," Bulletin No. 704, Series No. LI, 1959.

52. Johnson, H. D., and Ragsdale, A. C., "Effects of Constant Environmental Temperatures of 50° and 80°F on the Growth Responses of Holstein, Brown Swiss, and Jersey Calves," Bulletin No. 705, Series No. LII, 1959.

53. Johnson, H. D., and Ragsdale, A. C., with technical assistance of Robertson, Delano, "Temperature Effects on Thyroid I[131] Release Rate of Dairy Calves," Bulletin No. 709, Series No. LIII, 1960.

54. Kamal, Taymour H., Johnson, H. D., and Ragsdale, A. C., "The Effect of Long Exposure of Environmental Temperatures of 50° and 80°F on Glutathione, BEI[131], and Growth Rate of Dairy Calves," Bulletin No. 710, Series No. LIV, 1959.

55. Kibler, Hudson H., "Energy Metabolism and Related Thermoregulatory Reactions in Brown Swiss, Holstein, and Jersey Calves During Growth at 50° and 80°F Temperatures," Bulletin No. 743, Series No. LV, 1960.

56. Yeck, R. G., and Stewart, R. E., "Stable Heat and Moisture Dissipation with Dairy Calves at Temperatures of 50° and 80°F," Bulletin No. 759, Series No. LVI, 1960.

57. Johnson, H. D., Ragsdale, A. C., Sikes, John D., Kennedy, James I., O'Bannon, E. B., Jr., and Hartman, D., "Surface Area Determinations of Beef and Dairy Calves During Growth at 50° and 80°F Environmental Temperatures," Bulletin No. 770, Series No. LVII, 1961.

58. Johnson, H. D., Ragsdale, A. C., and Yeck, R. G., "The Effects of Constant Environmental Temperatures 50° or 80°F on the Feed and Water Consumption of Holstein, Brown Swiss and Jersey Calves," Bulletin No. 786, Series No. LIX, 1960.

59. Johnson, H. D., Ragsdale, A. C., Berry, I. L., and Shanklin, M. D., "Effect of Various Temperature-Humidity Combinations on Milk Production of Holstein Cattle," Bulletin No. 791, Series No. LXII, 1962.

60. Kibler, H. H., Yeck, R. G., and Berry, I. L., "Vaporization Rates in Brown Swiss, Holstein, and Jersey Calves During Growth at Constant 50° and 80° Temperatures," Bulletin No. 792, Series No. LX, 1962.

61. Kibler, H. H., "Energy Metabolism and Related Thermoregulatory Reactions to Thermal Stress in 50° and 80° Acclimated Dairy Heifers," Bulletin No. 793, Series No. LXI, 1962.

62. Cargill, B. F., Stewart, R. E., and Johnson, H. D., "Effect of Humidity on Total Room Heat and Vapor Dissipation of Holstein Cows at 65, 80, and 90°F," Bulletin No. 794, Series No. LXIII, 1962.

63. Berry, I. L., and Shanklin, M. D., "Physical Factors Affecting Thermal Insulation of Livestock Hair Coats," Bulletin No. 802, Series No. LXIV, 1962.

64. Bedwell, Robert L., and Shanklin, Milton D., "Influence of Radiant Heat Sink on Thermally-Induced Stress in Dairy Cattle," Bulletin No. 808, Series No. LXV, 1962.

65. Johnson, H. D., Ragsdale, A. C., Berry, I. L., and Shanklin, M. D., "Temperature-Humidity Effects Including Influence of Acclimation on Feed and Water Consumption of Holstein Cattle," in press, 1963.

Note: The following Environmental Physiology bulletins and publications are not included in the foregoing series:

66. Cobble, J. W., and Herman, H. A., "The Influence of Environmental Temperatures on the Composition of Milk of the Dairy Cow," Bulletin No. 485, 1951.

67. Singh, Ranjit, and Merilan, C. P., "Influence of Temperature on Vitamin Levels in Bovine Blood. A Study of B-Vitamins and Vitamin C Levels in the Blood of Brahman, Santa Gertrudis and Shorthorn Heifers Reared Under

Different Environmental Temperature Conditions," Bulletin No. 639, 1957.

68. Merilan, C. P., and Bower, K. W., "Influence of Daily Environmental Temperature Cycles on Composition of Cows' Milk," Bulletin No. 687. 1959.

69. Yeck, R. G., and Stewart, R. E., "A Ten-Year Summary of the Psychroenergetic Laboratory Dairy Cattle Research at the University of Missouri," *Transactions of the ASAE*, **2**, 71 (1959).

70. Yeck, R. G., "Environmental Research with Dairy Cattle," *Agr. Eng.*, **40**, 536 (1959).

71. Berry, I. L., Shanklin, M. D., and Johnson, H. D., "Dairy Shelter Design Data Based on Milk Production Decline as Affected by Temperature and Humidity," ASAE Paper 61–932, 1961.

72. Johnson, H. D., and Kibler, H. H., "Temperature-Humidity Effects on Thyroxin I^{131} Disappearance Rates in Cattle," *J. Appl. Physiol.*, **18**, 73 (1963).

25. Methods of Determining Vapor Losses from Cattle

ROBERT G. YECK

Agricultural Research Service, U.S. Department of Agriculture, Beltsville, Maryland

ABSTRACT

Vapor losses from cattle are a problem in livestock shelters. Their evaluation leads to design criteria for ventilation and air-conditioning systems. They are also valuable for determining and evaluating the mechanisms associated with animal adjustments to heat and cold, as well as for selecting animals according to their adaptability to variations in climate.

Methods of determining vapor losses may be grouped into systems that measure the respiratory vaporization, those that measure skin vaporization, and those that measure the summation of the two, total vaporization. Respiratory vaporization measurements require a mask over the cow's muzzle, a means of measuring exhaled air volume (without undue back pressure against respiration), and a system for measuring the change in moisture content of the air as it enters and leaves the respiratory system. Skin vaporization has been most successfully measured with aspirated capsules. Total vaporization in cattle has been determined either through measurements of weight loss using an industrial type scale with electronic recording equipment or with a hygrometric tent. The latter is a metal and plastic enclosure through which air is moved; the vaporization rate is determined by measuring the amount of air moved through the enclosure and the change in its psychrometric properties.

INTRODUCTION

Although cattle are not considered a sweating species, more than 2½ pounds of water per hour have been reported as being vaporized from their body surfaces. These vapor losses are significant for several reasons:

(1) They represent evaporative cooling—a primary means by which cattle dissipate heat in hot weather. The determination of vapor losses of individual animals leads to a better understanding of body temperature regulation. Geneticists look upon vaporization rates of individual animals as a possible means of selecting animals that are best adapted to a given climate.

(2) An understanding of the effectiveness of the various avenues of heat transfer (convection, conduction, radiation and evaporation) aids in selecting the most effective shelter design.

(3) In housing, the vapor losses increase humidity which may cause structures to deteriorate and contribute to illness among animals. The rates of vapor dissipation then become useful in establishing design criteria for ventilation systems.

Methods of measuring these vapor losses are the subject of this presentation. The methods of measurement can be divided into 3 categories—skin, respiratory and total. Skin vaporization refers to vapor that is dissipated from exterior body surfaces of the cow, somewhat like sweating in man except that water seldom appears in the liquid state. Respiratory vaporization refers to vapor that is dissipated through the mouth and nostrils. The summation of the two will be referred to as total vaporization.

MEASUREMENT OF TOTAL VAPORIZATION

The insensible weight loss technique was one of the first methods of measuring total vaporization. Early investigators[1] weighed animals at the beginning of a test and again several hours later. The change in weight was adjusted according to the weights of the feed and water consumed and the urine and feces excreted during the test. The net result was an estimate of vapor loss. The process required much time and labor and was subject to considerable error.

This process was later shortened by increasing the sensitivity of an industrial platform type scale, adding an electronic sensing and recording system, and recording weight loss over a short time period.[2] The key features of one such system are shown in Fig. 1. This technique, although having the advantages of obtaining results directly in a single basic measurement of weight within a 15-minute period, had disadvantages of: (a) limited precision (particularly if the animal shifted position on the platform); (b) urine and feces had to be trapped in a container from which essentially no water vaporized, and (c) adjustments had to be made for the weight loss associated with the difference in weight between the oxygen consumed and carbon dioxide and methane given off by the animal. The latter gaseous losses were determined with metabolism apparatus.

In 1954, a hygrometric tent was developed to measure total vaporization of cattle. In general, it was a metal and plastic enclosure[3, 4] through which air was moved. The amount of air and its change in psychrometric properties were determined. From these data, vapor dissipation rates were calculated. The tent was used in a controlled temperature room, and an animal was held in the tent for about 20 minutes. An example of this system is shown in Fig. 2. Prior to each day of use this system was checked by vaporizing a measured amount of water within the tent. The humidity sensing element (a Foxboro "Dewcel") was extremely critical, since the "Dewcels" measured the moisture content of incoming and outgoing air for the hygrometric tent. The change in the moisture content of the air was the primary variable in the calculation of

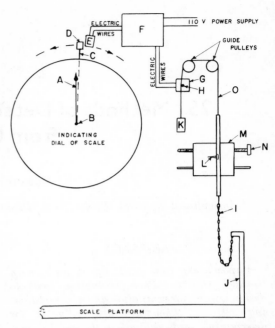

FIG. 1. Schematic diagram of mechanism used for recording insensible weight loss. A null or constant balance point of the scale indicator (A) was maintained by replacing any weight loss by links of chain (I) through a post (J). The chain was raised or lowered by a reversible motor (G) acting through its shaft (H) and a line (O) with line tension provided by a counterweight (K). The motor was actuated through an electronic relay (F) and a pick-up coil (E). In operation the indicating shaft (B) working through a balanced arm (C) causes the aluminum flag (D) to move, without contact, between the pick-up coils. Initial adjustment of the scale counterpoise weights was necessary to bring the flag to the point where it changed the energy in the electronic circuit, as indicated by the reversal of the motor when the flag was between coils. The movement of the chain was recorded by a pen (L) on a chart (M) which in turn was driven by a chart drive mechanism (N). Each inch of vertical travel represented 50 grams and each inch of horizontal travel represented ten minutes.

animal vaporization rates. The other variable, rate of air flow, was maintained approximately constant. The "Dewcel" manufacturer claimed an accuracy of better than $\pm 2°F$ dew-point temperature, but for small calves, $2°F$ dew-point temperature was about the total change in absolute humidity of the air as it moved through the tent. Therefore, a more precise method of calibration was needed.

The discrepancies in the "Dewcel" when

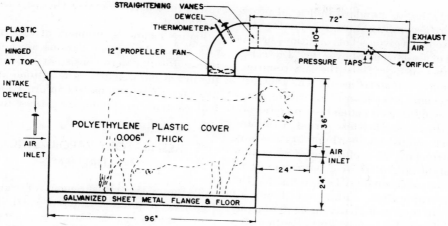

FIG. 2. The hygrometric tent as used for cows. The 36-in. wide floor was of 24-gauge sheet metal with the edges bent upward. The plastic cover was taped to these edges and supported by an angle iron frame. The detachable hood in the front part of the tent was lined with ¼-in. hardware cloth to prevent the cows from licking the plastic. Air was drawn into the tent by the fan through several small holes (4 in. and less in diameter) located in the flap and in the hood. Air flow was measured in the straight section of duct by measuring the pressure drop across the orifice with an inclined manometer. Air turbulence in the duct was reduced by 1 by 3-in. egg crate type straightening vanes. The moisture content of the intake and of the exhaust air was detected by the lithium chloride heated electrical elements and recorded in an adjoining room. The hood was not used for the calf experiments and air entered through the rear only.

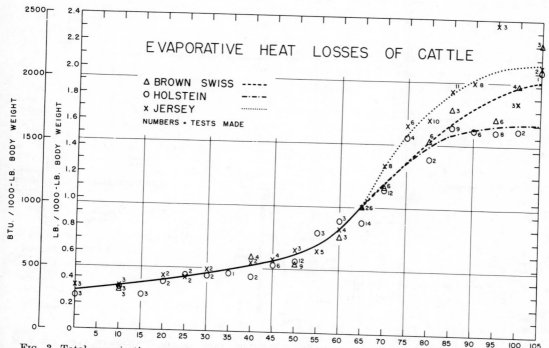

FIG. 3. Total vaporization rates from lactating cows. The relative humidity ranged from 55 to 70 per cent. Rates are on a per hour basis.

used according to standard industrial procedures were generally not erratic in nature but rather fixed for a given set of conditions such as the level of air movement over the "Dewcels", the number of days since the last resalting, the inherent characteristics of each "Dewcel", and the general level of air temperature. Since all these conditions remained reasonably constant within a one-day test period, a calibration check against another humidity-measuring instrument was effective. Calibration checks of the intake "Dewcel" were made with a wet-bulb psychrometer. This eliminated the error in calibration within the limits of accuracy of the wet-bulb psychrometer (about $\pm 0.5°F$ dew-point temperature). With errors reduced to less than $0.5°F$ dew-point temperature, the important part of measurement then became the precise determination of the difference in calibration between "Dewcels". This was accomplished by comparing the exhaust and intake air "Dewcels" under normal operating conditions except without the cow in the tent. The amount that one "Dewcel" calibration differed from the other was determined and applied, as a correction factor, to the differences between "Dewcel" values that were observed when the cow was in the tent.

Figure 3 shows a summary of vaporization rate measurements at various air temperatures.[5] Results were consistent enough with the insensible weight loss technique and the hygrometric tent to use the information from both systems in summarizing these data.

RESPIRATORY VAPORIZATION MEASUREMENTS

To date, the measurement of water loss from the respiratory tract of cattle has required the use of a mask over the cow's muzzle. Requisites are: an air supply and exhaust system that does not create unusual static pressures against which the animal must work in breathing; a method of measuring the volume of air; and a method of evaluating the moisture change of the air as it moves in and out of the mask. Hot wire anemometers have been used to evaluate air movement in the system but the more satisfactory systems used gas meters. Both gravimetric (with chemical absorbents) and psychrometric devices for

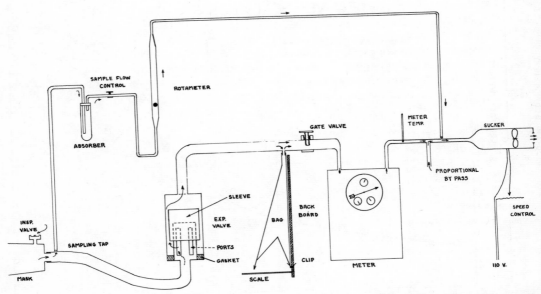

FIG. 4. Gravimetric apparatus for measuring respiratory vaporization. Respiratory vaporization is determined by the weight change of the absorber. The bag serves as an air mixing chamber and to minimize back pressure against the respiration process.

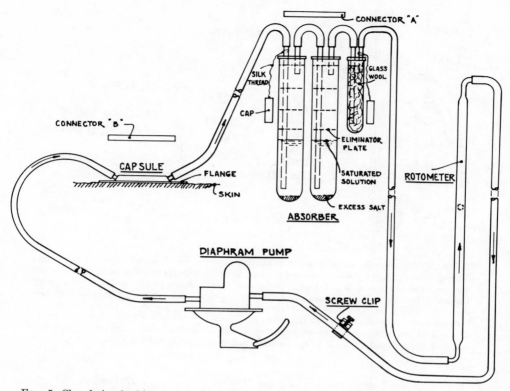

FIG. 5. Closed-circuit skin vaporization measurement apparatus. Respiration rate is measured by the change in weight of the salt solution in the absorber. Excess salt is provided to assure saturation and thus a constant vapor pressure at all times.

evaluating moisture content of the air have been used.[6, 7] Wet- and dry-bulb psychrometers and electric hygrometers (lithium chloride types) have been used. Figure 4 shows a schematic diagram of a gravimetric system. Apparatus for this purpose are cumbersome and there is a need for improvement.

SKIN VAPORIZATION

Skin vaporization is frequently estimated as the difference between total and respiratory vaporization. This, of course, has the advantage of convenience, but an error in either the total or respiratory vaporization measurement would result in an error in the skin vaporization measurement.

Spot skin vaporization measurements have proven their value in identifying the fact that the vaporization rate per unit area varies from place to place on a cow's body and in showing

the most effective areas of evaporative heat dissipation.

An inverted petri dish with calcium chloride impregnated paper was placed over the cow's body in an early attempt to measure spot skin vaporization.[8] The major disadvantages were: (a) the calcium chloride impregnated paper in the bottom of the petri dish provided an unnatural vapor pressure over that area, (b) there was no air movement, and (c) the necessary procedure for sealing the edge of the capsule might have affected vaporization within the capsule.

Two investigators have independently developed aspirated capsules that overcame many of these disadvantages.[9, 10] One featured a closed circuit (Fig. 5) for the air. The desired vapor pressure was provided by circulating the air through an appropriate saturated salt solution. The capsule was secured in place with a non-shrinking plastic cement. Figure 6 shows an open circuit system. In this, the

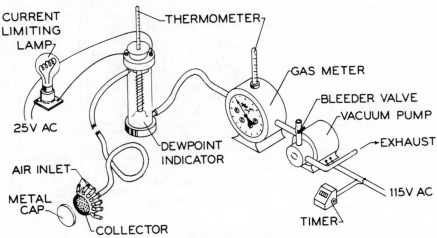

FIG. 6. Open-circuit apparatus for measuring vaporization from a limited surface area. The open-bottomed collector is placed over an animal surface, enclosing an area of 37.4 sq cm. Lithium chloride dew-point indicators measure the difference in moisture content of the air before and after it passes over the enclosed area. Leakage under the collector contact surfaces is negligible, since air enters freely at atmospheric pressure through tubes which pierce the walls of the collector around its periphery near the skin level. These inlet air tubes extend upward on the outside about 2 in. above the animal surface. Air flow is produced by means of a vacuum pump and measured with a meter.

capsule was aspirated with room air, air volume was recorded by a gas meter, and the change in moisture content as the air passed through the capsule was measured with electric lithium chloride dew-point indicators. This capsule was held against the skin so that there was no need to clip hair at any location and the capsule could be moved easily from spot to spot. There is some question as to whether or not the pressures applied to prevent leakage around the base of the capsule (and consequently take up vapor from an area greater than the area within the inner circumference of the capsule) may effect vaporization from the area of skin being measured. The greatest difficulty was the limited precision of dew-point measurements possible with the currently available instruments. This was overcome in part by taking the readings on the cow's back and following the observation by another reading with a plate inserted between the capsule and the cow's back. With the room temperature held approximately constant (as it was under the circumstances in which this particular instrument was used), the calibration of the two dew-point indicators could be compared.

SUMMARY

Vapor losses from cattle are a problem in shelter design and their evaluation leads to design criteria for ventilation and air-conditioning systems. They also are valuable data for determining and evaluating the mechanisms associated with animal adjustments to heat and cold and for selecting animals according to their adaptability to variations in climate.

Methods of determining vapor losses may be grouped into those systems that measure total vaporization rates, those that measure respiratory vaporization, and those that measure skin vaporization rates. Various techniques have been described. Several require dew-point detecting devices to measure the difference between intake and outlet air as it is moved through an enclosure that contains the subject to be measured.

References

1. Benedict, F. G., and Ritzman, E. G., "The Metabolism of the Fasting Steer," pp. 63–75, Washington, Carnegie Institution of Washington, 1927.

2. Thompson, H. J., McCroskey, R. M., and Brody, Samuel, "Influence of Ambient Temperature, 0° to 105°F, on Insensible Weight Loss and Moisture Vaporization in Holstein and Jersey Cattle," *Missouri Agr. Expt. Sta. Bull.*, **451**, 5–8 (1949).

3. Yeck, R. G., and Kibler, H. H., "Moisture Vaporization by Jersey and Holstein Cows During Diurnal Temperature Cycles as Measured with a Hygrometric Tent," *Missouri Agr. Expt. Sta. Res. Bull.*, **600**, 3 (1956).

4. Yeck, R. G., "Evaporative Heat Losses of Dairy Cattle at High Environmental Temperatures," Ph.D. Thesis, University of Missouri, 1960.

5. Yeck, R. G., and Stewart, R. E., "A Ten-Year Summary of the Psychroenergetic Laboratory Dairy Cattle Research at the University of Missouri," *Trans. ASAE*, **2**, 71–77 (1959).

6. Findlay, J. D., *The Effects of Temperature, Humidity, Air Movement, and Solar Radiation on the Behaviour and Physiology of Cattle and Other Farm Animals*, Hannah Dairy Research Institute Bulletin 9, p. 138, 1950.

7. Kibler, H. H., and Brody, Samuel, "Influence of Temperature, 5° to 95°F, on Evaporative Cooling from the Respiratory and Exterior Body Surfaces in Jersey and Holstein Cows," *Missouri Agr. Expt. Sta. Bull.*, **461**, 4–7 (1950).

8. Freeborn, S. B., Regan, W. M., and Berry, L. J., "The Effect of Petroleum Oil Fly Sprays on Dairy Cattle," *J. Econ. Entomol.*, **278**, 382–88 (1934).

9. McDowell, R. E., Lee, D. H. K., and Fohrman, M. H., "The Measurement of Water Evaporation from Limited Areas of a Normal Body Surface," *J. Animal Sci.*, **13**, 405–10 (1954).

10. Kibler, H. H., and Yeck, R. G., "Vaporization Rates and Heat Tolerance in Growing Shorthorn, Brahman, and Santa Gertrudis Calves Raised at Constant 50° and 80°F Temperatures," *Missouri Agr. Expt. Sta. Res. Bull.*, **701**, 9–11 (1959).

26. Aspects of Design for Moisture Control Within Controlled-atmosphere Storage Walls and Ceilings

R. T. LORENZEN

Cornell University, Ithaca, New York

ABSTRACT

A field study of controlled-atmosphere apple storages reveals the prevalence of high moisture conditions within structural walls and ceilings. Subsequent deterioration limits the useful life of wood framed CA storage structures, often requiring major replacement of many wood components in 8 to 10 years.

A coordinated analysis of the CA operating cycle and ambient climatological data indicates the existence of periods of wetting potential and periods of drying potential. This factor is theoretically combined with the natural moisture storage capacity of the building component, via a form of Fick's law, to achieve control of the degree of saturation.

Control of moisture within the wall may be maintained through the use of one or more design intricacies. Among these are discrete regulation of permeance by insertion of a vapor barrier, increase of drying potential by integral ventilation of structural components, and removal of excessive moisture by condensation and subsequent drainage.

Operational practices which will increase the drying potential are the maintenance of the maximum allowable storage temperature, and the quick warm-up of emptied storage rooms.

INTRODUCTION

Controlled-atmosphere storages require gastight wall construction so that designated levels of oxygen and carbon dioxide may be maintained in the storage environment. To assure gastight construction, impervious membranes or panels are installed in the floor, wall, and ceiling of the storage. Materials which are used to build up this gas seal are galvanized steel, aluminum sheets, aluminum foil, glass fabric, plywood, and asphalt roofing.

It is necessary that this gas seal be accessible for maintenance and testing. Maintenance requires annual caulking to arrest the leaks. Testing determines the adequacy of the gas seal. Because of the maintenance and testing requirements, the most practical location of the gas seal has been found to be the interior surface of the storage room. Two typical wall sections with the gas seal located on the interior surface are shown in Fig. 1. Gas seals on the exterior surface of the wall have been tried with little success.

An essential of moisture control in a wall is that the greatest resistance to moisture movement be on the warm side. The moisture accumulation which results from placing an impervious membrane on the cold side of a wall is demonstrated in research by Barre,[1] with the rapid development of a saturated condition.

The location of the gas seal on the interior surface of a CA storage wall and ceiling perpetuates this moisture accumulation problem by being on the wrong side to act as a vapor barrier. In New York State apple growing areas, with a storage temperature of 32°F, the warm side of the wall is the outside for eight to

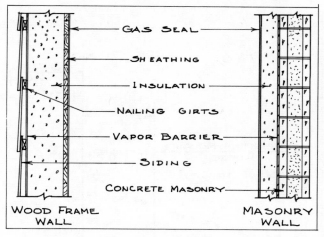

FIG. 1. Two typical wall designs for CA storages.

nine months of the year, and the inside for the remaining part of the year.

Because of the impervious gas seal on the inside surface and the reversal of the warm and cold sides of a CA storage wall, both a wetting potential and a drying potential exists during a given year. The wetting potential exists when the storage temperature is below the dew-point temperature of the exterior air. The drying potential takes over when the storage temperature is above the exterior dew-point temperature.

This reversal of the warm and cold sides of the wall generally complicates the design requirements for moisture control. One method of meeting these design requirements is to hermetically seal the wall and ceiling compartments. In general, the fabrication problems and the cost rule out this method. Another solution would be to utilize the moisture storage potential of the wall by controlled moisture ingress during the wetting period and facilitated moisture egress during the drying period.

The problem of the reversal of the warm and cold sides of the wall, as well as that of wall saturation, is significant in other structures besides CA storages. Refrigerated transport vehicles (trucks, railroad cars and ships) often travel through reversals of the exterior environment. A solution of the moisture problem pertaining to CA storages may be significant in these other areas.

MOISTURE STUDY OF CA STORAGE STRUCTURES

In order to determine the extent of the moisture accumulation problem in CA storage walls and ceilings, a field examination of 15 storages in New York State was made. During the spring and summer of 1961, a total of 79 moisture samples were taken from various locations in the walls and ceilings of these storages.[2] Of these samples, 47 were wood samples from various parts of the building frames, and 32 were samples of insulation. Several different types of wall and ceiling fabrication were represented. The one feature in common for all walls and ceilings was the interior gas barrier.

Out of the group of wood samples, 21 were found to be near equilibrium with outside air. Of the remaining wood samples, 15 were found to contain moisture in excess of equilibrium, but not saturated, and 11 were found to contain moisture in excess of 26 per cent, and thus were considered to be saturated.

Equilibrium moisture data is not generally available for many types of insulation. The moisture content of the insulation was determined and then the sample was categorized by pairing with an adjacent wood sample. The results of this CA storage field study are plotted in Fig. 2.

Insulation and wood members in ventilated attic spaces were found to be universally dry.

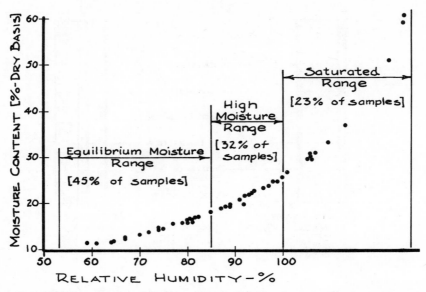

FIG. 2. CA storage wood framing sample classification by moisture content.

This observation is substantiated by work done by Sainsbury on ordinary apple storages.[3] Outside of this, there was no consistent pattern of dryness or wetness. Some walls with exterior vapor barriers were found to be dry, and some were found to be wet. This was also true of walls without exterior vapor barriers. Three out of four bar-joist ceiling compartments examined, which had a sheet metal ceiling supported by the lower chord, were found to have free standing water on the gas seal. Figure 3 shows this free moisture found in this type of ceiling structure.

The above field study indicates the extent of the problem of moisture control in CA storages but gives very little clue to the solution. The fact that a given wall is found dry and a wall of the same type of construction at another location is found saturated, indicates a variable which is not fully appreciated.

FIG. 3. Drops and pools of moisture in CA ceiling structure.

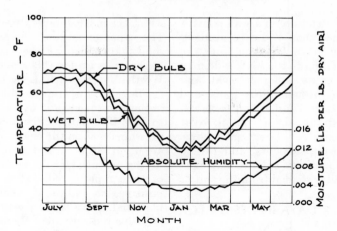

Fig. 4. Time series of the seven year average weekly mean ambient air temperature and moisture content, 1951-58, Westhampton Beach, Long Island, New York.[4]

The known factors which influence the level of moisture in a wall are the exterior and interior environment, the hygroscopic properties of the structural materials, and the mechanisms of movement of moisture. More intense study of these factors, and their mutual interaction should lead to more precise design for moisture control within walls.

SIGNIFICANCE OF WEATHER DATA

In general the Weather Bureau has accumulated climatological data in most areas which can be used for defining the exterior environmental conditions for the purpose of building design. As was found true for design of potato storages,[4] this weather data is often not in a form which is immediately usable for CA storage design purposes.

Figure 4 represents a major weather data analysis for Westhampton Beach, Long Island, made for the purpose of potato storage design by Arthur H. Bennett.[4] This Figure shows the annual climatological cycle as it is composed of dry-bulb and wet-bulb readings, along with computed absolute humidities. The plotted points are the average weekly readings over the seven-year period of 1951–58.

Weather data in this form would also serve for the design of CA storages. For this purpose, weather data needs to be analyzed and put into this form for the Hudson Valley, Lake Champlain, and Lake Ontario regions of New York State, and for other major apple growing areas throughout the United States. This type of analysis would promote a more positive design of apple storages, as well as other agricultural and industrial buildings in these areas.

It is anticipated that inland climatological data will follow the same general cyclic conformation as the coastwise data of Fig. 4. However, the inland data can be expected to show larger temperature fluctuations and a wider spread between wet-bulb and dry-bulb temperatures. This would result in reduced atmospheric vapor pressures which would improve the drying potential for inland areas.

Together with the annual climatological cycle, the diurnal cycle needs to be explored for possible effects on moisture balance within CA storage walls. Figure 5 presents climatological data from Rochester, New York, for the month of April 1961. The average diurnal temperature cycles for the month of April is portrayed, with the same data presented as a histogram of 24-hour temperature averages. The histogram shows a drying potential during 13 days, or parts of days, for this specific data.

A limitation of the use of the average cycle for design purposes can be seen when the diurnal cycle of Fig. 5 is studied in conjunction with the histogram. As noted above, the histogram shows a drying potential during seven whole days and six parts of days. The average diurnal cycle for April shows no drying potential. This same limitation would apply to the average annual cycle of Fig. 4.

Orientation and exposure of a wall relative to moisture balance should also be studied. The variations of the microclime from the north side of a building to the south side may be sufficient to cause different heat and moisture balances through these walls, and thus warrant separate design for each exposure. Direct exposure of a wall to solar radiation may create a different microclime within the wall compartments, and thus a different heat and moisture balance may exist than when the wall is shaded from the sun.

USE OF WEATHER DATA IN DESIGN FOR CONDENSATE CONTROL

Climatological data, in the particular form it appears in Fig. 4, is useful for determining the potential annual moisture balance within a CA storage wall. It can be rationalized that if the potential outward movement of moisture is greater than the potential inward movement, the wall will be comparatively dry, at least part of the year. If the potential inward migration of water is greater, the wall will eventually become water-logged, and other provisions for drying it out become necessary.

Figure 6 contains the data of Fig. 4 altered to indicate the partial pressure of moisture at the gas seal (which is the ultimate condensation surface) and in the exterior air. The partial pressure of the moisture at the gas seal is represented by the broken line. This line is traced for an operating temperature of 32°F, and a close-down period of two months during which the inside temperature is given as 70°F. The vapor pressure in the exterior air is the solid line connecting the weekly averages of vapor pressure for this seven year period at Westhampton Beach, Long Island.

These two lines representing vapor pressure in the atmosphere and at the gas seal combine to form boundaries of cumulative differential pressure areas on the chart. When these areas are negative, as indicated in Fig. 6, there is a drying potential for the wall during the period of time represented. When these areas are positive, as indicated, there is a wetting potential. The relative size of the positive and negative pressure areas should be relatable to the cumulative effect of these wetting and drying potentials. Balancing these wetting and drying potentials should provide a basis for design which would prevent the wall from becoming saturated through this moisture cumulative effect.

The relative size of these areas of wetting and drying potentials in Fig. 6 are dependent on the relative positions of the lines representing vapor pressure at the gas seal and vapor pressure in the air. Higher interior temperatures will increase the vapor pressure at the gas seal and thus favor the drying potential. Lower absolute humidity in the exterior air (generally related to lower exterior temperatures) also favors the drying potential. Thus, the need for climatic data in the form of Fig. 4 to be used for positive design of CA storages becomes apparent.

The nature of Fig. 6 is such that it becomes

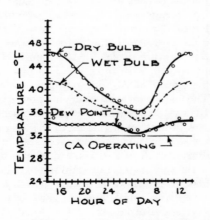

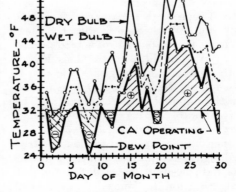

HOURLY AVERAGE FOR MONTH　　　　　HISTOGRAM OF DAILY AVERAGE

Fig. 5. Diurnal temperature cycles and fluctuations, April 1961, Rochester, N.Y.

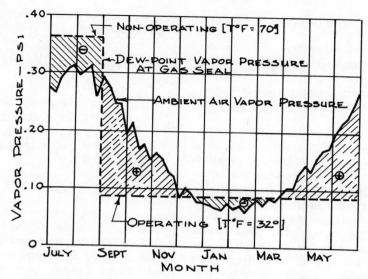

FIG. 6. Wetting and drying potential for CA structural components at Westhampton Beach, Long Island, New York.

an average representation of a number of annual temperature histograms, a sample of which is shown in Fig. 5. Average data is not always applicable for design purposes. Sometimes a statistical treatment gives a better design basis. Such a treatment, of outdoor design dry-bulb temperatures, is represented by the recommendations of H. C. S. Thom[5] for heating loads and of the technical advisory committee of A.S.H.V.E. for cooling loads.[6] Design for moisture control should also be analyzed in this manner to determine the percentile level of data most appropriate as a design basis for defining wetting and drying potentials.

MOISTURE MIGRATION AND STORAGE WITHIN CA STORAGE WALLS

In order to achieve a design which will maintain a favorable moisture balance in building components, two processes must be considered. One is the movement of moisture in the wall and the mechanics of this movement. The other involves the storage of moisture in building materials and the mechanics and capacity of this storage.

The moisture storage capacity of a wall, short of saturation, is dependent on the moisture in the ambient air, the hygroscopic properties of the material, and the amount of material present. Hygroscopic properties are measured by determining the equilibrium moisture content of the material. Hygroscopic properties and equilibrium moisture content are influenced by temperature.

When we consider the following equilibrium moisture content data for wood extracted from the Forest Products Laboratory Wood Handbook:[7]

T (°F)	RH (%)	m (%)
70	90	20.6
70	30	6.1

where m is the equilibrium moisture content, dry weight basis, the moisture storage capacity of the wall becomes apparent and is represented by the equation:

$$M_s = W(m_2 - m_1) + I(m_2' - m_1') \quad (1)$$

where

M_s = moisture storage capacity, lb
W = wood components (dry weight), lb
m_2 = allowable equilibrium moisture content of wood at end of wetting cycle, per cent
m_1 = equilibrium moisture content at end of drying cycle, per cent

I = insulation component (dry weight), lb

m_2' = allowable equilibrium moisture content of insulation at end of wetting cycle, per cent

m_1' = equilibrium moisture content of insulation at end of drying cycle, per cent

This equation would be extended for other hygroscopic materials in the wall. For each 10 pounds of wood, 1.45 pounds of moisture may safely be accumulated and stored as the equilibrium moisture content is raised from 6.1 to 20.6 per cent. Insulation will store a proportionate, but generally lesser amount of water than the wood. The equilibrium moisture contents for most insulations are not readily available and need to be determined before wall storage capacities can be fully computed. The material which first approaches saturation would govern the moisture storage capacity of the system.

In order to arrive at the point of storage, moisture must move through the wall materials. There are three mechanisms by which moisture may move within a wall structure. These mechanisms may be listed as movement by volume transfer, movement by diffusion and movement by hygroscopic action. All three of these moisture transfer methods may be in operation in a wall structure at a given time. These moisture transfer mechanisms are explained in detail by McDermott.[8]

Movement of moisture by volume transfer takes place when convection or induced currents are set up in the air within a wall chamber. Convective air movement picks up the moisture on warm surfaces of the chamber and deposits it on colder surfaces. The dewpoint temperature of air in the compartment is controlled by the coldest surface.

Transfer of moisture by diffusion is actuated by a pressure differential of the vapor from one location to another in a gaseous media. Molecules of moisture will diffuse through a gaseous media at a velocity which is dependent on temperature and at a rate depending on the pressure differential, in accordance with a form of Fick's law.[9] The partial pressure of moisture in a given location is dependent on the number of molecules present.

The rate of vapor flow through the wall of a building by steady-state diffusion is expressed by the equation:[10]

$$M = \frac{A K_0 (p_1 - p_2)}{7000} \qquad (2)$$

where

M = water transmitted per hour, lb

A = area of wall surface, ft^2

K_0 = overall vapor permeability of the wall, grains water vapor/(hour) (ft^2) lb/in.^{2}

p_1 and p_2 = vapor pressures on opposite sides of the wall, lb/in.^{2}

The permeability (K_0) is affected by the hygroscopic moisture in the wall, and the temperature of the wall, and thus published values are only approximate. Other limitations of the above equation are that it represents only diffused moisture and that it is based on steady state vapor transfer.

When a gas barrier is present in the wall structure, the vapor can no longer pass through the wall. If the gas barrier is on the cold side of the wall, the pressure differential is positive. The moisture will then diffuse into the wall until it reaches a point of storage, the maximum penetration being to the gas barrier. If the gas barrier side of the wall becomes the warm side, the pressure differential is negative and the diffusion process transfers moisture out of the wall. This diffusion to storage during the wetting potential and from storage during the drying potential may be represented by the equation:

$$M_s = \frac{A K_s \theta (p_1 - p_3)}{7000} \qquad (3)$$

where

M_s = moisture diffused to (or from) storage, lb

A = area of wall, ft^2

K_s = vapor permeability of wall from open side to point of storage, grains/hour-ft^2-lb/in.^{2}

θ = time, hours

p_1 = vapor pressure at open side, lb/in.^{2}

p_3 = vapor pressure at point of storage, lb/in.^{2}

The moisture which is diffused to storage will be stored as hygroscopic moisture until wall materials reach the saturation point. After saturation is reached, the moisture will run off as free water.

Since all entering moisture may not be diffused through the entire wall to the gas seal and all exiting moisture may not originate at the gas seal, Eq. (3) is a functionary, rather than a quantitative representation. Recognizing the above possibilities, both permeability and pressure differential to the point of storage would be indeterminable quantities.

Condensation may take place during this diffusion-to-storage process. This condensation will take place at the location where dew point is reached, which may be at the gas barrier or at other planes within the wall structure. Condensate may be transferred hygroscopically, or it may run as free water.

Hygroscopic transfer of moisture is accomplished by film or capillary action in or around solid media. This is generally referred to as absorbed moisture. The direction of flow will depend on the hygroscopic moisture balance within the solid media.

It is possible for moisture to be transferred within a wall by two, or even by three of the above mechanisms simultaneously. Volume transfer and diffusion will always result in the movement of water in a given direction through the wall when the volume transfer is by convective currents. Volume transfer can be opposite to diffusion when instigated by mechanical ventilation. The movement of moisture by hygroscopic transfer may be in the same given direction as by diffusion and by volume transfer, or it is possible that the hygroscopic transfer may be in the reverse direction.[8]

DESIGN FOR VAPOR BALANCE IN CA STORAGE WALLS

The foregoing discussions point out three factors which must be considered in designing for vapor balance within CA storage walls. The first factor is concerned with the environment, both within and outside the storage, and its wetting or drying effect on the wall. The second factor to be considered is the potential moisture storage capacity of the wall. The third factor is concerned with the movement of moisture into and out of this wall and with the resistance to this movement by various materials and types of construction.

These factors—vapor environment, movement and storage—are interdependent on each other and must be considered as a combinational whole when designing for vapor balance within structural walls.

When Eq. (3) is examined in the light of Fig. 6, the relationship between the environment and the movement of moisture into and out of the wall can be seen. The term, $\theta(p_1 - p_3)$, from Eq. (3) is an area function in Fig. 6 with a positive area representing the wetting potential and the negative area representing the drying potential. This graphical area is a product of time (θ) on the abscissa and pressure differential ($p_1 - p_3$) on the ordinate. The rate at which vapor will diffuse to storage in the wall, during the wetting potential, or from wall storage during the drying potential is dependent on the pressure differential and the permeability (K_s).

The same type of relationship exists when Eq. (3) is examined in the light of the dew-point temperature of Fig. 5(b). This dew-point temperature line may easily be interpreted as vapor pressure by use of a psychrometric chart.

The amount of vapor which may be allowed to be transmitted to storage within the wall is limited by the moisture storage capacity of the wall. Thus the wall storage capacity of moisture, as indicated by the computations of Eq. (1), limits the allowable moisture movement during the wetting cycle.

Although the moisture storage capacity of a wall can be determined, the distribution of moisture within a wall is not always uniform. Some CA storage walls were observed to be saturated near the bottom and in a dryer state higher up.[2] Barre concluded that in walls where convective air currents are possible, condensation took place near the bottom, while insulation filled walls showed a more even distribution of moisture.[1] Uniformity of moisture storage needs to be considered when the storage potential is determined.

Design for the achievement of vapor balance within a CA storage wall then deals with two variables, each of which can be controlled to a degree. The first of these variables is the storage or disposal of moisture once it has been transmitted into a wall structure. The second variable is the rate at which the moisture is

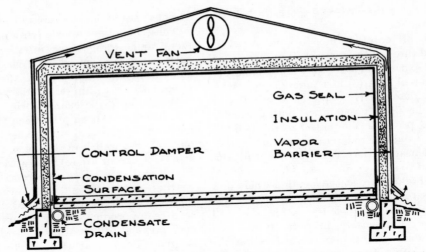

Fig. 7. Design essentials for vapor control within CA storage structural components.

transmitted into the wall during the wetting potential and out of the wall during the drying potential.

Storage capacity for moisture may be designed into a wall to a certain extent. The practical limit to this storage capacity would be dictated by the hygroscopic properties of materials which have a primary function of structural framing and thermal insulation. The effect of the storage of moisture on these primary functions, as well as the storage capacity of many of these materials, needs to be determined.

Moisture disposal systems may also be built into a CA storage wall. The purpose of such a system would be to carry off moisture transmitted into the wall in excess of the moisture storage capacity of the wall. One possibility would be controlled condensation of excess moisture, such as on the back of the gas seal, and then the draining away of this condensate. Such a scheme is presented in Fig. 7.

The rate of transmittance of vapor into and out of the wall can be regulated by the permeability of the wall. This permeability is represented by (K_s) of Eq. (3). The control of this permeability can be achieved by inserting a vapor barrier of the desired resistance to vapor flow. The design problem then is to control the ingoing moisture during the wetting cycle so that the vapor storage potential of the wall is not exceeded, and to achieve the

maximum drying potential during the drying cycle in preparation for the next wetting cycle. If the wetting potential (as shown by the positive areas in Fig. 6) exceeds the drying potential, it may be desirable to have an outer vapor barrier of varying permeability. This would promote fast drying and slow wetting of the wall. This variable permeability could be achieved by inserting vent ports through the vapor barrier and using forced ventilation. These vent ports would be opened when the drying potential exists. Such a scheme is also shown in Fig. 7.

MANAGEMENT ASPECTS OF VAPOR BALANCE IN CA STORAGE WALLS

Management can contribute to the drying potential of CA storage walls. If a room is warmed up soon after its storage function is completed, this will facilitate the movement of moisture out of the wall to the exterior air. Also, if a choice can be made of the variety of apples to be stored, those storing at the higher temperatures will promote a greater drying potential for the wall than those storing at 32°F. The drying aspects of the nonstorage period and the advantage of a warmer storage temperature can be analyzed by manipulation of the line representing the gas seal vapor pressure in Fig. 6.

CONCLUSIONS

Theoretically, a CA storage wall with the gas barrier on the inside can be designed to facilitate a favorable moisture balance within the wall. Three factors need to be considered in such a design. These factors are the exterior environment, the transfer of moisture into and out of the wall compartments, and the hygroscopic storage capacity of the wall. The wetting potential of the environment, the rate of moisture transfer into the wall, and the storage capacity of the wall need to be considered in unison so that the hygroscopic storage potential will not be exceeded. The drying potential and the rate of moisture transfer out of the wall also need to be considered in unison.

The above factors also offer a plausible explanation for the fact that when two CA storage walls of like construction are compared, one may be found saturated and the other one at equilibrium moisture content. The determination of a saturated or unsaturated condition hinges on the moisture balance of the wall. The use of a vapor barrier cannot guarantee an unsaturated wall. The vapor barrier will affect the rate of ingress or egress of moisture, but the cumulative effect may still add up to a saturated condition.

In order that it may be possible to design for moisture control, research pertaining to several elements which affect such design is necessary. Exterior environmental data needs further interpretation regarding its effect on building design. The mechanisms of moisture transfer and storage need to be better understood. A practical approach to design for moisture control needs to be worked out.

The above theory and the recommended research are based on present practical necessity of locating the gas barrier on the interior side of a CA storage wall. Some of the moisture accumulation problems of a CA storage wall would be eliminated if the gas barrier could be located on the side of the wall which is the warm side the greater part of the year, thus also serving as a vapor barrier. A study should be made regarding this possibility.

References

1. Barre, Henry J., "The Relation of Wall Construction to Moisture Accumulation in Fill-type Insulation," *Iowa State Univ. Res. Bull.*, **271** (1940).
2. Lorenzen, R. T., and Blanpied, G. D., "Condensate Moisture Conditions Within Wall and Ceiling Structures of Controlled-atmosphere Apple Storages," Unpublished research report, Agricultural Engineering Dept., Cornell University, September, 1961.
3. Sainsbury, G. F., "Roof Insulating Methods," *Refrig. Eng.*, **61**, 286 (1953).
4. Bennett, Arthur H., "Use of Weather Data as an Aid in the Design of Potato Storages," Masters Thesis, Agricultural Engineering Dept., Cornell University, 1959.
5. Thom, H. C. S., "Revised Winter Outside Design Temperatures," *ASHAE Trans.*, **61**, 387 (1955).
6. *ASHAE Guide*, **37**, 170 (1959).
7. "Wood Handbook," *U.S. Dept. Agr., Agr. Handbook*, **72** (1955).
8. McDermott, P. F., "Moisture Migration, a Survey of Theory and Existing Knowledge," Paper presented at 28th spring meeting of the American Society of Refrigeration Engineers, June 1941.
9. *ASHAE Guide*, **37**, 129 (1959).
10. Barre, Henry J., and Sammet, L. L., "Farm Structures," New York, John Wiley & Sons, Inc., 1950.

27. Vapor Barriers for Farm Buildings

NORMAN C. TETER

United States Department of Agriculture, Agricultural Research Service, Beltsville, Maryland

ABSTRACT

Farm structures must withstand severe internal moisture loads. The problem of moisture is created by high density population, low net heat input available for heating air and supplying building heat loss, moisture from animal wastes, and evaporation of water in plant materials.

Broiler houses and farrowing houses present the greatest problem because the population is dense, usable animal heat input is low, and moisture input is high. Sources of water input and output are discussed.

Major emphasis is on the problem of water vapor movement into walls and its control. In livestock shelters, the vapor pressure maximum differential is about 1.3 cm of mercury, and vapor barriers are essential for good construction. Because of the difference in temperature of operation, the differential of a bright leaf tobacco curing barn may be over 15 cm of mercury, yet a vapor barrier is not necessary because condensation is temporary causing no trouble. Permeable walls are desirable for crop drying structures used in warm seasons. Paint on the exterior of such buildings is short-lived unless the exterior cover is well-vented. A permeance of one perm is suggested as acceptable in livestock shelter if the space between the insulation and the exterior cover is ventilated.

Moisture problems on the farm require considerable agricultural engineering time for solution. Broiler houses, farrowing and nursery units, dairy stables and crop curing, drying and storage buildings are the major buildings with moisture problems.

Livestock buildings have severe internal moisture loads because:

(1) Population is dense,
(2) Heat supply is limited,
(3) Body wastes add to the moisture load.

Water input into a building equals water output on a yearly basis. Sources of input and output are:

Water Input into Buildings	Water Output from Buildings
Drinking	Drainage
Washing	Water in manure removed
Intake air	
Leakage of rain	Exhaust air
Moisture in animals or crops brought in	Vapor permeation
	Moisture in animals or crops taken out
Oxidation of	
Feed (metabolism)	
Litter (decomposition)	
Crops (respiration)	
Open flame burners (combustion)	

The likelihood of water input equaling water output during any given hour or day is small. Building materials and litter store water when hygroscopically drier than the ambient vapor pressure, and they release it when the vapor pressure gradient is in the other direction. Since oxidation generates water, more water must come out of a livestock building than is taken into the building.

Animals obtain water from three sources—drinking, air intake and food oxidation—and release it in three ways—body wastes, air exhaust and surface evaporation. Animal processes in moisture exchange are well defined for poultry,[1] hogs[2] and dairy cattle.[4]

The function of a structure in relation to the

TABLE 1. STRUCTURAL DIMENSIONS AND OCCUPANCY USED TO ILLUSTRATE MOISTURE LOADS

Building	Size			Housed Units		Floor Area (m²)	Cubic Vol. (m³)	Building Surface (m²)
	Width (m)	Length (m)	Ht. Eave (m)	No.	Wt. (kg)			
Broiler house	10	50	2	5000	7500	500	1417	785
Farrowing nursery	8	50	2	30 litters	6000	400	1050	669
Dairy	11	54	2.5	80	36000	594	1485	919
Flue-cured tobacco barn	5	5	5	600 sticks	2230 to 245	25	135	131

moisture balance of animals is poorly defined. Thompson[4] stated that "Dairy barns dissipate a higher per cent of their normal heat production by vaporization than the animals within." The data indicate that at air temperatures from 40 to 50°F, the evaporation from stall surfaces ranged from 38 to 63 per cent of the total moisture load."

Skorokhodz'ko[5] estimated that floor evaporation contributed 20 to 25 per cent of the moisture load, and water in outside air brought into the building for ventilation contributed 10 to 15 per cent to inside humidity of stables. Borowski[6] found moisture contribution from the outside air to amount to 39 to 93 per cent of the humidity in the inside air. The latter figure refers to a profusely ventilated pen.

Thompson[4] defined the functional relation between water output from a dairy stable and temperature of the stable as:

$$W = \frac{16,870}{49 - °C} - 9.07 \qquad (1)$$

where

W = grams of water per hour from a stall housing a 454 kg animal
°C = Celsius degrees temperature.

The equation gives good definition of moisture release in a temperature range between -16 and 33°C.

Table 1 describes typical buildings used to illustrate the moisture problem.

Heat generated within buildings, either the metabolic heat of animals or the combustion fuels, vaporizes moisture and creates an energy potential inside the building that is higher than the energy potential outside. Air at 0°C and 30 per cent RH has an enthalpy of about 6.4 kg-cal/m³ (0°F base). If the inside of a building is 10°C, energy is added to the air on the inside in the approximate amounts given in Table 2.

Assuming a building heat loss of 7670 cal/hour and a balance of vapor generation to moisture withdrawal, 5.1 air changes per hour

TABLE 2. ESTIMATES OF HEAT AND WATER VAPOR GENERATION IN BUILDINGS DESCRIBED IN TABLE 1

Building	Total Heat Generation (kg-cal/hour)	Water Vapor Generation (kg/hour)	Hourly Heat Generation per m³ of Building Volume		
			Latent (kg-cal)	Sensible (kg-cal)	Total (kg-cal)
Broiler house	59,400	52	21	21	42
Farrowing nursery	15,500	15	8	7	15
Dairy	72,800	34	13	36	49
Flue-cured tobacco barn*	41,000	28	121	183	304

* Barn taken at maximum moisture load between yellowing and drying stages. Inside temperature, 62°C.

(5.1 air changes equals 0.85 cfm per bird) in the broiler house results in 10°C, 95 per cent humidity inside air with energy of 13.4 kg-cal/m³ (0°F base). The differential of 7 kg-cal/m³ between inside and outside air consists of 3.3 kg-cal of latent heat in water vapor and 3.7 kg-cal of sensible heat in the air and water vapor. Thus, a broiler house under the assumed conditions has a potential of 4680 calories in the vapor inside over that in an equal volume outside the building—a potential of 2,000,000 kg-m.

This energy is expressed in a higher vapor pressure inside than outside of 0.72 cm of mercury (9.8 cm of water). Obviously the vapor "leaks" into most walls—even liquid water at this depth would run rather freely into most wall construction. These conditions are ordinary. When the weather outside gets colder and air exchange or ventilation is decreased to maintain inside temperatures at a desirable level, the severity of the problem increases. Moisture may accumulate, condensation may occur, or supplemental heat may be added to eliminate the problem.

A similar analysis of the farrowing-nursery house indicates a need for 2.2 air changes per hour (2.2 air changes equals 45 cfm per litter.) plus about 64,000 calories per hour of supplemental heat to give 10°C, 80 per cent RH inside. The moisture load and ventilation needs are less than those in the broiler house, but heat loss from the building uses most of the sensible heat needed to maintain temperature.

The dairy barn presents a better and more easily controllable moisture balance. Ample sensible heat and lower moisture input make it possible to use 10 air changes per hour (10 air changes per hour equals 109 cfm per cow) to maintain a 54 per cent RH at an inside air temperature of 10°C and still remove water at a balanced rate.

No problem would exist if vapor could move freely from high to low potential as a vapor, but in the broiler house example, vapor condenses at a temperature of 9°C, causing condensation on the surface or within the walls. Water in the walls of buildings is intolerable because:

(1) Water supports life that deteriorates organic materials;
(2) Water speeds corrosion of metals;

(3) Water changes cause dimensional changes—a change from water to ice is especially destructive;
(4) Water weakens many building materials;
(5) Water may prolong the life of disease organisms.

Moisture in walls affect heat flow—not simply but with a complexity of qualifications that make almost any one statement on the functional association of moisture content to insulative value erroneous in some aspect. Hygroscopic moisture in insulating materials has little influence on insulating value.[8] After condensation has formed in insulating material the insulation value is decreased,[9] but while condensate is forming, heat flow may be reduced to increase the apparent insulating value. On the other hand, frost crystals in walls may increase the insulating value.

Ellenberger and Camburn[7] observed moisture and temperature in several dairy stable walls and ceilings over a ten-year period, with intensive studies for two years.

In walls protected by vapor barriers the greatest moisture variation was 3.4 per cent in nine and a half years. "Evidently the vapor barrier was very efficient."

"In contrast, the moisture content for the section of the side wall that had no covering (no vapor barrier with covering) on the inside of studdings ranged from 13 to 25 per cent during the same period."

Vapor pressure differential across a building wall does not imply per se that a vapor barrier is needed. The flue-cured tobacco barn in the latter stages of yellowing or early stages of drying may have a vapor pressure differential across the wall of 15 cm of mercury (204 cm of water); yet, it has been repeatedly demonstrated that vapor barriers are useless for tobacco barns. Energy input is sufficient, and extreme moisture load lasts such a short time that the possible condensation quickly vaporizes, doing no damage.

Other crop buildings such as tobacco ordering and grading rooms or sweet potato curing and storage houses that are kept humid over prolonged periods need exceptionally good vapor barriers on the inside. Cold storage buildings used for fruits, meats, etc., need vapor seals on the outside.

Vapor barriers should be installed on the warm side (inside) of insulated livestock buildings. It is not practical to obtain an absolute vapor barrier so the question arises, "What is a vapor barrier?"

A vapor barrier is any material that is sufficiently impermeable to water to prevent harmful amounts of water from entering the wall. It is difficult indeed to give specific values for adequate barriers. Usually the leakage occurs at holes or joints in barrier film if the barrier is any acceptably good material like polyethylene film, kraft paper with asphalt laminations, metal foils, or other equally good plastic films or vapor barrier papers. Since it is almost impossible to seal all joints, it is quite important to ventilate the walls and roof between the outside of the insulation and the exterior cover. The exterior cover should allow the passage of vapor through the wall and in addition should permit air movement to sweep vapor from the outside of the insulation.

To avoid the mistake of installing a material that is permeable to water, all materials used for vapor barriers should have a permeance of 1 perm or less. A vapor barrier that has a rating of 1 perm will pass 1 grain of water through 1 sq ft of surface area in one hour when the vapor pressure difference across the barrier is 1 in. of mercury (1 perm = $0.69 \, \text{g/m}^2$ in one hour at a differential of 2.54 cm).

Irish and Layer[10] suggest barriers as follows for cold storage rooms:

Operation Temperature	Perm
30°F or above	0.2
29 to 0°F	0.1
−1 to −40°F	0.01

This publication summarizes permeabilities and other aspects of barriers installed in farm buildings.

Permeable walls are desirable for crop drying structures used in warm seasons. Paint on the exterior of such buildings is short-lived unless the exterior cover is well vented.

References

1. Longhouse, A. D., Ota, Hajime, and Ashby, Wallace, "Heat and Moisture Design Data for Poultry Housing," *ASAE J.*, **41**, 567 (September 1960).
2. Bond, T. E., Kelly, C. F., and Heitman, Hubert, Jr., "Heat and Moisture Loss from Swine," *ASAE J.*, **33**, 148 (March 1952).
3. Moss, E. G., and Teter, N. C., "Bright Leaf Tobacco Curing," *N. Carolina State College Agr. Expt. Sta. Bull.*, **346** (1944).
4. Thompson, H. S., and Stewart, R. E., "Heat and Moisture Exchanges in Dairy Barns," *ASAE J.*, **33**, 201 (1952).
5. Skorokhodz'ko, A., Gigiena sel'skokhoziaistvennykh zhivotnykh [Hygiene of farm animals] Ed. 4, Rev. Moskva, Gos. Izd-vo Selkhoz lit-ry, 1950.
6. Borowski, W., "Okrslanil charakterystycznej wilgotnosci pomieszczen inwentarskich (Determination of the characteristic humidity of livestock sheds)," *Roczniki Nauk Rolniczych Ser. B.*, **74**, 199 (1959).
7. Ellenberger, H. B., and Cambern, O. M., "Dairy Barn Materials and Construction," *Vermont Univ. Agr. Expt. Sta. Bull.*, **562** (1951).
8. Henriksson, Rolf, "Varmeforluster genon vaggar provade under praktiska forhallanden," Sweden, stat. Forskanst. f. Lantmbyggnader. *Medd.*, **47** (1959).
9. Powell, F. J., "The Effect of Moisture on Heat Transfer Through Insulated Flat-Roof Constructions," Paper from National Bureau of Standards presented to International Institute of Refrigeration, Aug. 20–25, 1962.
10. Irish, W. W., and Layer, J. W., "Vapor Barriers," *Cornell Univ. Agr. Eng. Extension Bull.*, **333** (1962).

28. The Effect of Relative Humidity on the Application of Pesticides to Agricultural Crops*

Clarence F. Becker and Gerald L. Costel

University of Wyoming, Laramie, Wyoming

ABSTRACT

In recent years the interest in use of selective pesticides for weed and insect control in crops has been increasing. The use of granular carriers for these pesticides has received considerable attention recently because of the ease of handling and possible better residual characters; however, this created a need for accurate, easily calibrated equipment for metering and distributing the granular carrier.

Tests were made on several different principles of operation for metering the granular attapulgite carrier. It was found that for all principles, the weight metering rate changed for different moisture contents of the carrier and the equilibrium moisture content of the granular carrier was a function of the relative humidity of the atmosphere it was in equilibrium with. Sigmoid equilibrium moisture and wetting curves for the carrier were determined by maintaining various relative humidities with saturated salt solutions. On the basis of this information, it was determined that the error in application rate based on calibration tests will not be great if both the formulation of the herbicide and the calibration are done in atmospheres where the relative humidity is between 30 and 75 per cent. However, granular carriers treated with the herbicide when in equilibrium in an atmosphere at 30 per cent and calibrated with a metering device when in equilibrium in an atmosphere at 10 per cent RH will result in application of the pesticide at an approximate 10 per cent greater rate than calculated. The error, however, could be as great as 40 per cent.

INTRODUCTION

In recent years the interest in the use of a sorptive inert granulated material known as attapulgite as a carrier of selective pesticides for weed and insect control in crops has been increasing. The pesticide is impregnated on the granular carrier and is held by the carrier until they come in contact with water at which time the pesticide is released. The per cent of toxicant on the carrier varies from $2\frac{1}{2}$ to 20 per cent by weight. Use of the granular carrier is increasing because it possesses several valuable inherent characteristics: namely, reduced drift due to particle weight, elimination of the handling of water, possibly better residual characteristics, and elimination of the need for mixing. It has been estimated that 9 million acres of corn in the midwest alone were treated in 1960 with row application of soil insecticides. In addition, millions of acres have been treated with herbicides on granular carriers.

It has been reported that results from surface applications of pesticides are frequently erratic[5] and that these erratic results may be due in part to inaccurate metering of the granular carrier of the pesticide. There is need for accurate, easily calibrated equipment for metering and distributing the granular carrier, since in many cases the range of application rates for good weed or insect control and

* Paper authorized for publication as Journal Article No. 204 of the Wyoming Agricultural Experiment Station.

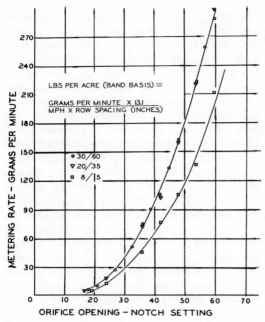

FIG. 1. Metering rate of various sizes of RVM attapulgite by a variable-orifice metering device with rotor-bar agitator turning at 25 rpm.

injury to the crop is not great. Because of this need, a project was initiated at the University of Wyoming Agricultural Experiment Station in cooperation with the Holly Sugar Corporation and the Great Western Sugar Company to study different principles of operation for metering. The metering rate of

various commercially available and experimental devices was determined by connecting them to an electric motor through a variable-speed reducer.[1] The material metered was caught in a container and weighed. A strain-gauge weight transducer was used to determine the weight of the metered materials continuously with time on some of the tests. Figure 1 shows the results of a series of tests for one of several devices tested. Metering tests for these types, reported in more detail elsewhere,[2] indicated a wide range of metering rates for most principles tested. The rates were very nearly proportional to the agitator speed for all devices except those which used a rotor-bar or rubber-flanged agitator, thus facilitating nearly equal application rates for ground-driven units even though the forward speed may vary. The metering rate, as a function of time after filling the hopper, did not change appreciably for all principles of metering studied.

MOISTURE EFFECTS

During one test a marked difference in the weight-metering rate was noted when the batch of the attapulgite was changed. It was determined that the difference could be attributed to variations in moisture content. Figure 2 shows the results of a series of tests conducted to determine the effect of moisture content on the weight-metering rate of

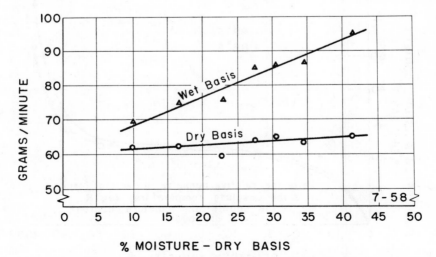

FIG. 2. Effect of moisture on the metering rate of 30-60 RVM attapulgite by brush-type metering device (0.265-in. diameter hole, 40 rpm).

attapulgite by a brush-type metering unit. The metering rate of the carrier on a wet basis increased approximately 12 per cent with a 10 per cent increase in moisture content. This indicates that the potential error in the amount of pesticide applied per acre due to moisture changes of the attapulgite carrier between the time of the formulation of the pesticide and the calibration of the metering device can be quite significant. However, the number of granules metered in a given time is affected to a lesser degree, as shown by the curve for metering on a dry basis. This suggests that, if the carrier is treated with the toxicant and calibration of the metering device is completed with no change in the moisture content of the carrier, there will not be an appreciable error in the metering rate even if the moisture content changes after calibration.

Equilibrium Moisture Content of Attapulgite

For completely accurate calibration, it is necessary to know the moisture content of the attapulgite at the time it is treated with the pesticide and at the time when the metering device is calibrated for field application. However, moisture determination is impractical because a temperature of about 780°F is necessary to dry the attapulgite

completely and to determine its moisture content. It is easier to measure the temperature and relative humidity of the atmosphere with which the attapulgite carrier is in equilibrium and then refer to equilibrium moisture curves of the material. However, this information was not available and had to be determined. The static method, in which the atmosphere in a closed container is maintained chemically at a desired relative humidity by a saturated salt solution, was used for determining the equilibrium moisture content at two temperatures, 68 and 86°F. The atmosphere surrounding the product comes to equilibrium with the product without mechanical agitation of the air or product. Thermodynamically, equilibrium is reached when the free energy change for a material is zero. Some of the salts used to produce the saturated solutions were calcium nitrate, cobaltous chloride, potassium chloride, lithium chloride, and magnesium nitrate.

The relationship between the equilibrium moisture content (or hygroscopic equilibrium) of a particular material and its equilibrium relative humidity at a particular temperature can be expressed by means of equilibrium moisture curves or isotherms. The isotherms for attapulgite turned out to be similar to those for grain,[4] i.e., type II sigmoid isotherms

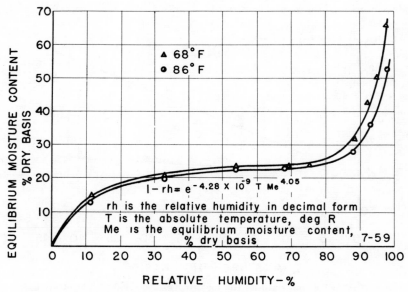

FIG. 3. Equilibrium moisture content of attapulgite.

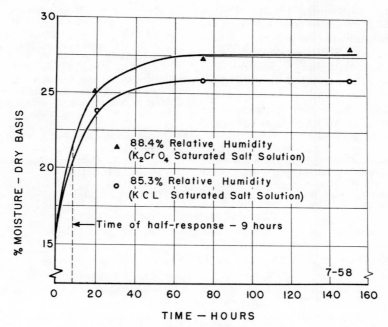

FIG. 4. Wetting curves for attapulgite.

according to the Brunauer classification.[3] An empirical equation is used to represent the equilibrium moisture content:

$$1 - RH = e^{-cTM_e^n} \qquad (1)$$

where

RH = the relative humidity in decimal form

T = the absolute temperature, degrees R

M_e = the equilibrium moisture content, % dry basis

c and n = empirical constants varying with the material.

The curves and solution of the empirical equation are shown in Fig. 3.

The time of half-response (Fig. 4) was determined to be approximately nine hours, indicating that the material will obtain moisture equilibrium with the atmosphere quite rapidly.

An examination of Fig. 3 indicates that the error in the application rate of pesticides carried on attapulgite due to change in moisture content will not be great if both the formulation of the pesticide and the calibration of the metering device are done when the

attapulgite is in equilibrium with atmosphere where the relative humidity is between 30 and 75 per cent. Conversely, attapulgite treated with the herbicide when in equilibrium at 30 per cent and calibrated with a metering device when in equilibrium in an atmosphere at 10 per cent RH will result in application of the herbicide at an approximate 10 per cent greater rate than calculated. In more extreme situations, the error could be as great as 40 per cent.

SUMMARY

Granular carriers for pesticides are being used more and more, thus creating a need for accurate, easily calibrated equipment for metering and distributing the granular carrier. Tests were made on several principles of operation for metering the carrier. It was found that for all principles the weight-metering rate changed for different moisture contents of the carrier and that the moisture content of the carrier was a function of the relative humidity of the atmosphere it was in equilibrium with. Sigmoid equilibrium moisture and wetting curves were determined for the carrier by maintaining various relative humidities with saturated salt solutions. It was determined that the error in the application rate based on calibration tests will not be great if both formulation of the pesticide and calibration of the metering device are done when the carrier is in equilibrium with atmospheres where the relative humidity is between 30 and 75 per cent. The error, however, could be as great as 40 per cent.

Acknowledgment. The project on which this paper was based was partially financed by the Holly Sugar Corp. and the Great Western Sugar Co. through research grants to the Wyoming Agricultural Experiment Station.

References

1. Becker, C. F., Costel, G. L., Hood, G., and Alley, H. P., "Equipment for Metering, Distributing and Mixing Granular Herbicides into Bands," *Agr. Eng. Trans.*, **2**, 108 (1960).
2. Becker, C. F., and Costel, G. L., "Metering and Distributing Granular Carriers For Pesticides," Paper No. 62–609, American Society of Agricultural Engineering, 1962.
3. Brunauer, S., "The Adsorption of Gases and Vapors," Princeton, N.J., Princeton University Press, 1945.
4. Hall, C. W., "Drying Farm Crops," Edward Brothers, Inc., 1957.
5. Wooten, O. B., McWhorter, C. G., and Ranney, C. D., "Underground Application of Herbicides and Fungicides," *Agr. Eng.*, **43**, 30 (1962).

29. Humidity and Moisture Problems associated with the Handling and Storage of Cured Tobacco*

James H. Young and Joe M. Bunn

Agricultural Engineering Department, University of Kentucky, Lexington, Kentucky

AND

Wiley H. Henson, Jr.

Harvesting and Farm Processing Research Branch, AERD, ARS, U.S. Department of Agriculture

ABSTRACT

To design systems for controlling the "case" of tobacco, more information was needed on the rate at which moisture was absorbed by the tobacco leaves when placed in a controlled wetting environment.

An analysis of the problem led to the derivation of the equation

$$\frac{M_e - M}{M_e - M_0} = \left[\frac{a}{a + t} \right]^b$$

where M_e = equilibrium moisture content, M_0 = moisture content at time $t = 0$, M = moisture content at time $t \geqslant 0$, t = time, a = experimental constant, and b = experimental constant. This equation was tested as to its fit of experimental data and was found to give very good approximations of the actual curve if the parameters a and b were properly selected and the values of the initial and equilibrium moisture contents could be accurately obtained.

Also, this relationship was compared with the equation

$$\frac{M - M_e}{M_0 - M_e} = e^{-ut}$$

where u is a parameter depending on the air velocity and other variables which may be termed "drying conditions" which has been used for drying operations and was found to give a better least squares fit of the data.

The values of the parameter b were tested for variation between grades and environmental conditions. The value of b was found to be significantly affected by the grade of tobacco, and this variation appeared to be due to differences in color and quality rather than to differences in stalk position.

The curve given by using the average values of a and b was felt to be of value in approximating the response of grades for which the parameters have not been evaluated.

INTRODUCTION

Many problems associated with the handling and storage of biological materials culminate into one major problem, the dynamics of moisture movement into and out of the biological materials as influenced by the environment. This is particularly true with tobacco since the moisture content required for proper handling of tobacco is higher than that allowable in proper storage. Also, at certain stages in the handling of the tobacco, it is advantageous to exchange moisture between the tobacco and the atmosphere as

* The investigation reported in this paper (No. 64-2-13) is in connection with a project of the Kentucky Agricultural Experimental Station and is published with approval of the Director.

231

rapidly as possible to facilitate mechanization.

In order to design systems for controlling the "case" of tobacco, more information is needed on the rate of moisture sorption of tobacco in terms of the physical properties of the leaves and of the environmental conditions. A review of the literature revealed no relationship which was judged to be satisfactory for describing the sorption curve of tobacco subjected to a wetting environment. However, some indication of the factors which might affect the moisture sorption was obtained from a study of relationships which have been used for drying operations. Sherwood[3] stated that a useful equation of a simple form can be derived by assuming that the rate of drying of a slab is directly proportional to the moisture content. He stated that although this assumption is only a rough approximation, it leads to an equation which fits the drying data surprisingly well. The integrated form of the equation is:

$$\frac{M - M_e}{M_0 - M_e} = e^{-ut} \qquad (1)$$

where

t = time
M_0 = moisture content at time zero
M = moisture content at time t
M_e = equilibrium moisture content
u = a parameter depending on the air velocity and other variables which

may be termed "drying conditions." It varies inversely with the slab thickness.

Sherwood concluded that the proportionality constant u in Eq. (1) needed to change with moisture content for a better fit of his drying data. This implied that u was a function of time.

Jeffrey[1] worked with Kentucky Agricultural Experiment Station No. 16 Burley tobacco and found that the equilibrium moisture content of cured tobacco varied with relative humidity as shown in Fig. 1. The relationship is nonlinear in the range of humidities between 50 and 80 per cent. This range is of particular importance in tobacco conditioning because it corresponds to a change in the condition of the tobacco from the brittle state to the satisfactory case state. The nonlinear characteristic of the equilibrium moisture content *vs* relative humidity relationship also implies that the resistance to moisture movement into tobacco is a function of the moisture content or time. Therefore, the present study was undertaken to develop a more suitable relationship for expressing moisture content as a function of time.

ANALYSIS OF THE PROBLEM

Many properties of tobacco leaves and environmental conditions were considered in an attempt to describe their influence upon the

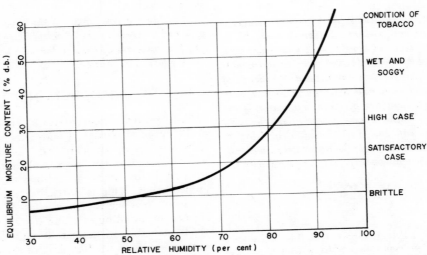

Fig. 1. Effect of relative humidity on the equilibrium moisture content of Burley tobacco.[1,p.375]

moisture transfer. After a careful consideration of each, the following factors were selected as those believed to influence the moisture movement: (1) leaf thickness, (2) pore space, (3) density of the leaf, (4) the difference between the equilibrium moisture content and the initial moisture content, (5) the velocity of the water molecules in the environment, (6) the density of the water vapor, and (7) time. Temperature and relative humidity were not considered directly, but their influence was assumed to be included in the velocity and density of the vapor molecules in the environment. Also, it was assumed that the moisture moved only in a direction perpendicular to the plane of the leaf.

These factors were combined into a mathematical relationship through the use of dimensional analysis. The result of the dimensional analysis procedure was:

$$\Delta t = C\left[\frac{x}{V}\right](P)^e\left[\frac{\gamma t}{\gamma w}\right]^f(\Delta M)^g \qquad (2)$$

where

Δt = the time between the initial subjection of a leaf to a wetting environment and the instant at which a new equilibrium is reached

C = dimensionless proportionality constant

x = thickness of leaf

V = velocity of vapor molecules in the environment

P = percentage pore space based on bulk volume of leaf

γt = dry matter density of tobacco leaf

γw = density of water vapor

ΔM = difference between equilibrium moisture content and initial moisture content expressed as a percentage of the oven dry weight of the leaf

$e, f,$ and g = exponents to be determined experimentally.

It may be noted that all the right-hand terms of Eq. (2) will remain constant, except the moisture content difference, for a given sample at constant conditions. This allowed the following simplification of Eq. (2).

$$\Delta t = K(\Delta M)^g \qquad (3)$$

where

$$K = C\left[\frac{x}{V}\right](P)\left[\frac{\gamma t}{\gamma w}\right]^f \qquad (4)$$

From Eq. (3) the following equation for the moisture ratio was developed:

$$\frac{M_e - M}{M_e - M_0} = \left[\frac{t_e - t}{t_e}\right]^h \qquad (5)$$

where

M_0 = moisture content at time, $t = 0$

$h = 1/g$ = exponent to be evaluated

t_e = time at which an equilibrium moisture content is reached

M_e = equilibrium moisture content

M = moisture content at time $t \geqslant 0$

t = any general time $t_e \geqslant t \geqslant 0$.

EXPERIMENTAL PROCEDURE

The method chosen by which to determine the form of the experimental transient moisture curve was to bring the tobacco into equilibrium with a low relative humidity environment and then subject it to a high humidity environment and record the weight with respect to time until a new equilibrium was reached. This was done, through the use of three environmental control chambers. The first chamber was used to condition the tobacco leaves to a low initial equilibrium moisture content. The leaves were then transferred to one of the other two chambers where they were subjected to a wetting environment.

The environmental chambers designed to meet these needs were constructed of $\frac{1}{2}$-in. plywood with dimensions of $30'' \times 30'' \times 45''$. These chambers were equipped with resistance heaters for controlling the temperature and with metal pans which were used to hold saturated salt solutions which controlled the relative humidity within the boxes. The two chambers used for maintaining high relative humidities were insulated to reduce the heat loss and eliminate moisture condensation on the walls. Condensation was not a problem, and insulation was not necessary in the chamber used for maintaining low humidities.

Powerstats were used to control the voltage across the resistance heaters in the high humidity chambers. Since the boxes were located in an air-conditioned room with a fairly constant temperature, it was possible to maintain a more constant temperature within the boxes by adjusting the power input than by using a thermostat. This was important since a sudden change in temperature due to the differential of a thermostat would have caused a large change in the relative humidity and introduced large experimental errors.

Four different environmental conditions were tested using different combinations of two initial and two final conditions. The two initial conditions were maintained by a lithium chloride solution at 86°F and a sodium chloride solution at 104°F. The two final conditions were maintained by potassium chromate and barium chloride solutions at 86°F. The relative humidities maintained by these four different solutions were measured with a Foxboro "Dewcel"* and found to be 15, 65, 80, and 87 per cent respectively.

The top of each of the two high humidity chambers was constructed with six 5″ by 5″ hinged trap doors. Each of these doors had a 1/2-in. diameter hole with a wire hook passing through and a cork stopper holding it in place. These trap doors allowed the placing of leaves in the chambers without greatly changing the conditions. The leaves were hung on the wire hooks which could then be weighed by removing the cork stopper and placing one end of the hook on a load cell.

A load cell with a range 0 to 0.75 ounce was used in connection with a digital strain indicator to record the weight of the leaves. The sensitivity of the weight determination was ± 0.005 ounce.

Tests were conducted on six different Federal Government grades. Eight samples consisting of one leaf each were randomly selected for each environmental condition from each of the grades. Thus a total of 192 leaves was tested.

The six grades selected for testing were chosen from a list of possible Government grades for Burley tobacco. These were selected to represent a wide variation in quality and stalk position. The grades selected were: B2FR, X5G, X2L, T3FR, C2F, and T5GR.

* Mention of company or trade names of specific equipment is for the purpose of identification and does not imply endorsement by State Agencies or U.S. Government.

ANALYSIS AND DISCUSSION OF RESULTS

Initial empirical analysis of Eq. (5) and the experimental data showed both t_e and h to be negative. Therefore, Eq. (5) is not valid if t_e has the physical meaning of time which it was originally given. For this reason, Eq. (5) was transposed by replacing t_e by $(-a)$ and h by $(-b)$. This generalization effectively relocates the origin of reference for the equation and results in the following equation form:

$$\frac{M_e - M}{M_e - M_0} = \left[\frac{a}{a + t}\right]^b \qquad (6)$$

where a and b are positive quantities as applied to the data of this study.

Other than the removal of any physical significance from the parameters, the primary difference between Eqs. (5) and (6) is that Eq. (5) describes a leaf reaction which can reach absolute equilibrium and Eq. (6) describes a reaction which only approaches equilibrium values asymptotically. In this respect, Eq. (6) is more like the equation given by Sherwood.[3] However, in the actual tests the moisture content was found to reach a maximum and then to decrease. In any case, it should be pointed out that the maximum moisture content obtained was used as the equilibrium moisture content in the analysis of the data.

The decrease in weight that occurred may have been due to deterioration starting in the leaves after they were subjected to a very high humidity for a period of about three days. Results of preliminary tests at 96 per cent RH indicate that such leaf deterioration does significantly affect the moisture uptake curve. Figure 2 shows two forms of curves which resulted from the exposure of tobacco leaves to a relative humidity of 96 per cent. The first form is characterized by a sudden increase in moisture content, while the second is characterized by a long period of moisture uptake at a near constant rate. These changes in the expected moisture uptake patterns were accompanied by mold formation on the leaves or other visible leaf deterioration. Because of these results the formal study was confined to environment relative humidities below 90 per cent.

By a numerical method given by Scarborough,[2] a least squares fit of Eq. (6) to

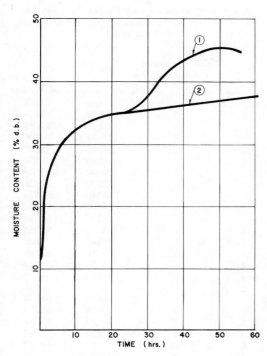

FIG. 2. Moisture uptake of tobacco leaves in a 96 per cent RH environment.

the average values of the moisture ratio at the various values of time was obtained for each of the 24 different combinations of grade and environmental condition. Also, the coefficients of correlation between the experimental values of the moisture ratio and the values computed by Eq. (6) were calculated. The results of these computations are given in Table 1.

To compare the relationship given by Eq. (6) with that given by Sherwood,[3] it was necessary to compute the best value of u in Eq. (1) and to compute the coefficient of correlation between the experimental values of the moisture ratio and the values computed by Eq. (1). The results of these computations are given in Table 2.

Equation (6) was found in each case to give a higher correlation between experimental and computed values of the moisture ratio than the relationship given by Sherwood.[3] A graphical comparison of the two equations is shown in Fig. 3. The plotted points represent the average of all the experimental data at each testing period. The curves representing each of the equations was determined by

using the average value for the parameters.

In contrast to Eq. (1), which assumes that:

$$\frac{dM}{dt} = u(M_e - M) \qquad (7)$$

where u is constant throughout the test, Eq. (6) gives a relationship which allows a decrease in the proportionality constant. By differentiation of Eq. (6) the following relationship may be obtained:

$$\frac{dM}{dt} = \left[\frac{b}{a + t}\right](M_e - M) \qquad (8)$$

Thus, Eq. (6) indicates that the rate of moisture movement is not directly proportional to the free moisture content but is equal to a function of time multiplied by the free moisture content. This function of time decreases in value as time increases. By examining Fig. 1 in light of Fick's Law which states that the rate of moisture movement is proportional to the vapor pressure difference, it can be seen why the function of time should

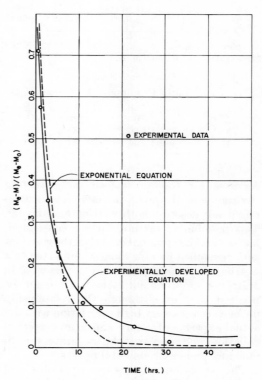

FIG. 3. Comparisons of the regression equations and experimental data given for average values.

TABLE 1. VALUES OF THE PARAMETERS a AND b IN EQ. (6) AND THE CORRESPONDING CORRELATION COEFFICIENTS

Grade*	Environmental Conditions**	a	b	r
1	1	3.10908	1.57569	.99960
1	2	1.96808	1.19839	.99988
1	3	3.87634	1.92162	.99982
1	4	3.89004	1.56780	.99980
2	1	.45685	.78392	.99812
2	2	.61254	.64923	.99786
2	3	.82817	.96585	.99974
2	4	.77714	.92979	.99910
3	1	1.07749	1.07456	.99896
3	2	2.58246	1.32171	.99953
3	3	2.46678	1.51874	.99991
3	4	3.99889	1.77480	.99973
4	1	.64249	.92289	.99875
4	2	5.33549	1.77114	.99852
4	3	2.24688	1.19938	.99965
4	4	2.88598	1.26621	.99922
5	1	.70829	1.04274	.99910
5	2	1.63751	1.12122	.99925
5	3	1.08929	.84048	.99920
5	4	2.84225	1.41137	.99936
6	1	.26855	.65798	.99706
6	2	2.38936	.81151	.99834
6	3	1.62484	.98174	.99911
6	4	3.59942	1.31786	.99981

* Key to grades: (1) B2FR; (2) X5G; (3) X2L; (4) T3FR; (5) C2F; (6) T5GR.

** Key to Environmental Conditions:

	Initial Conditions	Final Conditions
1	15%; 86°F	80%; 86°F
2	65%; 104°F	80%; 86°F
3	15%; 86°F	87%; 86°F
4	65%; 104°F	87%; 86°F

TABLE 2. VALUES OF THE CONSTANT u IN EQ. (1) AND THE CORRESPONDING COEFFICIENTS OF CORRELATION

Grade*	Environmental Conditions**	u	r
1	1	.27366	.99544
1	2	.23352	.98945
1	3	.29113	.99633
1	4	.22751	.99706
2	1	.31038	.93972
2	2	.13290	.95268
2	3	.29096	.96325
2	4	.27050	.95830
3	1	.30940	.97516
3	2	.18205	.98552
3	3	.30599	.99340
3	4	.25934	.99683
4	1	.30147	.94226
4	2	.20310	.99686
4	3	.23531	.99344
4	4	.20128	.99475
5	1	.45333	.96146
5	2	.25651	.98854
5	3	.21753	.98479
5	4	.25748	.99551
6	1	.26273	.90173
6	2	.10113	.99113
6	3	.21745	.99645
6	4	.16965	.99541

* Key to grades; (1) B2FR; (2) X5G; (3) X2L; (4) T3FR; (5) C2F; (6) T5GR.

** Key to Environmental Conditions:

	Initial Conditions	Final Conditions
1	15%; 86°F	80%; 86°F
2	65%; 104°F	80%; 86°F
3	15%; 86°F	87%; 86°F
4	65%; 104°F	87%; 86°F

decrease for tobacco placed in a wetting environment. However, the same relationship might not describe both wetting and drying. This possibility was not further considered, but it should be remembered that the relationship developed was for tobacco subjected to a wetting environment and may not be valid in a drying environment. Also, it should be realized that even though the relationship developed has a very high correlation with the actual experimental curves, it is an empirical equation and may not be accurate for all moisture and environmental ranges.

The variation of b between grades and environmental conditions was tested by an analysis of variance conducted on the em-pirically determined values of b. The parameter b was found to vary significantly between grades at the 0.01 level of F. However, the variation was not significant for environmental conditions at the 0.05 level of F. Further observation of the computed values of b indicates that the variation occurs due to differences in quality and color rather than to stalk position. The two grades which gave the lowest values of b were T5GR and X5G. Thus, both were green and of poor quality, and yet they were from opposite ends of the stalk. Also, the grades X2L and T3FR, which gave considerably higher values of b than those given by the previously mentioned grades, were from opposite ends of the

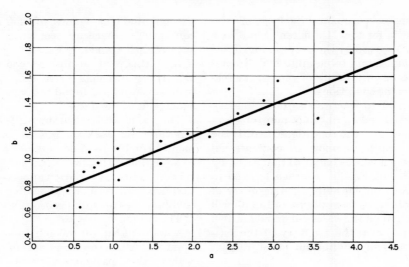

FIG. 4. Relationship between a and b.

stalk but both of reasonably good quality.

The variation of parameter a was tested in the same manner and was found to vary significantly between both grades and environmental conditions at the 0.05 level of F.

A further study of the values obtained for a and b for the 24 different tests indicated that there could be a relationship between the two. The values of a and b were plotted against each other as shown in Fig. 4. The relationship appeared to be linear or of the form:

$$b = \alpha + \beta a \qquad (9)$$

The values of α and β were computed by the method of least squares to obtain

$$b = 0.70 + 0.23a \qquad (10)$$

The coefficient of linear correlation between a and b was calculated and found to be 0.89.

Since the values of a and b were not determined for all possible grades nor all environmental conditions and extensive experimentation would be required to determine the values under all these conditions, a further study of the data obtained in this experiment was made to determine what errors could be expected if the average values of a and b from the 24 different conditions of this investigation were used in Eq. (6). Figure 5 shows the curve given by Eq. (6) using the average values of a and b which were found to be 2.12 and 1.19 respectively. Also shown is a 95 per cent confidence interval for the values of the

moisture ratio which was obtained by assuming that the values of the moisture ratio for a given time were normally distributed about the values given by the curve. The correlation

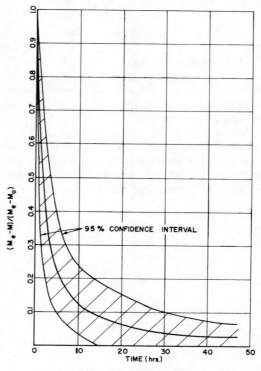

FIG. 5. Relationship between moisture ratio and time given by average values of a and b in Eq. (6).

between the experimental values of the moisture ratio for the 24 different conditions and the values given by the curve in Fig. 5 was computed and found to be quite high despite the variation in the values of the parameters for the different conditions.

To put Eq. (6) to practical use, it is necessary that the initial and equilibrium moisture contents be known for the conditions used. If the initial and equilibrium moisture contents can be taken from a curve similar to that given by Jeffrey[1] (Fig. 1), Eq. (6) can then be used to describe the transient state. The accuracy of the values obtained from the use of Eq. (6) will depend both upon the values of a and b which are used and upon the accuracy of the estimated initial and equilibrium moisture contents.

A comparison of the equilibrium moisture contents obtained in this investigation with the curve given in Fig. 1 indicates that more investigation is needed to determine the equilibrium moisture content of different grades of tobacco at a wider range of environmental conditions, particularly in the range of relative humidities above 80 per cent.

SUMMARY

To design systems for controlling the "case" of tobacco, more information was needed on the rate at which moisture was absorbed by the tobacco leaves when placed in a controlled wetting environment.

An analysis of the problem led to the derivation of Eq. (6). This equation was tested as to its fit of experimental data and was found to give very good approximations of the actual curve if the parameters a and b were properly selected and the values of the initial and equilibrium moisture contents could be accurately obtained.

Also, this relationship was compared with Eq. (1) which has been used for drying operations and was found to give a better least squares fit of the data.

The values of the parameter b were tested for variation between grades and environmental conditions. The value of b was found to be significantly affected by the grade of the tobacco, and this variation appeared to be due to differences in color and quality rather than to differences in stalk position.

The curve given by using the average values of a and b in Eq. (6) was felt to be of value in approximating the response of grades for which the parameters have not been evaluated.

Acknowledgment. The work reported herein was conducted jointly by the Agricultural Engineering Department, Kentucky Agricultural Experiment Station, and the Harvesting and Farm Processing Research Branch, Agricultural Engineering Research Division (ARS), U.S.D.A.

References

1. Jeffrey, R. N., "The Effect of Temperature and Relative Humidity During and After Curing, Upon the Quality of White Burley Tobacco," *Kentucky Agr. Expt. Sta., Bull.,* **407** (1940).
2. Scarborough, James B., "Numerical Mathematical Analysis," Chapter 16, Baltimore, The John Hopkins Press, 1955.
3. Sherwood, T. K., "The Drying of Solids, IV. Application of Diffusion Equations," *Ind. Eng. Chem.,* **24**, 307 (1932).
4. Young, James H., "Development of a Relationship Between Moisture Content and Time for Burley Tobacco in a Controlled Environment," Unpublished M.S. Thesis, University of Kentucky, Lexington, Ky., 1964.

SECTION III

ENVIRONMENTAL CHAMBERS

30. Principles in the Design of Cabinets for Controlled Environments*

K. R. Solvason and N. B. Hutcheon

Division of Building Research, National Research Council, Canada

ABSTRACT

The design or selection of a conditioned cabinet should only be made after thorough consideration of the requirements. Failure to recognize all the basic elements of the problem may often lead to unreasonable requirements in respect to some factors, while ignoring others which may equally influence the final performance. In the air-conditioning design special emphasis should be placed on reducing heat and moisture exchanges between the cabinet and ambient and on air circulation or stirring to reduce spatial variations in temperature and humidity to a practical minimum.

The product temperature will be governed not only by air temperature but also by radiant energy exchange with the cabinet walls and furnishings. The design should, therefore, ensure minimum radiant transfer and high convective heat transfer to the product when it is desired to control the product to air temperature. Close control of humidity, especially where relative humidity sensing is used, also requires close temperature control because of the dependence of relative humidity on temperature. All cabinet and equipment surfaces must be designed to operate above the desired dew-point temperature.

Precision in control can only be obtained by careful attention to the response characteristics of the conditioning equipment and the cabinet itself, as well as to those of the control devices.

* This paper is a contribution from the Division of Building Research, National Research Council, Canada and is published with the approval of the Director of the Division.

Though the performance is influenced by each component, it is the interaction of one with the other and with the product being conditioned that determines the ultimate performance.

INTRODUCTION

Conditioned cabinets are used to provide small spaces of less than room size where one or more atmospheric factors, including temperature, humidity, air motion, and pressure, can be controlled within acceptable limits. The practical and technical considerations associated with them almost always pose a challenging problem for the designer. Too often the potential user, who may not be aware of the problems involved, will set unrealistic requirements, which may be met by the designer or supplier at unnecessarily high cost or ignored at the risk of subsequent dissatisfaction and recrimination. Ideally, all requirements should be carefully explored in extensive discussions between the user and the supplier or designer to establish clearly the minimum performance actually required, unless the user himself has had extensive experience. This paper will be concerned mainly with some of the basic principles and considerations with which the user or purchaser, as well as the designer, ought to be familiar. It will be limited also to cabinets for use at atmospheric pressure at temperatures from —60 to 200°F.

The provision of the desired conditions within a cabinet has all the engineering problems of air-conditioning. The system may be considered in three parts: the enclosure, the conditioning equipment, and the control system. Though each of these merits consideration individually, it is their interdependence and the interaction of one with the other and with the product being conditioned that is the real core of the design problem and ultimately governs the final performance.

THE BASIC CONDITIONING PROBLEM

The elements of the basic problem, involving heat, moisture, and radiant energy exchange between the product, the cabinet atmosphere, and the cabinet enclosure, are illustrated in Fig. 1. The product may be material being conditioned, or it may be an apparatus for which a controlled environment is being provided. In either case, both the product and the cabinet enclosure may be exchanging sensible heat, H, and water vapor, M, with the cabinet air. In addition, if the product and the cabinet wall are not at the same temperature, there will be a radiation exchange, R, between them. Such other contents of the cabinet as furnishings and equipment may at any given time be exchanging both heat and moisture with the cabinet air and radiant energy with the enclosure surface in a manner similar to that of the product.

The net result of these exchanges will be the addition of an amount of sensible heat, H, and an amount of moisture, M, in unit time, to the cabinet air being circulated through the cabinet at a rate W, based on weight of dry air in unit time. H and M may be positive or negative. If h and m are the enthalpy and moisture content, respectively, for a unit weight of air, and assuming that conditions are not changing rapidly, simple mass and energy balances may be written as follows:

$$H = W(h_2 - h_1) \qquad (1)$$

$$M = W(m_2 - m_1) \qquad (2)$$

Examination of these equations leads to three important conclusions:

(1) Conditions throughout a conditioned space can *never* be uniform so long as there are heat or moisture exchanges between product or cabinet and the conditioned air.

(2) For a given air circulation rate, the spatial variations in conditions will be in proportion to the heat and moisture exchanges involving the air.

(3) For constant heat and moisture exchanges, the differences in air condition throughout the space will vary inversely with the air circulation rate.

Thus, when spatial variations must be kept small, it is necessary either to keep heat and moisture loads, i.e. H and M, as small as possible or to provide a high circulation or stirring rate, or both. As will be shown, there are other substantial advantages to be gained in this direction, so that minimizing the conditioning load and maintaining a high circulation rate become important basic objectives in cabinet design for highly uniform conditions. The primary entering airstream will show the greatest departure from average conditions, but this effect is modified rapidly along its path as mixing occurs as a result of the induced secondary circulation. The condition of the leaving air will generally reflect more closely the average cabinet conditions.

Consider, next, the conditioner shown in Fig. 1. Its function is to reverse the change in heat and moisture conditions of the airstream from those at 2 to those at 1, but an additional heat load, S, which is always positive, must

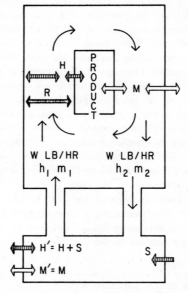

Fig. 1. The basic conditioning problem.

be introduced. This is the energy input to the fan or blower required to circulate the conditioned air. The conditioner must then reject sensible heat at a rate $H' = H + S$ and water vapor at a rate $M' = M$. It may, in the process, condense the water vapor, rejecting it as liquid, in which case a further amount of sensible heat, L, representing that released on condensing, must be added to H', the reverse being true if water is added.

For the general case, the four basic functions required in addition to stirring are heating, cooling, humidifying, and dehumidifying. The provision of all four requires complex equipment and control, but simpler systems may be used when the nature of the requirements is such that the loads do not change sign, as from heating to cooling or humidifying to dehumidifying. Heating may be accomplished readily with electric heaters or heated liquid coils. Cooling may be obtained with cooled liquid coils or with the new thermoelectric cooling devices. Dehumidification may be accomplished by chemical means or by condensation on cooled surfaces.

THE STIRRING PROBLEM

It is recognized that there is potential conflict in the desired objectives of minimizing loads and keeping circulation rate high. High circulation can only be accomplished by the expenditure of energy to drive a fan that, in turn, eventually appears as sensible heat in the air. A distinction may be made, however, between the heat load, S, introduced by the fan, and that portion of it, called here the stirring load, that appears in the cabinet proper.

In the arrangement thus far discussed, stirring within the cabinet is provided by the kinetic energy of the entering air; as it is gradually dissipated and converted to sensible heat, it induces a secondary circulation throughout the space. Only that part of the load, S, that appears as kinetic energy in the entering air contributes directly to the load within the cabinet, and it is of importance in this respect only when velocities are high. The dissipation of an entering velocity of 2000 fpm results in an increase in air temperature of 0.1°F. In other arrangements separate fans may be installed for stirring in the working space, contributing their total energy input to the space.

THE RADIATION PROBLEM

It was noted earlier that the product and the interior surface of the cabinet enclosure might be at different temperatures. There would, therefore, be a radiant energy exchange between them as shown in Fig. 1. This might readily occur under transient or cyclical conditions of operation or during periods when the product is adjusting to cabinet conditions. It is not so readily appreciated that such a difference can exist even under certain steady-state conditions, with the result that the product temperature may differ appreciably from the cabinet air temperature.

When cabinet conditions are markedly different from ambient, there will be a heat flow through the enclosing wall of the cabinet, depending upon the differences in conditions and the wall thermal conductance. This will result in an interior wall surface temperature different from the interior air temperature at which the combined convective and radiative heat exchanges of the surface are in balance with the heat exchange through the wall. It can readily be demonstrated by calculation that for a relatively poor cabinet wall, consisting of 1 in. of wood and ambient temperatures differing by 20 or 30°F from cabinet air, the product temperature may differ by as much as 1°F or more from air temperature.

Under these conditions the product is in thermal equilibrium, but it is exchanging heat by radiation with the enclosing wall surface at a rate balanced by its exchange of heat, opposite in sign, by convection with the air. These differences are calculable under steady-state conditions provided that the appropriate convection coefficients and emissivities for both product and wall surfaces are known. Somewhat similar conditions may result when heating or cooling surfaces, warm motors, light bulbs, or window surfaces at temperatures different from cabinet air temperature are located so that they can exchange thermal energy by radiation with the product.

It will be evident that, when precise control over the product condition is to be maintained, the product must be protected from such radiative exchanges. It will be apparent also that thermostats and humidistats must be similarly protected. Radiation shielding may be employed to advantage, but it will usually be best to eliminate the basic cause of the difficulty, whenever possible, by removing heating or cooling devices from the space and by using a well insulated enclosure so that its surface temperature will be closer to cabinet air temperature.

Once again, the maintenance of high rates of air circulation is shown to be desirable. The higher the velocity, the higher will be the convection coefficients, thus increasing the importance of convective heat exchange over radiative exchange and bringing all surfaces closer to the cabinet air temperature.

THE HUMIDITY PROBLEM

The requirement for simultaneous control of temperature and humidity poses special problems. The main one arises out of the temperature dependence of relative humidity. For a constant humidity ratio (water vapor to dry air, by weight) and changing temperature at constant barometric pressure, the water vapor partial pressure, e, is also constant. Relative humidity (e/e_{sat}), therefore, varies inversely as the saturation pressure, e_{sat}, corresponding to the temperature. Changes in e_{sat} for 1 F deg change at various temperatures can be obtained from tables. The change in relative humidity for 1 F deg temperature change decreases as temperature increases, at high humidities being roughly 5 per cent per F deg at 0°F and 3 per cent at 100°F. The proportional change in relative humidity, (not percentage points) for 1 F deg temperature change from a particular temperature is independent of relative humidity.

When precision in relative humidity is required, the temperature control must also be precise. This applies not only to the temperature of the conditioned air but also to the temperature of the product and the humidity sensing devices, spatial temperature variations, as well as radiation exchanges, being particularly important in this respect.

The physics and thermodynamics of the air-vapor system are the basis for air-conditioning theory and must be fully appreciated as a prerequisite in design for humidity conditioning. Only a few of the practical considerations will be discussed.

Advantage is often taken of the constancy of vapor pressure at constant barometer with changing temperature in the dew-point method of control. A saturated mixture is produced at the dew-point temperature of the desired final condition so that, upon heating to the required final dry-bulb temperature, the required relative humidity is produced. Account must always be taken of the heat released when water vapor is adsorbed or condensed and of the opposite effect when it is desorbed or evaporated.

Cooling below the dew-point is a means of dehumidifying. No portion of the cabinet or conditioner system must operate unintentionally at temperatures below the desired final dew-point, or this will produce dehumidification and thus prevent the attainment of the desired relative humidity. This is particularly important in cabinets operated at temperatures well above ambient and in systems in which heat and moisture adjustments are made separately in different devices. In such cases a large coil operating at high air velocity to produce the required heat exchange at an acceptably small differential with air temperature may be employed, or cooling may be followed by rehumidifying. It may be noted that in a cabinet having a cooling requirement at high humidity provided by a conditioned airstream, the relative humidity that can be carried can never be greater than that corresponding to saturation at the entering air temperature. Conversely, when extremely high humidities must be produced, spatial variations in temperature, including those involved in the conditioning airstream, must be reduced to appropriate low levels. Heat gains to the cabinet must be eliminated, as far as possible, and high rates of air circulation maintained. The maintenance of precisely 100 per cent RH without fogging is impossible in practice.

THE CONTROL PROBLEM

All possible variations and solutions of the control problem cover a broad range, which has become a full-time specialty in itself. The main features of a system, however, that make the control problem easy or difficult can be readily appreciated. Consider a simple cabinet requiring heating only, with an air thermostat operating an electric heater on and off as required. The first determinant is the reliability and sensitivity of the control itself. Next to be considered is its time of response to a given change in air temperature, in relation to the rate at which the heater is capable of raising the air temperature as well as the speed of response of the heater to the on-off switching.

These same considerations apply equally well to humidity control with the sensitivity, reproducibility, and speed of response of the humidity sensing element being of paramount importance. Again the correcting device, humidifier, or dehumidifier must respond rapidly to the on-off switching, and its output must be controlled in relation to the moisture loss or gain. The moisture capacity of the air in small cabinets is very small, and the cabinet and its furnishings may not provide appreciable moisture storage unless a hygroscopic material is purposely provided.

Over-shooting of the control point will result with on-off systems controlling temperature or humidity if the heat or moisture capacity of the cabinet is small, the correcting device is of large capacity and slow to respond, and the sensing element is sluggish. Occasionally the extreme cycling control provided in this manner may be acceptable if it maintains a constant mean value. The time response of the cabinet may change, however, if ambient conditions change, thus shifting the mean control condition.

On-off control is widely used in conditioned cabinets and leads to simple control and conditioning equipment. Precision is increased if:

(1) the response time of the sensing element can be decreased,

(2) the response time of the correcting devices can be decreased,

(3) the response time of the system to the restoring action can be increased.

The response time of a thermal sensing element and of a heating or cooling element will be a function of its heat capacity and overall heat transmission characteristics. The lighter the element and the larger its ratio of surface to volume, the faster its response will usually be. Elements immersed in air will have a much longer response time than those in liquid by a factor of as much as 100 because of the lower heat transmission characteristics of air or vapor compared to liquid. Increasing the velocity of flow over an element will decrease the response time. Fortunately there are now available temperature sensors having low capacity and providing relatively fast response in air. Electric heaters usually provide relatively fast response, but liquid-filled coils including their associated liquid heating or cooling devices will be relatively sluggish. It will often be of advantage to operate cooling devices continuously at capacities just over the maximum cooling capacity required, and to follow them with fast-response electric heating to provide the final precise control.

The time response of a cabinet will be a function of the heat and moisture losses or gains, its thermal and moisture storage capacity, and the capacity of the restoring action being called into play. Improvement in control capability can, therefore, be achieved if the losses or gains can be kept small, the restoring action limited only to that required, and the cabinet response time increased.

Relative humidity sensors generally react like a hygroscopic material; that is, their moisture content varies in relation to the relative humidity of the air. If the element is maintained at constant temperature, the speed of response to a given vapor pressure change is inversely proportional to the moisture capacity of the element and the resistance to water vapor flow from the air to the element. Elements of the electrical resistance type are now available, having an accurately reproducible rapid response to small changes in relative humidity at normal temperatures. At low temperatures, however, as the water vapor pressure is very low and, hence, the vapor pressure difference for a given change in relative humidity is extremely small, much slower response will result. In many cases it may be impractical to attempt humidity control using relative humidity sensors at low temperatures, and some form of dew-point control may be necessary.

Where on-off control is not suitable, proportional controls capable of continuously varying the restoring action in relation to the need can be used. All system components must again be carefully selected with regard to response times to achieve stable control.

Modifications to these and to still other types of controls with increasingly complicated characteristics can be used in the more extreme and more difficult cases. The designer may make use of the thermal storage capacity of liquids in the system when this is an advantage and avoid this when it is not.

CYCLING CONDITION CABINETS

The design of cycling condition cabinets depends largely upon the objective to be achieved, but it will almost always be difficult. Some thought will show that when rapid cycling is involved the conditioning loads may be very high, the spatial variations large, and the product condition will not necessarily follow the cabinet conditions closely.

It may only be desired to expose the product to some prescribed cycle of cabinet conditions, with the product condition cycling in response to this. A change in the product with respect to kind of material, size, or shape will then change the pattern of conditions produced in it by a given pattern of cabinet conditions.

When the product consists of a number of samples to be conditioned uniformly, it becomes necessary to ensure that the conditions are the same for each sample. Each must be exposed to the same radiation exchanges. If the cabinet air is to be circulated over a number of samples in series, conditions will change along the air flow path. For slowly changing conditions this change may not be significant. In most cases, however, it will be necessary to distribute the heat and moisture sources and sinks among the samples to achieve equal exposure, unless the samples are arranged for one-pass parallel air circulation. The relative humidity at the sample will not be that of the main airstream but will be determined by the temperature and vapor pressure at the sample surface.

SOME FEATURES OF CABINETS AND EQUIPMENT

The size and arrangement of a cabinet will be influenced by the intended use and the conditions and the control precision required. If it is to be used only for conditions close to room temperature, a relatively simple enclosure may suffice. On the other hand, if operation is required at temperatures below room dew point, air locks may be needed to facilitate insertion and removal of samples without disturbing cabinet conditions or damaging samples. Where samples must be manipulated inside the cabinet, gloved openings may be used, or where temperatures are not too different from ambient, say 35 to 110°F, a walk-in cabinet may be considered. Even at 35°F, however, difficulty may be experienced in walk-in cabinets from condensation of moisture from the operator's hands and breath on samples, particularly where precision weighing is required. At lower temperatures most manipulation may have to be done remotely; weighing, for example, can be carried out by attaching samples to an external balance by a connection through the cabinet wall. Remotely controlled machinery inside the cabinet may be required in some cases for tests or product manipulation.

The cabinet-conditioner system thus far discussed is fully recirculating, with the conditioner separated from the cabinet, but other arrangements are possible. Only a portion of the air drawn from the cabinet may be passed through the conditioner, to be mixed with the main stream and returned. Where the product is a source of contamination, which would increase in concentration under full recirculating conditions, ventilation may be introduced by rejecting a part of the air drawn from the cabinet and replacing it with ambient air. The necessary adjustments in heat and moisture content of this entering ventilating air will then contribute to the heat and moisture loads.

The conditioner may also be located within the cabinet but separated from the controlled space, as in the design shown in Fig. 2. In this case the air duct connections between conditioner and cabinet are eliminated, though the system is fundamentally unchanged. There is, however, a marked practical advantage. When the equipment is external to the cabinet there can be substantial loads from air leakage into the system resulting from the pressure differences along the air flow circuit. This is a common fault in many cabinets. It is also possible to locate the essential components of the conditioner within the controlled space, particularly when the functions required and, therefore, the number of com-

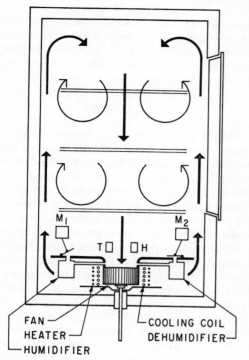

M$_1$ M$_2$

T☐ ☐H

FAN
HEATER ┐ ┌ COOLING COIL
HUMIDIFIER   DEHUMIDIFIER

Fig. 2. Cabinet with conditioning equipment inside.

ponents are reduced. The advantage of reduced spatial variations resulting from proper juxtaposition of components and good mixing of the conditioned airstream may then be lost.

Special designs of systems can often be devised for particular requirements. When spatial variations and radiation exchanges in the conditioned space are likely to be a problem, the cabinet may be completely lined with coils or hollow metal plates, or made of double-walled tank construction through which a controlled temperature liquid is circulated. Thermal loads arising from ambient conditions are, thus, intercepted; the conditioned space is provided with a uniform radiation environment; the small stirring load can be taken out with very small temperature differences from the large enclosing surface. In such a case it will usually be adequate to control jacket liquid temperature rather than air temperature, and the large thermal capacity of the liquid then facilitates control.

In the design of a freeze-thaw apparatus the authors found it possible to utilize rather than minimize heat exchange by radiation in the cabinet. This was for an automatic cycling apparatus to employ air freezing and liquid thawing of concrete specimens on a 12-hour cycle. It is a problem in such cases to achieve uniform conditions throughout a cabinet, even with high circulation, because of the heavy thermal load, the unavoidable differences in air flow over specimens, and the marked differences between entering and leaving air temperature. In the design employed the specimens were placed in rows between liquid-cooled plates, which could be held at a uniform temperature from end to end with liquid circulated from a tank. Each specimen was, thus, subjected to nearly identical conditions of cooling by radiation on two faces. In addition, high air circulation was maintained parallel to the plates and rows of specimens to promote even further by forced convection the rate and uniformity of heat exchange. As the circulating airstream was not cooled outside the cabinet, it always entered at exactly the same temperature as it left, heat transfer being effected largely at right angles to the direction of air flow. Very uniform temperatures from specimen to specimen were achieved in this design.

In another case, this time for a high-humidity cabinet, the necessary saturator was, in effect, wrapped around the inside of the cabinet. The small room was completely copper lined, the bottom forming a sump with the working floor provided by slatted panels. Water, recirculated from the sump and conditioned to constant temperature, was sprayed from the top downward over the copper wall lining. This provided, in effect, a jacketed room as well as a very powerful saturator. The air-pumping action of the water jets was used to induce air circulation behind a light inner wall, gapped top and bottom, and into the room. A wet blanket lining without free air circulation to the room would, in most cases, be preferable, because the sprays produce an aerosol effect in the space. This was not undesirable in this application for concrete curing where some wetting of the product was acceptable as long as leaching was not appreciable.

One feature of the liquid conditioning system used in the humid room design is worthy of attention. Experience over many years indicated that small refrigerator units used for cooling and operated on-off for control gave much trouble. Consequently, it has been the practice to operate them continuously on a full-load liquid-cooling function whenever appropriate. The cooling coil is followed by an electric heater operated from an immersion thermostat and proportioning controller. A damper motor drives a variac and, thus, varies the electrical input to offset the excess capacity of the refrigerator.

In another case a similar arrangement was used for air-cooling with very satisfactory results. The refrigeration unit was run continuously to supply a direct expansion air coil. An open-wire electric heater was constructed over the face of the coil to provide fast heater response and fed from a proportioning electrical input arrangement, as described above, actuated by a fine-wire resistance type thermostat.

Small humidifiers, often required, have been found particularly troublesome pieces of equipment; heated types tend to have unsatisfactory time response or to be unreliable. Very satisfactory results have been obtained with a simple device consisting of a water surface in a small tank over which an airstream is blown by a small electric blower of suitable capacity, operated on-off. A small float valve maintains the water level. In order to prevent evaporation while the motor is shut off, gas mask valves, actuated by the blower pressures, are used.

Much might be said on the subject of cabinet construction. Cabinets must, in general, be heavily insulated and constructed to provide adequate resistance to air and vapor leakage. Doors should be well gasketed and all external parts of the system should be reasonably air-tight to eliminate unnecessary heat and moisture loads as far as possible. Vapor barriers may have to be incorporated to prevent condensation and, finally, special interior finishes may sometimes be necessary for special purposes.

CONCLUSION

The design of controlled-condition cabinets almost always presents a challenge to the designer. It is highly desirable, when purchasing or constructing a cabinet, to identify clearly the essential requirements and to appreciate the ease or the difficulty with which these can be obtained. An attempt has been made to present the principles and some of the more important considerations to assist this. The stated requirements must be realistic and capable of achievement. There is little point in specifying extreme precision in the control system if time, spatial variations, and radiation exchanges within the cabinet lead to large departures in product conditions from those desired. If cost is an important consideration or when extreme precision is required, it will often be necessary to restrict the range of conditions the cabinet must provide to permit design or selection for optimum performance. The capability of controlling conditions over a wide range will usually necessitate compromise, so that it should only be called for when actually required.

The ultimate performance of a cabinet depends not only upon the characteristics of the individual parts of the system but also upon the ways in which they interact in determining the final product condition. All aspects of the design must be considered for their possible effect upon the final performance.

31. Designing Humidity Controls for Environmental Chambers

Honeywell Controls Ltd., Toronto, Canada

ABSTRACT

This paper discusses selection of relative humidity controls for environmental rooms with special reference to test laboratories and growth chambers operating in a temperature range from 35 to 100°F.

Factors affecting design of the control instruments covered in the paper include the time constant of the process loop, necessary air changes needed to dissipate internal heat loads and obtain close temperature gradients across the room, and problems related to control of more than one variable.

The paper also discusses dehumidification using cold coils (which can present frost problems), programmed temperature and humidity changes to simulate seasonal variations, and close tolerance relative humidity requirements which in turn demand extremely tight limits on dry-bulb temperatures.

It is concluded that close relative humidity conditions can be obtained by giving full consideration during design to the control aspects of the air conditioning system.

INTRODUCTION

Environmental chambers serve to provide a specific environment under laboratory conditions. Such chambers may be required to artificially produce any condition of temperature, humidity, or pressure that may exist in nature.

This paper deals with the application of commercially available humidity controls for such purposes as material testing, physio-logical tests, and plant growth experiments. Rather than selecting one specific system for description, the author has reviewed the application of controls on several environmental installations in Canada. From this analysis, an attempt has been made to describe the reason certain components may be the most suited to the control of relative humidity. Many problems have been evident, and some of the conclusions derived may be of value to others in future system design.

In all instances, the tests have required a full-sized laboratory room, suitable for occupancy. The conditions to be maintained have necessitated the design of a forced-circulation air conditioning system. An indication of the scope of conditions maintained is outlined in Table 1.

Note that in each instance, the test requirements have been for conditions of relative humidity rather than water vapor content (absolute humidity) of the air. Relative humidity is expressed as: the ratio in per cent of partial pressure of water vapor present in a space to the saturation pressure on water at the same dry-bulb temperature.

$$\% \ RH = \frac{P}{P_\text{sat}} \times 100 \qquad (1)$$

EFFECT OF TEMPERATURE CHANGE ON RELATIVE HUMIDITY

From the definition of relative humidity it is noted that the ratio of pressures is taken at the same temperature. If air with a given moisture content is subjected to an increase in

249

TABLE 1. TYPICAL INSTALLATIONS ON WHICH PAPER IS BASED

Building	Chamber	Relative Humidity (%)	Tol. (%)	Temperature (°F)	Approximate Room Size (ft)	Approximate Room Air Change Rate (sec)
Defense Research Medical Lab. Downsview—Ontario	Tropical	48 to 80 12 to 84 12 to 26	1	60 110 160	20 × 18	30
	Wet cold	Over 85	—	35 to 70	22 × 18	30
	Dry cold	min.	—	−70 to 50	30 × 18	30
Ontario Hydro Research Lab. Toronto, Ontario	Power apparatus	50	2	74	19 × 19	170
	Plastics	50	2	73	20 × 10	60
	Spectographic	45	2	73	20 × 10	35
	Organic const.	50	2	73	15 × 10	60
	Infrared	45 max.	2	72	10 × 8	60
	Masonery	25 to 75	2	35 to 80	12 × 11	30
	Non metallic	30 to 90	2	50 to 100	19 × 10	30
Dept. Lands and Forests Forest Biology Lab. Maple, Ontario	Plant growth	50 to 93	2	50 to 80	10 × 8	30

Information is also based on control systems installed at the following locations:

University of Western Ontario—London Ont.—Science Service Labs.
Dept. of Agriculture—Ottawa, Ont.—Light and Dark Growth Chambers.
KVP Company—Espanola—Ont.—Test Laboratory.
IBM Company—Toronto, Ont.—Production Lab.
Dept. of Agriculture—Belleville, Ont.—Bacteria Lab.
Ontario Research Foundation—Toronto, Ont.—Test Chamber.

temperature, the percent relative humidity will fall due to the higher value of saturation pressure (P_{sat}) for the new temperature. Thus, with constant grains of moisture content of the air, the relative humidity ratio will change inversely with changes in temperature.

This effect is observed on the psychrometric chart example shown in Fig. 1. With the amount of water per pound of dry air at a fixed value of 70 grains, an increase in temperature from 70 to 75°F will cause a change in relative humidity from 65 to 55 per cent.

A stable humidity condition is desired, one which does not cycle back and forth or permanently drift away from the desired set point. Since temperature change effects the relative humidity, it is necessary that the room temperature conditions be kept as constant as possible. It is often necessary to design for temperature tolerances within much closer limits than those specified in order to keep within the relative humidity tolerances that are desired.

EFFECT OF FAST AIR CHANGE RATE

It is also noted from the list of typical applications that the air change rate is much faster than with comfort air conditioning. In many test rooms the air is changed at a rate of once each 60 seconds or faster.

Some of the factors that determine the required air change rate are as follows:

(a) The rate must be fast enough to remove the sensible and latent heat loads. For test rooms, the internal loads are often as significant as the wall losses and, in addition, may be intermittent in nature.

(b) As control tolerances are reduced, the air change rate is increased proportionately.

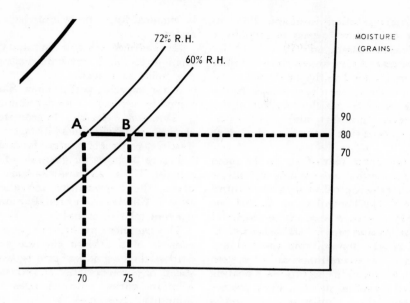

Fig. 1. Relative humidity error due to temperature change.

(c) High relative humidity room conditions require a faster air change rate, due to the limitation on sensible cooling possible, since the room temperature is close to the saturation line.

(d) Many rooms require the close tolerances to be held across the entire room or at least within a critical area comprising a large portion of the room. To achieve this, the diffusion temperature of the air entering the room must be very close to room conditions and is obtained by increasing the rate of air change.

(e) Over-sized mechanical equipment may also contribute since air conditioning components are normally selected at the nearest larger type and size commercially available.

Let us now visualize that all of the air in the room is drawn through the mechanical equipment and back into the space within a 60-second time period. When a control sensing device detects a change in room conditions, not only must it be capable of making the correction quickly, but also the overall mechanical system must be of a type which will respond within this short time period.

This timing effect is illustrated in the simplified process loop shown in Fig. 2.

We have assumed a humidification process using direct steam injection.

(a) Humidity sensor S detects a drop in relative humidity level in the room. Its sensing signal is transmitted to the control instrument I.

(b) The instrument compares the low humidity signal with the set point index and transmits a corrective signal to valve V.

(c) The control valve by action of the

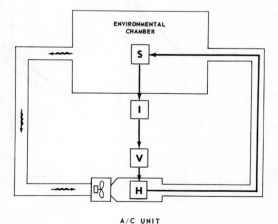

Fig. 2. Simplified control loop.

changed signal repositions itself and allows an increase of steam flow to pass to humidifier H in the air-conditioning unit.

(d) Room air is drawn across the humidifier and moisture is added to the air stream.

(e) The air stream then passes back to the sensing element S which recognizes the corrected room humidity and informs the control instrument that no further adjustment is required.

Since every cubic foot of air in the room passes the humidifier once each 60 seconds, it is obvious that the control sensor S, the control instrument I, the control valve V, and the humidifier H must each be of a type which will respond quickly and provide stable operation.

As well as the humidifying process described above, the overall mechanical system will contain a dehumidifying process, a heating process, and a cooling process. Each process may be shown in a similar manner and is subject to the same response considerations.

We will now look at each of the four processes in detail keeping in mind that the most suited components will provide fast response with minimum upset of other room conditions.

HUMIDIFYING PROCESS

Sensing Elements

The following means are commercially available for sensing relative humidity.

(1) Direct relative humidity measurement—mechanical hygrometer and electrical hygrometer.

(2) Indirect relative humidity measurement—wet- and dry-bulb instrument and dew-point instrument.

A far superior performance has been obtained by controlling relative humidity using a Dunmore electric hygrometer sensing element, primarily due to its fast response and its direct control of relative humidity.

Figure 3 shows an example of this direct control. The room conditions are shown between the temperature tolerance lines of $80 \pm 1°F$ and relative humidity lines of 50 ± 1 per cent relative humidity.

The Dunmore hygrometer sensing element consists of a lithium chloride salt solution embossed on a gold leaf grid between two fine sheets of porous plastic. The resistance of the solution varies with changes in relative humidity. Response is dependent on the porosity of the plastic covering and commercial types are available with a response time of approximately 10 seconds. Accuracies are available to within 1 per cent RH and minimum drifting in the order of 1 per cent per year is present with aging. Control ranges are available from 5 to 95 per cent RH. Dunmore elements are not recommended for atmospheres containing certain contaminants, mainly of an ionic nature, nor for operation where they will come in contact with drops of moisture.

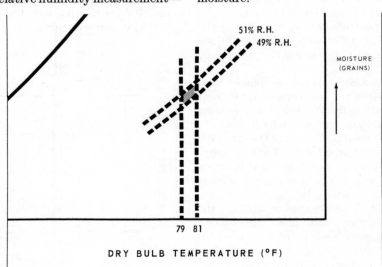

Fig. 3. Direct relative humidity sensing.

In comparison, direct relative humidity sensing using mechanical force is derived from a change in physical length of a material that occurs with a change in relative humidity. Materials used include human hair, wood, paper, animal membrane, and certain plastic materials.

They have not proven successful for applications with fast air change rates, due to a relatively slow response of from 4 to 15 minutes. The limited mechanical force makes accuracy more difficult and considerable drifting of the set point with age has been experienced.

Indirect humidity sensing using a wet-bulb instrument is obtained by applying a wet wick over the sensing bulb of a temperature controller. Room air is passed over the element at a rate of 15 fps, and the resulting depressed temperature corresponds to the room wet-bulb temperature.

This form of measurement has been used successfully for manual measurement of relative humidity for scientific and meteorological purposes. When applied to an automatic controller, however, it has certain limitations, such as an increased response time and a wet-bulb depression error. This error is due mainly to mechanical problems, such as the maintenance of a proper temperature of water applied to the wick, dirt accumulation on the wick, and response time considerations,

which are often difficult to eliminate on an automated control system.

Of special note, due to the indirect relative humidity sensing, very close wet-bulb and dry-bulb temperature tolerances are required to hold close relative humidity levels. This is illustrated in Fig. 4.

With dry-bulb temperature maintained at 80°F plus or minus 1°F and wet-bulb conditions at 67°F plus or minus 1°F wet-bulb, the relative humidity may vary between 47 and 58 per cent RH. To obtain plus or minus 1 per cent RH, it would be necessary to control both dry-bulb and wet-bulb temperature to a small fraction of 1 degree.

In a similar manner, control of relative humidity using a dew-point sensor is also limited, due to its slower response and its indirect relative humidity control action. A further consideration might be its accuracy limits of approximately 1.5° dew point.

A dew-point sensor consists of a cell of lithium chloride solution through which an electric current is passed, causing the solution to heat. The temperature to which it rises is dependent upon the absolute grains of moisture content of the air. By inserting a temperature controller inside the heated cell, the measured temperature can be calibrated as a measure of the dew point of air passing over the element.

Again of special note is that very close dry-

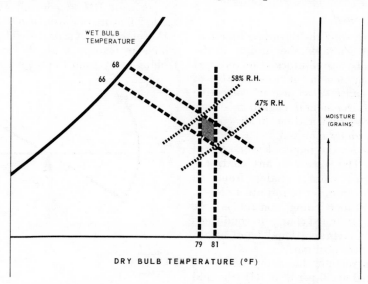

Fig. 4. Indirect relative humidity sensing using wet bulb.

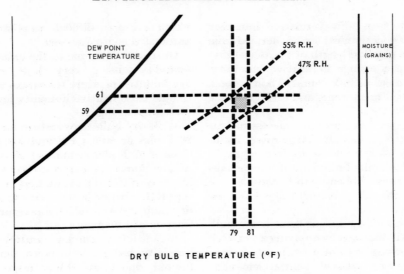

FIG. 5. Indirect relative humidity sensing using dew point.

bulb and dew-point tolerances are required to obtain close relative humidity conditions. Figure 5 shows that at $80 \pm 1°F$, dry-bulb, and $60 \pm 1°F$ dew-point temperature, the relative humidity may vary between 47 and 55 per cent RH.

An advantage of a dew-point instrument is its wide control range, from 11 to 100 per cent RH within a dew-point range of from -50 to $+160°F$ and a temperature range from -50 to $+260°F$.

Control Instruments

As well as providing the recording function, the instrument contains the brains of the control system. By use of information received from the sensing element, it must be able to establish and initiate a proper corrective action. For environmental chambers it has been experienced that a three mode control instrument is usually required.

Mode 1 provides the required proportional control action. The essence of any control is that it must first sense a change from the control set point in order to initiate a corrective action. Proportioning control is one which for each continued change in conditions sensed within the proportional band establishes a fixed valve position.

Since the controller in the example shown in Fig. 6 is indexed at 50 per cent RH (the mid point of its 20 per cent RH proportional band),

the only time it will maintain its set condition will be when the load requires the valve to be ½ open. For any other loading requirement, the conditions maintained will be at a point either above or below the set point.

A drop to 40 per cent RH is required to open the valve fully. To maintain stable control action on systems with fast air change rates, a 20 per cent proportioning band or even wider may be necessary. Since it is desired to keep the room control condition at the set point of 50 per cent RH, a controller including the mode 2 feature of automatic reset is required.

Automatic reset is provided by a component which recognizes that the system is controlling away from the set point and adds an

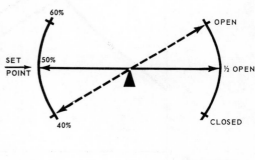

Fig. 6. Proportional band analyses.

independent correction to the valve position, sufficient to restore the desired room condition.

The further refinement, mode 3, is a control feature called rate action. Its effect is to cause a control correction to be made at a faster rate when conditions in the room are upset by a fast load change.

Control Valves

It follows that the controlled device, in this case a control valve, should be as responsive as the other components in the system and of equal quality.

In general, steam and water valves should be of industrial quality with characterized seats. Low flow characterization may be required and replaceable valve seats and discs, if included, may save changing a complete valve should the initial selection of size be incorrect. Valve and damper motors should include travel positioners for precision operation.

Electrically operated motors have given equal performance to pneumatic motors, provided a fast motor timing is selected. Motors with 15-second full travel time have been used successfully.

Humidifiers

Selection of the humidifier is equally important to the selection of the control system. It should have a fast response and an ability to be finely proportioned under control action. Consideration should also be given to insure that the by-product sensible heat factor is minimized.

Our experience indicates that these conditions are best met with direct steam injection. This may be compared with the other humidifiers as shown on the process curves in Fig. 7.

The process of steam injection follows line A-B and is close to an isothermal action. Air entering the humidifier is at point A; air leaving the humidifier will be at a point along line A-B. Steam injection has proven very successful, due to its fast response and the minimum upset in temperature conditions. The amount of steam injected may be accurately controlled by a proportioning steam valve.

Water atomization is essentially an adiabatic process and falls on the wet-bulb line from A to C. The water is reduced to very minute particles which are totally absorbed by the air. Regardless of water temperature, the sensible heat quantity of the spray is small in proportion to the latent heat quantity, and the process closely follows the line A-C. Atomization has fast response but is quite difficult to control, since a proportioning action would destroy the atomization.

The water spray humidifier process falls on line A-D; the slope of the line may be varied

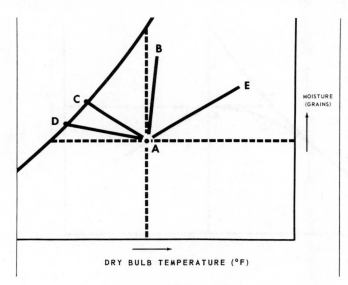

Fig. 7. Humidifying processes.

depending on the temperature of the water. The water droplets are bigger, and a large volume of water is sprayed. The greater proportion of the water is not absorbed by the air and is recirculated by pumping action. Response to change is relatively slow, as the mass of water must be heated or cooled to provide the change. Also, the recirculated water acts as a cooling or heating coil, causing a relatively large by-product temperature upset. It is not possible to proportion the quantity of water pumped without destroying the spray characteristics.

In a pan humidifier, water is heated to various temperatures below its boiling point, and the process follows line A-E. The capacity of the system is low, and it is not practical to use pan humidifiers to maintain high relative humidities. A very large temperature upset occurs as approximately one third of the heat added is transferred to the air in the form of sensible heat. Proportioning control action is possible; however, response is very slow, due to the mass of the water involved.

Therefore, in summary, the best humidifying process control has been experienced by utilizing the following components:

(a) Dunmore electric hygrometer sensing
(b) 3-mode recording controller
(c) Industrial grade steam valve with positioner
(d) Direct steam injection humidifier.

This arrangement has provided a fast response system with full range proportioning control action.

DEHUMIDIFICATION PROCESS

In dehumidification, the same factors as for humidification apply for:
(a) The sensing element
(b) The recording controller
(c) The control valve.

In some applications a common sensing element and controller are used to sequence the humidification and dehumidification equipment.

The dehumidifier component, however, requires a close analysis and actually is very difficult to control accurately. The choice of dehumidifier falls between:
(a) Passing recirculated air over a cold coil
(b) Employing chemical dehydration
(c) Air washer.

Dehumidification process curves are shown in Fig. 8.

A cooling coil will act as a dehumidifier, provided its coil surface temperature is below the dew point of the entering air. With the air entering the coil at condition A and a coil surface temperature at condition B, the air leaving the coil will be at condition C. Point C will vary on the curve, depending on the number of rows of tubes in the coil. Control is

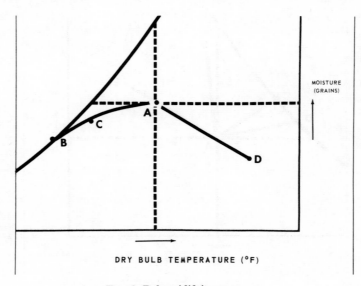

Fig. 8. Dehumidifying processes.

obtained by varying the coil temperature B and, therefore, changing the curve A-C-B relationship.

Both liquid cooling coils and direct expansion refrigeration coils are available for dehumidification. Liquid coils are preferred, as they are more readily controlled by the use of a proportioning valve. Some controversy exists over the merits of a constant volume *vs* a variable volume water flow within the coil. The choice probably depends on the overall system design, as each has its advantages.

Refrigeration coils have been successfully varied by the use of a compensated back pressure valve. However, the control performance may be limited by the accuracy and response of the self-contained control action of this valve form and also by possible set-up difficulties of the thermal expansion valve and low pressure cut-outs.

In both cases, the coil mass is relatively large and response to a new requirement is extremely slow. In addition, a by-product effect of lowered temperature occurs with this process.

On the other hand, chemical drying does not offer an improvement. Here the air is passed over a drying agent such as silica gel, and moisture is adsorbed on its surface. The process is adiabatic and follows wet-bulb line A-D, and a very large by-product temperature rise occurs. Proportional control may be achieved only by using face and bypass dampers, a form which has experienced some difficulty in accurately controlling this application.

Chemical drying falls off in efficiency, for air entering conditions above 50°F. Its primary application is for a very low relative humidity at low temperatures.

The air washer method of dehumidification causes moisture to condense from the airstream into relatively large drops of water which are sprayed into the air stream. In effect, the water drops perform a function very similar to the cooling coil dehumidification process, since moisture is condensed on the cold surface of the water droplets.

A greater amount of moisture may be removed by employing an air washer in which a chemical solution is sprayed into the air stream. Lithium chloride or bromide solutions are commonly used.

With both chemical dehydration and chemical air washing, auxiliary heating is required to restore the chemical properties, in the former instance to provide reactivation, and in the latter to provide regeneration to maintain solution concentration.

Therefore, in summary, the most suited dehumidification process has been experienced using the following components:

(a) Dunmore electric hygrometer sensing

(b) 3-mode recording controller

(c) Industrial grade water valve with positioner

(d) Chilled water dehumidifying coil.

Full range control is obtained; however, the response time is very slow and a large temperature upsetting effect is present.

HEATING PROCESS

Sensing Elements

Temperature may be sensed either with an electric or a mechanical thermometer, but the requirements for fast response dictates the use of the electrical means. Electrical sensing may be achieved by the use of a thermocouple, a resistance bulb, or a thermistor. All types may be classed as very responsive due to their low mass.

A further consideration is the control range required. A thermocouple has a wide control range; a resistance bulb has a narrow range, while a thermistor has a very narrow span. Sensing element selection should be made by a combined analysis of response and control range requirements of the environmental chamber.

Heating Coils

Heating coils are available using electricity, hot water, or steam as the controlled medium.

Figure 9 shows the process curve for the heating cycle. Regardless of the medium used, air entering the coil at condition A will fall along line A-B as it is heated by the coil. The choice of coil type is determined by response and control capabilities.

The electric heating coil, due to its low mass, provides very fast response. Full proportional control is obtainable by the use of a magnetic amplifier and a saturable core reactor which acts as an electric heat valve. Motorized variable transformers have also been used

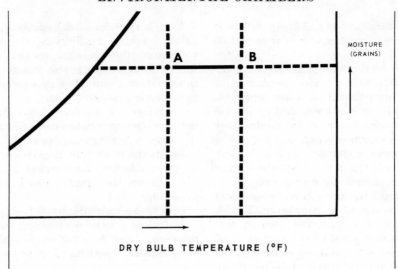

DRY BULB TEMPERATURE (°F)

FIG. 9. Heating processes.

successfully, and in the near future, silicon controlled rectifiers will be available for proportioning control action.

In contrast, the hot water heating coil, with its larger mass, is less responsive to changes. Conditions of overshooting and undershooting may be minimized by adjusting the base water temperature supplied to the coil at the source.

The steam coil may provide an adequate response to change. It is limited, however, in its control action by the fact that the steam

temperature is supplied at a level above 212°F. Under light load conditions when the coil is partially filled, the steam coil is subject to nonuniform leaving temperatures across the coil face, which may contribute to distribution problems.

Therefore, in summary, the most suitable heating process arrangement would consist of the following:

(a) Thermocouple, resistance bulb, or thermistor sensing element

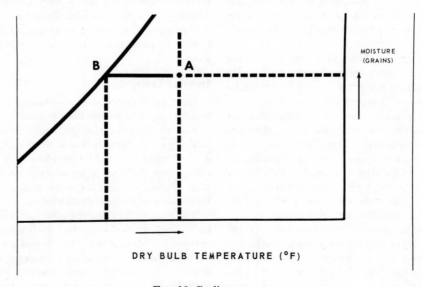

DRY BULB TEMPERATURE (°F)

FIG. 10. Cooling processes.

(b) 3-mode recording controller

(c) Magnetic amplifier and saturable core reactor

(d) Electric heating coil, preferably an open coil type.

The above arrangement will be capable of providing very fast response coupled with full proportioning control action.

COOLING PROCESS

The cooling process is performed by a cold coil and normally is achieved from the same coil providing the dehumidification. This is outlined in Fig. 10. Air entering the coil at condition A will leave at a point on line A-B, depending on the control valve position. If point B is lower than shown on the diagram, dehumidification will also occur.

Again, the liquid cooling coil is preferred to the refrigeration coil, although adequate performance has been obtained using both mediums. In either instance, due to its large mass, the coil responds slowly to change.

Since the other process control components are similar to those listed for the heating process, the overall cooling process may be summarized as follows:

(a) Thermocouple, resistance bulb or thermistor sensing

(b) 3-mode recording controller

(c) Industrial grade water valve with positioner

(d) Chilled water cooling coil.

Full range control is possible; however, this control process is difficult due to the slow response of the coil.

COMBINED CONTROL SEQUENCES

In air conditioning design there are many combinations of equipment and controls available to the designer. In all probability, most have been considered in constant temperature and relative humidity room applications. From the arrangements with which the author has had experience, two control sequences which have been designed for stable action with fast response are now discussed.

The first control arrangement is shown in Fig. 11.

Room relative humidity is sensed by element Hs and controlled by recording instrument HI, which acts to proportion in sequence the water valve V1 for dehumidification and steam valve V3 for humidification, as required.

Room temperature is sensed by element Ts and controlled by recording instrument TI, which acts to proportion in sequence the hot water valve V1 for cooling and the saturable

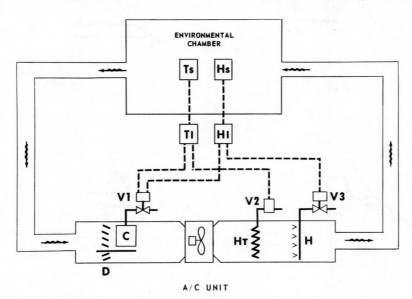

Fig. 11. Typical system. Method 1.

core reactor V2 for heating, as required.

Since water valve V1 is under control action from both temperature and humidity and cannot satisfy both, the valve is arranged to take the position of greatest demand. For example, if the dehumidification requirement was the greatest demand, V1 would be controlled from HI and by-product overcooling would occur. Space temperature would fall, and the temperature control system would automatically increase the output from the electric heating coil to compensate for the overcooling.

A manual face and bypass damper arrangement D is shown ahead of the cooling coil C. It has been found that a portion of the air may bypass the cooling coil in some applications where the large air quantity is required for diffusion purposes. With this arrangement, care must be taken to thoroughly mix the cooled and bypassed air.

Cooling coil bypass may also be achieved by careful selection of the number of rows of tubes in the cooling coil, as long as the coil runs dry. If a spray coil is used, much of the bypass effect may be lost, and the coil cooling

characteristics may be appreciably changed. The performance of this system is shown in Fig. 12.

As stated before, under the direction of temperature instrument TI the room air may be cooled or heated; and under direction of the humidity instrument HI room air may be dehumidified or humidified. Two control functions, one from each instrument, are possible simultaneously and in the following combinations as shown in the diagrams:

(a) Heat (AB) and humidify (BC)
(b) Dehumidify (AB) and heat (BC)
(c) Cool (AC) and humidify (CD)
(d) Dehumidify (AC) and cool (AB).

Under combination (c), cool and humidify, the ability to add humidity is decreased as the temperature leaving the cooling coil approaches point B, and the desired humidity levels will not be maintained. One solution is to include a bypass factor at the cooling coil, so that the mixed quantity of cooled and bypassed air will leave the coil at point C, which will support humidity addition. Of course, increasing bypassed air would necessitate increasing the design air volume. If

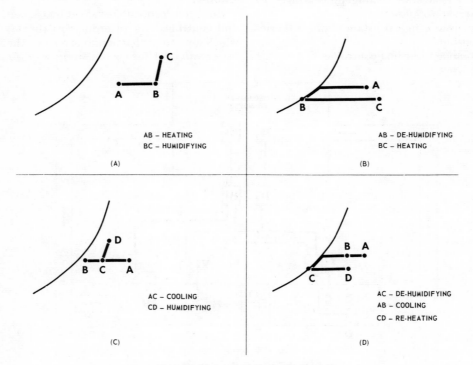

AB – HEATING
BC – HUMIDIFYING

(A)

AB – DE-HUMIDIFYING
BC – HEATING

(B)

AC – COOLING
CD – HUMIDIFYING

(C)

AC – DE-HUMIDIFYING
AB – COOLING
CD – RE-HEATING

(D)

FIG. 12. Process analysis. Method 1.

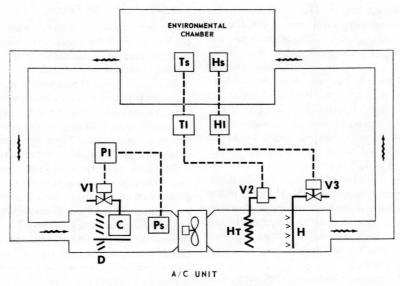

F<small>IG</small>. 13. Typical system. Method 2.

bypass air is not possible, one solution may be to add the moisture directly in the room. Introduction of moisture within the room is often awkward, and uniform humidity conditions are difficult to obtain.

Under condition (d), dehumidify and cool, the valve V1 will be controlled from the dehumidification requirement AC since it is a greater demand requirement than cooling AB. By-product overcooling will occur and the room temperature will fall. Temperature instrument T<small>I</small> will sense the fall and bring on the required reheat CD.

As the figures show, this control arrangement is capable of providing corrective action for any load change requirement in the room. The area of control difficulty is likely to be a condition where either de-humidification or cooling is required. Correction may be sluggish due to the slow response coil characteristics. Also, on diagram D, at a condition of balance between the requirement for de-humidification and cooling, the air leaving the cooling coil can alternate between two temperatures several degrees apart if there is the slightest load change. An upset in room temperature may occur as the room dry-bulb control endeavours to adjust for this inter-action.

The control arrangement shown in Fig. 13 has also been successfully applied and has provided excellent control performance while removing problems of control sequence interaction.

Control of the slow response cooling coil has been such a problem in environmental rooms that it has been compared to "prodding an elephant with a pin." To minimize this problem, a preselected condition of overcooling and over-dehumidification leaving this coil is established by sensing element Ps, control instrument P1, and valve V1. This arrangement will allow for a wider cooling and de-humidification tolerance, provided sufficient overcooling and over-dehumidification are maintained. However, due to the fast air movement through the coil, a control with fast sensing and automatic reset may still be required. The sensing may be by dry-bulb temperature or dew-point temperature leaving the coil, or by controlling the temperature of the coil medium.

With the base condition preset by P, the temperature control sequence Ts, T<small>I</small>, and V2 can precisely operate the electric heating coil as required. Similarly, the humidity control Hs, H<small>I</small>, and V3 can precisely control the steam humidifier. It is noted that the temperature instrument T<small>I</small> and humidity instrument H<small>I</small> now control only one device, and sequencing is eliminated.

Manual bypass damper D is again shown and serves the same purpose as described for the first control arrangement. The system process is shown in Fig. 14. Room air enters the cooling coil at point A and leaves at condition B. It is then mixed with bypass air, and the mixture is shown at point C on the line connecting points A-B. The condition at point C is maintained by the action of control instrument PI, and, as mentioned before, a wider tolerance may be permitted, since reheating and humidification are to follow.

Reheat occurs along line C-D and humidification occurs along line D-E. Point E is the air temperature condition diffused into the room and, dependent upon the length of lines C-D and D-E, may be established at any condition in a circle around point A, as dictated by the room loads.

As the diagrams illustrate, the successful application of this control sequence will provide for all loading conditions, with fast system response and without loading upset due to control sequence interaction. The one sacrifice is an increased operating cost due to the longer refrigeration running time and additional reheat requirements; however, it will likely be a worth-while investment.

MISCELLANEOUS CONSIDERATIONS

Listed below are a few control problems that have been encountered and which may be worthy of consideration during system design.

Variable Room Set Points

In general, the control system is more easily designed for one fixed temperature and relative humidity condition, such as 70°F and 50 per cent RH.

For conditions that require several sets of temperature and relative humidity conditions, an analysis must be made of the psychrometric chart of the overall system operation for these various conditions. Then equipment can be selected that is suitable for all circumstances.

In plant growth chamber simulation, the room may require several sets of temperature and relative humidity conditions which are automatically and continuously being varied on a time program pattern. To achieve this programming, instruments are used which employ a means of resetting the control point index, either by the use of cut cams or by the use of incremental timers.

Special attention must be given to the rate at which the conditions are reset. If conditions are raised too rapidly, the walls and floors (due to their mass) may not heat up as quickly as the air. It is possible that the wall temperature, in lagging behind, may be at a temperature that is below the room dew point, and moisture will condense on these surfaces. This same condition can occur in rooms that are set manually at various conditions. In changing to higher conditions it might be necessary to bring the room temperature to the new setting for a fixed period of time before elevating the humidity conditions.

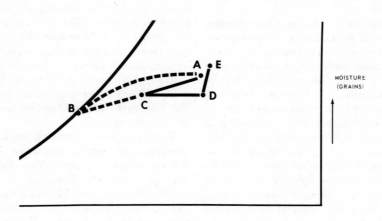

MOISTURE
(GRAINS)

DRY BULB TEMPERATURE (°F)

FIG. 14. Process analysis. Method 2.

Defrost

Many of the tests conducted will require dew points in the cooling coil which are below 32°F, and ice build-up will, therefore, occur on the coil surfaces. One method to provide defrost with continuous operation is to use a parallel coil arrangement where the coils are used alternately under control of isolating dampers.

This method has been used successfully, although it is difficult to control the change-over without some upset in the room conditions.

Systems using a sprayed glycol coil wash have been used to provide continuous defrost. However, an electric hygrometer using a Dunmore sensing element will experience considerable control point drift (due to the action of the glycol) and should not be used. Dew probe sensing has been successfully used, provided the glycol vapor carry over is at a minimum. Stable control operation has been experienced for periods up to one week, after which dew probe element retreatment is necessary. For continuous operation, it is desirable to have a second retreated sensing element available for immediate replacement.

Wire Insulation Requirements at Low Temperatures

In low temperature control rooms, consideration should be given to the insulating material used on the control lead wires between the sensing element and the instruments. A material should be used that will withstand the low temperatures without cracking. Some test conditions require that the sensing probes be moved throughout the critical area in the room; here the consideration of wire insulation is of even greater importance.

High Humidities

For high relative humidity areas, such as between 95 and 100 per cent, the electric hygrometer requires an extended recovery time. There is a possibility of the element calibration being destroyed due to condensation.

Control within this range has been successfully obtained by the use of a differential wet- and dry-bulb instrument. Over broad temperature spans, a fairly linear relationship exists between relative humidity and wet-bulb depression.

Air Distribution Pattern

The control system will sense the humidity and temperature conditions only at the point where the sensing elements are located in the room. The resulting conditions at all other points in the room are dependent upon a uniform air flow pattern. It is not intended to describe how this uniformity is to be provided, but merely to point out the limitations of the sensing elements in this regard. However, it should be noted that any unbalance in conditions, due to the nonuniform air flow pattern, is minimized by providing diffusion conditions entering the room close to the required design conditions.

CONCLUSIONS

The selection of relative humidity controls for environmental chambers should be made only after a thorough analysis of the air-conditioning system requirements. These requirements usually call for close control tolerances to be maintained on a system designed for very fast air change rates.

Stable relative humidity control conditions within close tolerances are possible, provided the system is designed to:

(a) Control within very close temperature tolerances

(b) Measure and correct conditions at a sufficiently fast rate.

(c) Minimize by-product sensible heat upsets inherent with the humidifying and dehumidifying processes.

(d) Minimize the effects of the slow response operation of the cooling and dehumidifying processes.

(e) Minimize complicated control sequences.

32. Environmental Control Facilities at the Agricultural Engineering Department, University of Kentucky*

JOE M. BUNN AND WILEY H. HENSON, JR.

Agricultural Engineering Department, University of Kentucky, Lexington, Kentucky

ABSTRACT

This paper outlines special design considerations which were made to obtain, within a single unit, equipment to control dry-bulb and dew-point temperatures and air flow rates over ranges which include ambient conditions. A discussion is given of some of the considerations made in designing, selecting components, and installing and operating such equipment.

The equipment will control environmental conditions over the ranges of 35 to 200°F dry-bulb temperature, 0 to 142°F dew-point temperature, and air flow rates of 1200 to 2000 cfm. By the use of an air bypass duct built into the control unit, air velocities within detachable test chambers can be varied over an even wider range. Desired environmental conditions are controllable over the operating ranges of the equipment to within ±1°F dry-bulb temperature and ±2 per cent RH.

Control is accomplished by sensing the dry-bulb temperature with a resistance thermometer and the dew-point temperature with a "Dewcel." These temperatures are then recorded, using continuous balance wheatstone bridges. Each Wheatstone bridge is a part of a pneumatic controller which positions steam heating and humidifying valves by proportioning and reset action. A circular chart-recorded indication of control temperature and a cam-operated pro-gram control are also featured in the controller.

Six independently operated conditioning units with characteristics similar to those described above were built and installed in the Agricultural Engineering Building at the University of Kentucky. Special attention was given to design considerations which made it possible for the equipment to operate at any time of the year. Many special features of the equipment make it useful for a wide variety of environmental investigations.

INTRODUCTION

The selection or design of equipment and facilities for research work is at best an intelligent guess. Without first having some idea of the expected results of the research one can only guess what range, degree of accuracy, and utility the equipment must have for the proposed investigations to have meaningful conclusions. Not having these results and, in most cases, having only a general knowledge of the scope and variability of the problems to be investigated, the investigator makes his designs for maximum accuracy and versatility, limited mainly by economic considerations. Economic considerations have generally resulted in limiting the selection of commercially available environmental control equipment to two types: (1) equipment which operates above ambient conditions, and (2) that which operates below ambient conditions. Environmental research equipment for botanical systems' control necessarily must be

---

* The investigation reported in this paper is in connection with a project of the Kentucky Agricultural Experiment Station and is published with approval of the Director.

capable of operating over ranges which include ambient conditions.

In considering environmental equipment to be used for tobacco research, the authors anticipated both plant production and processing investigations. Installation space was limited. Available commercial equipment was limited to ranges above or below ambient conditions. Therefore, specially designed equipment was needed. It is the objective of this report to relate some of the considerations made in designing, selecting components, installing, and operating environmental equipment built for tobacco research at the Agricultural Engineering Department of the University of Kentucky.

DESIGN CONSIDERATIONS

Temperature, relative humidity, air flow rate, and light radiation are the environmental factors which the authors considered of major importance in tobacco production and processing. The design requirement was the building of equipment for control of these factors over ranges wide enough to facilitate investigations of optimum and limiting plant responses to environmental restraints.

Light radiation is an environmental factor associated directly with the material under test. This, in contrast to the other environmental factors, suggested that the design might best be done in two parts; i.e., one should first design equipment for conditioning the air as an integral unit, separate from the test chamber and the light source. The test chamber could be detachable; thus, individual chambers could be designed for specific research needs and not research fitted to specific test chamber limitations. Therefore, this discussion will center around the design of a unit to condition air and deliver it to an attached test chamber in such quantity as different research investigations might require.

Air Flow

Desired air flow rates ranged from those needed to simulate wind velocities in a field of growing plants to those required in a forced air crop drying installation. The quantities of air needed to establish this range of air flow rates was dependent upon the size of test

chambers to be employed and the minimum air flow rate needed for the proper functioning of the heat exchange equipment. Upon considering these requirements along with a space limitation in which a test chamber could be located, the designers agreed upon an air flow range of 1200 to 2000 cfm.

A forward curved-blade centrifugal fan was selected in order to obtain a nearly constant air delivery rate over a range of static pressures from free delivery to that of $1\frac{1}{2}$ in. of water. The fan selected was a Carrier 27N5, which has the desired performance range of 1200 to 2000 cfm delivery when driven by a U.S. Varidrive motor. The motor and variable drive assembly provides the means for a manual adjustment for fan speed in the range from 380 to 760 rpm.

To accomplish all the widely varied air flow requirements within the 1200- to 2000-cfm range, the air flow path within the conditioning unit was established as shown in Fig. 1. The air is conditioned to the desired environmental levels in section A. From here it is blown into section B where it can be delivered to the test chamber through section C; or, up to 60 per cent of the air can bypass the test chamber through section D. Bypassing some

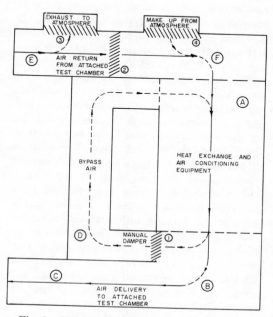

Fig. 1. The air flow path within a conditioning unit.

air helps to reduce the air flow in the test chamber while maintaining enough air flow over the conditioning equipment for proper heat transfer and control. After passing through the test chamber, the air is returned to section E where it can either reenter the conditioning cycle through section F or it can be exhausted to the atmosphere through damper 3. If the air is exhausted to the atmosphere, makeup air from the atmosphere enters the cycle through damper 4. Dampers 2, 3, and 4 are mechanically linked in such a way that as damper 2 is closed dampers 3 and 4 are opened. The amount of exhaust and makeup air can be adjusted up to 100 per cent of the total air flow in the conditioning cycle; hence, with the dampers and a 2-to-1 variable speed fan drive, a wide range of air flow can be obtained within moderately sized test chambers.

Air Conditioning

Lower limiting temperatures for plant growth are near the freezing temperature of water. The upper practical temperature limit for drying biological materials is near the boiling point of water. All major tobacco responses of interest would be expected to occur within these temperature limits. By similar reasoning, relative humidities of major interest to tobacco researchers should be included within the limits of 20 to 95 per cent RH throughout the above dry-bulb temperature range of 35 to 200°F.

The process considered most efficient for conditioning the air consists of first establishing the desired amount of water vapor (dew-point temperature) and then reheating this air to the desired dry-bulb temperature. Control of the environmental conditions within the conditioning unit was obtained by reheating and rehumidifying the air after it had been cooled down to approximately 3°F below the desired dew point. This method of conditioning was selected because heating and humidification was accomplished with steam which can be metered and controlled very precisely over a wide range. Operational efficiency was sacrificed to accomplish this range and control. That is, the cooling and dehumidifying equipment was sized to the maximum expected need and was set to operate continuously in association with a variable preheat coil. The preheat coil was needed to reduce frosting and, hence, air flow restriction by the cooling system at low external cooling loads.

In sizing the compressor and cooling coils, some projections into expected research problems were required. Low moisture and temperature storage, evapotranspiration, curing and drying, and several other possible biological cooling and dehumidifying loads were considered. The maximum load among those considered, plus an added safety factor to aid in covering any unforeseen needs, resulted in a cooling capacity of 64,800 Btu/hour at standard ASHRE 23R Group IV rating conditions at a 1200-cfm air flow rate. Expressed in another way, the coil had to accommodate a 44,000 Btu/hour sensible heat load and a 20,800 Btu/hour latent heat load with 1200 cfm of air entering at 80°F dry-bulb and 60°F dew-point temperatures. The preheat coil was sized to furnish a maximum supplementary load of 36,000 Btu/hour at 5-psi steam pressure with 60°F entering air temperature. An open-type compressor with a water-cooled condenser coil was selected to accomplish the cooling and dehumidifying. The compressor was equipped with all the necessary safety controls to assure the safety of the equipment in an automatically operated system.

The heating coil was sized to a system rate of response which would enable the control temperature to be changed from 35 to 200°F in 30 minutes with an air flow rate of 1200 cfm. A heating coil with a capacity of 129,000 Btu/hour based on a 100°F temperature rise across the coil when supplied with 10-psi steam was selected. Humidification was accomplished with and Armstrong Air-operated Model AM32 humidifier by dispersion of 10-psi dry steam through a metered orifice. This humidifier has a maximum capacity of 80 pounds of water per hour. This is a capacity determined by a desired response of the system, such as changing from 60°F and 20 per cent RH to 75°F and 95 per cent RH in one hour.

INSTRUMENTATION AND CONTROL

Botanical systems inevitably respond variably to even constant environmental restraints. Because of this there is little justification for precision instrumentation and controls. However, the desire of those doing botanical research is for control equipment with as close control as possible in order that variations in research results can be ascribed to the test systems rather than to the equipment.

A pneumatic control system was selected because of the time proven dependability of these systems. The mode of control was proportional-plus-reset with proportional band and reset rate adjustments. These features are exemplified in the Minneapolis-Honeywell "Air-O-line" control system incorporated in the controllers installed in the conditioning units.

Dew-point Control

Relative humidity is established and maintained by controlling the dew-point temperature of the air. This is sensed with a Foxboro Model 2711AG "Dewcel" element which consists of a resistance thermometer covered with a woven glass tape impregnated with lithium chloride. The tape is wrapped with two resistance heater wires connected to a 25-VAC power supply.

Dew-point determination by the "Dewcel" element is based on the principle that for every water vapor pressure in contact with a saturated salt solution there is an equilibrium temperature at which the solution neither absorbs nor gives up moisture. If, for example, the temperature of the element is below

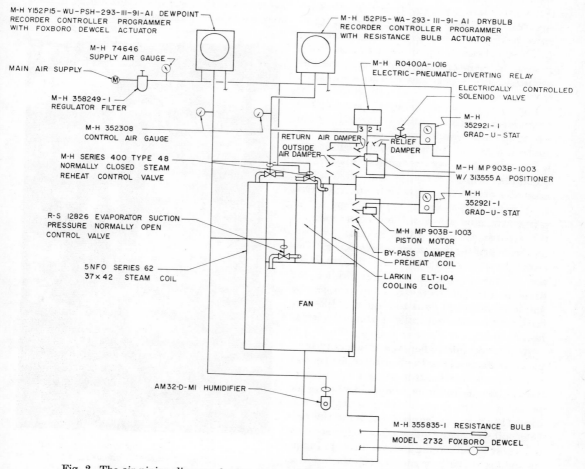

Fig. 2. The air piping diagram for the pneumatic control system in a conditioning unit.

equilibrium temperature, the salt adsorbs moisture from the air, the conductivity of the solution around the heater wires increases, and the current flow increases, thereby raising the element to equilibrium temperature. This temperature, measured by the internal resistance thermometer, is calibrated to the dewpoint temperature of the air. By making the resistance thermometer a branch of a wheatstone bridge in a Minneapolis-Honeywell "Electronik" Circular-Chart pneumatic cam-program controller, dew-point temperature control and recording was obtained.

Another way to use the controller effectively is to move the control index with respect to the recording pen. Systematically changing the control index is called programming. The Minneapolis-Honeywell control instruments accomplish programmed control by moving the control index with a driven plastic cam cut to the desired process pattern. Cam patterns can be varied over a range from 0 to 150°F dew-point temperature and controlled to a combined instrument and sensing element accuracy of ±1 per cent of the instrument span.

Figure 2 shows the piping diagram for the pneumatic control system installed in an environmental conditioning unit. Elements controlled by the dew-point controller are: (1) a normally closed steam control valve which regulates steam to the preheat coil, (2) a normally open suction pressure control valve that regulates, over a limited range, the refrigerant flow between the cooling coil and the compressor, and (3) a normally closed metered orifice dry steam humidifier. The elements are controlled by adjusting, through the pneumatic system of the controller, air pressure supplied to them. They also can be manually adjusted so as to require a different pressure from the controller for initial activation.

As an example, when the dew-point temperature decreases or the control index setting is increased, the control system operates to restore balance in the system by increasing the pressure to the controlled elements. In this case: (1) the steam control valve for the preheat coil will open to furnish a larger sensible heat load to the cooling coil, therefore reducing its dehumidifying capacity; (2) the suction pressure control valve in the refrigerant line

will throttle to reduce the refrigerant flow through the cooling coils which will further reduce the dehumidifying capacity; and (3) the humidifier will open to add dry steam for humidification. Altogether the action raises the dew-point temperature and restores balance to the system.

To protect against rupture of the cooling coil at high temperature operations, a high limit switch is used to stop automatically the refrigerant flow when the conditioned air temperature rises above approximately 110°F. During high-temperature operations cooling and dehumidification are accomplished by automatically adjusting the dampers with the dry-bulb temperature controller. Ambient air is taken in, heated, and humidified to the desired conditions; then the air is passed through the test chamber, after which it may be recycled through the conditioning unit or exhausted to the atmosphere.

Fig. 3. An environmental conditioning unit installed in the Agricultural Engineering Building at the University of Kentucky.

Another automatic control is a cooling coil temperature indicator and assorted instrumentation to defrost the cooling coil when ice builds up during low dew-point operations. Even with the preheat coil, frosting of the refrigerant coils cannot be prevented when operating at controlled dew-point temperatures below approximately 45°F. This is because of the need for a temperature difference between the air and the refrigerant coil surface in order to effect proper heat transfer. In such cases, the units operate automatically to defrost the coils and then reestablish control conditions. When the surface temperature of the coil decreases to a preset temperature, owing to lack of heat transfer because of ice formation, the defrost instrumentation stops all of the conditioning equipment. Electrical heaters mounted through the fins of the coil are energized to melt the ice which drains away as water. After the ice has melted the compressor is operated for one minute, to refreeze any liquid left on the coil, before the fan and other conditioning equipment is put back into operation.

Dry-bulb Control

Dry-bulb temperature control and measurement are obtained with a Minneapolis-Honeywell controller, the same as is used for dew-point control except for the sensing element and range. The sensing element used is a regular resistance thermometer and the range of the dry-bulb instrument is from 0 to 220°F, with a combined instrument and sensing element accuracy of 0.5 per cent of the instrument span. A normally closed steam control valve is the controlled element. This regulates reheating of the environmental air after it has been cooled to slightly below the desired dew-point temperature.

As well as the steam heating control valve,

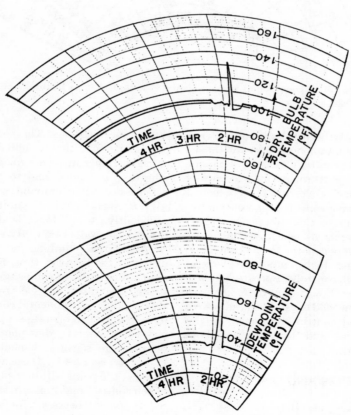

Fig. 4. An indication of the time required for an automatic defrost cycle.

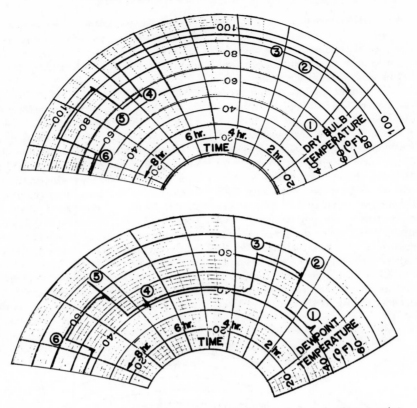

Fig. 5.   A conditioning unit's response to abrupt changes in the set-point
settings.

Fig. 2 shows that the dry-bulb controller is connected to the motor positioner for the air return, air intake, and air exhaust dampers. The connection is through an electrically operated pneumatic-diverting relay which is wired into the refrigerant compressor circuit. When the compressor is stopped for high temperature operations, the diverting relay connects the damper motor to the controller. Therefore, during high-temperature operations the dry-bulb controller operates to reach a balance between the amount of make up air and the heating needed to establish the desired conditions. Final control is reached, in this case, by heating and humidifying above ambient conditions.

INSTALLATION AND OPERATION

George Koch Sons, Inc., of Evansville, Indiana, designed and fabricated six environmental control units according to the pre-ceding specifications. The components composing the conditioning units were mounted on rigid frames in such a manner as to avoid vibration and noise and to make the components accessible for maintenance and repair. All duct work within the units was insulated sufficiently to reduce heat transmission through the walls below 0.125 Btu/hour-sq ft-°F. All internal plumbing and wiring was completed at the factory; thus, final installation required only direct connections to the proper steam, air, water, and electrical supplies.

Since the environmental conditioning units were designed to operate separately from the test chambers, the dew-point and dry-bulb temperature sensing elements were put on 12-ft extension leads. These allow researchers to select the point within the test chambers at which control conditions are to be maintained. Safety controls necessary for fail safe operation when the units function as completely automatic machines were included. Figure 3 shows one of the completed units as it was installed.

Installation

The six environmental control units were installed in the Agricultural Engineering Building at the University of Kentucky. High pressure steam for heating and humidification was furnished by attaching the units to the University's heating system. Electrical power was obtained from the University system. An air supply for the air operated controls and a water supply for condensing refrigerant had to be designed and constructed as part of the laboratory.

An air compressor equipped with strainers, dryers and pressure regulators was installed to furnish a clean, dry air supply to the equipment. A water system was designed to enable the conditioning units to be operated throughout the year. Instead of maintaining a water supply in the water cooling towers located on the roof of the building, the towers are drained to an indoor storage tank. This was done to protect the water from freezing during winter operations.

From the storage tank the water is pumped through the refrigerant condensers and returned to storage, except when the stored water temperature exceeds 84°F. In the latter case the water, coming from the refrigerant condensers, passes through a diversion valve to the cooling towers. After passing through the towers the water flows back, by gravity, to the indoor storage tank to start the cycle over.

Operational Examples

Even though the six environmental control units are connected to common steam, electrical, air and water supplies, they operate independently. Each unit has separate regulating controls, and they are installed such that any single unit or all units can be operated at any time. Because of the wide ranges of temperatures and air flow over which the units

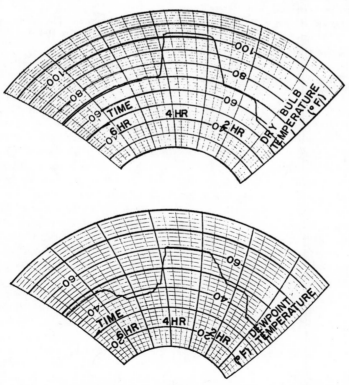

Fig. 6. An indication of the controlled temperatures when operating a conditioning unit by automatic programmed control.

can operate and the versatility designed into them, it is difficult to show examples of all of the operational features. However, a few examples of some extremes should establish an appreciation of the utility of the units.

Figure 4 shows an example of the time required for automatic defrosting. It also shows how control of the environmental conditions is reestablished at the end of the defrost cycle. However, the deviation of the temperatures during the time defrosting was being accomplished is not an exact indication of what the temperatures were in the test chamber during the defrost cycle. This is because the sensing elements are designed to operate in a steady air velocity and the fan is stopped during defrost. Hence, as the defrost cycle starts, the sensing elements must adjust from a finite air velocity past them to a stagnant air. At the end of the defrost cycle an opposite adjustment must be made.

Two other operating extremes are (1) response to an abrupt change in set point, and (2) operating by programmed control. Records of the controlled conditions for these two operations are shown in Figs. 5 and 6 respectively.

Figure 5 shows the response rate of a conditioning unit when an abrupt change is made in the set point. At point (1) the set point of

the dry-bulb temperature controller was abruptly increased from 61 to 94°F. The set point of the dew-point temperature controller was increased from 43 to 63°F at point (2). Points (3) and (4) represent abrupt decreases of the dew-point and dry-bulb set points respectively. Point (5) shows the response when both dry-bulb and dew-point were increased simultaneously, and point (6) is where both were decreased simultaneously. Control unit response to automatic program control is shown in Fig. 6.

The equipment controls to very close tolerances over ranges of 35 to 200°F dry-bulb temperature, 0 to 142°F dewpoint, and 1200- to 2000-cfm air flow rate. Detachable test chambers facilitate designs for specific research problems, rather than to have research projects designed to specific test chambers. These features make the equipment useful for a wide variety of environmental studies, ranging from low-temperature storage to high-temperature curing and drying.

Acknowledgment. The work reported herein was conducted jointly by the Agricultural Engineering Department, Kentucky Agricultural Experiment Station, and the Harvesting and Farm Processing Research Branch, Agricultural Engineering Research Division (ARS), U.S.D.A.

33. Humidity, Temperature, and Air-flow Control Cabinets for Experimentation in Processing Agricultural Products

I. J. Ross and J. M. Myers

University of Florida, Florida Agricultural Experiment Station, Gainesville, Florida

ABSTRACT

Ten cabinets in which samples of crop materials can be placed under controlled temperature, humidity, and air flow have been constructed by the Agricultural Engineering Department at the University of Florida. These environmental control cabinets are being used in factorial experiments to determine the functional specifications for bulk curing bright leaf tobacco and for other work considering the influence of environment on crop materials.

Each cabinet is made in three distinct parts connected by sealed metal ducts. Air is delivered by a fan to a spray chamber where a dew-point temperature is established. The water temperature in the spray chamber is controlled to $\pm 0.2° F$. The air then flows through the heating chamber to establish the desired wet- and dry-bulb temperatures of the air. Heat input is controlled by a variable transformer connected to resistance heating elements. A 16-element thermopile is used to measure the temperature increase in the heating section. The conditioned air is then forced through the crop material where it absorbs moisture. Rate of air flow is controlled manually in the system and is measured with a calibrated orifice plate and a differential manometer.

Drying rates and air temperature during coloring of bright leaf tobacco are two of the important treatment variables considered in this work. Air temperature is controlled to $\pm 1° F$. In replicated tests, average drying rates of 0.00130, 0.00259, and 0.0039 lb water re-moved per min. were established for treatment variables. The limits of mean at 95 per cent confidence for these drying rates were respectively 0.000056, 0.000061, and 0.00011 lb of water removed per min.

INTRODUCTION

Optimum conditioning, curing, or storage of agricultural materials requires a knowledge of the effects of various environments on these materials. Agricultural engineers working with agricultural scientists to establish specifications for those operational processes are faced with frequent recurrence of similar questions about environmental influences on different crop products. These questions relate to such things as changes in weight, moisture, color, or other physical or chemical qualities of a crop material which are influenced by the conditions under which it is held and the time it is held.

This report describes an experimental facility developed and in use at the University of Florida for studying the effects of various environments on agricultural materials.

Ten cabinets have been constructed by the Department of Agricultural Engineering at the University of Florida for conducting various types of experiments in which it is necessary to control air temperature and humidity and air-flow rate around samples of agricultural materials or experimental animals. The cabinets were designed primarily for controlling relative humidities above 60

273

per cent, but they can be used for any air-vapor mixture condition above a dew-point temperature of 32°F and any dry-bulb temperatures in the range of 32°F to 180°F.

Ten cabinets were constructed so that three by three factorial experiments could be conducted. Also, experiments involving three replications of three levels of a single factor can be conducted. In each of these cases, an extra cabinet is available if mechanical or electrical trouble should develop during a test in one of the cabinets being used in the experiment.

The cabinets thus far have been used in two different experiments. The first of these involves curing bulked tobacco samples. It is the objective of this experiment to determine how the chemical and physical characteristics of bulk cured tobacco are affected by air temperature and humidity and air-flow rate through the bulked tobacco during curing. Also, the physical arrangement of the bulked tobacco in the curing container is being studied in this experiment. The second experiment involves the degreening of citrus under conditions of controlled temperature and humidity. It is the objective of this experiment to determine the effects of air temperature and humidity on the rate of degreening and subsequent physiological breakdown of citrus following such various treatments.

The authors have been involved directly with the tobacco curing experiments. These experiments will be referred to later in this paper to illustrate certain characteristics of the control system being discussed.

DESCRIPTION OF THE CONTROL CABINETS

A schematic diagram of a control cabinet is shown in Fig. 1. A portion of a psychrometric chart is shown on the right side of Fig. 1. This chart will be used to help describe the operation of the control cabinet.

The cabinet consists of three basic parts: a spray chamber for the control of the dew-point temperature and humidity, a heating chamber, and a drying or curing chamber. The section of the cabinet designated as the drying and curing chamber is the portion of the cabinet in which samples of the experimental material is placed.

Air is forced by a fan through the temperature and humidity control chamber. This chamber is located between points 1 and 2 on the diagram in Fig. 1. Twenty-four nozzles are used to spray water into this chamber. Air passing through the chamber is saturated with water vapor, and its dew point is established. This state condition is noted as point 2 on the psychrometric chart. Water is circulated through the nozzles in the spray chamber. Approximately 28 gallons per minute of

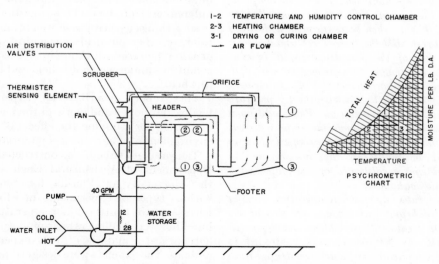

FIG. 1. Schematic diagram of laboratory curing unit.

water is returned to the 40-gallon storage tank. The return pipe and the suction pipe from the water storage tank are arranged to give the water in the tank a swirling action to assure mixing.

Water temperature in the tank is regulated by an on-off temperature control. The on-off control is basically a transistorized bridge-type instrument with a thermistor sensing element. The sensing element is located in the pipe line running from the pump to the spray chamber. The on-off control regulates the flow of the control agent into the tank. Both cold water and steam are provided as control agents. Steam is used when the enthalpy of the air-vapor mixture entering the humidification chamber is lower than the enthalpy of the air at the dew-point condition that is being established in this chamber. Conversely, cold water is used if the enthalpy of the air-vapor mixture entering the chamber is greater than the enthalpy of the air at the dew-point condition being established.

The air is forced through a fiber glass scrubber at the top of the humidification chamber to remove any free moisture that may be carried in the air as a result of air currents in the chamber. The chamber was designed for air velocities in the range of 4 to 40 feet per minute.

After passing through the scrubber, the air moves through a header to the heating chamber which is the section of the cabinet between point 2 and point 3 in the schematic diagram in Fig. 1. In the heating chamber the air-vapor mixture is heated to the desired dry-bulb temperature. This process is indicated by points 2 and 3 on the psychrometric chart in Fig. 1.

Three individually controlled resistance heating elements are used in the heating chamber; two 500-watt elements and one 1000-watt element. A variable auto-transformer is used to regulate the voltage to one of the 500-watt elements so that a full range of heat input from 0 to 2000 watts can be obtained. Since the dew-point temperature is controlled in the humidification chamber, it is necessary only to provide a constant supply of heat to the air passing through the heating chamber to control the dry-bulb temperature and relative humidity at the condition indicated at point 3 on the psychrometric

chart in Fig. 1. Thus, no temperature or humidity controller is used in the heating chamber.

After passing through the heating chamber the air is directed through a footer into the drying or curing chamber. This chamber is the section of the cabinet between points 3 and 1 as shown on the schematic diagram in Fig. 1. This chamber provides the controlled environment and space for holding the experimental material. The dimensions of the chamber are 24 inches wide by 24 inches deep by 30 inches high.

In the tobacco experiments, samples of tobacco were placed in the curing chambers. The temperature and relative humidity of the air entering the chamber and the air-flow rate through the tobacco were the controlled variables. The air passing through the tobacco would become saturated by an approximate adiabatic process. This process is designated as line 3-1 on the psychrometric chart in Fig. 1.

After passing through the tobacco, the air is directed back to the fan through sheet metal ducts. Air-flow rate is measured in this return line with a calibrated orifice. Also, a set of three air distribution valves are provided in this return line. By manually adjusting these valves it is possible to control the air-flow rate in the systems and (1) allow for complete recirculation of the air in the system, (2) allow for complete air change in the system, or (3) allow for partial air change and partial air recirculation in the system.

A one-eighth horsepower centrifugal fan used to force the air through the system is capable of delivering 110 cubic feet of air per minute against a static pressure of 1.5 inches of water.

TEMPERATURE MEASUREMENTS AND ACCURACY OF CONTROL

Temperature was measured in the cabinets at four different points with copper-constantan thermocouples. The temperature of the water entering the humidification chamber was measured at the thermistor sensing element with a single element thermocouple. The dry-bulb temperature of the air-vapor mixture leaving the fan was measured with a single element thermocouple. The dry-bulb temperature of the air-vapor mixture was measured in the header and the footer with four-element, parallel-connected thermopiles. In addition to these temperature measurements, the temperature rise of the air passing through the heating chamber and the temperature drop across the drying or curing chamber were measured with 16-element, series-connected thermopiles.

The water temperature in the spray chamber was maintained at the set point to within plus or minus 0.2°F. The accuracy of this temperature control was determined with a calibrated ASTM, extreme precision grade, Fahrenheit thermometer. The set point temperature was accurate to within plus or minus 0.5°F.

Dry-bulb temperatures of the air-vapor mixture in the header were generally the same as that of the water as determined with the ASTM thermometer. However, when air-flow rate was increased to 100 cubic feet per minute through the humidification chamber, header temperature increased to as much as 0.5°F above the water temperature. The water-flow rate through the humidification chamber was maintained so that the average water temperature in this chamber would not drop more than 0.2°F. Temperatures of the air-vapor mixture in the drying or curing chamber varied less than plus or minus 0.5°F.

The relative humidity of the air-vapor mixture in the header and footer was determined with wet-bulb thermometers and with a narrow-range electrical hygrometer. These measurements indicated complete saturation of the air-vapor mixture in the header.

Perhaps a better estimate of the accuracy of control can be drawn from the tobacco curing experiment. In 1960 three series of bulk curing tests were conducted. Each test consisted of a three by three factorial experiment in which the dry-bulb temperature of the air entering the tobacco column and the drying rate during the coloring period were the two factors considered. The experimental design is illustrated in Fig. 2. Three levels of drying rate were used. These are designated in Fig. 2 as Slow, Medium, and Fast and represent a moisture removal rate of 10, 20, and 30 per cent, respectively, of the total moisture in the sample in 48 hours. Adiabatic drying was assumed for making calculations to determine

DRYING TIME

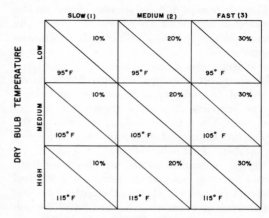

(1) 10% of total water in sample removed in 48 hours.
(2) 20% of total water in sample removed in 48 hours.
(3) 30% of total water in sample removed in 48 hours.

FIG. 2. Design of tobacco curing experiment.

the dew-point temperature (water temperature) of the air-vapor mixture. Also, it was assumed that the air leaving the curing chamber would be saturated. Making these assumptions and knowing the moisture content of tobacco samples, the moisture removal rate was determined. The actual moisture removal rates obtained in the experiment are given below for three tests.

Per Cent of Moisture Removed in 48 Hours

Slow Drying	10.6%
Medium Drying	21.2%
Fast Drying	31.9%

Average Drying Rate

Slow Drying	13.0×10^{-4} lb/min.
Medium Drying	25.9×10^{-4}
Fast Drying	$39 \ \times 10^{-4}$

Limits of the Mean at 95 Per Cent Confidence

Slow Drying	0.56×10^{-4} lb/min.
Medium Drying	0.61×10^{-4}
Fast Drying	$1.1 \ \times 10^{-4}$

The limits of the mean of the actual drying rate in pounds per minute give a good indication of the accuracy with which the conditions were reproduced in the cabinets. The limits of the mean are less than 4.5 per cent of the average drying rate in every case.

All of the air handling portions of the cabinets are insulated with styrofoam or fiber glass. Enough insulation was provided to limit heat losses so that the temperature drop in the air-vapor mixture would be less than 0.5°F.

Air-flow rate was measured with a calibrated orifice plate. The actual accuracy of these measurements have not been determined, but results of the tobacco curing experiments indicate that no large discrepancies existed.

OPERATING CHARACTERISTICS

Four to five hours is required to bring the cabinets into control from a cold start. Adjustment of the water temperature set point is the most tedious operation in this procedure, but once this adjustment is made, the control is very stable. Along with this adjustment, the flow of the control agent has to be regulated manually so as to minimize deviation from the set point.

Heat input to the heating chamber can be calculated very accurately, and the adjustment for heat input is practically instantaneous.

In operation, the air-vapor mixture temperatures in the header and footer were monitored continuously with a recording potentiometer. These measurements give a continuous and accurate indication of cabinet control.

After the conditions in the cabinets have stabilized, the product samples are placed in the curing chamber through a door. Opening this door disturbs the conditions in this chamber. Approximately five to ten minutes is required to restabilize these conditions. To minimize the problems involved in opening and closing the door in this chamber, an automatic strain gage weighing system is being installed in the cabinets. The weighing device will have an accuracy of plus or minus 0.1 pound and can be programmed to weigh test samples on any desired time schedule.

Two major difficulties have been encountered in the operation of the cabinets. The spray nozzles tend to become stopped with rust and calcium carbonates, although two separate mechanical filters have been provided to minimize this difficulty. Also, line voltage fluctuates as much as five volts during the course of a day. Steps are presently being taken to correct both of these difficulties by adding a chemical water filter to remove iron and various carbonates, by replacing the steel water tank and associated tubing with a stainless steel tank and tubing, and by providing regulated voltage to the electrical components of the cabinets.

SUMMARY

Optimum conditioning, curing, or storage of agricultural materials requires a knowledge of the effects of various environments on these materials. Agricultural engineers working with agricultural scientists to establish specifications for those operational processes are faced with frequent recurrence of similar questions about environmental influences on different crop products. These questions relate to such things as changes in weight, moisture, color, or other physical or chemical qualities of a crop material which are influenced by the conditions under which it is held and the time it is held.

The ten temperature, humidity, and air-flow rate control cabinets provide a means for conducting replicated experiments under accurately controlled conditions. The cabinets are basically simple in concept although some skill and knowledge of the internal functions of the control means are required for successfully operating them.

The cabinets cost in labor and materials approximately $1250 each.

34. A System Providing Close Long-term Control of Environmental Humidity for Physical Tests on Cut Tobacco

P. S. H. Boyce, A. Horseman and W. G. Iles

The Imperial Tobacco Company (of Great Britain & Ireland), Ltd., Bristol, England

ABSTRACT

The system to be described has been in full operation for over five years for measurements of tobacco properties that are very sensitive to moisture content. Precise estimates of equilibrium relative humidity (to within $\pm\frac{1}{4}$ per cent) are required to permit reduction of the results to the standard relative humidity of 60 per cent.

The main features of the system are:

(1) The humidity and temperature of the air supplied to the laboratory are controlled at fixed levels, and there is no attempt to compensate for heat or moisture gains within the room. The tobacco samples are conditioned and tested in extensions of the air supply duct, thus eliminating much of the random variation which occurs in conventional systems. The remaining variations are, however, still too large to be neglected, so that determination of actual levels and correction for departure from standard are necessary.

(2) The tobacco samples are slow to respond to the variations resulting from imperfect control. In consequence the relative humidity observed by a conventional hygrometer at the time of test is not, in general, the humidity with which the sample is in equilibrium. Certain tobacco samples are therefore designated for use as hygrometers; they respond at the same rate as the experimental samples and the effective relative humidity with which they are in equilibrium may be determined at any time from their weight. The method of calibrating

these "tobacco reference samples" (weight vs relative humidity) is described.

(3) All readings of relative humidity are ultimately based on a photoelectric dew-point hygrometer. The essential requirement for this device is long-term stability and no claims are made in respect of absolute accuracy. A portable electrical resistance hygrometer is used as a link in the calibration of the tobacco reference samples, and both hygrometers are described.

INTRODUCTION

The physical properties of cut tobacco are profoundly affected by moisture content and hence by atmospheric humidity. For example, one property of importance alters by about 3 per cent for a change of one third of 1 per cent moisture content, corresponding to a change of 1 per cent RH.

Some time ago a demand arose for this particular measurement to be made regularly in such a way that samples tested on different occasions, perhaps years apart, could be validly compared. It was clearly impossible to maintain the standard test humidity (60 per cent RH) to within plus or minus one quarter of 1 per cent which was the tolerance that would allow the test results to be compared directly with the desired precision; a method of making corrections for deviations from 60 per cent RH was therefore needed. This in turn required a means of knowing the humidity with which the samples were in equili-

FIG. 1. Testing hoods.

brium at the time of test, again to high precision. The main features of the system were therefore specified as follows:

(1) The variations in humidity and temperature at the point where the samples were conditioned and tested had to be reduced as much as possible.

(2) Since the remaining variations in humidity even with the best available control system were likely to be too large, a method was required for estimating the effective humidity in equilibrium with a sample at the time of test so that the measurements could be corrected to the nominal humidity.

(3) A reliable method of checking the nominal humidity was required. The hygrometer used had to give very reproducible readings over a long period.

DESCRIPTION OF THE SYSTEM

Conditioning

In a conventionally conditioned laboratory the differential resulting from the action of the control gear can usually be detected at all points in the room, while in addition there are variations in the average humidity level over the working space, due, for example, to the presence of observers.

This second type of variation is of a random nature, and the design of the installation now in use makes no attempt to eliminate it in the room as a whole. Instead, the air supplied to the room is controlled as closely as possible at the standard humidity and temperature, and all measurements on the samples are made in extensions of the inlet duct. The working benches are arranged under hoods (Fig. 1) resembling fume hoods, and the freshly conditioned air flows through the hood from the duct above, over the bench, past the operator and out into the room. The flow is adjusted to be fairly uniform over the front apertures of the hoods at a linear velocity of about 40 fpm. This is not so high as to feel drafty to the operators, and yet it is high enough to prevent moist exhaled air or general room air from disturbing the conditions over the bench.

FIG. 2. Conditioning racks.

The samples are conditioned in racks (Fig. 2) supplied with air from the same duct. The air flows into a plenum chamber at the back and then horizontally forward over the sample trays. Each tray accommodates one 8-ounce sample and equilibration is normally considered complete in about 2 days, the time constant being about 6½ hours; that is, about 63 per cent of the eventual moisture change occurs in 6½ hours.

The air-conditioning plant uses a conventional spray type air washer in which all the air recirculated from the laboratory, plus a small fresh air supply, is cooled and moistened at an appropriate temperature so that the correct relative humidity is obtained after reheating to the required dry-bulb temperature. The temperature of the spray water is controlled by a servo-operated valve which mixes water recirculated from the sump of the washer with chilled water in appropriate proportions.

The position of the mixing valve can be controlled by a temperature sensing element located in the air emerging from the washer (the so-called dew-point system). However, control by a humidity-sensing element located in one of the testing hoods is preferable, being

less sensitive to variations in washer efficiency. Records taken with an electrical resistance hygrometer, to be described later, in hoods served by plants using the two types of control are reproduced in Fig. 3. Record "D" shows the humidity variations in a plant using "dew-point" sensing with single-term (proportional) electronic control gear and on-off chilled-water temperature control. Record "C" shows the variations for a plant with more sophisticated control gear: two-term (proportional and reset) control of humidity and dry-bulb temperature, and modulated control of chilled-water temperature.

The dry-bulb temperature is sensed by an electrical resistance thermometer located, like the humidity element, in the air supply to the hoods and racks. Electrical air heaters are used, supplied from a servo-operated variable-ratio transformer.

As mentioned previously, accuracy of control in the laboratory itself is deliberately sacrificed, by locating the sensing elements in the air supply duct, in order to obtain the best possible control in the racks and hoods for conditioning and testing the samples. Nevertheless, the air-flow requirements of the racks and hoods result in a high rate of air circulation through the laboratory (about one air change per minute) so fairly stable conditions are maintained there, too.

Estimation of the Humidity in Equilibrium with an Experimental Sample

The humidity within a hood or rack normally lies within a range of about ±1 per cent RH of the nominal value and will settle down at an average level somewhere within this range. It is therefore necessary to determine the actual humidity in equilibrium with the sample at the time of test so that appropriate corrections may be made, since the target is plus or minus one quarter of 1 per cent RH. Readings taken with any normal hygrometer are of no use because the tobacco samples respond to changes relatively slowly; this has the advantage of smoothing out the short-term fluctuations, but as a consequence the tobacco is in equilibrium with some sort of an average of the conditions prevailing over the preceding few hours, and not with the current condition indicated by a hygrometer.

This difficulty is overcome by using

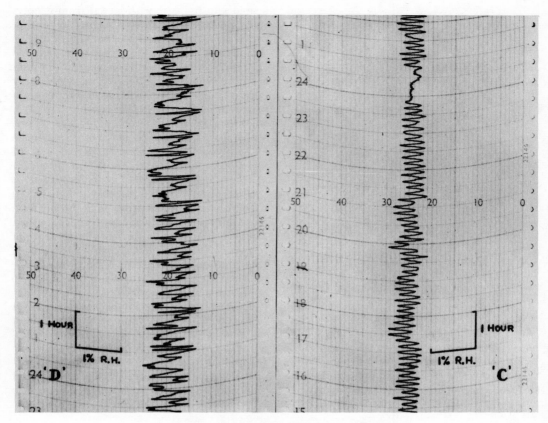

FIG. 3. Humidity fluctuations in two installations.

standard samples of tobacco as hygrometers. These tobacco reference samples ("TRS") are calibrated (see below) so that the variation of their weights with equilibrium relative humidity is known. They are accommodated in small open tins and exposed in the conditioning racks alongside the experimental samples. The quantity of tobacco in a TRS is such that it responds to changing humidity at about the same rate as the experimental samples. Provided, therefore, that a TRS and an experimental sample have been conditioned together for an adequate period, the TRS has only to be weighed to give an estimate of the effective humidity in equilibrium with the experimental sample. The tobacco reference samples cannot, unfortunately, be used over long periods because their characteristics change. Replacement every few months by freshly calibrated samples is necessary.

Calibration of the Tobacco Reference Samples

Measurement of Equilibrium RH: the "Humel". The hygrometer used to define the standard humidity is a dew-point instrument which will be described later. Unfortunately, the operating characteristics of this instrument preclude its direct use for calibrating the tobacco reference samples and a transfer instrument is required. For this purpose an electrical resistance element (referred to as a "humel") is used (Fig. 4); its design was based on that described by Dunmore.[1]

The humel is of cylindrical shape, about 1 in. long and $\frac{3}{4}$ in. diameter, and is composed of four circular discs of perspex and three intermediate discs of palladium sheet (about 0.003 in. thick) clamped firmly together and lightly machined after assembly to give a smooth cylindrical surface. The two outer metal discs are electrically connected internal-

F_{IG}. 4. Humel and guard.

scopic film by slow withdrawal from a poly-vinyl acetate solution containing an appropriate concentration of lithium chloride. This design was adopted for three main reasons: (1) the electrode spacing is very stable and easily reproduced; (2) the spacing is relatively large so that small particles of contaminant do not unduly alter the calibration; and (3) a smooth surface is presented for the hygroscopic film. The time constant of the humel is about 3 seconds for small increases and 15 seconds for small decreases in humidity.

For some applications a guard is needed. It consists of a perforated metal cylinder covered with thin paper which protects the humel from contamination but readily transmits moisture. There is, of course, a decrease in the rate of response of the humel when fitted with a guard (the time constants are increased by a factor of about 3) but this is not important in the application to be described.

The resistance of the humel is measured by a balanced AC bridge circuit. The humel and a multi-turn helical potentiometer are connected in opposing arms of the bridge, which is supplied from a 35-cps oscillator. Any out-of-balance voltage is amplified and indicated by a simple valve voltmeter. The capacitance

ly to one of the base pins and the center one is connected to the other pin. The effect is of three very narrow electrodes set in the cylindrical surface. The humel is coated with its hygro-

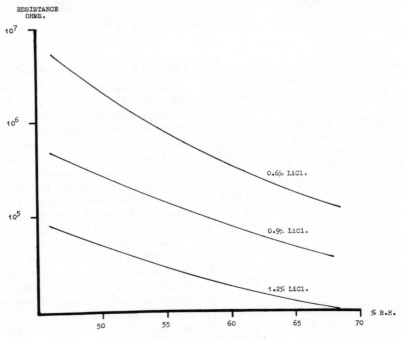

F_{IG}. 5. Typical humel calibrations.

FIG. 6. Calibration cans for tobacco reference samples.

of the humel varies, so an uncalibrated capacity balance control is fitted.

The specimen calibration curves (Fig. 5) for three humels having different ranges show relative humidity plotted against humel resistance. No attempt has been made to produce humels to accurately specified resistances since frequent calibrations are always needed.

Calibration Cans for Tobacco Reference Samples. Calibrations of the tobacco reference samples in terms of weight *vs* equilibrium relative humidity are carried out in small weighable cans (Fig. 6). Each can contains a humel, with guard, for in situ humidity measurement and is fitted with two tubes to permit circulation of moist or dry air so that the tobacco moisture can be changed. These tubes are plugged when they are not in use.

During calibration, the can is maintained at 70°F, the temperature at which the TRS is to be used and at which the humel has been calibrated. The procedure is as follows:

(1) After a period of about 24 hours for equilibration, the humidity inside the can is measured with the humel and the can is weighed.

(2) The tobacco moisture content is altered slightly by circulating moist or dry air through the tubes, and after a further period for equilibration the two measurements are repeated.

(3) This process is continued, to build up a weight/humidity calibration covering the required humidity range, about 55 to 65 per cent RH.

The specimen calibration curve (Fig. 7) shows the weight of a TRS plotted against equilibrium humidity from which it can be seen that a change of one tenth of 1 per cent RH corresponds to a weight change of about 18 mg.

The Dew-point Hygrometer. Humels cannot be relied upon to maintain their calibrations over long periods and reference to a more standard hygrometer is required. A dew-point hygrometer has been constructed for this purpose. In Fig. 8 the top of the aluminium cylinder forms the mirror, which has a thermo-junction set in its surface. The lower end is

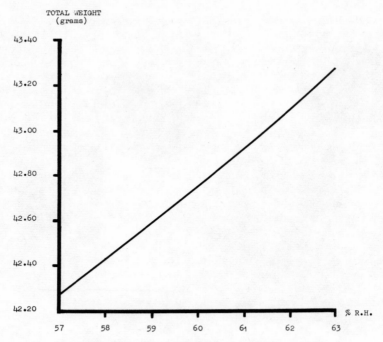

FIG. 7. Typical calibration of tobacco reference sample.

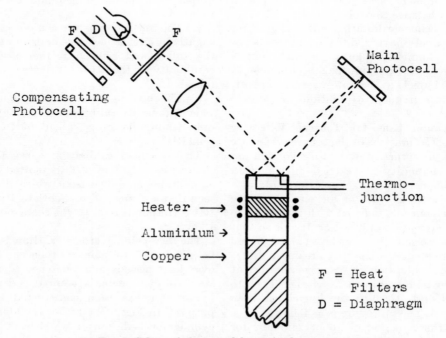

FIG. 8. Schematic layout of dew-point hygrometer.

screwed to a copper rod which is immersed in a cooling mixture while a heater coil with manually adjustable power input is wound around the anodised central section. The whole structure is of fairly large thermal capacity and in consequence its temperature changes quite slowly; this characteristic is convenient for measurements on very stable air. Oblique illumination of the mirror is provided through a heat filter, the specularly reflected light being focused at the main photocell slit. The presence and quantity of dew are indicated by the main photocell output. Figure 9 shows the form of the photocell output as a function of temperature; the early stages of dew formation do not provide a sufficiently well defined indication of the dew point, and it is necessary to work on the steeper and more linear part of the curve. The operating point is arbitrarily chosen at 60 per cent of the output obtained under clear-mirror conditions. The output of the compensating photocell offsets the output of the main cell in order to reduce the effect of

variations in the intensity of the light source, and the overall output is arranged to be zero at the operating point. The method of operation is to adjust the mirror temperature until the output remains steady at zero. In this state presumably the rates of evaporation and condensation are balanced and the corresponding mirror temperature is taken as the dew point.

The main interest is in reproducibility; both the specification of a constant definite photocell output and the care in operating contribute to this, and results appear to be satisfactory.

Calibration of the humels is carried out in an apparatus described by Cram.[2] After passing over the humels in the temperature-controlled calibrating chamber, the constant humidity air flows through the dew-point instrument. The variations in the relative humidity of this air stream are shown in Fig. 10. Over the short period required for obtaining one calibration point, the relative humidity is constant to within about plus or minus one twentieth of 1 per cent.

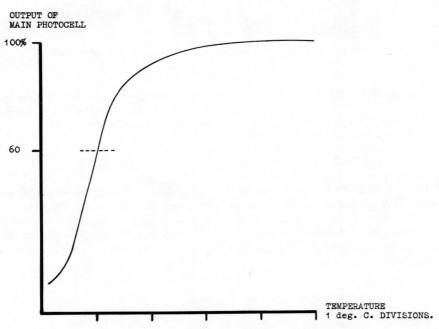

FIG. 9. Relation between photocell output and mirror temperature.

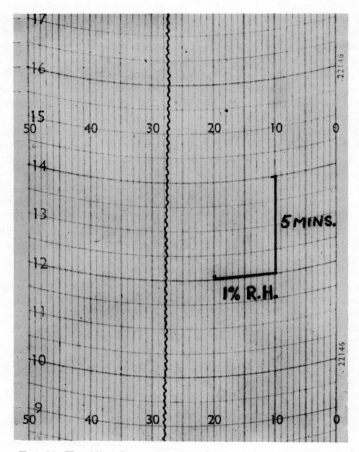

Fig. 10. Humidity fluctuations in humel calibration apparatus.

CONCLUSION

The system described has now been in continuous operation for about five years for routine tests on large numbers of tobacco samples. It is thought that the target of plus or minus one quarter of 1 per cent RH has been met and that no drift in the humidity standard has occurred. However, it is intended to make a comparison between the dew-point instrument and some other standard hygrometer when one of adequate sensitivity and accuracy becomes available.

Acknowledgment. The authors are grateful to the Directors of the Imperial Tobacco Company for permission to publish this paper.

References

1. Dunmore, F. W., "An Improved Electric Hygrometer," *J. Res. Natl. Bur. Std.*, **23**, 701 (1939).
2. Cram, L. A., "An Apparatus for Producing Air of Controlled Relative Humidity for Hygrometer Calibration and Testing," *J. Sci. Instr.*, **33**, 273 (1956).

35. Control of Relative Humidity and Temperature in Rubber Laboratory of National Bureau of Standards

Frank L. Roth and Robert D. Stiehler

National Bureau of Standards, Washington, D.C.

ABSTRACT

The effect of moisture on the properties of rubber compounds made it necessary to control the humidity in the rubber laboratory at the National Bureau of Standards when the establishment of standard materials for rubber compounding was undertaken in 1948. A relative humidity near 30 per cent was found necessary to achieve the best reproducibility of results. The system installed for controlling humidity consisted of a silica gel dehumidifier, a steam injector for humidification and a Dunmore electric hygrometer. Operational difficulties with the dehumidifier were overcome by modifications in the design of the rotating drums. The hygrometer sensing element had to be replaced about every 18 months because the electrical resistance gradually increased during use until resetting the control point was no longer possible. When functioning properly, the system maintained the relative humidity within 0.5 per cent of the set point. Under unfavorable conditions, the humidity fluctuated about 2 per cent above and below the set point.

INTRODUCTION

The moisture in a rubber compound at the time of vulcanization affects the properties of the vulcanizate. This moisture is derived from two sources; namely, the compounding materials and the air. During the mixing and storage of the compound prior to vulcaniza-tion, moisture may be lost or gained depending on the relative humidity of the air and the moisture content of the compounding materials. Using the same materials, seasonal and daily changes in relative humidity are reflected in the measured properties of the compounds. For this reason, control of relative humidity is essential in a laboratory engaged in the evaluation of rubbers. Humidity control is also essential in the evaluation of materials used in rubber compounding. These materials must be evaluated by mixing them in rubber since their effect in rubber can not be predicted from their chemical composition.

When the National Bureau of Standards undertook the establishment of standard materials for rubber compounding in 1948, it was decided to air condition the rubber laboratory in order to control moisture ex-change between the rubber compound and the air. At that time, standard conditions for rubber compounding had not been established. The most uniform vulcanizates and best reproducibility would be obtained when the moisture content of the rubber compound is in equilibrium with the humidity level of the air. Since the rubber compound is at an elevated temperature during mixing, the equilibrium condition after mixing is at a low relative humidity, generally less than 30 per cent. Since it is not economical to condition labora-tories at very low humidity throughout the year and since a significant effect is caused by a humidity change of 5 per cent, a relative humidity of 30 $\pm$ 2 per cent at 25 $\pm$ 1°C was selected for the design conditions. This paper was prepared to describe the essential features of the system that was installed and the operational problems encountered during the past 15 years, including modifications made in the system, in order to assist others confronted with the task of conditioning a laboratory at or near this humidity level.

DESIGN OF AIR-CONDITIONING SYSTEM

A survey was made of various constant temperature and humidity rooms at the National Bureau of Standards and elsewhere. This survey indicated that the following characteristics of an air-conditioning system were necessary for close control of temperature and humidity:

(a) Rapid response

(b) Low hysteresis

(c) Separate control of humidity and temperature

(d) Sensitive humidistat and thermostat

(e) Chemical dehumidification for low levels of humidity

(f) Absence of moisture sources that appreciably affect humidity

(g) Absence of thermal radiation

(h) Adequate capacity for the range of heat and moisture loads.

The most rapid response with minimum hysteresis was observed in systems where temperature and humidity were controlled by proportioning air streams by means of positively positioned dampers. Little or no lag occurred in such systems. This system in conjunction with a Dunmore electric hygrometer[1] and an electrical resistance thermostat was selected as the means most likely to produce close control of temperature and humidity. A dual duct system prior to the central circulating fan was specified for controlling humidity and another dual duct after the fan was specified for temperature control. In order to avoid frosting of the cooling coil, chemical dehumidification was specified but the type was optional. These specifications led to the installation of the system shown schematically in Fig. 1.

The fresh and recirculated air is proportioned by dampers A and B in a ratio dependent on the outside ambient conditions.

Minimal quantities of fresh air enter the system under extreme winter and summer conditions. After the mixture of fresh and recirculated air is filtered, it is proportioned by dampers C and D into the dry and moist air ducts. Moisture is removed or added as required to maintain a constant relative humidity in the conditioned space. A silica gel dehumidifier is used to remove moisture and steam is injected to add moisture. The air having essentially a constant dew point passes through the central circulating fan and is distributed by a dual duct system. A steam coil is located in one duct to supply heat when needed, and a refrigeration coil is located in the other duct to provide the cooling required. The air in the hot and cold ducts is proportioned by a damper (E in Fig. 1) consisting of a single blade suspended vertically and rotated about the top edge to maintain constant temperature in a room. There are fourteen of these dampers, one for each room of approximately 4000 cu ft. There is, on the average, one change of air every 8 minutes in each room, except that a change every 4 minutes occurs in the mill room where the humidistat is located. In the rooms where temperature and humidity must be held within the specified limits, the windows are covered with aluminum foil and thermal insulation in order to minimize heat transfer by radiation and convection.

CONTROLS

The proportioning dampers C and D, the dehumidifier, and the humidifier are controlled by a single humidistat located in the area near the mills on which the rubber is mixed. This humidistat consists of a Dunmore electric hygrometer[1] and a combination electronic recorder and pneumatic controller with adjustable throttling range and reset. Full scale range of the recorder is about 12 per cent RH. The humidity at the sensing element can be controlled within 0.5 per cent relative humidity of the set point. This precise control at the humidistat is necessary to maintain the humidity throughout the conditioned spaces within 2 per cent RH. Humidity control at a single point is possible since the only significant sources of moisture in the conditioned spaces are the few occupants. The pneumatic

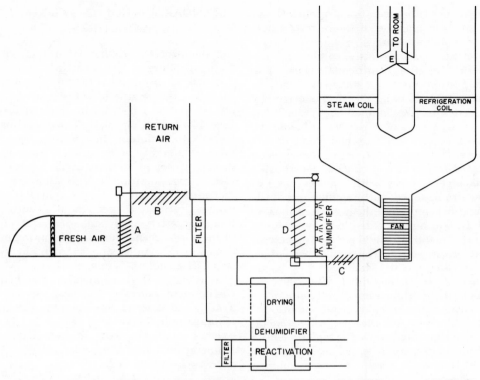

Fig. 1. Schematic diagram of air-conditioning system in NBS rubber laboratory: (A) Fresh air damper. (B) Return air damper. (C) Dry air damper. (D) Moist air damper. (E) Temperature control damper.

controller governed by the humidistat starts and stops the dehumidifier as required and regulates the amount of air passing through it by positioning dampers C and D in Fig. 1. It also throttles the steam valve when moisture must be added to the air to maintain the desired relative humidity. This valve is closed when the dehumidifier is operating and damper C is open.

In order to maintain precise control of relative humidity, the temperature at the location of the humidistat must also be precisely controlled. A resistance sensing element and a combination electronic recorder and pneumatic controller with adjustable throttling range and reset is used for this purpose. The recorder has a full scale range of about 20°C. It is necessary to control the temperature of the air at the hygrometer within ±0.3°C in order to control the relative humidity within ±0.5 per cent.

In each of the conditioned spaces other than the space in which the humidistat is located, a separate thermostat is used to control a damper like E in Fig. 1 to proportion the air from the hot and cold ducts. These thermostats have a throttling range of 100 per cent for a change in temperature of about 1.5°C. The temperatures in the hot and cold ducts are also controlled by thermostats. The set points of these thermostats and the ratio of fresh to recirculated air are determined by controls in the fresh air duct.

All throttling valves and dampers have positive positioning devices in order to eliminate hysteretic effects from friction. Safety controls and interlocks are provided where required and all controls are designed to fail "safe."

PERFORMANCE OF DEHUMIDIFIER

The dehumidifier gave more operational difficulties than any other part of the system. The difficulties were finally overcome so that a discussion of the operational problems and their solution may be of interest to others using a similar system.

As mentioned previously, a silica gel dehumidifier of the continuous-regeneration, rotating-drum type was installed for removing moisture from the air. The drums originally furnished with the dehumidifier retained the silica gel by means of a wire screen (about 60 per cent open area) and had good drying capacity. However, the wire screen soon separated from the end rings and permitted the silica gel to escape. After a second set of similar drums failed, the manufacturer of the dehumidifier replaced them with drums in which the silica gel was retained by means of perforated metal (about 25 per cent open area) instead of wire screen. The smaller percentage of open area greatly reduced the drying capacity of the dehumidifier. The silica gel pellets in these drums were rapidly ground to a fine powder that entered the air-conditioned spaces. Cracking of the perforated metal through fatigue made repair or replacement of the drums necessary at least once a year. Air leaks at the rubber seals were also a common occurrence.

During rotation, both the original wire screen and the replacement perforated metal drums exhibited irregular motions. Measurements of the drums indicated that the end rings on which the drums rotated were out-of-round by more than 2 per cent and deviated from right cylinders. Fatigue of the drums was attributed to stresses from flexing and twisting during rotation.

New drums were designed and constructed that had end rings which formed right cylinders and were circular within 0.05 per cent. Perforated metal having an open area of about 45 per cent was used to retain the silica gel. This larger open area increased the drying capacity, but not to the original designed capacity of the dehumidifier. Within the limit of their capacity, these drums have performed satisfactorily since they were installed two years ago. Interestingly, there has been no evidence of the silica gel pellets being ground to a powder in these drums. No silica gel has been added and no maintenance of the drums has been required since they were installed. Wear and damage to the rubber air seals by the drums has been minimized.

STANDARDIZATION OF LABORATORY CONDITIONS

Soon after the rubber laboratory at the National Bureau of Standards was conditioned, it was decided to condition laboratories in the synthetic rubber plants then owned by the Government. Since many of these plants were on the Gulf Coast, it was not feasible to maintain these laboratories at a relative humidity of 30 per cent. Since it was decided to condition them at 35 $\pm$ 5 per cent RH, the set point in the NBS laboratory was increased from 30 to 35 per cent RH. This change facilitated year-round control of humidity, particularly since the replacement of the wire-screen drums by perforated metal drums made it impossible to maintain 30 per cent RH during the summer months.

Since the initial installation, the Federal Government and the American Society for Testing and Materials have adopted a standard laboratory temperature of 23 $\pm$ 1°C. In order to conform with this standard, the temperature in the rubber laboratory has been decreased from 25 to 23°C.

PERFORMANCE OF HUMIDISTAT

Since the key element in humidity control is the humidistat, a Dunmore electric hygrometer was selected for its ability to detect quickly small changes in relative humidity. The electrical resistance of this sensing element has consistently increased with time in service. As a consequence, the element has had to be replaced after 12 to 24 months of service.

When the increase in resistance was first observed, contamination from the air in the laboratory seemed a possible cause. Therefore, the sensing element was covered with a porous cellulose thimble impregnated with silver nitrate to remove any sulfide or chloride contaminant that might be in the air. The thimble also prevented dust particles from settling on the element. This protection of the element had no effect on its change in electrical resistance.

Sensing elements that are in shelf storage do not change in their electrical characteristics. Therefore, the increase in electrical resistivity of the sensing element during use appears to be

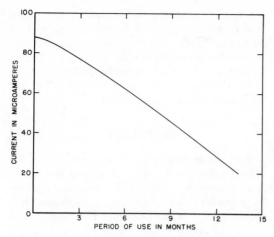

FIG. 2. Change of current in Dunmore electric hygrometer during continuous use at 35 per cent RH.

caused by the electric current continuously passing through the element. Figure 2 shows the decrease in electrical conductivity of a typical element during use. Because of this behavior, the humidity must be verified by independent means. A hygrothermograph is used to indicate drift in relative humidity over long periods. At approximately monthly intervals, the relative humidity recorded on the hygrothermograph is verified by means of wet- and dry-bulb thermometers. As the resistance of the sensing element changes, the

set point on the controller must be adjusted to maintain the desired humidity. Usually, adjustment at monthly intervals is sufficient.

PERFORMANCE OF HUMIDIFIER

The humidifier consists of a corrosion-resistant metal pipe in which a series of holes are drilled. The pipe is connected to a throttling steam valve. During a change in conditions from removal to addition of moisture or vice versa, there is some hunting in the control system. The relative humidity fluctuates at the sensing element about 2 per cent during this transitory period. Figure 3 is a recorder chart showing periods of good control and periods when the humidity fluctuated about ± 2 per cent from the control point. Similar fluctuations of unknown cause occur at times. Other than the usual maintenance of steam valves, the humidifier is free of operational problems.

DISCUSSION

The Dunmore electric hygrometer is capable of controlling relative humidity within a narrow range. However, the hygrometer is not an accurate instrument since the electrical characteristics of the element change slowly during use. It is interesting to note that Dun-

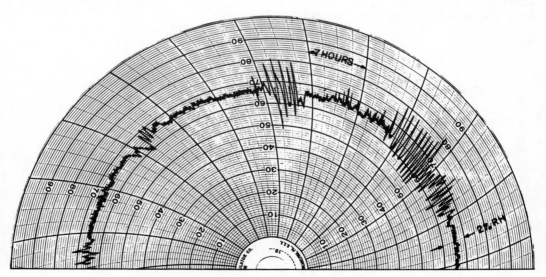

FIG. 3. Chart showing control of humidity in NBS rubber laboratory. Chart is graduated in microamperes.

more[1] found an increase in resistance when metal wire other than platinum or palladium was used. He reports no change in resistance during a six-month period when palladium wire was used, but he gives no details of his experiment. It is not known whether his hygrometer was in intermittent or continuous use during the six-month period. Our findings indicate that present commercial hygrometers of the Dunmore type wound with palladium wire also increase in resistance during continuous use. In spite of this instability, these hygrometers are very useful, provided other means are employed for verifying the humidity level.

Since the Dunmore electric hygrometer senses the relative humidity, good control of temperature is necessary to maintain close control of humidity. For this purpose, the proportioning of hot and cold air by a mixing damper controlled by a sensitive thermostat is very effective. Response is rapid, and there is no lag in cooling or heating to cause the temperature to overshoot or undershoot. Dampers and the pneumatic motors for operating them require little or no maintenance.

Fracturing and powdering of the silica gel granules during operation of the dehumidifier is commonly attributed to the large temperature changes in going through the dehumidification and reactivation cycles. In some dehumidifiers, temperature change may have been responsible but in our dehumidifier, mechanical grinding rather than temperature change has been found to be the cause. Our experience indicates that in a silica gel dehumidifier properly designed and operated at a reactivation temperature below 320°F, there is little or no fracturing of the granules and little maintenance is required.

SUMMARY

Relative humidity has been controlled in the rubber laboratories of the National Bureau of Standards since 1948. The Dunmore electric hygrometer used for the humidistat has enabled the relative humidity to be controlled within a narrow range, but the element is not stable since the electrical resistance increases slowly during use. When used with an independent means for verifying the humidity level, it has been very effective. Humidification of the air has been through steam injection. Dehumidification has been done by a silica gel dehumidifier. Poor design and workmanship of this dehumidifier has caused many operational difficulties and excessive maintenance. Through a modification in design, these difficulties have been overcome and maintenance has become negligible.

Reference

1. Dunmore, F. W., "An Improved Electric Hygrometer," *J. Res. Natl. Bur. Std.*, **23**, 701 (December 1939).

36. A Versatile Environmental Test Chamber for Thermal Stress Research

C. M. HUMPHREYS AND AUSTIN F. HENSCHEL

U.S. Department of Health, Education, and Welfare, Public Health Service, Cincinnati, Ohio

ABSTRACT

The paper describes a new environmental test chamber recently built by the Division of Occupational Health, U.S. Public Health Service, at Cincinnati, Ohio, for studying the effect of thermal stress on human subjects. The room is designed to operate at any desired temperature from 50 to 150° F, and near the middle of this range, the relative humidity can be controlled at any point from 25 to 75 per cent. Air movement, radiant environment and work rate also can be controlled over a wide range of conditions. Design features and operating characteristics are discussed.

INTRODUCTION

Man's thermal comfort or discomfort is determined by the combined effect of four environmental factors, namely, the temperature, relative humidity and velocity of the air, and the temperature of the surrounding surfaces. Much has been accomplished during the last ten or fifteen years in providing more comfortable environmental conditions in industry. In spite of this general trend, however, there are still many workers exposed daily to heat stresses of varying severity.

Many of the problems associated with thermal stress are not fully understood, and further research on the subject is needed. In preparation for such studies, a new thermal test chamber has been constructed, in which all four of the above named environmental factors can be controlled at any desired level over the ranges normally encountered in the field. Two treadmills provide means for varying the work rate of the test subjects. This paper presents a description of the test room and an outline of some of the studies which will be made in it.

GENERAL DESCRIPTION OF ROOM

The thermal test chamber is located within the air-conditioned building occupied by the Occupational Health Research and Training Facility at 1014 Broadway, Cincinnati, Ohio. Adjoining the test chamber is a pre-test room. The size and the general arrangement of the rooms are shown in the floor plan, Fig. 1. Some of the construction details may be seen in Fig. 2 which shows a sectional view of the test room. Basically, the rooms consist of a wood frame covered with plywood on both sides. A vapor barrier, consisting of 40-pound kraft paper between two layers of aluminum foil, is cemented to the interior plywood surfaces of the test room and plenum chamber. Walls, floor and ceiling are insulated with 2-in. thick glass-fiber blanket.

The inside surfaces of the test room walls consist of 0.063-in. thick painted aluminum panels spaced 2 in. from the interior plywood surfaces. The bottom of these panels is 2 in. above the floor.

A suspended ceiling is located at a height of 9 ft, thus forming a plenum chamber above it. Two rows of fluorescent lights and five 12-in.

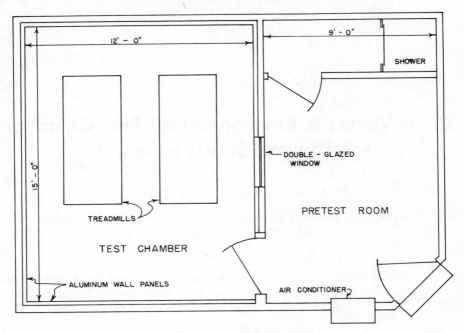

FIG. 1. Plan of test chamber.

wide panels of perforated aluminum are located in the ceiling as shown in Fig. 2, and the remaining ceiling area consists of acoustic panels. Because of the high temperatures which will at times be maintained in the room, the ballasts for the lights are remotely located.

Figure 3 is a photograph of the interior of the test room.

Air Distribution System

The air distribution system for the test room may be visualized from Fig. 2. Conditioned air

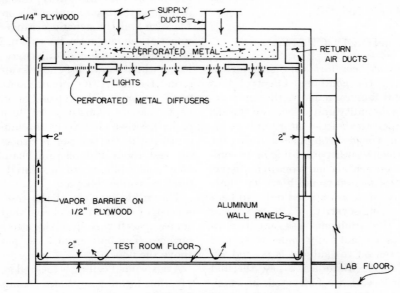

FIG. 2. Section through test chamber.

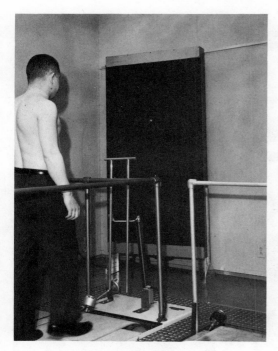

FIG. 3. Interior view of test chamber.

panels, and it flows upward through the 2-in. space in back of the panels to a return air duct in the plenum chamber. This method for removing air from the room was adopted as a means of maintaining the wall surface temperature at or very near the room air temperature.

Air is supplied to the room at the rate of 100 air changes per hour (2700 cfm), but in spite of this high rate of delivery, the maximum air velocity in the occupied zone of the room, as measured with a thermal anemometer, is approximately 30 fpm.

Air-conditioning System

The air-conditioning system which is shown diagrammatically in Fig. 4, was designed to provide close control of temperature and humidity in the test room. Moisture may be removed from the air by a sorption-type dryer having an air capacity of 1000 cfm. Humidification is accomplished by a capillary-type air washer having a capacity of 2700 cfm. Spray water is heated by one 6-kW and one 7.5-kW immersion heater located in the discharge line of the spray water pump.

After the moisture content of the air has been properly established, sensible heat is removed or added by cooling or heating coils located on the discharge side of the fan. Chilled water/ethylene glycol solution is circulated through the cooling coil from a 220-gallon tank, the contents of which is cooled by

enters the plenum through two ducts of perforated aluminum, thus providing distribution in the plenum with minimal velocity. From the plenum, air enters the test room through the perforated panels in the ceiling.

Air leaves the room through the 2-in. slot between the floor and the aluminum wall

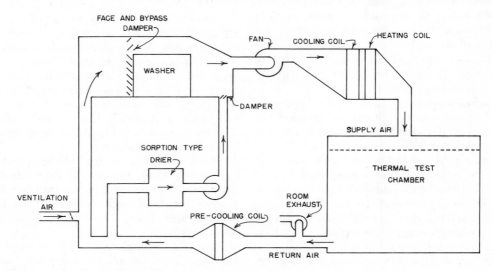

FIG. 4. Diagrammatic arrangement of air-conditioning equipment.

Fig. 5. Air-conditioning equipment and control panel.

means of a 15-hp refrigeration compressor and liquid chiller. An air-cooled condenser permits operation of the refrigeration system at any season of the year.

Hot water is circulated through the heating coil from a 220-gallon tank, which is heated by a gas-fired water heater.

During some tests the internal sensible load in the room will be quite high because of the operation of radiant panels which are described later. A pre-cooling coil is located in the return air duct ahead of the washer and drier to remove most of this sensible load. Chilled liquid is supplied to this coil from the chilled liquid tank by a separate pump.

Figure 5 is a photograph showing a part of the air-conditioning equipment. A window-type air conditioner has been provided to maintain comfortable conditions in the pre-test room.

Control System

Aspirated resistance type wet and dry bulbs are used as the sensing elements for the control of temperature and humidity in the test room. Signals from these sensing elements are transmitted to a pneumatic controller-recorder by two millivolt-to-pressure transmitters. The pneumatic controller-recorder is a two-pen instrument with a 12-in. circular chart. The instrument has adjustable proportional band and automatic reset.

To maintain a given dry-bulb temperature in the test room, the pneumatic controller, upon receipt of an error signal from a MV/P transmitter, throttles in sequence three-way mixing valves in the lines to the heating and cooling coils.

Similarly, to maintain a given wet-bulb condition, the pneumatic controller, upon receipt of a signal from the second MV/P transmitter, throttles the two damper motors in sequence. For example, if additional humidification is required, the dryer damper is first closed, after which the washer damper is opened and the bypass damper is closed.

Water temperature in the pre-cooling coil is maintained constant by a pneumatic controller which operates a three-way mixing valve. The controller set point is adjusted manually to the desired point.

The temperature of the liquid in the hot and cold storage tanks is controlled by two transistorized relays, with the sensing elements located in the respective tanks.

The "Freon" compressor and condenser are on pump-down control. The usual safety devices, including high- and low-pressure cutouts, oil pressure switch, and a freeze protection thermostat on the chiller, are connected into the control circuit. An extra contact on the switch for the chilled water circulator is also connected into the control circuit to prevent the operation of the compressor unless the circulator is running.

The control circuit for the gas-fired water heater is so connected that the water heater cannot be turned on unless the hot water circulator and the fan which exhausts the products of combustion are in operation.

The temperature of the washer spray water is controlled by an electric insertion type thermostat in the coil circuit of a three-phase contactor. This circuit is also connected through extra contacts on the switches for the washer pump and main fan so that the heaters cannot be energized unless these two pieces of equipment are running.

The room usually reaches equilibrium within 30 to 60 minutes after start-up, depending upon the magnitude of the changes required. It is anticipated that to obtain very low humidities, an even longer period of time may be required. To prevent loss of testing time each morning while equilibrium is being attained, the air-conditioning system can be operated by an electric timer, The desired conditions for a morning test can be set up the previous evening, and the room will be ready for the starting of tests when the subjects and observers arrive. The timer has a mechanical drive which will automatically take over for a period of up to 8 hours in case of current failure. It can also be set to skip operation over weekends and holidays.

Air Movement

As previously stated, the normal air velocity in the test room is quite low. To provide greater air movement over the subjects when so desired, two banks of fans will be used. Each bank consists of five 10-in. propeller fans mounted one above the other and equipped with a variable transformer to provide speed control. Any desired air velocity up to about 1,000 fpm can thereby be obtained.

Fans may be readily moved so that the air stream may be directed at the subject from any direction.

Thermal Radiation

Thermal irradiation of the subjects is provided by two electrically heated panels, each 3 ft wide by $5\frac{1}{2}$ ft high, and having vertical heating elements located 3 in. on centers. The panels are standard, commercially available units usually used in the construction of industrial ovens, except that a cover of 18-gauge black steel has been placed over the heating elements to provide a flat radiating surface. One of the panels may be seen in Fig. 3.

Panels of this type are designed to operate at rather high temperatures. For thermal stress studies the maximum desired temperature of the radiant surface is approximately 400°F. To obtain low-temperature operation, panels designed for 480-V operation and rated at 36,000 watts, were selected. The units are operated at 208 V, and at this lower voltage, the heating capacity is reduced to 6760 watts.

Regulation of panel temperature is obtained by controlling the percentage of the time during which energy is supplied to the heating elements. Controllers work on a 30-second cycle, and may be set to supply power from 4 to 100 per cent of each cycle. The average temperature of the radiant surface is determined by several copper-constantan thermocouples silver-soldered to the panel face.

Like the fans, the radiant panels may be readily moved to any desired position with respect to the subjects.

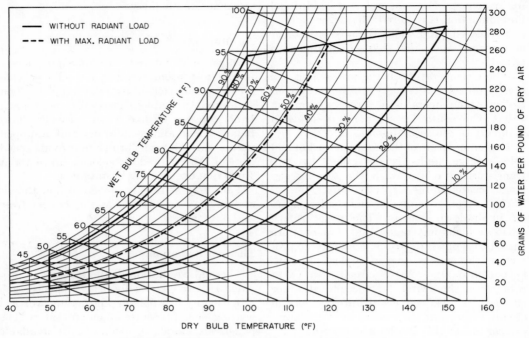

FIG. 6. Environmental conditions attainable in chamber.

Range of Test Conditions

The room was designed to operate at any temperature from 50 to 150°F. The design relative humidity varies depending upon the temperature and the internal radiant load. In Fig. 6 design conditions are outlined on the psychrometric chart. Solid lines indicate conditions without radiant heat load, and the dotted line shows the design conditions with the two radiant panels operating with a surface temperature of 400°F or 300°F above room temperature, whichever is lower.

Tests have not yet been made at all of the limiting conditions shown on the figures, but spot checking suggests that most of the conditions can be reached without difficulty.

TEST PROGRAM

Most of the research programs contemplated for the room will be carried out by the Physiology Section of the Division of Occupational Health. The following is a list of ten projects which have already been suggested for study:

(1) Standardize methods and techniques for estimating the physiological strain imposed on workers in hot occupational environments.

(2) Determine relative and absolute protection from radiative and convective heat gain provided by various clothing and shielding devices under simulated hot industry situations.

(3) Define physiological strain from radiative heat in terms of equivalent increment in air temperature.

(4) Determine the relative physiological strain imposed by equal calorie stress from endogenous and oxegenous sources and define the physiological mechanisms utilized in maintaining thermal balance under the two situations.

(5) Study the effects of thermal and work stress upon pulmonary dynamics.

(6) Study the effects of age and years of exposure to heat on physiological responses to a standardized heat and work test.

(7) Determine the psychological, physio-

logical and cultural aspects of comfort and discomfort in a wide range of thermal environments.

(8) Determine the decrement on physical and mental performance capacity as a function of the severity of heat stress.

(9) Determine the degree of heat acclimatization normally developed in a population as a function of season.

(10) Determine the impact of heat stress upon the tolerance to other types of industrial stresses.

SECTION IV

AIR CONDITIONING

37. An Investigation of Psychrometric Measurement Techniques in Air-conditioning Calorimetry

J. C. DAVIS AND P. R. ACHENBACH

National Bureau of Standards, Washington, D.C.

ABSTRACT

During a series of tests of several models of air-to-air heat pumps for a range of test conditions, reasonably close agreement was obtained between simultaneous measurements of cooling capacity made by the psychrometric method and the refrigerant-side method. Of the 55 cooling tests performed in which comparisons could be made between the two methods, the difference between the cooling capacity values was less than 4 per cent in 78 per cent of the cases, and less than 2 per cent in 44 per cent of the cases.

Dry-bulb and wet-bulb temperature measurements were made with thermocouple psychrometers. Relative humidities calculated from these measurements differed from those determined with electric hygrometers by 1 per cent RH or less in about 60 per cent of the comparison tests. The design and application techniques of thermocouple psychrometers are described in detail, and the methods used to obtain good air mixing at the stations of temperature and humidity measurement are discussed. Some of the sources of error in the measurement of temperature were investigated and the possible errors in the measurement of air and refrigerant flow rates were recognized and are discussed. Areas of instrument and thermodynamic data deficiencies and other factors affecting the reliability of air-conditioning calorimetry are summarized.

INTRODUCTION

It is difficult to obtain satisfactory agreement between capacity values for air conditioners and heat pumps measured by two commonly used laboratory methods; namely, the psychrometric method and the refrigerant-side method. The psychrometric method employs measurements of the air flow rate through the indoor heat exchanger and the wet-bulb and dry-bulb temperatures of the air at the inlet and outlet of the heat exchanger. These temperature measurements involve many possible sources of error due to radiation and conduction effects, low air velocities, inadequate air mixing, deviations from steady-state conditions with respect to time, heat and moisture flow in the wicks of the wet-bulb elements, and uncertainties in converting the observed temperature values into accurate values of moisture content of the air. The refrigerant-side method employs measurements of the refrigerant flow rate and the temperatures and pressures of the refrigerant at the inlet and outlet of the indoor heat exchanger. Temperature measurements are not as critical for this latter method since nearly all of the enthalpy change in the refrigerant between the inlet and outlet of the heat exchanger is represented by the latent heat of evaporation. However, the accuracy of the refrigerant-side method is dependent on the accuracy of published values of the thermodynamic properties of the refrigerant, on the measurement of low flow rates of refrigerant, on determinations of the effect of oil in the refrigerant, and on having refrigerant in a single phase at each station of temperature and pressure measurement.

A large number of tests were made at the National Bureau of Standards on several models of air-to-air heat pumps to determine heating and cooling capacity under a variety of test conditions using the psychrometric and refrigerant-side test procedures. The dry- and wet-bulb determinations in the psychrometric cooling tests were made with thermocouple psychrometers. The principal purpose of this paper is to describe the design and application of the thermocouple psychrometer used in the cooling tests, and to show the satisfactory agreement between values of relative humidity obtained with this instrument and with the electric hygrometer.

The agreement obtained between the psychrometric and refrigerant-side determinations of cooling capacity is summarized in the following section as evidence of the satisfactory results obtained by the methods described.

COMPARISON OF CAPACITY VALUES BY TWO TEST METHODS

Comparison of cooling capacity values of several heat pumps determined by the psychrometric and refrigerant-side methods was possible in 55 tests. In some other tests such a comparison was not possible because a mixture of refrigerant liquid and vapor existed at the refrigerant flowmeter or at one of the stations of temperature and pressure measurement. In the 55 cooling tests, the difference between the two capacity values was less than 4 per cent in 78 per cent of the cases, and was less than 2 per cent in 44 per cent of the cases. The cooling tests were selected for this analysis since wet-bulb psychrometers were an important part of the instrumentation.

Table 1 shows the distribution of cooling test determinations with respect to selected ranges of disparity between the psychrometric and refrigerant-side capacity values. The table shows that the refrigerant-side values were higher than the psychrometric values in about three-fourths of the tests. Only two of the 55 tests showed a disparity greater than the 6 per cent permitted by the American Society of Heating, Refrigerating and Air-Conditioning Engineers Standard 16–56,[1] which was used as a guide in the design of the calorimeter apparatus.

TABLE 1. COMPARISON OF PSYCHROMETRIC AND REFRIGERANT-SIDE CAPACITY VALUES FOR COOLING TESTS

Selected Ranges of Disparities Between the Two Values (%)	No. of Tests with Higher Psychrometric Values	No. of Tests with Higher Refrigerant-side Values
0–0.99	4	6
1.0–1.99	4	10
2.0–2.99	1	11
3.0–3.99	2	5
4.0–4.99	3	6
5.0–5.99	0	1
6.0–7.00	0	2
	14	41

DESCRIPTION OF PSYCHROMETRIC TEST APPARATUS AND PROCEDURE

Description of the Psychrometric Calorimeter

A drawing of the psychrometric calorimeter is shown in Fig. 1. The indoor unit of the heat pump was surrounded by a wooden enclosure and the discharge opening in the unit was connected to a discharge duct containing an ASME long-radius nozzle, air mixers, and an array of psychrometers for measuring the outlet conditions of the circulated air. The wooden enclosure permitted most of the cooling effect of the casing of the indoor unit to be included in the measured cooling capacity of the unit. The discharge duct was insulated from the point where it leaves the wooden enclosure to a position a short distance downstream of the psychrometers in the duct. A mixing chamber and a propeller fan near the inlet psychrometers were used to promote uniformity of temperature and humidity at the upstream station, and a baffle and an unpowered fan provided mixing for the downstream station, as indicated in Fig. 1. An auxiliary blower, connected to an extension of the discharge duct downstream of the nozzle, was used to overcome the additional pressure drop introduced into the air circuit by the nozzle and mixing devices. The auxiliary blower is not shown in the Figure. The outdoor unit of the heat pump, which houses the compressor, another finned heat exchanger, and other components, was located in an adjacent temperature-controlled space and connected to the indoor unit in the

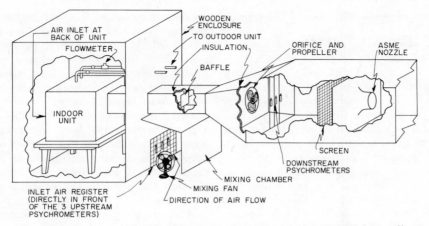

FIG. 1. The psychrometric calorimeter used in the tests for determining cooling capacity. An auxiliary blower, downstream from the nozzle, for overcoming pressure drop due to mixing devices and nozzle in the discharge duct, is not shown in the diagram.

wooden enclosure by a vapor line and liquid line.

Air Mixing

In order for a few wet-bulb and dry-bulb elements to satisfactorily represent the average condition of the air entering and leaving the calorimeter, it was necessary that the air stream be well mixed at the inlet and outlet measuring stations with respect to temperature and humidity. As indicated in Fig. 1, a propeller fan was located near the inlet of the wooden enclosure upstream of the indoor unit. A mixing chamber with one open side was built around the inlet air grille to confine the mixing process. Sometimes it was found advantageous to place another fan in the back of the chamber facing the first fan. The air entered the enclosure through a grille having a gross area of 2.0 sq ft and a net free area of about 1.4 sq ft .The fan positions were adjusted by trial and error.

For downstream mixing, the air leaving the blower of the indoor unit, was forced against and around a wooden baffle about 10 in. square, and then passed through an orifice having a 20-in. diameter and an area of about 2.2 sq ft. The unpowered fan placed at the center of the orifice was rotated by the flow of air. The orifice served two purposes: to help mix the air and to produce a suitable velocity at the thermocouple psychrometers. A screen, located upstream of the nozzle, helped to pro-

vide suitable entrance conditions for the nozzle. These elements of the psychrometric calorimeter are shown diagrammatically in Fig. 1.

Dry-bulb and Wet-bulb Measurements

During the psychrometric tests, readings of dry-bulb and wet-bulb temperatures of the moving air were made at stations upstream from the indoor unit at the entrance to the wooden enclosure and downstream from the unit at stations in the insulated metal duct. The dry- and wet-bulb elements of the thermocouple psychrometers employed 30-gauge (0.010-in.) copper-constantan wire taken from spools of wire from which a sample of wire had been removed and calibrated. These psychrometers were used because of the satisfactory performance described in the literature.[2-4] They were reported as giving accurate readings at low velocities, and were suited to remote reading and multiple measurements of the dry- and wet-bulb temperatures of the air. The design of these psychrometers was the same as that used by Wexler and Daniels of the National Bureau of Standards in a study of the performance of a two-pressure humidity generator.[5] Their data showed that the differences between the indications of the thermocouple psychrometer and the two-pressure humidity apparatus averaged ± 0.4 per cent relative humidity and in only two of the 30 cases were the differences 1 per cent or greater.

A schematic drawing of the initial design of the wet-bulb element of the psychrometer is shown in Fig. 2(a). A distilled water supply was provided in a test-tube fitted with a one-hole stopper. The thermocouple junction was located $\frac{1}{2}$ in. above the top of the stopper, and the cotton wick reached from near the bottom of the test tube, through the stopper, to a distance of one inch or more above the thermocouple junction. The thermocouple junction was formed by twisting the two wires and soldering and had no added mass loading in the initial design. The wick was held snugly around the thermocouple wires and the junction by three thread ties as indicated in Fig. 2(a). The dry-bulb element in each case was placed alongside its corresponding wet-bulb element at a distance of about 3 in. A $\frac{1}{4}$-in. brass washer was soldered to the dry-bulb thermocouple junction to damp momentary temperature variations. The leads to the wet-bulb and dry-bulb junctions were securely supported to minimize vibration and cold working. Care was also taken to minimize errors due to heat conduction along the wires.

The wicks for the wet-bulb element, as received from the manufacturer, were boiled in distilled water and allowed to dry in the open air prior to use. For each test of the heat pump, clean wicks, properly tied and oriented, were used. An array of three psychrometers, about 7 in. apart, was placed in a horizontal line at midheight in the duct upstream from the indoor coil, and another array of three, about 5 in. apart, similarly arranged, was placed downstream from the coil, as shown in Fig. 1. Thermocouple lead lengths of at least 15 in. beyond the point of support were provided in the moving air stream to minimize conduction of heat from the ambient air through the leads to the copper-constantan junctions.

A set of 5 thermocouples, connected electrically in parallel, was placed upstream of the array of psychrometers at the inlet and outlet stations. The five thermocouples in each of these parallel circuits were located so as to provide a good space average of the dry-bulb temperatures in the entire cross section of the duct. For this reason, the dry-bulb readings as obtained by the parallel thermocouples, upstream and downstream, were used in the calculations where only dry-bulb temperatures were required. The averages of the psychrometer dry- and wet-bulb readings, upstream and downstream, were used for determining the relative humidity values employed in the calculations.

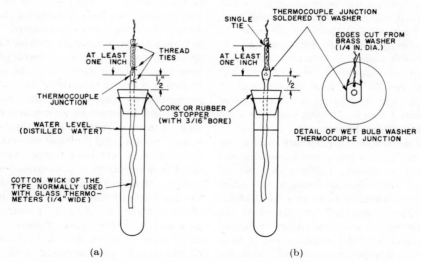

(a)   (b)

FIG. 2. (a) Original design for wet-bulb element for thermocouple psychrometer.
(b) Modified design for wet-bulb element for thermocouple psychrometer.

No test was started unless the disparity of the readings between any two of the six psychrometers upstream and downstream of the unit was 0.1°F or less when the compressor was stopped and the blower was running. This comparison was used to indicate the adequacy of the air mixing and of the preparation of the wet-bulb elements at the beginning of each test. In making this comparison, the temperature rise produced by the heat from the blower motor of the indoor unit was subtracted from the downstream temperature indications.

The readings of the sets of parallel thermocouples at the calorimeter inlet and outlet were observed on two potentiometers, a manually operated semiprecision indicator, and a self-balancing indicator which was carefully adjusted until readings could be estimated to the nearest 0.1°F. The thermocouple psychrometer readings were obtained using the self-balancing indicator because of the need to observe the temperatures of the twelve junctions in the minimum length of time. The readings of the two potentiometers were continuously monitored at two temperature levels by comparing the indications of two calibrated thermometers and thermocouples attached to the thermometers' bulbs and immersed in vacuum bottles of water at room temperature and at about 180°F. The indication of 32.0°F on the self-balancing potentiometer was periodically checked by an ice-bath thermocouple, and appropriate correction was made if the ice bath indication deviated from 32°F. Selector switches with copper and constantan contacts were used to eliminate junctions of dissimilar metals. Switching was accomplished manually.

The temperature and humidity of the air at the inlet to the psychrometric calorimeter were regulated manually by adjustment of a humidifier and a heater in the test room. A test period was not started until steady-state conditions were maintained for one hour, and a test was not considered valid unless such conditions had prevailed for at least one additional hour. A set of readings for all points of measurement, including those for the refrigerant-side determinations, was taken every ten minutes. The wet-bulb depression was determined for each of the upstream and downstream psychrometers for each set of readings, and the sets were averaged for each

psychrometer. If the deviations among these averages for the three upstream psychrometers and for the three downstream psychrometers did not exceed 0.3°F, the space temperature distribution was considered satisfactory for the one-hour test. If the variation in indicated temperature at either of the parallel arrays of dry-bulb thermocouples or at any of the single wet-bulb and dry-bulb junctions did not exceed 0.2°F during the several sets of readings in a one-hour test, the time variation in temperature was considered satisfactory.

Under some operating conditions, it was not possible to obtain the desired degree of temperature control in the refrigerant lines or in the air flowing through the calorimeter apparatus. In most such cases the test period was extended to 3 or 4 hours to obtain the average value of a larger number of readings. Sample readings were taken between the periodic recorded values to monitor the control of the indoor and outdoor test conditions. Experience showed that the greatest disparity between the psychrometric and refrigerant-side values of cooling capacity occurred when the fluctuations of temperature and humidity in the apparatus were greater than average. The water level in the psychrometer test-tube reservoirs was lowered excessively by evaporation from the wicks for tests lasting longer than one hour. In such cases, the test-tube reservoirs were refilled at a time midway between sets of readings.

At the beginning of the series of tests, the primary instrument for measuring relative humidity was a series of 5 electric hygrometer elements spaced evenly at the upstream and downstream stations. During this period, three wet-bulb thermocouple elements were located at the upstream station and one at the downstream station. The electric hygrometers were calibrated within 60 days of the time of use. Calibration in most cases was made with the pressure-humidity apparatus described in NBS Research Paper No. 2312.[5] A comparison of the relative humidity values as determined by the two types of instruments is shown in Table 2. Considering the upstream and downstream determinations collectively, the average of the relative humidity values observed with the two types of instruments agreed within 1 per cent RH in 60 per cent of the cases and within 2 per cent RH in 91 per

TABLE 2. DIFFERENCE IN RELATIVE HUMIDITY VALUES OBTAINED WITH THE CALIBRATED ELECTRIC HYGROMETER AND WITH THE THERMOCOUPLE PSYCHROMETERS

No. of Tests	Differences in Relative Humidity Values (% RH)
Upstream from the Coil (*DB Temperature Range 75 to 85°F, RH Range 45 to 55%*)	
20	0.0 to 0.9
6	1.0 to 1.9
3	2.0 to 3.0
Downstream from the Coil (*DB Temperature about 60°F, RH Range, 75 to 85%*)	
15	0.0 to 0.9
12	1.0 to 1.9
1	2.0
1	3.3

cent of all cases, for the cooling tests in which comparisons were possible. The ranges of temperatures and humidities that prevailed at the upstream and downstream measuring stations are indicated in the Table. The agreement between the two instruments appeared to be a little better for the conditions at the upstream station where the wet-bulb depression was greater.

The use of the electric hygrometer was discontinued later because of the need for frequent recalibration.

In the latter part of the study, a modified thermocouple wet-bulb element was used which involved only one tie around the wick. A washer was soldered to the junction of the thermocouple and pushed down the core of the wick to its proper position. Because the washer fitted snugly into the hollow wicking material, it was not necessary to make the two ties near the junction, and only the tie at the top of the wick was necessary. A schematic drawing of the modified wet-bulb element is shown in Fig. 2(b). A number of tests showed that the performance of this type of wet-bulb element was essentially the same as for the original design without the washer, even though the addition of the washer increased the effective area for convection, radiation, and evaporation at the thermocouple junction.

Errors in Psychrometric Measurements

Separate investigations were made to determine the errors in the wet-bulb and dry-bulb measurements caused by the combined effects of low air velocity and radiation to the sensing elements, lack of perfect air mixing, and inadequate sensitivity of the self-balancing potentiometer. During these tests, the water level in the test-tube reservoirs of the psychrometers was maintained at a distance of about $\frac{1}{8}$ in. from the bottom of the stopper.

The average net air velocity at the stations of temperature measurement for inlet and outlet conditions to the calorimeter was in the range of 400 to 725 fpm for the capacity tests described in this report. However, the local velocities may have been higher than these values because of the fans used for air mixing. Calculations based on the formulae of Eckert and Drake,[6] showed the possibility of a small error, due to radiation, in the readings of the wet-bulb element at the upstream station when the wet-bulb temperature was 15°F less than that of the surroundings. Also, some error might have occurred at either station due to factors associated with the wick and reservoir.

For investigation at the upstream psychrometers, the wet-bulb depressions of the three psychrometers were observed for a range of net air velocity from 240 to 850 fpm while the dry-bulb temperature and relative humidity of the air were kept constant. Since the air at the inlet to the calorimeter was at essentially the same temperature as the surroundings, and the dry-bulb thermocouples were shielded from the cooling coil by parts of the test apparatus, there was little error in dry-bulb temperature due to radiation even at low air velocity. The moisture content of the inlet air was controlled to produce constant readings of three electric hygrometers located close to the thermocouple psychrometers. Since the electric hygrometers were sensitive to small humidity changes and were unaffected by air velocity in the range used, they served as good monitors of constant relative humidity. The milliammeter used with this instrument to indicate relative humidity could be read to 0.25 per cent RH.

Three dry-bulb and three wet-bulb readings were taken in rapid succession for each of the three upstream psychrometers for each of eight values of net air velocity in the range from 240 to 850 fpm. Three readings of each of the three electric hygrometers were also taken for each air velocity. During the tests at these 8 air velocity levels, the average relative humidity indicated by the electric hygrometers varied less than 0.25 per cent at two stations and less than 0.40 per cent at the third station. The wet-bulb depressions of the three thermocouple psychrometers did not vary more than 0.1°F during the series and showed no tendency to increase at the lower air velocities. At the same time the variation among the three dry-bulb temperatures and among the three wet-bulb depressions did not exceed more than 0.1°F for a given test condition. It was concluded from this study that the state conditions of the air were nearly uniform across the air stream and that radiation from the surroundings to the wet-bulb elements was not causing a significant error at the inlet to the calorimeter.

The determination of possible errors with change in air velocity at the downstream station was more difficult because the walls of the discharge duct were at a temperature of about 66°F when the discharge air temperature was 62°F under typical cooling conditions. Consequently, the indications of the three dry-bulb thermocouples in the downstream psychrometers were first compared with those of two shielded thermocouples for a range of air velocity from 300 to 600 fpm. For this comparison, the two shielded thermocouples were located between adjacent pairs of the psychrometers, about 5 in. apart and at a height about 5 in. below the three dry-bulb elements. The shields were cylindrical, having a diameter of 3 in. and a length of 10 in. The relatively large diameter served to allow a free flow of air, and the 10-in. length excluded angular radiation from the duct wall through the ends. Both ends faced material that was at approximately the same temperature as the dry-bulb temperature. The shields were fabricated from heavy cardboard, covered inside and outside with aluminum foil, which did not overlap the cardboard separator. Calculations, based on methods described by Eckert and Drake,[6] for this shield design, predicted little radiation effect for air velocities as low as 200 fpm. On the basis of a calculated convective heat transfer coefficient of 20 Btu/hour(ft)^2(deg R), an emissivity of 0.05 for the aluminum foil on the shield and 0.7 for the thermocouple junction, and the assumption that the shield assembly consisted of a single reflective surface, the radiation error at the thermocouple junction was computed to be less than 0.01°F for a temperature difference between duct surfaces and air of 4°F and an air velocity of 200 fpm.

The indications of the two shielded thermocouples and the three unshielded dry-bulb elements were compared for a range of air velocity from 280 to 615 fpm using one of the shielded thermocouples as a control for adjusting the air temperature. During this series of comparisons, the deviations among the two shielded thermocouples and one of the unshielded thermocouples never exceeded 0.1°F. The indications of each of the other two unshielded thermocouples were consistently about 0.1°F higher than that of the control element, revealing a small deficiency in air mixing. There was no trend toward greater deviations between any pair of thermocouples as the air velocity was decreased. The five thermocouples showed no measurable difference in temperature when immersed in a water bath after completion of these investigations.

The effect of change of air velocity on the downstream wet-bulb measurements was then observed using an electric hygrometer at each of the three psychrometers for comparison of relative humidity indications. First, at an air velocity of about 600 fpm, the dry-bulb temperature was set at 62.0°F at the reference shielded thermocouple, by means of a reheat coil immediately downstream from the heat pump coil and by some supplemental heat at the inlet to the enclosure. Humidity was adjusted by introduction of steam into the system ahead of the blower. Using one of the electric hygrometers as a monitor, its indication was noted when the three dry bulbs registered 62.0 $\pm$ 0.1°F and the three wet bulbs, 58.0 $\pm$ 0.1°F. At each lower velocity setting, the dry-bulb temperature and relative humidity indications on the reference shielded thermocouple and hygrometer elements, respectively, were adjusted to these same initial values, and repetitive readings of each instrument were taken and averaged. This procedure was repeated for 11 velocity settings in the range from 220 to 595 fpm. The dry-bulb temperature around the calorimeter was maintained at approximately 80°F, and the inside wall temperature of the discharge duct was about 66°F.

The results of this series of measurements showed that the dry-bulb temperatures varied only 0.1°F for the range of velocities, and the relative humidity indications of two of the three electric hygrometers varied as much as 1.0 per cent RH in a random fashion. As the air velocity was decreased there was a small increase in the indication of each of the three thermocouple wet-bulb elements, beginning at a velocity of about 340 fpm. The increase amounted to about 0.1°F, 0.2°F, and 0.3°F for the three elements. There was no similar trend in the readings of the electric hygrometers. Thus there appeared to be a small effect on the thermocouple psychrometers at the downstream station for air velocities below 340 fpm. This effect was probably not significant for the tests summarized on p. 308 of this report since the downstream air velocity was always greater than 400 fpm.

The sensitivity of the self-balancing potentiometer was investigated by impressing incremental changes of emf of 2.2 μV, equivalent to a temperature change of 0.1°F for the thermocouple wire employed, on the instruments while each of several observers looked for a change in indication of the instrument. The observers interpreted a 2.2-μV change in input as 0.1°F change in indication about 50 per cent of the time and either 0.0 or 0.2°F about 50 per cent of the time. These observations included both the effects of insensitivity of the instrument and interpretation errors of the observers.

Impact Error

The impact effect on the temperatures indicated by the thermocouple junctions was calculated. The results of the computations

TABLE 3. COMPUTED IMPACT ERROR OF THERMOCOUPLE JUNCTIONS AT SELECTED VELOCITIES

Velocity (fpm)	Error (°F)
150	negligible
1000	0.009
2000	0.038

for the range of velocity of interest are shown in Table 3. A recovery factor of 0.60 for a thermocouple junction was assumed for this calculation, based on the analysis of Moffat.[7]

The errors were calculated using the following relationship:[8]

$$\text{Error} = T_0 - T_j = (1 - \alpha)\left(\frac{v^2}{2gJC_p}\right) \quad (1)$$

where

T_0 = total or stagnant temperature, °F
T_j = junction temperature, °F
g = acceleration due to gravity, 32.2 ft/sec²
C_p = constant pressure heat capacity of air, Btu/lb(°F)
J = heat equivalent of work, 778 ft-lb/Btu
v = directed velocity, ft/sec
α = recovery factor for copper-constantan thermocouple junction.

The calculated errors shown in Table 3 indicate that the error due to impact at an air velocity of 725 fpm, the highest net air velocity occurring in any of the tests, was insignificant.

Air Flow Measurements

The 7-in. ASME nozzle was calibrated in place, in accordance with techniques outlined in NBS Research Paper No. RP-49.[9] An aluminum band was placed snugly around the outside of the throat of the nozzle to make the cross section more nearly circular. The diameter of the throat was then measured carefully in three directions to the nearest 0.001 in. in order to obtain an accurate value for the area used in the calculation of the rate of air flow. A calibrated manometer was used to measure the pressure drop across the nozzle. The uncertainty in the determination of the air flow rate under these conditions of measurement was estimated at ± 1 per cent.

Calculation Procedures

Ferrel's formula,[10, 11] as shown below, was used to calculate the partial pressure of the water vapor in the air based on the observed dry-bulb and wet-bulb temperature and using his empirical coefficients. From this property and the dry-bulb temperature it was possible to determine the enthalpy of the air at the upstream and downstream stations.

$$P_W = P_{s(WB)} - .000367 P(t - t_{WB})$$
$$\left(1 + \frac{t_{WB} - 32}{1571}\right) \quad (2)$$

where

t = dry-bulb temperature, °F

t_{WB} = wet-bulb temperature, °F

P_W = partial pressure of the water vapor in the air at the observed temperature, in. Hg

$P_{s(WB)}$ = saturation pressure of the water vapor at the temperature t_{WB}, in. Hg

P = barometric pressure, in. Hg.

Assuming that the ideal gas laws applied to the air and water vapor in the mixture, relative humidity was determined by the following equation:

$$\text{Relative Humidity, } \phi = \frac{P_W}{P_s} \quad (3)$$

where P_s is the saturation pressure of water vapor at dry-bulb temperature, in. Hg.

Values for ϕ were used to compute the degree of saturation in accordance with the relation

$$\mu = \frac{\phi(P - P_s)}{P - \phi(P_s)} \quad (4)$$

where μ is the degree of saturation of air at standard barometric pressure.

The unit enthalpy values of the air at the upstream and downstream stations were calculated from the general relation,

$$h = h_a + \mu(h_{as}) \quad (5)$$

where

h = enthalpy of the mixture, Btu/lb of dry air

h_a = enthalpy of dry air at the observed dry-bulb temperature, Btu/lb

h_{as} = difference in enthalpy for saturated air and dry air at the observed dry-bulb temperature, Btu/lb of dry air.

Values for h_a and h_{as} were obtained from the Goff and Gratch tables of the Thermodynamic Properties of Moist Air.[12]

The psychrometric capacity q_t, in Btu/hr, was then determined from

$$q_t = (h_1 - h_2)(M_a)$$
$$- (W_u - W)(t_3 - 32)(M_a) \quad (6)$$

where h_1 is the unit upstream enthalpy and h_2 is the unit downstream enthalpy in Btu/lb of dry air. M_a represents the mass air flow rate in lb/hr, W_u and W, the humidity ratio at the upstream and downstream stations, respectively, and t_3 the dew-point temperature at the downstream station, °F. The term $(W_u - W)$ $(t_3 - 32)(M_a)$ represents the heat that is lost to the system in the condensate drained from the cooling coil, Btu/hr.

DESCRIPTION OF REFRIGERANT-SIDE TEST APPARATUS AND PROCEDURE

Refrigerant temperatures were measured near the inlet and outlet of the cooling coil using calibrated 30-gauge (0.010 in.) copper-constantan thermocouples. The temperature of the liquid line was measured by a thermocouple junction soldered to the copper tube, with the lead attached to the tube for a distance of 8 in. and covered with insulation $\frac{3}{4}$ in. thick for a distance of 3 in. each way from the junction. The temperature of the refrigerant vapor was measured in a thermocouple well about 6 in. deep inserted into the vapor line at an elbow. The well was filled with oil. Refrigerant pressures were measured near the temperature-measuring stations at the inlet and outlet of the cooling coil using test quality Bourdon gauges, which were calibrated periodically with a dead-weight tester. Pressure indications were corrected for liquid lift in the pressure line between the gauge and the point of attachment to the system.

The corresponding temperature and pressure readings were used to determine the amount of subcooling of the liquid refrigerant at the coil inlet and the amount of superheating of the refrigerant vapor at the coil outlet as well as the enthalpy of the refrigerant at these two stations. It was necessary that the refrigerant be all liquid at the inlet and all vapor at the outlet in order to make valid determinations of enthalpy of the refrigerant, and of cooling capacity by the refrigerant-side method. Mass flow rate of the refrigerant was measured with a turbine-type flowmeter. Because the refrigerant was volatile and the amount of liquid subcooling was limited, the formation of gas bubbles was possible in the flowmeter if the pressure drop through the meter was excessive. Experience showed that for the $\frac{3}{8}$-in.

meter used for these tests, the pressure drop through the meter should be less than 8 lb/in.^{2}. During most of the tests the pressure drop was in the range from 5 to 7 lb/in.^{2}.

Since turbine-type flowmeters are somewhat sensitive to the viscosity of the fluid being measured, the flowmeter was calibrated with three relatively nonvolatile liquids having viscosities of 0.47, 0.91, and 1.18 centipoises. A meter calibration factor for refrigerant R-22 (monochlorodifluoromethane), with a viscosity of 0.23 centipoise was determined by extrapolation of the observed calibration data. The refrigerant flow rate determined with the extrapolated calibration factor was about 2 per cent greater than that indicated by the manufacturers' calibration, which was made gravimetrically with water.

Determinations of the amount of oil in the refrigerant were made, and appropriate corrections were made to the refrigerant flow rate.

The refrigerant-side computation of cooling capacity, q'_t, in Btu/hr was made using Eq. (7):

$$q'_t = (H_1 - H_2)M_r - q_m \qquad (7)$$

where H_1 and H_2 are the unit enthalpy of the refrigerant at the outlet and inlet of the cooling coil, respectively; M_r is the mass flow rate of refrigerant after correction for oil content in lb/hr, and q_m is the heat equivalent of the power dissipated in the blower motor in Btu/hr.

DISCUSSION AND CONCLUSIONS

Enthalpy values for the refrigerant were taken from the Tables of the Properties of Refrigerants published by E. I. du Pont de Nemours and Co., Inc.[13] The interpretation of these values of enthalpy involve a small uncertainty. There are small disparities between the enthalpy values for R-22 in the tables published by E. I. du Pont de Nemours and Company and those by the Allied Chemical Company,[14] although enthalpy differences for the respective tables are very nearly equal. The former company has stated that investigations are being made which may lead to revision of its tables. No corrections were made to the enthalpy values of the refrigerant for the heat of mixing of oil in the refrigerant.

Whereas Bambach[15] has reported that a 1 per cent concentration of a paraffin-base pale oil in refrigerant R-12 (dichlorodifluoromethane) caused a decrease in enthalpy of about 1 per cent under air-conditioning conditions, no similar data have been found for refrigerant R-22.

An inspection of Eqs. (6) and (7) used for calculating cooling capacity by the psychrometric and refrigerant-side methods, respectively, shows that two enthalpy determinations and one mass flow rate determination are involved in each calculation. Thus a 1 per cent error in the magnitude of each of these quantities could produce a 6 per cent difference between the two capacity determinations if all of the errors were cumulative. On the other hand, the several errors might be compensating, causing a smaller difference or even no difference between the two capacity values.

The experience gained during this series of tests indicated that the following precautions were necessary to produce satisfactory agreement in the measured values of cooling capacity of an air-conditioning unit by the psychrometric and refrigerant-side methods.

(a) All instruments and measuring elements must be calibrated;

(b) Near-perfect air mixing must be attained at the inlet and outlet of the calorimeter at the stations of wet-bulb and dry-bulb temperature measurement;

(c) Air velocities of 400 fpm or higher should be maintained at dry-bulb and wet-bulb elements of the type used in this investigation;

(d) Care in the design, installation and maintenance of the dry-bulb and wet-bulb elements, and frequent replacement of wicks are necessary;

(e) The ambient conditions around the calorimeter and the condensing unit must be accurately controlled to avoid fluctuations in either the air or refrigerant circuits;

(f) Wet-bulb and dry-bulb temperatures of the air must be interpreted to the nearest 0.1°F;

(g) The observers must be conscientious and careful.

This investigation also indicated that better instrumentation and more adequate published data in the following areas would assist in attaining better accuracy and reproducibility in tests of the type described in this paper:

(a) Wet-bulb elements for which the deviations of the indicated values from thermodynamic wet-bulb temperatures were known at various air velocities,

(b) A flowmeter that was less sensitive to fluid viscosity at low flow rates,

(c) Information on the heat of mixing of various refrigerants with oil,

(d) Information on the effectiveness of various types of air mixing devices,

(e) Reliable data on the thermodynamic properties of refrigerants.

References

1. "Methods for Rating and Testing Air Conditioners," Standard 16–56, American Society of Refrigerating Engineers, (1956).
2. Montieth, J. L., "Error and Accuracy in Thermocouple Psychrometry," *Proc. Phys. Soc. London, Ser. B*, **67**, 217 (1954).
3. Wile, D. D., "Psychrometry of the Frost Zone," *J. Am. Soc. Refrigerating Engineers*, 292 (October 1944).
4. Wile, D. D., "The Measurement of Moist Air Properties," in "Air Conditioning and Refrigeration Data Book of the American Society of Refrigerating Engineers," pp. 6–29 through 6–32, 1955–1956.
5. Wexler, A., and Daniels, R., "Pressure-Humidity Apparatus," *J. Res. Natl. Bur. Std.*, **48**, 269 (1952).
6. Eckert, E. R. G., and Drake, R. M., "Heat and Mass Transfer," 2nd ed., pp. 427–428, New York, McGraw-Hill Book Co., Inc., 1959.
7. Moffat, R. J., "Gas Temperature Measurement," Report GMR-329, General Motors Corporation Research Laboratories, pp. 8 and 51, 1961.
8. *Ibid*, p. 5.
9. Bean, H. S., Buckingham, E., Murphy, P. S., "Discharge Coefficients of Square-Edged Orifices for Measuring the Flow of Air," *J. Res. Natl. Bur. Std.*, **2**, 561 (1929).
10. Ferrel, W., Report of Professor Wm. Ferrel, Assistant, on Psychrometric Tables for Use in the Signal Service, Annual Report, U.S. Army Signal Corps, Appendix 24, pp. 233–259 (1886).
11. Eshbach, O. W., "Handbook of Engineering Fundamentals," 2nd ed., pp. 8–104, New York, John Wiley & Sons, Inc., 1952.
12. Goff, J. A., and Gratch, S., "Thermodynamic Properties of Moist Air (Standard Atmospheric Pressure)," in "Guide and Data Book," American Society of Heating, Refrigerating and Air-Conditioning Engineers, 1963.
13. "Properties of Commonly Used Refrigerants," Air Conditioning and Refrigeration Institute, 1957.
14. "Thermodynamic Properties of 'Genetron 22'," Allied Chemical Co., General Chemical Division, 1958.
15. Bambach, G., "The Behavior of Mineral Oil-F12 Mixtures in Refrigerating Machines," *Abhandl. Deut. Kaeltetech. Ver.*, **9**, 1–67 (1955).

38. Moisture Measurement and Control in Small Refrigerating Systems

L. C. FLOWERS

Westinghouse Research Laboratories, Pittsburgh, Pennsylvania

ABSTRACT

Excess residual moisture inside vapor compression refrigerating machines can lead to service failures. Most of the residual moisture in small, household-type units is lodged in the cellulosic products (e.g., paper slot cells and wedges) which comprise the major portion of the electrical insulation of the sealed-in motors. This moisture is relatively inaccessible and is virtually impossible to measure by a heat and vacuum moisture test. In an experiment, typical refrigerator units were alternately tested for moisture and operated in refrigerating cycles between each repetition of the test. The moisture that was "determined" each time the test was repeated did not diminish significantly from one test to the next, and no end point was in sight after 156 hours of heating and evacuating. Desorption of moisture from the interior of cellulose is inherently slow and appears to be diffusion-controlled. A method is described for estimating the "potential free moisture" in a refrigerating system at various temperatures. Questions concerning the possible hazards of moisture being transferred from cellulose to a dryer (desiccant) installed in a system are discussed. Tests on dryers taken from operating units at periodic intervals are cited as useful criteria of adequate moisture control.

INTRODUCTION

Many, if not most, of the papers in this book deal with new and sometimes sophisticated techniques for moisture measurement and with new problems in moisture control. The words "moisture control" mean different things to different people, but to a builder of refrigerating machines, "moisture control" normally means keeping the internal working parts of these machines sufficiently dry to guarantee many years of service in the field. This is an old problem, and usually, the techniques are neither new nor very sophisticated. The problem is not so much to find ways and means for measuring the moisture, as it is to get at the moisture that is to be measured.

In this discussion, we will consider only small vapor compression machines of the type used in household refrigerators. It has long been known that only a small amount of moisture can be present in these machines if operational failures are to be avoided. As a general rule, this knowledge has been acquired only with difficulty and often at great expense to the refrigerator manufacturer. More than one hundred million domestic or household-type refrigerating units have been manufactured in the United States alone, and the manufacturers of these units, except for those who have been very wise or very lucky, have had to learn through bitter experience that carelessness or nonchalance in respect to moisture content can lead to almost astronomical rates of failure when the systems are subsequently put into operation in the field. Any manufacturer surviving such an experience needs no further lesson on the importance of moisture control.

TYPES OF FAILURE ATTRIBUTED TO EXCESS MOISTURE

The principle types of possible failure are outlined in Table 1. Here the hazards to be avoided are listed in relation to the solubility of water in refrigerant.

TABLE 1. TYPES OF MOISTURE HAZARDS

Solubility of Water in Refrigerant	Hazard
Relatively high solubility	
Ammonia	Corrosion
Sulfur dioxide	(hydrolysis)
	Sludge
	Attack on motor insulation
Relatively low solubility	
Dichlorodifluoromethane (R-12)	Corrosion (hydrolysis)
Monochlorodifluoromethane (R-22)	Sludge
	Attack on motor
Dichlorotetrafluoroethane (R-114)	insulation
	Ice clogging
Hydrocarbons, etc.	

If excess water is present, it may or may not be completely dissolved by the particular refrigerant employed in the system. If the solubility is relatively high, as in systems containing ammonia or sulfur dioxide, the dissolved excess water can lead to corrosion of the metal parts, sludge in the lubrication oil, and if the system encloses an electric motor, chemical attack on the motor insulation.

If the solubility of water is relatively low, as is the case with the modern halocarbon refrigerants, there is a fourth hazard more to be feared than the first three mentioned, at least in small, domestic refrigerators which operate below the freezing point of water. The real danger is "ice-clogging." Ice clogging occurs when the refrigerant is unable to dissolve the excess water that circulates in the system, and this water then freezes to solid ice which stops the circulation by plugging small restricted passages, such as expansion valve orifices or capillary tubes.

SAMPLING DIFFICULTIES IN SETTING MOISTURE LIMITS

Various attempts have been made to define quantitatively the tolerable moisture content of a refrigerating system. Perhaps to no one's surprise, the limits specified often appear to be quite arbitrary. Not only is the measurement of the actual moisture content an elusive quantity, as will be dealt with later, but also moisture tolerances may differ according to the mechanical design of the system and its operating characteristics.

Some of the published limits for tolerable moisture contents in small systems are given in Table 2. According to ASHRAE[1] the moisture contents of small R-12 systems that are considered sufficiently dry for normal operation range from 20 to 37 ppm. This same authority also gives a figure of 60 ppm for a system that is considered "too wet." The principal criticism of the parts per million limits reported by ASHRAE is that these limits are apparently based on a sample of refrigerant which is withdrawn or somehow segregated from the system but the conditions of sampling are indefinite.

The published literature contains many references to laboratory tests dealing with the corrosiveness of various refrigerants in contact with water, but it is difficult to relate these data to machines in operation. It is generally assumed that the quantity of moisture required to produce corrosion is greater than

TABLE 2. TOLERABLE MOISTURE CONTENTS FOR NORMAL OPERATION
(ppm IN REFRIGERANT; AS RECORDED IN LITERATURE)

To Avoid:	Considered Satisfactory	Considered Excessive	Authority
Ice clogs in small R-12 systems	20–37 ppm*	60 ppm	ASHRAE
Corrosion and sludge	Not stated	Not stated†	
Motor failure		> 50 ppm	Steinle
* Also, 200 mg "total" moisture in ¼ hp machine when tested by evacuating 12 hours at 300°F (150°C).			Knight
† Moisture content required for corrosion presumably higher than that required for ice clogs.			ASHRAE

that which would cause ice-clogging, hence moisture limits which eliminate the latter hazard should also exclude corrosion of the type due to water.[1]

Since most refrigerating systems today are of the "hermetic" type, the electric motor windings are in direct contact with the circulating refrigerant. During operation these windings and the surrounding fluid reach temperatures ranging upward from about 175°F (80°C). In the presence of excess moisture, the rate of refrigerant hydrolysis increases rapidly with rising temperature and there then exists a potential hazard to the motor insulation. The limiting moisture content of 50 ppm reported by Steinle[2,3] was obtained under carefully specified conditions, namely in laboratory life tests with R-12 refrigerant accelerated by operating the motor windings at 284°F (140°C).

The difficulties in sampling were publicly recognized by J. L. Knight as long ago as 1949.[4] Knight suggested that moisture contents based on refrigerant samples were apt to be meaningless, and he recommended a procedure for determining the "total" moisture by vacuum pumping the whole system for 12 hours in an oven at 300°F (149°C).

Several other schemes which try to avoid the problem of representative sampling have appeared in the literature. Knight's 300°F vacuum method was to be applied to the entire unit before it was charged with refrigerant. Brisken[5] and also Steinle[3] installed electrohygrometers in a bypass circuit so that the moisture content of the circulating fluid could be measured without withdrawing a sample. Their specially constructed circuits were necessarily somewhat artificial, and they were not intended to duplicate production-made machines exactly. Elsey, Kelley, and Sharpe[6] recognized that the heart of the moisture problem would lie in the compressor. Like Knight, these authors advocated a heat and vacuum method, but they also pointed out that this test could be made in much less time if applied directly to compressors.

SOURCES OF MOISTURE IN SYSTEM

For the benefit of those who may not be completely familiar with the construction of small refrigerating systems, Fig. 1 shows the essential components of a typical domestic

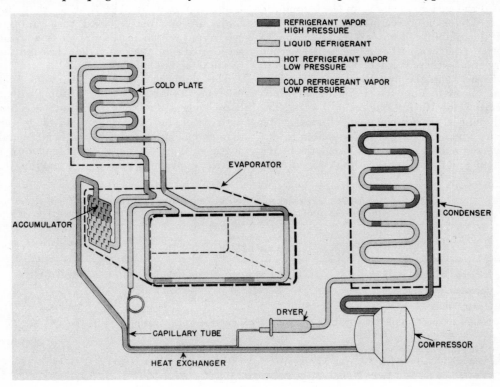

FIG. 1. Domestic unit components.

unit. We need to note only those components that are pertinent to the moisture problem. All of the circulating liquid must pass through the small capillary tube on its way to the evaporator, and it is at this point that excess moisture can cause ice clogging. Hence it is common practice to install a dryer—that is, a cartridge containing a desiccant—in the line ahead of the capillary tube. Sometimes this device is replaced by a simple filtering screen, as in room air conditioners where the temperature in the capillary does not fall below the freezing point of water. The compressor shell to the right of the dryer contains the refrigerant pump and an electric motor to drive the pump, both being splashed rather liberally from a fairly large sump of lubricating oil.

The difficulty of moisture measurement in such a system generally has its origin in the paper products and other materials of a cellulose nature that are normally used to insulate the windings of the sealed-in motor. The ability of cellulose to sorb and desorb moisture under changing conditions of temperature and humidity is, of course, well-known, and as the other authors in this book have pointed out, it is difficult to gain access to this moisture by the usual moisture measuring techniques.

In building refrigerating units of the type shown in Fig. 1 it is customary to oven-dry or dehydrate the component parts either separately or as a completed assembly (except for the dryer). Subsequently the dryer may be installed if required, and appropriate quantities of refrigerant and lubricating oil are charged into the compressor.

The major sources of moisture entering the unit in manufacture are listed in Table 3.

The moisture introduced with the oil and

TABLE 3. POTENTIAL SOURCES OF MOISTURE ENTERING DOMESTIC UNIT AT POINT OF MANUFACTURE

	milligrams
1. Refrigerant charge	2
2. Lubricating oil charge	21
3. Residual moisture in motor windings	$\begin{cases} ? > 115 \\ ? > 500 \end{cases}$
4. Accidental contamination	$? \begin{pmatrix} \text{Excluded from} \\ \text{consideration} \end{pmatrix}$

refrigerant can be estimated with a fair degree of reliability. For example, the system may be charged with 8 ounces (227 grams) of refrigerant and 25 ounces (710 grams) of oil. Refrigerant manufacturers guarantee a maximum moisture content of 10 ppm and the oil as received from oil refiners may contain about 30 ppm as dissolved water.[7] On the basis of these values, approximately 23 mg of moisture could enter the system with the combined charges of oil and refrigerant.

The weight of the motor insulation, probably 80 per cent of which is cellulose, may be about 100 grams. It has sometimes been speculated that the usual forms of oven dehydration reduce the moisture content of cellulose to about 0.1 per cent. On this basis, one would expect the insulation to contribute about 100 mg to the total water content.

One experiment[8] that was performed with a motor containing 80 grams of cellulose indicated a "residual moisture" content of approximately 115 mg when the motor was dried for nine hours at 266°F (130°C) in a stream of very dry nitrogen gas. This so-called residual moisture was determined by continuing the drying for seven hours more and measuring the additional water evolved.

However, as will be shown shortly, a test based on moisture evolution does not determine with any degree of certainty the true residual moisture in the motor insulation. The difficulty here is the virtual impossibility of reaching a zero moisture level at which the cellulose has lost all its sorbed water and has become truly dry. Without such a zero basis, one must arbitrarily define a so-called bone dry condition which depends on the operations performed. The moisture that is actually measured as being sorbed or desorbed by the cellulose is thus merely a differential increment for which the base line is the arbitrarily defined "bone dry" condition. However, whether this increment constitutes a large or small fraction of the total water residing in the cellulose is a question that cannot now be answered.

In more extensive experiments which we are about to describe, it appears that the residual moisture after nine hours drying at 266°F (130°C) must be much higher than the first mentioned figure, and is probably well over 500 mg.

Accidental contamination in the factory

may be a troublesome source of moisture at times. However, this is a problem that is too indefinite for general considerations.

FUTILE ATTEMPTS TO MEASURE TOTAL MOISTURE CONTENT

The experiments now to be described furnish a striking illustration of the difficulties encountered in attempts to measure the total residual moisture content of systems containing sealed-in motors. These experiments were performed as part of a larger scale program of improving moisture control techniques. "Moisture contents" were measured with the simple heat and vacuum scheme shown schematically in Fig. 2.

Starting at the left of Fig. 2, the compressor portion of a refrigerant-charged unit was placed in a hot oven and held for three hours to allow the temperature of the motor windings to become stabilized at 266°F (130°C). The attached piercing valve at P was then turned to puncture the suction tube of the unit. The escaping refrigerant was drawn by the vacuum pump at a low rate through the sequence of traps and was finally condensed in the liquid oxygen trap. This required about one hour and the absolute pressure in the system was then about 1 or 2 mm of mercury. Most of the moisture was caught in the dry ice trap and the small amount passing into the liquid oxygen trap was determined by analyzing the condensed refrigerant. These moisture collecting traps were exchanged for new traps and pump-

ing was continued for a total of 44 hours without disturbing the unit in the 266° oven. During this time the traps were exchanged periodically to measure the evolved moisture.

In the course of the testing program, three dehydrated domestic units which had been built without dryers were taken from the factory production line at widely separated times. Each of these units was then put through the moisture test several times in succession. That is, the unit was put through one 44-hour test, then was resealed and later given a charge of gas and oil, operated for a time, put through another 44-hour test, resealed and recharged with gas, operated and tested again, and so forth. Figure 3 shows the cumulative evolution of moisture from one of these units plotted against the accumulated hours on test.

The repeated evolution of moisture shown in Fig. 3 was typical of all the units that were tested. In each successive 44-hour run the pattern was essentially the same: an initial fairly rapid rate of moisture evolution was followed by a gradually declining rate which did not level off in the 44-hour period. The testing was discontinued at the end of 156 hours, which included three complete 44-hour tests and the two shorter time tests at the end of the experiment. These last two tests represented attempts to "purge" moisture from the unit by gas pressurizing techniques.

As a result of this protracted testing, the unit for which complete data are shown in Fig. 3 yielded approximately 600 mg of

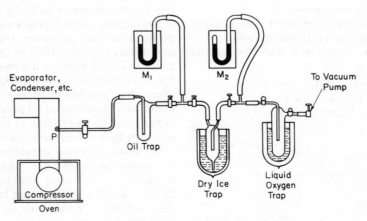

FIG. 2. Apparatus for measuring moisture evolved during evacuation of refrigerator units in oven at 266°F (130°C).

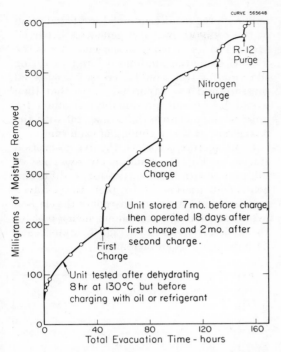

CURVE 565648

FIG. 3. Cumulative removal of moisture by five repetitions of heat and vacuum moisture test on the same unit at 266°F (130°C).

accidental source of moisture that would produce a systematic error of the magnitude required. Random errors of small magnitude no doubt occurred, and in fact such errors are apparent in the tabulated data to follow in Table 4. However, care was always taken to exclude moisture from the outside during the manipulations and operations between one run and the next, and all three units, handled at different times, showed essentially identical patterns of moisture evolution. Averaging the total amounts of moisture evolved by the three units gave a figure of 540 mg per unit.

It was also plausibly but erroneously suggested that the repeated evolution of moisture might be due to thermal decomposition of the cellulose insulation during the long hours of testing at an elevated temperature. It is true that the long polymeric chains in a cellulose molecule will break and liberate gases including water vapor at an appreciable rate when heated at temperatures above 212°F (100°C). This liberated water would indeed become a significant factor in the experiment if the temperature was raised to, say, 347°F (175°C). But it also appears to be true that under the actual conditions employed, the moisture liberated by thermal decomposition of cellulose would not be sufficient to explain the observed behavior. Support for this belief is found in data reported by E. J. Murphy[9] and later analyzed by Dushman.[10] From these data one may calculate the amount of moisture that is generated by cellulose decomposition at temperatures ranging from 176°F (80°C) to 284°F (140°C). In the present experiment, no more than approximately 3 mg of moisture could have been thermally generated by 80 grams of cellulose in the longest operating time between tests (two months), and this

moisture. This was a much larger amount than expected from a well-dehydrated unit. Moreover, it was surprising to see that the extra, and presumably exhaustive, drying given by a preceding 44-hour test of heat and vacuum had so little bearing on the moisture that was subsequently evolved in the next 44-hour test.

The first logical suspicion was that accidental contamination had allowed moisture to enter the system after the completion of each of the moisture tests. However, a careful scrutiny of the testing conditions disclosed no

TABLE 4. "FREE" AND "TOTAL" MOISTURE FROM TEST UNITS

Motor windings at 266°F (130°C)		Evolved Water Collected in Freezing Traps	
		Pumped out with refrigerant (mg H_2O)	Total evolved in 44 hours (mg H_2O)
Three repetitions with same unit, charged and recharged	(1)	69*	191
	(2)	40	170
	(3)	83	156
Statistical means from 35 charged units		53 ($\pm$19 std. dev.)	140 ($\pm$32 std. dev.)

* Pumped out first time with air.

amount assumes an average winding temperature of 230°F (110°C) which is higher than is ordinarily observed. When the unit was heated in the oven during the several moisture test cycles, the winding temperature was higher, 266°F (130°C), but the accumulated time at this temperature was only 156 hours. By chance, thermal decomposition under these conditions of time and temperature also accounts for 3 mg of moisture. The total of 6 mg is obviously a negligible portion of the more than 500 mg of moisture evolved by the unit.

DIFFUSION CONTROLLED RELEASE OF SORBED MOISTURE

In retrospect, it is possible to explain the behavior observed in Fig. 3 without recourse to extraneous sources of moisture. We now believe that the greater part of the 600 mg of moisture measured in this experiment was moisture retained by the windings after dehydration and actually existed as sorbed moisture in the cellulose when the moisture tests were started. Note that the unit was either stored or operated for a relatively long time before a moisture test was repeated. Hence, one can assume that the distribution of sorbed moisture in the cellulose structures would be fairly uniform at the start of each 44-hour run. But the surface layers of these structures are the first to dry, and as Hermans and Vermaas[11] have shown, the velocity with which moisture molecules diffuse through dry cellulose is very slow and takes place with difficulty. Moreover, the paper slot cells and pressboard wedges comprising these structures are relatively thick and massive in terms of molecular dimensions. The surface moisture passes off quickly, but in doing so, it tends to seal the pores through which moisture from the interior of the cellulose must escape. Therefore, the cellulose structure can retain a substantial amount of deep-seated moisture even when very little is being evolved at the external surface.

However, the laws of physics teach us that the slow diffusion from the interior does not stop abruptly when a 44-hour run is completed. Since the unit is then resealed, we may also assume that the continuing diffusion not only restores a uniform moisture distribution in the cellulose but also generates a partial pressure of water vapor in the gas space of the unit. Heating the windings before puncturing the unit for test would increase this partial pressure and the vaporized water that then would be present presumably accounts for most of the moisture that comes off with the refrigerant at the beginning of each run.

If this picture is correct, the five desorption stages in Fig. 3 should show evidence of diffusion control. One test for a diffusion-controlled process is to plot the evolved moisture against the square root of the elapsed evolution time. Figure 4 shows such a plot for the moisture evolved in Fig. 3, taking each 44-hour result as an increment.

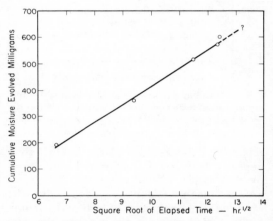

FIG. 4. Diffusion-type behavior shown by evolution of moisture from refrigerator unit of Fig. 3.

The straight line in this plot is characteristic of the early stages of a diffusion-controlled desorption process. In the later stages of desorption, this line should bend over more or less abruptly toward the horizontal and should become almost flat if the cellulose has already lost all of its sorbed moisture. From the fact that the line remains straight and does not bend over after an accumulation of 156 hours on test, we are led to believe that much sorbed moisture is still in the cellulose, and therefore, there is little or no hope of determining the actual moisture content of refrigerator units by a practical heat and vacuum method.

ESTIMATION OF "POTENTIAL FREE MOISTURE"

Although it obviously appears impractical to measure the total moisture in a refrigerating system with the apparatus of Fig. 2, this does not preclude the use of the method to estimate the "potential free moisture" in the system. For this purpose a much shorter time than 44 hours is required. One essential is to allow time for the vapor pressure in the unit to become stabilized before the suction tube is punctured.

If the test is subsequently carried on for approximately one hour after the refrigerant begins to flow, almost no vapor will remain in the system. The traps will then contain the moisture that was present as vapor when the suction tube was pierced plus an additional amount that diffuses from the motor windings during the hour of test. This latter amount is usually a minor fraction of the whole, and does not require correction or consideration in a practical test procedure. A comparison of the so called "free" moisture with the amount evolved in 44 hours is shown in Table 4.

Items numbered (1), (2), and (3) in Table 4 refer to the first three runs in Fig. 3. Taking each run in turn, and allowing for variables in the experiment, there seems to be crude relationship between the two columns of figures. The final item shows a statistical comparison of the relative amounts of moisture evolved by 35 units tested by this procedure.

Actually, the major concern of a designer of refrigerating systems is with the vaporized moisture in the gas space. Any moisture that remains sorbed and is essentially locked in the pores of the motor insulation is of little concern unless there is fear that this moisture will be set free eventually when units are placed in operation. Such an event is improbable if, in the moisture test procedure, the motor windings are heated to a higher temperature than they will reach in operation and are held at this test temperature for a time sufficient to generate a moisture vapor pressure approaching a stabilized condition. Needless to say, the test temperature should not be so high as to generate moisture by thermal decomposition.

If the "free" moisture is determined at the testing temperature, this amount may then be related to the "potential free moisture" at other winding temperatures as may exist when the unit is idle, or even when it is in operation if the sole requirement is to insure freedom from field failures. In estimating the "free" moisture at different temperatures, one may employ published charts which show the equilibrium distribution that exists between moisture vapor pressure and moisture sorbed by cellulose over a range of temperatures. Suitable charts for this purpose have been published by Piper.[12] Confirmation of Piper's charts as applied to refrigerator motor windings was reported several years ago by Elsey, Kelley, and Sharpe.[6]

In Table 5 the moisture distribution is estimated for a hypothetical unit with a gas space of 4 liters and a motor containing 80 grams of cellulose. This unit is supposed to have yielded 100 mg of "free" moisture on test, as shown by the asterisk in the second row of figures. Neglecting temperature variations in the unit, the partial pressure of water vapor in the 4-liter gas space would be about

TABLE 5. DISTRIBUTION OF MOISTURE IN HYPOTHETICAL UNIT

Gas Space = 4 *liters*	*Cellulose* = 80 *grams*			
	Temperature			
°F (°C)	266 (130)	230 (110)	176 (80)	77 (25)
Vapor pressure of H$_2$O, mm Hg	35	18	4.3	0.09
"Free" moisture, mg	100*	54†	14†	0.4†
"Residual" moisture** in motor insulation, mg	144	190	230	244

* Hypothetical result of moisture test at 266°F.
** Equilibrium amount in 80 grams of cellulose at indicated vapor pressure and temperature.[12]
† Computed for nonoperating conditions and uniform temperatures.

35 mm of mercury. According to Piper's charts, the residual moisture in the motor insulation would then be 144 mg. This, of course, is not the total sorbed moisture but, as has been mentioned is a differential increment above an arbitrary "dry" basis chosen by the original experimenter.[13] Assuming that the moisture to be accounted for is always 244 mg, that is, the sum of the "free" and "residual" moistures in the first column, Piper's data can then be used to compute the values at other temperatures shown in Table 5.

It is apparent from Table 5 that the winding temperature has a great influence on the moisture that is measured when a sample of refrigerant is withdrawn from the system and analyzed. Knight's objections to the validity of tests on refrigerant samples are well-grounded if the winding temperature is not strictly controlled and well-established before the sample is taken. Moreover, if a sample is taken from an idle unit at room temperature such a test is apt to be worthless since, under this condition, practically all of the moisture present will be lodged in the cellulose and the little that is associated with the refrigerant is likely to be too small to be significant. If the sample is taken when the unit is operating, concern must be given to controlling the winding temperature. According to Table 5, a moisture test on the refrigerant with the windings at 230°F (110°C) may show a fourfold increase over a test with the windings at 176°F (80°C) even though the moisture in the unit is the same in both instances. This view has been confirmed by the findings of Brisken.[4]

TRANSFER OF MOISTURE TO DRYER

The use of a dryer does not lessen the importance of adequate dehydration and moisture control. The function of the dryer is essentially to lower the moisture vapor pressure by extracting water from the refrigerating fluid circulating through the system. As Steinle[2] has mentioned, the circulating refrigerant acts simply as an agent in transferring sorbed moisture from the hot windings to the cooler desiccant in the dryer. But the desiccant itself generates a partial pressure of moisture vapor in relation to its temperature and moisture content, and if its moisture content exceeds a certain amount,

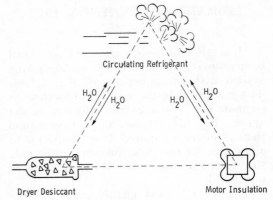

Fig. 5. Moisture transfer through circulating refrigerant in a system containing a cartridge dryer.

the desiccant can conceivably deliver moisture to the system. The possible movement of moisture back and forth from the motor insulation and from the desiccant through the vaporized and liquefied refrigerant is illustrated in Fig. 5. Since dryers are necessarily limited as to size, excessive amounts of moisture in the cellulose will, in time, lead to excessive amounts in the desiccant and may produce sufficient increase in moisture vapor pressure to the point where ice clogging can again occur. Thus, blind reliance on a dryer without proper attention to the need for adequate moisture control over other parts of the system may merely postpone the occurrence of moisture troubles in service.

Since it has been shown that the total sorbed moisture in a cellulose insulated winding may exceed 500 mg, a natural question is, whether all of this moisture will eventually be transferred to the dryer. Eventually, of course, may be taken to mean a very long time, and the best safeguard is to make certain that the quantity of desiccant in the dryer is adequate to accept this amount of moisture.

It is improbable, however, that all of the sorbed moisture will leave the cellulose. Dry cellulose is an excellent desiccant itself and apparently tends to retain most of its residual sorbed moisture at very low vapor pressures. Under such circumstances one may expect an eventual equilibrium, or at least a quasi equilibrium between the moisture sorbed by the desiccant cartridge and the moisture remaining in the cellulose.

The question becomes more serious, however, when one takes into account the possibility that additional moisture may be generated in the insulation by thermal degradation of the cellulose. In recent years there has been a seemingly inexorable trend toward higher motor operating temperatures which, if the trend continues, may eventually reach the point at which thermal degradation will become a definite hazard. Both Steinle[2] and Elsey[6] have carefully considered this question. Steinle puts the critical motor temperature at 248°F (120°C) and for safety suggests that a maximum limit be set at 230°F (110°C) to avoid thermal decomposition. Elsey employs Dushman's analysis[10] of Murphy's data to show that thermal decomposition would be expected to generate 975 mg of moisture in a motor containing 75 grams of cellulose insulation and held at 248°F (120°C) for twenty years. Operating temperatures of this magnitude, if maintained for long periods of time would obviously create an urgent demand for more thermally stable and otherwise satisfactory substitutes for cellulose insulation.

With motor winding temperatures at their present levels, there appears to be no immediate cause for alarm, at least in the experience of the writer. The available evidence indicates that most of the sorbed moisture does not transfer to the dryer in operation and that thermal decomposition is not now a significant factor. This opinion is supported by moisture analyses on 460 dryers taken after the units had been operated under supervised conditions for prescribed periods of time. Figure 6 shows the trend of these moisture analyses. The units were mainly of the type shown in Fig. 1, and the desiccant in the dryers was Type 4A Molecular Sieve. The conditions under which the units were operated before analysis were such that the motors ran continuously, but no attempt was made at this time to control the winding temperatures. To ascertain the changes in moisture content of the dryers with time of operation, analyses were performed after units had been operated for the stated time intervals of one week, two weeks, six weeks, and six months. Each dryer came from a different individual unit.

Over a period of 19 months, 294 dryers were analyzed from one-week units, 73 from two-

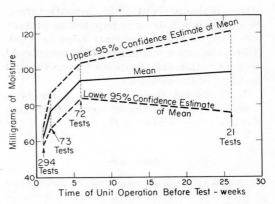

Fig. 6. Moisture found in domestic unit dryers over a period of 19 months.

week units, 72 from six-week units, and 21 from six-month units. The mean moisture content in each of these four groups of dryers was computed statistically and is plotted as the central curve in Fig. 6. To indicate the reliability of these mean values, broken lines have been plotted below and above the central curve at the 95 per cent confidence intervals. As expected from data affected by many variables, the mean value appears to be fairly reliable for the large number of tests made after one-week operation, but it is less reliable for the fewer tests made after longer times of operation.

According to Fig. 6, an average dryer on a unit in continuous operation can be expected to increase in moisture content for a period of time which may be as long as six weeks after the unit is placed in operation. The increase is rapid in the first week but gradually diminishes as would be expected if the windings and the desiccant tend to reach a moisture equilibrium during operation. The almost flat extension of the mean curve from six to twenty-six weeks seems to indicate that little or no further moisture transfer occurs after six weeks. Proof of this latter statement, of course, will depend on the study of more six-month test data than are now available.

In conclusion, it appears that there are three essentials for eliminating the moisture hazard in small, household-type refrigerating machines. First, the compressors as well as the other component parts must be adequately dehydrated, and to assure this, there must be strict moisture control in manufacturing. Second, when a dryer is required to prevent ice clogs, sufficient desiccant must be used. Third, the motor winding temperature should be kept within safe limits set by the thermal stability of the insulation.

By following these precepts, it has been possible to achieve almost complete freedom from moisture failures in the field.

References

1. ASHRAE Guide and Data Book, "Fundamentals and Equipment," p. 824, American Society of Heating, Refrigerating and Air-Conditioning Engineers, New York, 1961.
2. Steinle, H., "Water in Hermetic Units," Proceedings of the Tenth International Congress on Refrigeration, Copenhagen, Vol. 2, p. 70, 1959.
3. Steinle, H., "Wassergleichgewichte in Gekapselten Kältemaschinen," *Kältetchnik*, **11**, 336 (1959).
4. Knight, J. L., "Discussion at ASRE Meeting," *Refrig. Eng.*, **58**, No. 1, 52 (1950).
5. Brisken, W. R., "Moisture Migration in Hermetic Refrigeration Systems," *Refrig. Eng.*, **63**, No. 7, 42 (1955).
6. Elsey, H. M., Kelley, J. B., and Sharpe, R. B., "Estimating Water Content of Certain Dried but Uncharged Hermetic Refrigerating Compressors," *Trans. ASHRAE*, **65**, 651 (1959).
7. Divers, R. T., "Better Standards are Needed for Refrigeration Lubricants," *Refrig. Eng.*, **66**, No. 10, 40 (1958).
8. Elsey, H. M., Private communication.
9. Murphy, E. J., "Gases Evolved by the Thermal Decomposition of Paper," *J. Electrochem. Soc.*, **83**, 161 (1943).
10. Dushman, S., "Scientific Foundations of Vacuum Technique," p. 545, New York, John Wiley and Sons, Inc., 1949.
11. Herman, P. H., and Vermaas, D., "Density of Cellulose Fibers. I. Introduction and Experiments on the Penetration of Liquids Into Dry Cellulose," *J. Polymer Sci.*, **1**, 149 (1946).
12. Piper, John D., "Moisture Equilibrium between Gas Space and Fibrous Materials in Enclosed Electrical Equipment," *Transactions American Institute of Electrical Engineers*, **65**, 791 (1946).
13. Neale, S. M., and Stringfellow, W. A., "The Primary Sorption of Water by Cotton," *Trans. Faraday Soc.*, **37**, 525 (1941).

39. Residential Humidification

JOHN M. LIEBMANN

Research Products Corporation, Madison, Wisconsin.

ABSTRACT

Medical doctors have long been recommending high levels of relative humidity. With present day methods of home construction, this recommendation can cause condensation problems during the heating season. Proper humidity levels are beneficial to health and furnishings but these must be moderate and controlled. The humidity level in the home needs to be coordinated to the outdoor temperature. The recommended relative humidity values for the average home should be:

Inside Relative Humidity (%)	*Outside Temperature (°F)*
15	*—20*
20	*—10*
25	*0*
30	*10*
35	*20*

The effects of low humidity levels will absorb moisture from glue, fabrics, wood and other organic matter, increase the generation of static electricity, and decrease human comfort. High humidity levels will cause condensation to form on windows, allow water vapor to pass through walls and condense in insulation, tend to cause exterior paint failure, and cause roof sheating to buckle. The home owner will have to compromise between his comfort standard and damage to his home. A safe humidity level would be one in which no condensation would appear on the interior of double pane windows.

A survey of 150 unhumidified homes has shown that the relative humidity averaged 22 per cent, the lowest 15 per cent, the highest (due to unusual conditions present at the time) 70 per cent. This is well above the 7 to 15 per cent that would be present if no moisture were liberated in the home. The main sources of interior moisture are bathing, washing and drying clothes, mopping, cooking, washing dishes, human contribution, and house plants.

Many homes need moisture added to their air during the heating season. This can best be accomplished with a high-capacity humidistat controlled humidifier. There are many makes of residential humidifiers on the market today but they operate basically by throwing or "atomizing" particles of water by using a spinning disc, having air pass through a large wetted area of plates or pads, and exposing pans of water to air with and without an immersed electric heating element. The capacities of the above units are sometimes increased by exposing the wetted portions to heated air. It takes approximately 1000 Btu's or 350 watt-hours of heat to evaporate one pound of water.

The humidifier size requirement should be calculated on a pound of water per hour basis with inside design conditions of 73.5° F dry bulb, 35 per cent RH, and 20° F dry bulb, 50 per cent RH, outside conditions. The air volume can be determined by measurement and ASHRAE Guide air change procedures. A conservative approach of not including the interior sources of moisture should be used if fast humidity response is desired.

INTRODUCTION

Humidification has become increasingly more important to homeowners because of articles in national magazines, promotions of heating contractors, and advertisements by humidifier manufacturers. At present, there are over 100 humidifier manufacturers and the number keeps growing. Units are now being constructed with high capacity, good quality, and suitable controls.

Unfortunately, the subject of relative humidity is a very controversial topic and has been made confusing by the claims of medical doctors, building contractors, paint and insulation suppliers, and humidifier manufacturers. Considerable technical information is available regarding the standards of comfort and how these can be maintained under specified conditions, but the sources of information are scattered. This is particularly true in the case of residential humidification.

This paper is an attempt to assemble and evaluate the important factors that need to be considered in the application of humidifying devices in the home. Some of the areas will include a summary of the types of humidifiers available; what the moisture requirements and limitations are to maintain comfort and yet not damage the structure of the house; how humidity is measured in the home; humidification sizing and estimation; and some of the natural sources of water vapor in the home; and the medical aspects.

HUMIDITY INDICATORS AND LEVELS IN THE HOME

There are many ways in which humidity can be measured. A partial list of hygrometers would include: chemical, dielectric, dew-point, electrolytic, gravimetric, mechanical, thermistor, volumetric, and wet- and dry-bulb. A further breakdown of hygrometers is given by Mr. A. Wexler in his Bureau of Standards circulars.[2, 3] However, most of these are not readily usable in the typical American household.

The average homeowner does not have any direct readable humidity indicator device. He, of course, will notice heavier frost on his refrigerator coils in summer and condensation on his windows during the winter. He will feel summer mugginess and winter dryness with his body senses. His wife will notice the drawers sticking and his children will complain about the soggy cereal and in winter about static electricity shocks and dry noses.

Some homeowners will equip themselves with dial type humidity indicators that cost from two to twenty dollars, but these can be quite inaccurate. Dr. Proetz in his article, "Humidity, A Problem in Air Conditioning,"[4] indicated that the three dial indicators tested varied from −4 per cent RH, +5 per cent RH, and +11 per cent RH at room temperature when the humidity range was 26 per cent RH. Another home indicator device is paper impregnated with cobaltous chloride which will change from blue at low relative humidity through a series of lilac shades to pink at high relative humidity. This latter device is inexpensive but difficult to interpret accurately to within ±5 per cent RH.

At present, the most widely used instrument in accurately measuring residential humidity is the wet- and dry-bulb sling psychrometer. In order to obtain accuracies of ±1 per cent RH, it is necessary to take repeated wet-bulb readings, have the two bulbs move at velocities of approximately 1000 fpm,[5] use clean muslin wicks and distilled water. This instrument, however, is usually used by the engineer or air-conditioning contractor in checking an installation and is not readily available to the homeowner.

An ideal instrument would be one that would give direct relative humidity readings accurate to ±2 per cent RH, over a range of 10 to 50 per cent RH, at average room temperatures of 60 to 80°F, and would cost under $10.00. This instrument would be very helpful in informing home owners of their indoor winter conditions and would be valuable in determining humidity requirements over a large range of applications.

At present, information of humidity levels can only be obtained by actually measuring various residences. One survey is mentioned in a paper by Dr. Hitschler, "Humidification Indoors in Winter,"[6] in which he states that "In a series of 150 unhumidified houses near Lancaster, Pennsylvania, in February, the relative humidity averages 22 per cent, the worst being 15 per cent." These homes were occupied and contained normal family activities that liberated moisture by cooking, washing, etc. The humidity levels were above the 7 to 15 per cent one would expect to observe if there were no occupants or other internal sources of water vapor.

Studies made by Research Products Corporation indicated that levels of humidity in unoccupied spaces will become less than 10 per cent RH. In one case, the humidity level dropped as low as 4 per cent RH. These are based on readings taken on time-humidity recorders that were placed in three primary schools in Madison, Wisconsin during the winter of 1962–1963.

The humidity level of the home in the northern United States, during the heating season, will generally range from 10 to 40 per cent and will vary with the size of the home, rate of air change, indoor and outdoor temperatures, and internal moisture sources. The lowest readings will be found in the large unhumidified home that has frequent air changes, during a cold day, with a high thermostat setting.

THE SOURCES AND EFFECTS OF HIGH HUMIDITY

High humidity in homes during the winter months can cause problems. It can easily add $50 to $300 extra maintenance expense.[7] High humidity is generally caused by having a small home tightly constructed without adequate ventilation. The situation is usually aggravated by a number of high moisture producing sources.

Some typical sources of moisture would include:[8]

Human respiration and perspiration	0.2	lb/hour/person
Floor mopping	0.03	lb/sq ft
Clothes drying	26.4	lb/wash
Clothes washing	4.3	lb/wash

Cooking	*From Food*	*From Gas*	
Breakfast	0.34	0.58	0.9 lb
Lunch	0.51	0.66	1.2 lb
Dinner	1.17	1.52	2.7 lb
Bathing			
Shower			0.5 lb
Tub bath			0.1 lb
House plants			0.04 lb/plant

Other sources of water vapor that are not common or constant would be: unvented gas appliances (0.095 pounds of water/cu ft of natural gas consumed); freshly plastered walls and ceilings (approximately 700 gallons of water are required in the plaster to construct a six-room house),[9] damp crawl spaces, basement and slab floors that do not have a suitable water vapor barrier; and leaks in the siding, roofing, or flashings.

Excessive moisture will result in condensation forming on interior windows and walls. This forms on the surface and can be readily removed but may result in the finish flaking from the window frames or trim. A worse situation of interstitial condensation could result if the water vapor would move through the interior wall or ceiling and then condense or freeze in the insulation. Another effect of high humidity results in exterior paint failure. However, this latter situation has improved over the years because of better application of vapor barriers and improvements made in primer seals and oil-base paints.

A state of high interior humidity and cold exterior conditions can be a serious problem unless the home is designed to tolerate it. Surface and interstitial condensation can be eliminated by either reducing the humidity levels or raising the dew-point temperature. The latter can be raised by proper application of insulation, storm windows, or vapor barriers. The humidity levels can be lowered by ventilation or control of the moisture sources. Professors Rowley[10] and Teesdale[11] have written excellent papers on the readily available methods of reducing excessive moisture.

THE EFFECTS OF LOW HUMIDITY

Excessively dry air absorbs moisture from glue, fabrics, and other organic matter. Convincing proofs exist that wood shrinkage is related to relative humidity of air and that furniture is adversely affected by the drying action of room air in winter. The home owner can readily observe the widening of cracks between the floor boards and wood trim and can hear the change of tone characteristics of his piano.[12]

Positive evidence exists to the effect that generation of static electricity depends on the relative humidity of air. When the air is dry, static electricity is readily formed when one walks across a rug and the spark occurs when one touches a grounded object. This in itself is an annoyance, and it is also possible that static electrical charges on the surfaces of dust particles aid in keeping such particles afloat.[13]

Human comfort is greatly affected by low humidity. There are a number of articles by medical doctors which relate humidity to health. Dr. Proetz[4] states. "The nasal mucus contains some 96 per cent water. To begin with, it is more viscous than mucus elsewhere in the body and even slight drying increases the viscosity enough to interfere with the work of the cilia. Demands on the nasal glands are great, even under usual conditions, and they cannot cope with extreme dryness indoors in winter." Dr. Hitschler's[6] articles says, "The value of proper humidity in the prevention, amelioration, and relief of infection of the respiratory tract is pretty well established. Richards[14] comes to a similar conclusion in his article on postnasal drip. Andrews[15] states, "Humidity of 40 to 50 per cent with a temperature of 68 to 72°F produces the most healthful conditions for living and working areas and for recovery from diseases of the respiratory systems."

Dr. Lubart[16] states, "It is significant that coincidental with the institution of furnace heat in the fall, patients complain of smartings and burning in the pharynx, and the usual seasonal infections begin to make their appearance. These are popularly attributed to the inclement weather, but the actual cause of the coughs and colds is a dry nose and throat caused by artificial heating. An examination of the nose and throat of these individuals will show the characteristic dry spots, incriminating evidence against the low humidity. The irritations of the nose and throat usually will persist until the air in the individual's apartment, especially the sleeping quarters, is properly humidified. Among the many sins committed in the name of air conditioning, the worst offenses are those against humidity."

A paper by Dr. Gaul[18] indicates that humidity and skin conditions have a correlation. He states, "The remarkable action of rising dew points on chapped skin strongly suggests that the degree of air moisture is directly associated with softness, smoothness, and suppleness of the skin." He concludes his article in part by, "Resident and hospital heating engineers should provide means to adequately humidify the indoors."

The most important manifestations of low humidity levels during the heating season are those that affect the comfort and well-being of the occupants. Other effects are those of shrinkage or increasing the brittleness of products constructed of hygroscopic materials and the annoyance of static electricity.

HUMIDITY LEVEL RECOMMENDATIONS

Medical doctors will generally recommend high humidity levels. Dr. Proetz states, "Optimum relative humidity for 72°F and 74°F temperatures has been given as 40 per cent to 45 per cent, and some tests with human subjects have it as high as 73 per cent, but even the lower figures will be difficult to maintain in heated houses." Dr. Hitschler's article says, "So we would aim to produce a humidity of around 50 per cent and temperature of about 70°F. For reasons explained, such a state is not always possible; however, humidity as low as 30 to 35 per cent is still beneficial and worth striving for."

On the other hand, building material manufacturers are very concerned with possible condensation damage and tend to promote considerable lower humidity levels. Mr. Dunn,[18] a paint company representative, says, "The present status of the art (building construction) would indicate any house with an average inside temperature of 70°F and 40 per cent relative humidity can be expected to have condensation in insulated walls in zero weather." Professor Lund[19] of the University of Minnesota, stated that, "Tests we have made indicated that in a fully insulated wall. with a 70°F constant temperature and a 17 per cent relative humidity with a minus 15° below outside, no condensation will occur."

The home owner will want to weigh his comfort and well-being requirements with those of the construction of his dwelling. A conservative recommendation would not allow any condensation to form on or in the building structure. Generally, the first warning signs of this condition will appear on the interior of windows. The home with the double windows, of course, will tolerate a higher humidity level before this occurs.

We at Research Products Corporation recommend the following humidity levels for homes having indoor temperatures below 75°F.

Relative Humidity (%)	Outside Temperature (°F)
15	−20
20	−10
25	0
30	+10
35	+20

These recommendations are conservative for average home construction in the northern United States and are based on nearly 10 years of experience in the manufacture of high-capacity, humidistat-controlled humidifiers. These levels have proven to be safe and satisfactory for many thousands of applications.

HUMIDITY REQUIREMENTS

The factors that influence the amount of humidification required are: the amount of air in question, the comfort desired, and the outside temperature conditions. If, for example, one wishes to maintain 73.5°F and 35 per cent RH inside his home while the outside conditions are 20°F and 50 per cent RH, 3.7 pounds of water vapor should be added to every 10,000 cu ft of air changed. This can be calculated by using psychrometric chart values and is shown in Fig. 1.

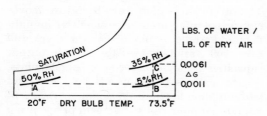

$$WA = WGT. \ OF \ DRY \ AIR = \frac{10,000 \ FT.^3}{13.5 \ FT.^3/LB.} = 740 \ LBS. \ OF \ AIR$$

HUMIDITY REQUIRED = WGT. OF AIR × AIR CHANGE RATE
× WATER CONTENT DIFFERENCE
= W_A × 1 × Δ G = 740 × 0.005
= **3.7 LBS./HOUR**

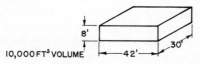

Fig. 1. Humidity calculations based on psychrometric chart values.

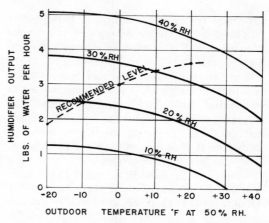

Fig. 2. Humidification requirements. Moisture required for 10,000 cu ft of space based on 73.5°F indoor temperature and one air change per hour.

This equation shows that the humidification requirements vary directly with the volume of air in question. The 10,000-cu ft volume is typical of ranch-style slab houses, but generally the homes located in the northern United States will have full basements and may have more than one floor. In either case, the volume of a home can be quickly and accurately determined by measurement or examination of floor plans.

The more difficult consideration is that of how often the air changes in a given time. There will generally be from ½ to 2 changes per hour depending on the house construction, wind velocity, temperature difference, and location of other adjoining buildings. A recent paper[20] indicates that air change rates below ½ can be obtained by extreme care in construction and insulation. On the other hand, a farm house constructed before 1930 can have more than 2 air changes per hour. The air change rate determination requires judgment and experience. The ASHRAE Guide[12] has a chapter on infiltration and ventilation in which the crack and air change methods of determination are explained in detail.

For those desiring a method of accurately measuring air change rates, a tracer gas technique could be used, the most common one being that which uses small traces of helium and measures the changes of thermal conductivity of air and helium concentration. Messrs. Coblentz and Achenbach[22] of the National Bureau of Standards list other alternate tracer-gas techniques. However, it has been shown that good agreement between measured and calculated air change rates can be obtained.[23]

Once the air change rate and home volume has been determined, it is a simple matter to determine the humidity requirements by referring to Fig. 2. If, for example, one wishes to know the requirements for a home of 20,000 cu ft that has an hourly air change at 0°F outside temperature and the home owner desires an inside humidity level of 25 per cent, a value of 6 pounds of water vapor can quickly be obtained. If there are continually interior sources of moisture within the home, i.e. human occupancy, house plants, etc., the amount of humidification required could be decreased.

Typical applications will show that some small tight homes require ventilation and not humidification during the heating season. Most homes need between two to ten pounds of moisture per hour and some large homes require twenty or more pounds per hour in order to maintain comfort conditions. It should be noted in Fig. 2 that the largest requirement for additional moisture of the recommended humidity level occurs when the outside temperature is 20°F and not at the extreme low temperatures that one might expect.

HUMIDITY LEVEL CONTROL

In order to maintain comfortable conditions and avoid condensation problems, it is necessary to have the proper humidification capacity as well as an accurate humidity control. The home owner expects to have a control that is reasonably accurate, responsive and inexpensive. At present, the most commonly used controls or humidistats are those that contain human hair or nylon elements which by hygroscopic elongation or contraction will operate an electric switch. This switch in turn could operate a relay which might open a valve, start a motor, move a damper, energize a heater, or cause some combination of these actions.

A control used for residential humidification need only operate in a humidity range of between 15 to 40 per cent and in temperatures between 60 to 80°F. The response rate of the control is not critical because usually the variation in the home will only be 5 per cent RH during an hour's time. This rate of humidity level change could be greater if the home were small compared to the rate of water vapor produced or if forced ventilation were used. The humidistat should be accurate to within ±3 per cent RH and should not require recalibration or attention for 5 or more years of operation. There are a number of manufacturers who currently make such a control.

The ideal control system would be one that sensed both the outdoor temperature and inside humidity so as to maintain a maximum comfort level without causing condensation damage. This same control could then be used either to actuate a humidifier or, in case of the small tight home, a ventilator. If an inexpensive (under $20 cost to the home owner) control were available, it would be of great interest to the manufacturers of residential air-conditioning equipment.

Residential Humidifiers

There are many types of humidifiers available to the home owner. They range in cost from $2 to $200 and have output capacities from $\frac{1}{2}$ to 25 lb/hour. Some are simple pans, and others are a combination of controlled humidifier, dehumidifier, and air filter devices. The author has read the sales literature of over eighty manufacturers of residential humidifiers and would estimate that there are well over 100 varieties available. Their output capacities are given in terms of pounds, pints, quarts, gallons per hour or day, with and without qualifications. A common rating of pounds per hour and a statement of operating conditions would have been helpful in comparing competing units.

It is very difficult to make a classification of the types of humidifiers available because of all the variables and combinations of components within the units. Some units are portable, while others attach into or onto existing heating systems. The ASHRAE Guide[24] has the following classification: (1) nozzle type, (2) rotary type, (3) cascade type, and (4) heater type. Another approach suggested in an *Air Conditioning News Magazine*[25] could be: (1) atomizing, (2) evaporating, and (3) vaporizing. A recent study by the National Warm Air Heating and Air Conditioning

Association gave nine separate classifications.[26]

In order to illustrate the most generally used methods of residential humidification, an arbitrary classification of (1) pan type, (2) atomizing type, and (3) wetted element type was used. The capacity ratings given are those that are most frequently stated in the manufacturers' sales literature. The output performance of most of the units illustrated could be increased by using heated water or hotter air, greater water-air surface contact area, or larger air volumes. It should be understood that this, by no means, shows all the variations of humidifiers but represents the author's attempt to illustrate the most generally used components currently available.

Figure 3 shows that a simple pan at room temperature and no air movement would be a very ineffective device. If the pan were placed on a radiator or in a further plenum, its output would be greatly increased. If plates or rotating discs were used to extend the water-air contact surface and then placed in a warm air stream, the output capacity would be adequate for many homes. Another version of the pan would heat the water directly by means of an immersion heater. As we know, it takes approximately 350 watt-hours or 1000

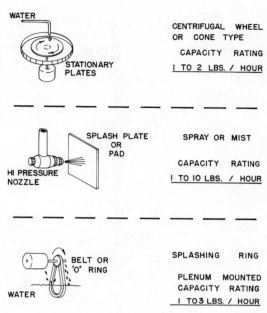

Fig. 4. Atomizing humidifiers.

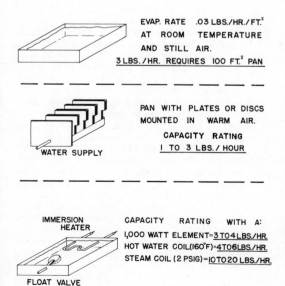

Fig. 3. Pan-type humidifiers.

Btu's in order to evaporate a pound of water, and the larger the heat source, the greater is the output. The heated pan is sometimes located in a warm air stream or is provided with a fan to move air over the water surface for increased capacity.

The top illustration of Fig. 4 shows how the mechanical (atomizing) process is accomplished by the centrifugal force of a rapidly revolving disc separating the water into small particles. The aspirating effect of the disc or cone will induce a moderate air movement to pass through the unit. The capacities listed are those of most commonly used portable humidifiers. The output can and is increased almost tenfold by using larger components and mounting the unit in a warm air stream. The nozzle method may be varied by the use of high-pressure water, hot water or steam, and by location in the warm air stream. Other methods of water separation that are employed include: a splashing belt, slinger "O" ring, and paddles. These latter atomizers are generally mounted in the warm air furnace plenum.

Figure 5 shows that the elements normally found in an evaporative cooler will produce enough moisture output if the air flow is large.

WETTED ELEMENT HUMIDIFIERS

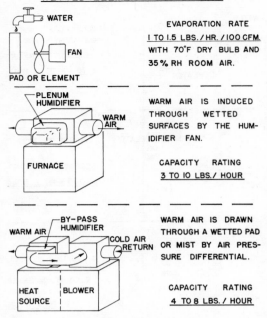

EVAPORATION RATE
I TO I.5 LBS./HR./I00 CFM.
WITH 70°F DRY BULB AND
35% RH ROOM AIR.

WARM AIR IS INDUCED
THROUGH WETTED
SURFACES BY THE HUM-
IDIFIER FAN.

CAPACITY RATING
3 TO I0 LBS./HOUR

WARM AIR IS DRAWN
THROUGH A WETTED PAD
OR MIST BY AIR PRES-
SURE DIFFERENTIAL.

CAPACITY RATING
4 TO 8 LBS./HOUR

Fig. 5. Wetted-element humidifiers.

If the air temperature is raised by the use of a heating coil, the capacity is also increased. Another way in which additional output is obtained is by flowing hot water through the wetted element. A more common method of increasing capacity is that of utilizing the warm air generated in the furnace. This is done either by inducing the air with the humidifier fan or using the air pressure differential of the furnace blower system.

As one becomes familiar with the practical applications of residential humidifiers, he will encounter problems. In some cases, the humidifiers simply do not have the capacity to do an adequate job, while others produce so much moisture that condensation damage will occur unless a proper control is employed. Another problem is that of corrosion of the metal parts contacting water or water vapor. Also, there is the problem of solids that remain after the water has evaporated. The solids result in white dust in case of the atomizers or scale and lime build-up in the other units. The lime problem can be challenging for if a thousand pounds of water (a conservative figure) are evaporated during a heating season, approximately 3 to 4 pounds of solids will remain unless they are continually removed.

CONCLUSIONS

(1) The home owner will have to compromise between his comfort standards and well-being and the condensation damage to his home. A safe humidity level should always be related to outdoor temperature. Generally, the first warning signs of exceeding this level will result in condensation forming on the interior surfaces of windows.

(2) Some small modern homes are built so tightly that their problem is that of excess humidity and they require ventilation and not humidification. Most homes require an additional two to ten pounds of moisture each hour, but it must be controlled. There are some large and/or older homes that require more than twenty pounds of water vapor to maintain comfort conditions.

(3) Humidification requirements should be based on 73.5°F and 35 per cent RH inside and 20°F and 50 per cent RH outside conditions. Judgment and experience are required in determining the air change rate.

(4) High-capacity, well-engineered, and accurately controlled humidifiers are readily available. The manufacturers of humidifiers should try to rate their units in terms of pounds per hour output and state the conditions of their operating performance.

References

1. Penman, H. L., "Humidity," Institute of Physics, London, Chapman and Hall Limited, (1955).
2. Wexler, A., and Brombacher, W. G., "Methods of Measuring Humidity and Testing Hygrometers," *Natl. Bur. Std. (U.S.) Circ.*, **512** (September 28, 1951).
3. Wexler, A., "Electric Hygrometers," *Natl. Bur. Std. (U.S.) Circ.*, **586** (September 3, 1957).
4. Proetz, A. W., M.D., "Humidity, A Problem in Air Conditioning," *Annals of Otology, Rinology, and Laryngology*, **65**, 376 (June 1956).
5. Queer, E. Z., and McLaughlin, J. R., "The Measurement of Water Vapor in Air and Other Gases," p. 7, Pittsburgh, Pa., Pittsburgh Lectrodryer Corp., (1955).
6. Hitschler, W. J., "Humidification Indoors in Winter," *Archives of Otolaryngology*," **72** (July 1960).
7. Miller, W. T., and Morse, F. B., "Excessive Moisture in Homes," *Purdue Univ. Eng. Bull. Res. Ser.*, **82**, 17 (September 1953).
8. Hite, S. C., and Bray, J. L., "Research in Home Humidity Control," *Purdue Univ. Eng. Bull. Res. Ser.*, **106**, 24 (1948).

9. Liebmann, J. M., "Residential Humidification," (thesis), p. 31, University of Wisconsin, Department of Mechanical Engineering, January, 1961 .

10. Rowley, F. B., Algren, A. B., and Lund, C. E., "Methods of Moisture Control and Their Application to Building Construction," University of Minnesota, Engineering Experiment Station, Bulletin No. 17.

11. Teesdale, L. V., "Remedial Measures for Building Condensation Difficulties," Report E 1710, Madison, Wisc., Forest Products Laboratory, September 1947 .

12. Konzo, S., Carroll, R., and Bareither, H., "Winter Air Conditioning," p. 18, New York, The Industrial Press, 1958 .

13. Kratz, A. P., "Humidification for Residences," p. 8, University of Illinois, Engineering Experiment Station, Bulletin No. 230, July, 1931 .

14. Richards, L. G., "The Problem of Postnasal Drip," *Annals of Otology, Rinology and Laryngology*, **64**, 55–68 (March 1958).

15. Andrews, A. H., Jr., "Clinical Cardiopulmonary Physiology," pp. 258–261. New York, Grune & Stratton, Inc., 1957 .

16. Lubart, J., M.D., "The Common Cold and Humidity Imbalance," *N.Y. State J. Med.*, 817 (March 15, 1963).

17. Gaul, E., and Underwood, G. B., "Relation of Dew Point and Barometric Pressure to Chapping of Normal Skin," *J. Invest. Dermatol.*, **19**, 19 (1952).

18. Dunn, E. J., "Water Permeability of Paint Materials for Wall Construction," Building Research Advisory Board, "Condensation Control in Buildings," p. 44, Conference Report No. 4, National Research Council, National Academy of Sciences, 2101 Constitution Avenue, Washington, D.C., September, 1952 .

19. *Ibid*, p. 96.

20. Jordon, R. C., Erickson, G. A., and Leonard, R. R., "Infiltration Measurements in Two Research Houses," *ASHRAE J.*, **5**, No. 5, 76 (May, 1963).

21. Heating Ventilating Air Conditioning Guide and Data Book, "Fundamentals," p. 421, New York, American Society of Heating and Air Conditioning Engineers, Inc., 1961 .

22. Coblentz, C. W., and Achanbach, P. R., ASHRAE Research Report No. 1616, "Design and Performance of a Portable Infiltration Meter," *ASHRAE Trans.*, **63**, 478 (1957).

23. Bahnfleth, D. R., Moselay, T. D., and Harris, W. S., ASHRAE Research Report No. 1615. "Measurement of Infiltration in Two Residences. Part II," *ASHRAE Trans.*, **63**, 465 (1957).

24. Heating Ventilating Air Conditioning Guide 1957 , p. 860.

25. *Air Conditioning Heating and Refrigeration News* (January 18, 1960).

26. *Air Conditioning, Heating and Ventilating*, **59**, No. 8, 10 (August 1962).

40. Condensation Problem Solutions in the Insulation of Buildings in Hot Climates

H. T. MEI

Lamar State College of Technology, Beaumont, Texas

AND

W. R. WOOLRICH

The University of Texas, Austin, Texas

ABSTRACT

For several decades builders of insulated houses have been advised to install moisture infiltration barriers on the warm side of the building wall to prevent condensation from forming within the walls. In the case of designs of heating for homes and other buildings, the warm side was next to the heated room wall. By contrast, in the case of cold storage rooms, the moisture infiltration barrier was placed on the outside of the insulation next to the outer (or warmer) wall.

With the advent of summer cooling of the same rooms that are to be heated in winter, new problems arose. If the owner of a building insisted on cooling his rooms below the dew point of the atmospheric air, then he will face with the same problem as the cold storage room designer, and for the summer period the vapor barrier should be placed at the outer wall. Does this mean that air-conditioned buildings should be insulated with vapor barriers on both the inner and outer walls?

This "reverse flow" of heat and vapor is a very real problem in certain buildings in hot climates unless some precautions are taken. Not the least of these is the careful calculation of the location of the vapor barrier.

For many years the recommended practice has been to place the vapor barrier on the heated side of the insulation. The reason is sound. In the heating season, the rooms, especially when the doors and windows are closed, accumulated a high humidity during occupancy due to excess moisture from washing, cooking and partying. As this warm humid air pushes toward the cold side of the wall with its lower vapor pressure, the migrating air is chilled below the dew point. Condensation results, and the insulation progressively gets saturated with moisture. For a cold-storage room the process would be reversed, especially in summer when the hot outside air (often with a relatively high absolute humidity) moved inward to the cold room, it would either deposit its condensation within the insulation or move into the storage room and deposit as frost on the refrigeration coils. Thus in each case the recommended vapor barrier is placed next to the warm side of the wall which is on the inside wall surface for winter heating and on the outside wall surface for cold-storage rooms.

For the hot-dry climates the most practical solution to prevent condensation is to maintain a room comfort temperature above the dew point of that region. For a climate to be classified as hot-dry, it must have, over a 24-hour period, a nearly constant wet bulb to some level from 20 to 40°F higher each afternoon. For some regions of the United States for several months the total change in wet-bulb temperature night and day for those months will not exceed 6 to 10°F. Condensation will not be a summer problem in homes in these areas if the rooms are maintained not lower than 78°F dry bulb during these months. Yet as a case example, a new $150,000 Texas home in a hot-dry climate came under the conditions stated above except that the owner had maintained the rooms at 67 to 70°F dry bulb. The insulation was installed with the vapor barrier on the inside as if for heating, the panelled walls were made up of special kiln-dried lumber and had been so tightly assembled that they not only buckled in every room but expanded with a one- to two-inch gap at the corners. The insulation in the outside walls adjoining the air cooled spaces was wet with condensation in each instance. The only walls of the mansion that had been occupied less than six months that did not require rebuilding were those that had the same temperature maintained on each side. The weather records of the past ten years indicate that if these rooms had been held not lower than 78°F dry bulb, this home would have remained undamaged.

With the advent of summer cooling for rooms that are to be heated in winter, more complex problems face the designer, if the owner of a building insists on cooling his rooms below the dew point of the atmospheric air, then he will face the same problem as the cold-storage room designer, and for the summer period the vapor barrier should be placed at the outer wall. Does this mean that all year-

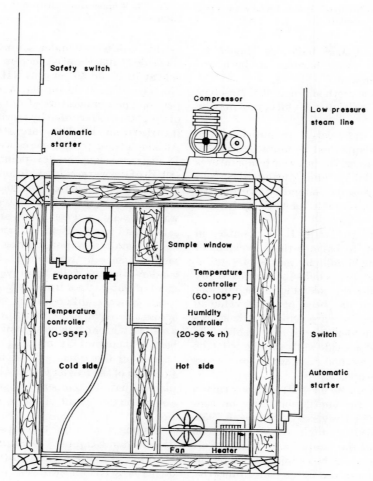

Fig. 1. Moisture chamber for testing wall samples.

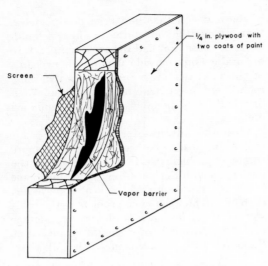

Fig. 2. Sample (No. 3) of insulated wall with vapor barrier inside the insulation.

Fig. 3. Temperature distribution through wall Sample 4.

round air-conditioned buildings should be insulated with vapor barriers on both the inner and outer walls?

Three possible methods suggest themselves by which condensation in a wall or roof may be prevented:

(1) Reduce the relative humidity of the warm side. This method is impractical since, during the summer, the outdoor temperatures are uncontrollable, and during the cold weather the relative humidity within the living spaces is desirable for both health and comfort.

(2) Ventilate the wall. It is possible, in theory at least, to balance the movement of moisture through walls by means of ventilation. This balance could be achieved by actually venting the cold side to the outdoor air. Ventilation has been of great value in minimizing moisture problems in attic spaces and on the under-side of flat roofs. The ventilation of some side walls appears to be the most feasible method that will allow excess moisture to escape.

A sample, No. 4, (see Fig. 3) was constructed to investigate the ventilation effect on condensation at The University of Texas in 1959. A perfect vapor barrier (glass) was installed on the cold side of the sample, and a total of six 1/2-in. diameter vent holes were drilled on the top and bottom of the frame (three on each), facing the cold room (see Fig. 1).

This was tested under summer conditions (hot side at 103°F and 65 per cent RH with cold side at 70°F and 50 per cent RH) with sample No. 3 (see Fig. 2) during the three weeks' test period. The temperature of the inside surface of the glass was recorded by thermocouple, and it varied from 71 to 73°F during the test period. Although these temperatures were more than 15 degrees below the dew-point temperature (89°F) of the warm side condition, there was no condensation shown on the glass during the test period. At the end of the test, the sample was in a very good condition, and no condensation was found inside the sample.

(3) Install a vapor barrier. This is the method generally recommended to eliminate condensation in walls to prevent the movement of water vapor from the warm side of the walls. Since a difference in vapor pressure across a wall can cause moisture to move into a wall faster than it moves out, water vapor can best be kept out by installation of a vapor barrier on the warm side of the insulation. Location of the barrier is critical. It must be so placed that its temperature will always be above the dew point of the warm side condition.

Assume that Fig. 4 represents the wall described in Example 1, p. 81, ASHRAE 1961 Guide and Data Book. A condition of 70°F and 50 per cent RH on the inside, and 0°F, 80 per cent RH exists on the outside in winter. This

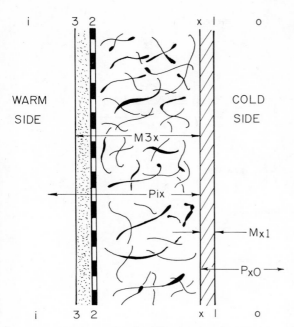

WARM
SIDE

COLD
SIDE

M3x

Pix

Mx1

PxO

FIG. 4. Wall with vapor barrier.

wall consists of painted plaster on lath, nailed over 2 × 4 studs, mineral wool fill, wood exterior sheathing, paper, and pine lap siding. Permeances, conductances, densities, and other physical data are specified. To substitute these data into the vapor flow formula indicated a rate of vapor transmission from the warm side of 0.30 grain/sq. ft/hour, and a rate of 0.06 grain transmitted through the cold side. Thus a vapor barrier is recommended to be installed at section 2-2 for winter protection.

Suppose this wall is part of an Austin, Texas, house. In summer it is exposed to an outside design condition of 100°F and 40 per cent RH, with indoor conditions remaining the same as in winter. A steady-state heat flow calculation indicated that the temperature of surface 2-2 is 71.84°F, and that the temperature of the vapor barrier surface is above the outside dew point of 71.2°F. It *looks* like there is no danger of condensation under these conditions.

Actually, there is a considerable danger of condensation with these existing conditions. The twin graphs of Fig. 6 shows the temperature variation, over a period of 24 hours, of the outer north and west wall surfaces of an air-conditioned building in Austin. By the

method of Mackey and Wright (ASHVE Transactions, 52), it can be shown that the temperatures of the vapor barriers in the north and west walls go as low as 71.03 and 71.27°F, respectively. Thus, it is seen that the north wall is likely to experience condensation that will certainly develop into a serious problem.

At 100°F and 40 per cent RH, on the psychrometric chart, the dew point is 71.2°F. At the same dry-bulb, but at 45 and 50 per cent RH, the dew points rise to 74.8 and 78°F, respectively. The time lag in cooling and heating of such a wall is about 6 hours. From the graph, the minimum wall temperature is 76°F, which temperature will occur 4 hours after midnight. The vapor barrier surface temperature will reach a dew-point temperature about 10 hours (4+6) after midnight, indicating an accumulation of condensation from about 9-30 to 10-30 a.m.

If the vapor barrier of Fig. 4 is moved from 2-2 to A-A, as in Fig. 5, which is 5⁄8 in. from 2-2, or 3 in. from X-X, the barrier temperature will be 56°F in winter, and 73.6°F during the cooling season. These temperatures are above the dew-point temperatures (51 and 71.2°F, respectively) of the warm side condition during the heating and cooling seasons, so that no condensation will accumulate in the walls.

Sample No. 3 illustrated in Fig. 2, has a

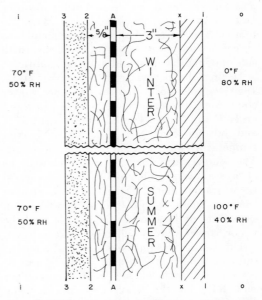

5⁄8″   3″

70° F
50% RH

WINTER

0°F
80% RH

70° F
50% RH

SUMMER

100°F
40% RH

FIG. 5. Wall with vapor barrier moved inward.

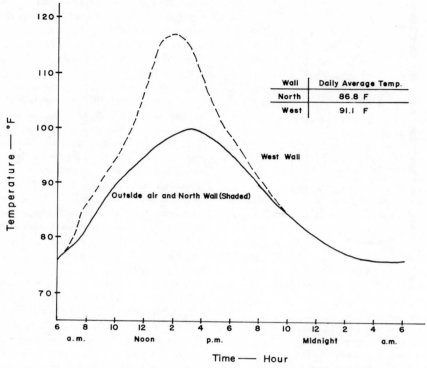

FIG. 6. Summer wall surface temperatures plotted against time for Austin, Texas.

vapor barrier inside the insulation and located about 1 in. from the plywood siding. This location was based on the calculation of winter and summer test conditions, so that the temperature of this vapor barrier should be above the dew-point temperature of the warm side under both winter and summer conditions.

During the period from November 9–15, 1959, Sample No. 3 was tested under winter conditions. The cold side conditions were set at 24°F and 70 per cent RH, hot side at 87°F and 50 per cent RH. The vapor barrier temperature was recorded by a thermocouple. The temperature during the test period was always above the dew-point temperature of the warm side (66°F). During and at the end of the test, there was no trace of condensation shown at any location in the sample, and the vapor barrier was dry and in perfect condition.

The sample was put back for test under the summer condition (hot side at 103°F and 65 per cent RH with cold side at 70°F and 50 per cent RH) for the next three weeks, from November 18 to December 5, 1959. The re-

corded barrier temperatures were above the dew-point temperature of 90°F. There was no condensation shown on the vision glass window during the test. At the end of the test, the barrier was in perfect condition, and there was no trace of condensation at any place inside the wall. One method, therefore, of solving the condensation problem is to place the vapor barrier inside the insulation where its temperature will always be above the dew point of the warm side condition.

The modern home, cooled below the atmospheric dew point in summer, and heated in winter against outside freezing temperatures, poses a design riddle. If vapor barriers are used on both sides of its insulation, the vapor in the ambient air may enter through smaller pinhole openings, forming droplets of condensation within the space. To avoid this, the intermediate insulated space should be amply ventilated. Extreme cases have been observed where the condensation was accumulated and trapped at the bottom of such a moisture barrier. A method that has been proposed involves the arrangement of each barrier with controlled ports so that the side which is warm can be made vapor-tight, while the cold side is allowed to breathe.

In conclusion, the authors want to emphasize that the location of the barrier is extremely important in air-conditioned buildings. To install a vapor barrier on the warm side of the wall requires a thorough investigation before application. At any rate, the vapor barrier will be most effective when it is installed so that the temperature of the barrier is above the dew point of the warm side condition. When this is not possible, a metal barrier may be the most acceptable alternative. If the occupants of an air-cooled house insist on very low temperature conditions in their rooms in the hot and humid summer periods, the only positive solution, under the present conditions of the insulating art, may be sheet vapor barriers on both the inside and outside surfaces, with provision for drainage and light ventilation of the insulation filling of the sandwich.

Within the semitropical humid areas of the United States too often the most expensive air-conditioned homes experience condensation within the insulation, while the cheaper air-conditioned homes go through a change of seasons without appreciable wetting of the insulation. The difference is obvious—the lower priced homes lack good workmanship, and although the two types of homes may have similar vapor barriers, there is a looseness of construction which enables the insulation of the cheaper house to dry out by natural ventilation.

References

1. Woolrich, W. R., and Mei, H. T., "Specifying Vapor Barrier for Year-round Air Conditioning," *Air Conditioning, Heating and Ventilating* (September 1959).
2. Mei, H. T., "Condensation and Vapor Barrier in Hot-dry and Hot-humid Climates," Dissertation, The University of Texas, June, 1960.
3. Mei, H. T., "Vapor Barrier Walls of Year-round Air-Conditioning," *Air Conditioning, Heating and Ventilating* (August, 1961).
4. Mei, H. T., "Summer Design Sol-air Temperatures for Eight U.S. Cities," *Air Conditioning, Heating and Ventilating* (July 1962).

41. Soil Covers Protect Basementless Houses from Wood Decay

JESSE D. DILLER

Northeastern Forest Experiment Station, U.S. Department of Agriculture, Upper Darby, Pennsylvania

ABSTRACT

Fifteen different materials were tested as soil covers in the crawl spaces of 150 basementless houses in four climatic zones of the eastern United States to reduce relative humidity and thus keep moisture content of underfloor wooden members below 20 per cent, the point above which wood-decay fungi attack the timbers and cause serious damage. The tests, begun in 1942, demonstrated that a soil cover of ordinary 55-pound asphalt roll roofing is effective in preventing wood decay. Within a few weeks after application of soil covers, moisture content of the wood dropped to about 14 per cent. Other types of soil covers were also effective. Relative humidity and air temperature in the crawl spaces were measured periodically with a hand-aspirated psychrometer, and an electrical resistance type of moisture meter was used to determine moisture content of sills and joists.

INTRODUCTION

Since 1941, many houses throughout the United States have been built without basements. Builders have assumed that ventilation in the crawl space of such houses prevents ground vapor from condensing on the sills, joists, and subfloor timbers, thereby eliminating the timber-decay hazard. However, the amount of ventilation usually provided has often proved to be inadequate, especially where the houses were built on moist sites, or during the cold winter months when the occupants frequently closed all vents for crawl-space warmth (Figs. 1 and 2). Because of the underfloor dampness that developed under such conditions, the sills and joists in many basementless houses rotted out within 5 to 15 years (Fig. 3).

In 1942, the U.S. Department of Agriculture began an experiment in which the ground in the crawl space of two basementless houses was covered with a single layer of roll roofing (Fig. 4). At the time, both of these houses had extensive underfloor dampness due to condensation moisture. The results of this preliminary experiment were phenomenal: within only 3 months all condensation had disappeared, even where vents were closed; the crawl-space air became noticeably drier; and the wood-moisture readings of the subfloor timbers averaged 14 per cent—well below the 20 per cent that is generally recognized as necessary for the growth and development of most wood-rotting fungi.

Encouraged by these results, the Department began a broader experiment to test further the practicability of ground covers for reducing the crawl-space relative humidity and allaying the wood-moisture decay hazard.

MATERIALS AND METHODS

Some 150 basementless houses were included in this study, which was made from 1943 to 1948 and repeated from 1952 to 1955. The houses were located in three distinct climatic zones: (1) cool (New England and Lake States), (2) intermediate (Middle Atlantic and Middle West States), and (3) warm and

FIG. 1. Moisture condensation on sills and joists is common during winter months in most states in houses built on moist sites where vents in the crawl space are kept closed to preserve heat.

FIG. 2. Moisture condensation caused severe corrosion of the plumbing in this 5-year-old house in eastern Tennessee.

FIG. 3. This No. 1 kiln-dried Douglas fir, in a newly constructed church in northern Virginia, failed in service after only 4 years due to attack by wood-decay fungi. The builders had failed to provide adequate crawl-space ventilation.

humid (South, particularly the Gulf States).

Many of the houses rested on piers, with crawl spaces enclosed by a skirting of wood or mineral-board. Some rested on continuous masonry or concrete foundation walls. The crawl spaces under all of the houses were damp. In some houses that were less than 10 years old, wood rot was already present in the sills and joists, and in others the underfloor water pipes had become badly corroded.

Fifteen different materials were tested as ground covers. Some of them were inexpensive, lightweight covers; others were heavier grades of roll roofings. Some manufacturers provided their own ground-cover products for use in the test houses—usually one house in each of the

FIG. 4. Roll roofing of either 55- or 90-pound weight is demonstrated to be an effective moisture barrier. A single layer covering the soil under a house prevents moisture from vaporizing and condensing on the sills and joists.

three zones. Some home owners purchased local roll roofing and installed it under their houses.

The moisture content of the subfloor in the crawl space was determined by means of an electrical resistance-type meter. For electrodes, copper nails (insulated, except for the head and the pointed tip, by a coating of spar varnish) were driven into the sills and joists to a depth of 1 in. at the four corners and center of each crawl space studied. The wood-moisture content readings at the time of each inspection were converted to a 70°F base.

The relative humidity and air temperature readings in the crawl space were also recorded. At the beginning of the study, several hygrothermographs were used to record relative humidity and temperature differences in crawl spaces with and without ground cover. An instrument was hung in the center of each crawl space. However, because of their rather delicate construction and the need for frequent adjustment (particularly after travel), these instruments were replaced by Friez hand-aspirated psychrometers.

In each house we took the climatic data at the center and four corners of the crawl space, and reported relative humidity and air temperature readings as averages. The wood moisture, air temperature, and relative humidity were measured at regular 4-month intervals in the 30 experimental houses in the Washington-Baltimore area, and annually in all other houses.

EXPERIMENTAL RESULTS

Before the ground covers were installed, the relative humidity ranged from 80 to 100 per cent, and the wood moisture, expressed as percentage of oven-dry weight, averaged approximately 20 per cent under the test houses, Thus wood moisture content was constantly at the critical level for the growth of the wood-decaying fungi.

Three months after the experiment was begun, a comparison was made of the relative humidity in the crawl space of basementless houses with and without ground covers. An instrument was placed at the center of the crawl space for a 1-week period. Comparisons were made at five widely separated locations. The results are shown in Fig. 5.

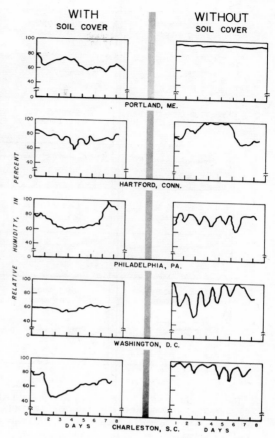

Fig. 5. Relative humidity in crawl space of basementless houses, with and without ground covers, at five locations. (Data taken from hygrothermograph records).

In Fig. 6, the effectiveness of various ground covers in reducing wood moisture by lowering the relative humidity in the crawl space of basementless houses is shown for periods that ranged from 8 to 10 years. The two original test houses have been under observation for more than 20 years, but data are included here for only 10 years. All test houses, except No. 2, No. 13, and No. 14, are located in the Washington-Baltimore area, and were visited every 4 months. The other houses were visited at yearly intervals. The most striking features of the various tests are described below:

No. 1. The ground cover in this crawl space proved to be the most effective of any tested, and it also represented the heaviest and most expensive grade of roll roofing materials tried. During the 10-year period, the relative

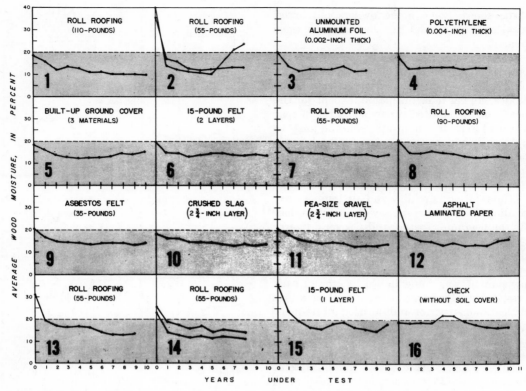

FIG. 6. Relative effectiveness of various ground covers in reducing wood moisture (i.e., relative humidity) in the crawl space of basmentless houses. All houses are located in the Washington, D.C.-Baltimore, Md. area except No. 2, No. 13 and No. 14, which are in Oak Ridge, Tenn., Charleston, S.C., and Portland, Me., respectively.

humidity was lowered from 84 to 67 per cent, and the wood moisture dropped from 18.7 to 12.0 per cent.

No. 2. (Two houses at Oak Ridge, Tenn.) The curves represent two basementless houses on the same housing project. At the beginning of this experiment the two houses appeared to be comparable in every respect, and both had equally moist crawl-spaces. A 55-pound roll roofing ground cover was installed under each. During the following 5-year period, the wood moisture of the subfloor timbers in both houses dropped uniformly at satisfactory rates. Then the owner of one of the houses removed his ground cover because, as he expressed it, "ground covers tend to breed sowbugs." By the end of the sixth year, his crawl space had again reached the critical 20-per cent moisture stage. Meanwhile, in the house with the undisturbed ground cover, the subfloor wood moisture had continued to remain at a constant

15 per cent, which afforded adequate protection against wood-decaying fungi.

No. 3. This relatively inexpensive, unmounted aluminum-foil cover showed considerable promise in preventing visible moisture condensation and in lowering the wood-moisture content of the sills and joists. After 8½ years the owner was convinced by an overzealous salesman that he could further improve the crawl-space condition of his house by nailing a tight, ½-in. thick, asphalt-impregnated insulation board to the bottom of the joists. During the installation of the ceiling the ground cover was completely destroyed, but this did not deter the owner: he had such complete confidence in the efficacy of the asphalt-impregnated ceiling, thanks to the salesman's pitch, that he did not even bother to replace the aluminum-foil ground cover.

However, he had occasion to regret his decision: within 6 months the crawl-space relative humidity had increased to over 90 per cent and termites had made inroads in the sills at one corner—their first appearance since the house was built. However, even though the aluminum foil had performed effectively for $8\frac{1}{2}$ years, it probably would have become less effective after a few more years. There is a tendency for water to collect in pockets of this ground cover and cause corrosion. And there is also a tendency for this lightweight material to become disarranged by wind or rapid water movement unless it is pegged to the soil.

No. 4. Polyethylene film—also a lightweight cover—performed satisfactorily as a ground cover for the 8 years of testing. It does, however, have the limitation of being disturbed by wind or water movement unless pegged; and because polyethylene is inflammable, it should not be placed directly underneath a subfloor, suspension-type heating furnace.

No. 5. An attempt was made to determine the minimum amount of ground cover material required to make a satisfactory moisture barrier in a wet crawl space. First the soil surface was sprayed with a deep-penetrating ($\frac{3}{16}$-in.) asphalt (soap) emulsion. This material, under previous laboratory tests, had shown considerable promise. Sprayed on top of sand and gravel in a pail containing free water, the emulsion developed a skin that prevented moisture evaporation. Cost of the material was less than 1 cent per sq ft. The asphalt-emulsion spray treatment in the crawl space of this house after a 7-month test period proved to be ineffective in reducing the relative humidity or in lowering the wood moisture content of the sills and joists, and visible condensation still occurred on the subfloor timbers. (This was the same experience observed in six other crawl spaces where asphalt emulsion was tried.) Next, we applied a single layer of unmounted aluminum foil (0.00035-in.) on top of the asphalt-emulsion sprayed soil surface. After 21 months this conbination of ground covers resulted in a slightly lower relative humidity and wood moisture, but it did not eliminate conpletely visible condensation moisture. Finally a single layer of 15-pound felt was rolled out over the aluminum foil. This combination then proved effective in controlling the relative humidity and wood-moisture content of the sills and joists. However, we do not regard this built-up ground cover as practical, in view of the readily available, reasonably priced roll-roofing materials.

No. 6. On the basis of initial cost and moisture-barrier performance, a 2-layer, 15-pound asphalt-saturated felt cover has thus far proved to be the most desirable ground cover. This felt cover lowered the relative humidity from 80 per cent to less than 62 per cent, and the wood moisture from 19.4 to 13.8 per cent. Though the strips of the second layer were placed at right angles to the strips of the first layer, overlapping of seams did not appear to be a very important consideration, covers with no overlap, or even on areas where there were gaps $\frac{1}{2}$ to 1 inch. wide between strips, gave as good control as covers with over-lapped and cemented strips.

In contrast, the effectiveness of a single layer of 15-pound felt as a moisture barrier, is demonstrated in frame *No. 15.* Its performance was only slightly better than that for the check house, shown in frame *No. 16.*

No. 7 and No. 8. These represent the two original test houses in which 55- and 90-pound roll roofings were applied as ground covers in December 1942. (See Fig. 7, in which their wood moisture is plotted for the 20-year period.)

No. 9. Here, cold application, asbestos felt, a specially manufactured product intended for ground cover use, was tried. It is manufactured entirely of mineral substances and, therefore, is inert to attack by either fungi or termites. Although it proved to be a very effective ground cover and is still durable after 16 years in service, this cover is still experimental and more costly than the heavier grades of roll roofing.

No. 10 and No. 11. At the request of certain maintenance superintendents of housing projects in the Washington, D.C., area, we installed respectively a $2\frac{3}{4}$-in. layer of crushed slag and an equally deep layer of pea-size gravel, in the crawl spaces of two houses. The maintenance superintendents felt that these two materials, both cheap and permanent, might serve to break up moisture capillarity in the soil and prevent its vaporization into the crawl space. Although the curves show that wood moisture in both houses decreased gradually over a period of 5 years, the decrease was not so rapid as that produced by roll-roofing covers. At the end of the fifth year, a tight insulation ceiling (comparable to the one described above—see *No. 3*), was installed in the house with the crushed slag, and from then on, there was a gradual rise in the subfloor wood moisture. By the 7th year, relative humidity had reached the 90 per cent level, and (as in *No. 3*) termite damage was noted in the sills at one corner of the crawl space. As a result of this experience neither of these materials was recommended as a satisfactory ground cover.

No. 12. This lightweight, reinforced, asphalt-laminated paper began to deteriorate badly after the eighth year, at which time there was also a rapid decline in its moisture-barrier effectiveness. At the tenth year, another layer of the same material was superimposed on the old cover; and within less than 2 years the wood moisture had again dropped to well below 13 per cent. Because of the initial high cost of this lightweight material, it is probably more practicable to purchase a longer-lasting and more substantial ground cover.

No. 13. Although the 55-pound ground cover proved as effective in the crawl space of this house located in warm, humid Charleston, S.C., the curve shows that the drop of wood

moisture was not as rapid as in other less humid regions. But this does not rule out its usefulness in safeguarding the timbers from wood-rot fungi.

No. 14. (Two houses in Portland, Me). As a precaution against freezing in the underfloor water pipes, access doors as well as all crawl-space vents were fitted with outside storm windows, as typical in the colder climatic zones. The crawl spaces were virtually sealed for a period of 6 months. The two houses selected for inclusion in this study appeared to be similar in every respect with one exception: approximately one-fourth of the ground area under one house was permanently covered with a surface of water (2 ft deep at the extreme northern end); there was no standing water at any time in the other house. A loosely constructed platform was built over the water surface in the one crawl space, sufficient to support a ground cover. A 55-pound roll-roofing cover was installed in the crawl spaces of both houses. While the curves show that the cover was not quite as effective in the house with standing water, it is apparent that, even under these unusual circumstances, the cover afforded sufficient protection to keep the wood

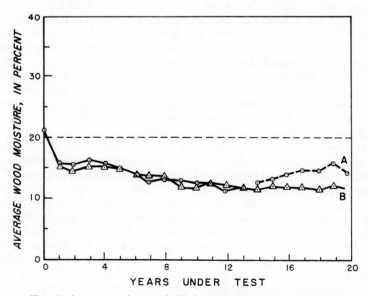

FIG. 7. Average moisture of sills in two basementless houses with ground covers: a single layer of 90-pound roll roofing was used in house "A," and a single layer of 55-pound roll roofing was used in "B." After the thirteenth year, a ½-in. thick, tight insulation ceiling was installed under the joists in the crawl space "A."

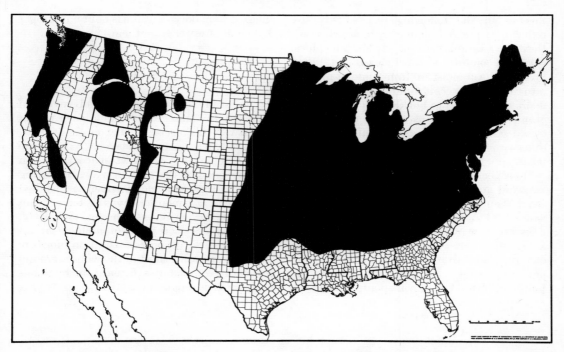

FIG. 8. Dark sections indicate where climatic conditions are apt to cause condensation during winter months and where ground covers are recommended for basementless houses. Also, under certain local conditions, ground covers can be used successfully in other areas.

moisture well below the 20 per cent level.

No. 15. The single layer of 15-pound felt is not recommended for use.

No. 16. Throughout the 10-year period, the relative humidity in the crawl space of this house ranged from 80 to 90 per cent, and the wood moisture ranged from 18 to 19 per cent. During at least one third of all the inspections over the 10-year period, there was visible condensation on the sills and joists. By the seventh year it was necessary to remove and replace the entire northern sill because of its rotted condition.

Figure 7 shows the average wood moisture per cent of the sills in the two original basementless houses with roll-roofing ground cover during the entire 20-year test period. Although both covers are still effective moisture barriers, after the thirteenth year an insulation ceiling was installed in the crawl space of one of the two houses (cf. *No. 3* and *No. 10,* above). Even though this also tended to increase the subfloor timber moisture in the crawl space, the increase was not great enough to create a wood-rot hazard.

Figure 8 shows the area in the continental United States where climatic conditions are apt to cause condensation during the winter months, and where ground covers are recommended for basementless houses. The mean temperatures within the dark areas average 45°F in January, and annual precipitation averages 20 in. or more. It is believed that under certain local conditions ground covers can be used successfully in other areas (e.g., *No. 13,* above).

On the basis of gross cost and moisture-barrier performance, for the 8- to 10-year test period, the most durable cover was found to be two layers of 15-pound asphalt-saturated felt. However, for crawl spaces where the ground cover was subject to physical wear from people or animals, durability of the material was a major consideration. Under the circumstances, therefore, an initial investment for a heavier material, such as 45-pound roll roofing or a heavier grade of asphalt-saturated felt, was recommended.

Besides the primary advantages mentioned elsewhere, ground covers also proved advantageous in the following respects: (1) by reducing the relative humidity in crawl spaces they also reduced corrosion of plumbing pipes, electrical conduits, and switch boxes; (2) they prevented soil moisture from moving upward into the house where it could easily have caused floors to swell and to buckle; and (3) after the ground covers were installed vents could be closed safely, thereby saving heat that would otherwise have been lost through uninsulated floors.

However, the ground covers used in these tests did not stop termites, and they did not strengthen wood already weakened by decay. neither did they protect wood that was getting moisture from other sources. (Before applying a ground cover, a check should be made on outside grades to make certain that they are not responsible for moisture under the building; also, the down-spouts should be checked to make sure there is not an improper diversion of water from them.)

SUMMARY

This study shows that ground covers of sufficient thickness and weight, such as 45-pound roll roofing or heavier grade asphalt-saturated felt, can effectively reduce the relative humidity of crawl spaces and can thereby prevent the growth of wood-rotting fungi. If a recommended cover is installed soon after a basementless house is built, it can extend the service life of the house indefinitely. Even in houses where decay of subfloor timbers is already present and condensation moisture is prevalent during most of the winter, ground covers can completely safeguard the buildings from further fungus decay.

42. Humidity Distribution and Rate of Evaporation of Water

Kamekichi Shiba

Faculty of Engineering, Toyo University, Saitama, Japan

AND

Masabumi Ueda

Faculty of Liberal Arts and Sciences, Gunma University, Gunma, Japan

ABSTRACT

The effect of natural convection on the rate of evaporation of water is investigated from the fine distribution of humidity. Experiments are performed for three cases of horizontal circular disks of various sizes facing upwards, a horizontal circular disk facing downwards, and a vertical plate. Using a small electric resistance hygrometer and a thermoelectric thermometer, measurements are made of the humidity distribution close to the evaporating surfaces, and from which effective thicknesses of the diffusion layers are determined graphically. It is found for the horizontal disks facing upwards that the data plotted as the effective thickness δ vs the distance x from the circumference give a single curve. A similar curve is obtained for the horizontal disk facing downwards except near the circumference where δ is somewhat larger than for the upward-facing horizontal disks. For the vertical plate, it is shown that the flow of air due to natural convection is laminar near the lower plate end and at the upper region it becomes turbulent. The results of experiments are correlated in the dimensionless form of x/δ versus Gs_D.Sc, and equations expressing the rate of evaporation of water in natural convection are obtained.

INTRODUCTION

When water evaporates from the surface of a liquid or solid body into the air, if the distribution of humidity in the diffusion layer immediately adjacent to the surface is known, then the rate of evaporation of water per unit area should be determined with the coefficient of diffusion. This matter had been known theoretically for long, but practically there was no experimental verification since it was nearly impossible to measure the humidity distribution in the diffusion layer. We have previously developed a small electric resistance hygrometer which enables us to measure the fine distribution of humidity in a thin air layer, and have presented experimental data on the rate of evaporation of water by measuring the 1–5 humidity distribution. In this paper we will describe in detail the effect of natural convection on the rate of evaporation of water.

APPARATUS AND PROCEDURE

Evaporating surfaces employed in our experiments are horizontal circular disks 2 to 60 cm in diameter facing upwards, a horizontal circular disk 60 cm in diameter facing down-

349

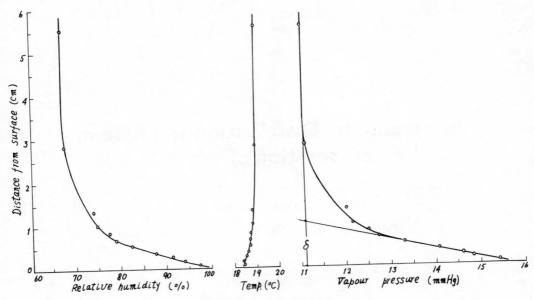

FIG. 1. Typical humidity distribution data.

wards, and a vertical plate 150 cm high and 30 cm wide. Each evaporating surface consists of a glass plate covered with wetted blotting paper of the same size. To measure the humidity distribution close to the surface, an electric resistance hygrometer and a copper-constantan thermoelectric thermometer are used; both of the sensitive elements are set on a moveable device having screw and vernier. The humidity sensitive element used is 10 mm long, 4 mm wide and 0.2 mm thick. Measurements of the humidity distributions normal to the evaporating surfaces are made at various distances: for the horizontal disks the distance is measured from the circumference, and for the vertical plate the distance is measured from the lower end. A typical example of the experimental data is shown in Fig. 1, in which relative humidity, temperature and water vapor pressure are plotted *vs* the distance from evaporating surface. Referring to the water vapor pressure curve, a region of the constant vapor pressure gradient which corresponds to the diffusion layer can be clearly recognized. As the thickness of the diffusion layer, we shall take the effective thickness δ, i.e., the distance from the evaporating surface to the point at which the vapor pressure becomes equal to that in the ambient air by extending the

linear portion of the water vapor pressure curve. The rate of evaporation of water per unit area, w, is given by the equation:

$$w = D' \frac{\Delta p}{\delta} \quad (1)$$

where Δp is the difference in water vapor pressure between the air at evaporating surface and the ambient air, and D' is a coefficient calculated from the following equation:

$$D' = \frac{DM}{RT} = 0.241 \left(\frac{T}{288} \right)^{0.75} \left(\frac{760}{P} \right)$$
$$\times 10^{-6} \text{ g/cm sec mm Hg} \quad (2)$$

where D is the coefficient of diffusion of water vapor in the air,[6] M is the molecular weight of water vapor, R is the universal gas constant, T is the temperature in degrees Kelvin, and P is the atmospheric pressure in mm Hg. For practical purposes, the value of D' at a temperature of $(15 + \Delta\theta)°$C may be obtained by

$$D'_{(15 + \Delta\theta)°C} = (0.241 + 0.0007 \, \Delta\theta) \left(\frac{760}{P} \right)$$
$$\times 10^{-6} \text{g/cm sec mm Hg} \quad (3)$$

The experiments are carried out in still air at temperatures of 5 to 30°C. The temperature

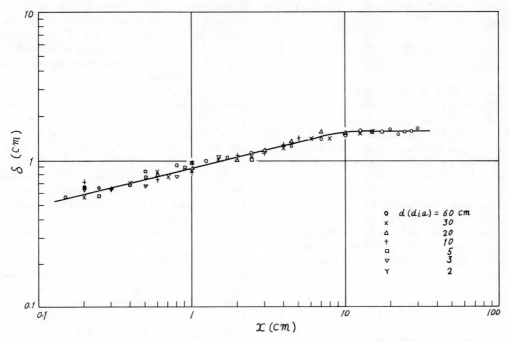

FIG. 2. Effective thickness *vs* distance from circumference for horizontal circular disk facing upward.

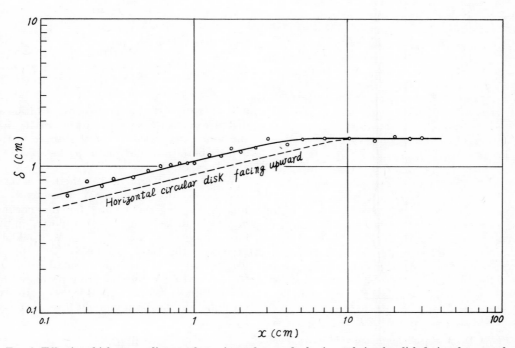

FIG. 3. Effective thickness *vs* distance from circumference for horizontal circular disk facing downward.

drops of the evaporating surfaces are within 2 deg.

EXPERIMENTAL RESULTS AND DISCUSSION

Values of δ obtained for the horizontal circular disks of various sizes facing upwards are shown in Fig. 2 plotted *vs* the distance *x* from the circumference. It is noticed that all the data points are on a single curve, independent of the size of disk: at $x < 10$ cm, δ increases with *x*, where the curve is linear on logarithmic coordinates with a slope of ¼, and at $x > 10$ cm, δ is kept constant at $1.5 \sim 1.6$ cm.

Figure 3 is a plot of δ *vs x* for the horizontal circular disk 60 cm in diameter facing downwards. The variation of δ with *x* is similar to that for the horizontal disks facing upwards (shown by broken line) except near the circumference, $x < 5$ cm, where δ is somewhat larger. The slope of the linear portion of the curve and the value of δ for the horizontal portion of that curve are in accordance with those of the horizontal disks facing upwards.

Figure 4 gives a graph of δ *vs* the vertical distance *x* from the lower end for the vertical plate. Near the lower plate end, δ increases with *x* and reaches a maximum value of $1.5 \sim 1.6$ cm at $x \approx 3$ cm. Exceeding $x \approx 5$ cm, δ decreases steeply, then it oscillates but the oscillation is gradually damped, and finally for $x > 120$ cm it becomes roughly constant. It seems that the flow of air along the surface due to natural convection is laminar for $x < 5$ cm and for the upper region it becomes turbulent.

The above-mentioned data suggest that in still air, natural convection caused by density difference has great influence on the rate of evaporation. Dimensional analysis predicts that in natural convection, the dimensionless quantity x/δ is a function of the Grashof number for mass transfer, Gr_D, and the Schmidt number, Sc, where x/δ, Gr_D and Sc are

$$\frac{x}{\delta} = \frac{w_x \, x}{D' \, \Delta p} \tag{4}$$

$$Gr_D = \frac{g x^3}{\nu^2} \left(\frac{\rho}{\rho_0} - 1 \right) \tag{5}$$

$$Sc = \frac{\nu}{D} \tag{6}$$

and where w_x is the local rate of evaporation at distance *x*, *g* is the acceleration of gravity, ν is the kinematic viscosity of the air, ρ is the density of the ambient air and ρ_0 that of the air at the evaporating surface.

We, now, shall analyze the effect of natural convection by dimensional consideration. Figure 5 gives the results for the various horizontal disks facing upwards plotted in the form of log x/δ *vs* log $(Gr_D \cdot Sc)$. As would be expected, the data points for $x < 10$ cm $(Gr_D \cdot Sc < 4 \times 10^4)$ except at small values of $Gr_D \cdot Sc$, and for $x > 10$ cm are represented by straight lines of slopes ¼ and ⅓, respectively; the equations for both straight lines are given by

$$\frac{x}{\delta} = 0.46 \, (Gr_D \cdot Sc)^{1/4} \tag{7}$$

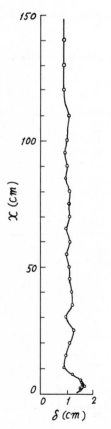

FIG. 4. Distance from lower end *vs* effective thickness for vertical plate.

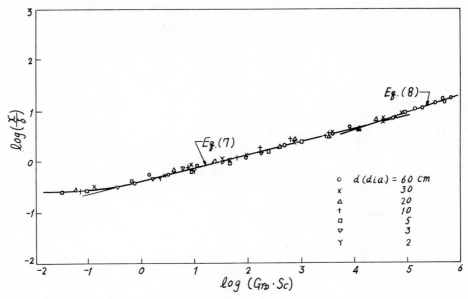

FIG. 5. Log (x/δ) *vs* log $(Gr_D{\cdot}Sc)$ for horizontal circular disk facing upward.

and

$$\frac{x}{\delta} = 0.21 \ (Gr_D{\cdot}Sc)^{1/3} \qquad (8)$$

At values of the product $Gr_D{\cdot}Sc$ smaller than about 1, the slope of the curve is substantially zero and it seems that the natural convection current almost vanishes.

Figure 6 is a plot relating log x/δ to log $(Gr_D{\cdot}Sc)$ for the horizontal disk facing downwards. The data points for $x < 5$ cm $(Gr_D{\cdot}Sc < 1 \times 10^3)$ are expressed by the equation:

$$\frac{x}{\delta} = 0.38 \ (Gr_D{\cdot}Sc)^{1/4} \qquad (9)$$

and the data points for $x > 5$ cm can be represented by Eq. (8).

Figure 7 shows the results for the vertical plate. The data points for $x < 5$ cm $(Gr_D{\cdot}Sc < 4 \times 10^3)$ and for $x > 10$ cm $(Gr_D{\cdot}Sc > 3 \times 10^4)$ gave straight lines, respectively: the equations of those lines are expressed by

$$\frac{x}{\delta} = 0.42 \ (Gr_D{\cdot}Sc)^{1/4} \qquad (10)$$

and

$$\frac{x}{\delta} = 0.37 \ (Gr_D{\cdot}Sc)^{1/3} \qquad (11)$$

It is evident from the above results that the dimensionless quantity x/δ is proportional to the nth power of the product $Gr_D{\cdot}Sc$, the power n depends on the flow of natural convection: for the laminar range $n = \frac{1}{4}$ and for the turbulent range $n = \frac{1}{3}$.

From Eqs. (7), (9) and (10) for the laminar range it is known that the coefficient 0.42 for the vertical plate is equal to the mean of 0.46 for the upward-facing disks and 0.38 for the downward-facing disk. This fact may be considered from the orientations of the evaporating surfaces.

Using the data shown in Fig. 6, we can determine the total rate of evaporation, w_r, from the whole surface of a horizontal circular disk of radius r facing upwards in still air. Now, we write Eq. (7) for the laminar range in the form

$$w_x = 0.46 \ D' \frac{1}{x} \ (Gr_D{\cdot}Sc)^{1/4} \ \Delta p \qquad (12)$$

and integrating the above equation, we obtain

$$w_r = 0.53 \ \pi \ r \ D' \ (Gr_D{\cdot}Sc)^{1/4} \ \Delta p \qquad (13)$$

where $Gr_D = [gr^3/\nu^2 \ (\rho/\rho_0 - 1)]$. Equation (13), as is known from Fig. 2, is valid for the disks of $r < 10$ cm. Putting the mean rate of evaporation, $w_r/\pi r^2 = w_m$, per unit area for the whole disk, Eq. (13) is written in the dimensionless form

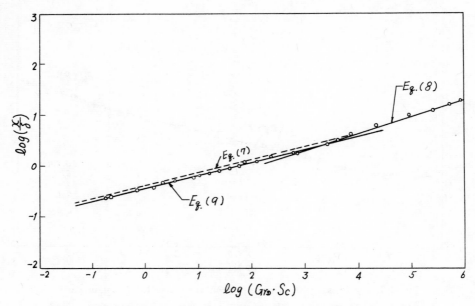

FIG. 6. Log (x/δ) vs $\log(Gr_D\cdot Sc)$ for horizontal circular disk facing downward.

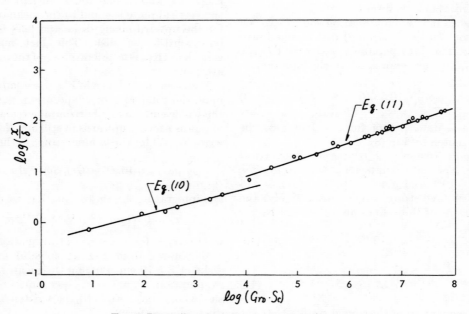

FIG. 7. Log (x/δ) vs $\log (Gr_D\cdot Sc)$ for vertical plate.

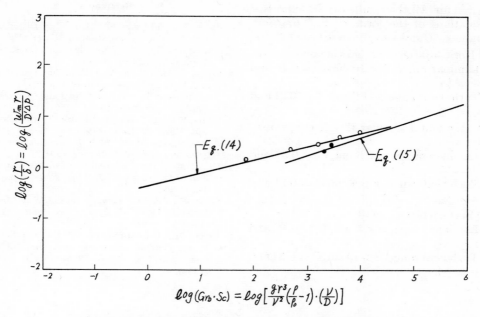

FIG. 8. Comparison with results of measurements by weighing.

$$\frac{w_m r}{D' \Delta p} = \frac{r}{\delta} = 0.53 \, (Gr_D \cdot Sc)^{1/4} \qquad (14)$$

Equation (8) for the turbulent range indicates that the rate of evaporation per unit area is independent of x since the term x is canceled from the equation, and consequently, we have

$$\frac{r}{\delta} = 0.21 \, (Gr_D \cdot Sc)^{1/3} \qquad (15)$$

This equation also holds for the turbulent range of the downward-facing horizontal disk.

Similarly, from Eq. (9) for the laminar range of the horizontal disk facing downwards, we have

$$\frac{r}{\delta} = 0.43 \, (Gr_D \cdot Sc)^{1/4} \qquad (16)$$

For the vertical plate, using Eq. (10) for the laminar range, the mean rate of evaporation, w_m, from the surface of length L and unit width is given by

$$\frac{w_m L}{D' \Delta p} = \frac{L}{\delta} = 0.56 \, (Gr_D \cdot Sc)^{1/4} \qquad (17)$$

where $Gr_D = [gL^3/\nu^2 \, (\rho/\rho_0 - 1)]$. For the turbulent range, from Eq. (11), we have

$$\frac{L}{\delta} = 0.37 \, (Gr_D \cdot Sc)^{1/3} \qquad (18)$$

To check the results, a comparison is made with the rate of evaporation calculated from the decrease of weight of circular dishes filled with water. In Fig. 8, the results of measurements by weighing are compared with the lines given by Eqs. (14) and (15). The white circles represent the data for dishes of $r = 1.2$ to 4.6 cm, while the black circles represent those for a dish of $r = 4.5$ cm, which is surrounded by a concentric circular pan of $r = 15$ cm filled with water to obtain the uniform rate of evaporation from the dish to be weighed. The white and black circles fit closely on the straight lines representing Eqs. (14) and (15), respectively, and it seems that the results obtained by humidity distribution are in good agreement with those obtained by weighing.

CONCLUSION

In the present work, from the data of δ vs x and x/δ vs $Gr_D \cdot Sc$ for the surfaces of horizontal circular disks, facing upward and facing downward, and a vertical plate, the effect of natural convection on the rate of evaporation is cleared up. All the results can be expressed by equations of the form $x/\delta = C(Gr_D \cdot Sc)^n$. The values of C and n are found to be as follows:

(1) Horizontal circular disks facing upwards.
Laminar range, $x < 10$ cm, $C = 0.46$ and $n = \frac{1}{4}$.
Turbulent range, $x > 10$ cm, $C = 0.21$ and $n = \frac{1}{3}$.

(2) Horizontal circular disk facing downwards.
Laminar range, $x < 5$ cm, $C = 0.38$ and $n = \frac{1}{4}$.
Turbulent range, $x > 5$ cm, $C = 0.21$ and $n = \frac{1}{3}$.

(3) Vertical plate.
Laminar range, $x < 5$ cm, $C = 0.42$ and $n = \frac{1}{4}$.
Turbulent range, $x > 10$ cm, $C = 0.37$ and $n = \frac{1}{3}$.

References

1. Shiba, K., and Ueda, M., "Humidity Distribution and Rate of Evaporation of Water (I)," Proceedings of the 6th Japan National Congress for Applied Mechanics, 1956.
2. Shiba, K., and Ueda, M., "Humidity Distribution and Rate of Evaporation of Water (II)," Proceedings of the 9th Japan National Congress for Applied Mechanics, 1959.
3. Shiba, K., and Ueda, M., "Humidity Distribution and Rate of Evaporation of Water (III)," Proceedings of the 11th Japan National Congress for Applied Mechanics, 1961.
4. Ueda, M., "Rate of Evaporation of Water by Forced Convection," *J. Appl. Phys. Japan*, **29**, 443 (1960).
5. Ueda, M., "Rate of Evaporation of Water from a Rotating Disk," *J. Appl. Phys. Japan*, **31**, 492 (1962).
6. Ueda, M., "Measurements of the Gradient of Water Vapour Pressure and the Diffusion Coefficient," *J. Appl. Phys. Japan*, **25**, 144 (1956).

43. An Experimental Study of the Effect of Surface Condensation on the Performance of Compact Heat Exchangers

E. W. JERGER

Department of Mechanical Engineering, University of Notre Dame, Notre Dame, Indiana

AND

F. L. COONAN

U.S. Air Force, Redstone Arsenal, Huntsville, Alabama

ABSTRACT

The heat transfer surfaces of compact finned tube air-conditioning coils were chemically treated to promote filmwise and dropwise surface condensation. Tests were made with a through circulation of air and with the coil as an evaporator in a F-12 vapor compression refrigeration system.

Air velocity through the coil was varied from 150 to 450 fpm, while the air temperature was held constant at 90°F with varying dew-point temperatures from 58 to 78°F.

Coil capacity (Btu/hour removed from the air) and the rate of condensation (lb/hour removed from the air) were determined with a mass and energy balance for the system.

In general, an increase of condensation rate was observed for the same entering air conditions for the filmwise treated coil and very little advantage was observed for dropwise treatment.

The data was correlated with a heat load ratio of total to sensible heat and the dimensionless Colburn factor for heat transfer.

INTRODUCTION

The overall objective of this study is to consider the effect of the mode of surface condensation on the performance of compact finned tube heat exchangers. Since, in general, the project was primarily intended to determine the overall effects on coil performance; no attempt is made to establish the theoretical mechanism of either condensation formation or heat transfer through the condensate film.

In order to separate the total heat transfer into sensible and latent heat transferred, the rate of condensation was measured directly. Accordingly:

$$q_l = Wh_{fg} \qquad (1)$$

where h_{fg} was taken at the dew-point temperature of the air mixture. Then:

$$q_s = q_T - q_l \qquad (2)$$

Baker and Beatty[1] report a temperature drop through the condensate film on a finned tube coil to be on the order of 0.5 to 0.8°F. Since this difference is small, the assumption is made that the coil surface temperature and condensate layer temperature are equal. In this case:

$$q_T = h_T A_e (T_1 - T_3) \qquad (3)$$

The air temperature varies continuously across the coil so some mean temperature must be defined to represent adequately a mean air side temperature. This air temperature (T_1) was taken as the arithmetic mean of the entering and leaving air dry-bulb tempera-

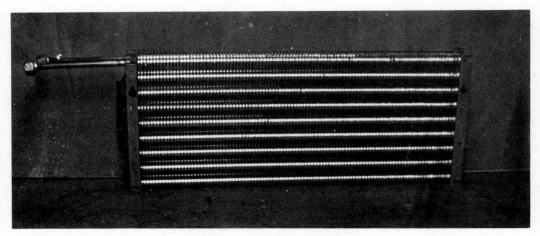

FIG. 1. Finned tube heat exchanger.

tures. Similarly, the surface temperature (T_3) was an arithmetic mean based on several measurements. However, since the refrigerant was evaporated at a constant pressure with only a few degrees of superheating, little tube surface temperature variation was observed. The entire surface area of the coil, however, cannot be considered to be at the surface temperature defined, because the fin temperature changes outward from the tube wall. This problem is resolved by adjusting the actual surface area to an effective area considered to be at a uniform temperature equal to the tube surface area. Schneider[2] defines a fin efficiency which makes such a modification for the case of a circumferential circular fin. It has been shown by Zabronsky[3] that the rectangular fin (essentially square) may be treated as a circular fin having the same surface area with negligible error. Based on these data and methods, the fin efficiency (η) was determined in each case, and the effective area (A_e) was calculated. Since, the overall heat transfer is used with an effective area and mean temperature difference, h_T must be considered as an average film coefficient for the entire coil.

EXPERIMENTAL PROCEDURE

Coils used in the tests were 9×20 in. nominal face dimension, 2-row, 5 fins/in., aluminum fins on copper tube heat exchangers.

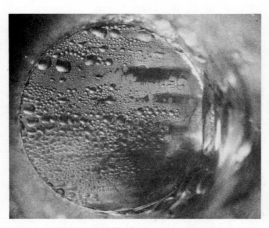

FIG. 2. Photograph of commercially clean fin surface illustrating typically mixed condensation.

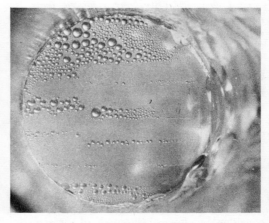

FIG. 3. Photograph of silicone treated fin surface illustrating typically dropwise condensation.

Fig. 4. Photograph of alodine treated fin surface illustrating typically filmwise condensation.

Fin width was 2 in. This coil is commercially available and is shown in Fig. 1. A commercially clean coil was observed to give a general mixed type of condensation as indicated in Fig. 2. By treating the surface of the coil with a solution of 2 per cent concentration of silicone* in heptane, the resultant surface gave the dropwise condensation as illustrated in Fig. 3. Filmwise condensation was obtained after the surface was coated with alodine,** as indicated in Fig. 4. Both treatments were "baked on," and the resultant coil

* Dow Silicone No. 1107.

** Parker Rust Proof Alodine 1200.

surface was not observed to change after some 14 months of testing and handling of the coils.

Figures 3 and 4 are photographs taken of a portion of the fin of a treated coil, and Fig. 2 of the untreated coil, after the surface was completely wetted. In Fig. 4, the entire surface is wet, i.e., it has a large area of very thin film that our photographic technique has failed to bring out clearly.

Prior to treatment, all coils were tested, and capacity and condensation "run off" were established. After treatment, the coils were first evaluated with an extremely low dewpoint air, so that no condensation on the surface occurred. Capacity comparisons of the treated and untreated coils for "dry" operation indicated no significant difference. It was concluded, therefore, that the surface treatment (of a thickness virtually impossible to measure) did not offer any additional resistance to heat flow through the fins.

The coils were tested in an air loop, with the air makeup carefully controlled. Figures 5 and 6 are schematic representations of the environmental synthesis system and coil test section. Air flow through the coil was varied by varying the fan speed and by a test section bypass arrangement. Dew point was maintained with a steam spray, chilled water coil and F-12 direct expansion coil while air temperature was maintained with a steam heating coil or F-12 direct expansion cooling coil. Temperatures were maintained to within $\pm\frac{1}{2}°$F. Air

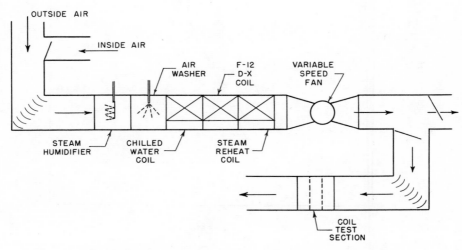

Fig. 5. Environmental synthesis system schematic flow diagram.

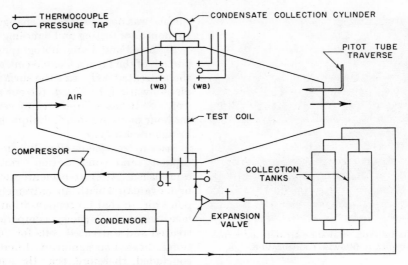

FIG. 6. Test section schematic flow diagram.

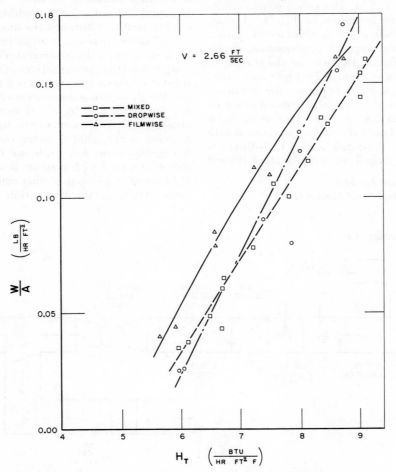

FIG. 7. Effect of rate of condensation on average heat transfer coefficients.

flow measurements were made with a calibrated Pitot tube traverse. Test runs were made with velocities maintained within a range of ± 15 fpm.

The coils were tested for flow rates corresponding to face velocities of 150, 300 and 450 fpm; entering air dew point was varied from 58 to 78°F, while all runs were made at an entering dry-bulb temperature of 90°F.

Each coil studied was used as an evaporator in a F-12 vapor compression refrigeration system. The capacity (q_T) of the coil was calculated from an energy balance made on the refrigerant side of the system. Refrigerant flow was established with calibrated cylinders, and the pressure and temperature of the refrigerant entering and leaving the coil were recorded. In all runs, the superheat temperature of the refrigerant leaving the coil and the suction pressure were held constant. A few degrees of superheating in the refrigerant coil

is necessary in order to accurately determine the enthalpy of the refrigerant leaving the coil.

The condensation "run-off" was collected and measured with a calibrated cylinder.

Coil surface temperatures were measured with thermocouples located at the tube surfaces. Variation of fin surface temperature was considered only in the use of a fin efficiency term to adjust the heat transfer surface area.

CORRELATION OF DATA

Figures 7, 8, 9 show a reasonably linear relationship between the weight of condensate per unit area of heat transfer surface and the average heat transfer film coefficient, for each of the air velocities used. In each case, the filmwise surface condensation data indicated a greater condensation rate than the other two

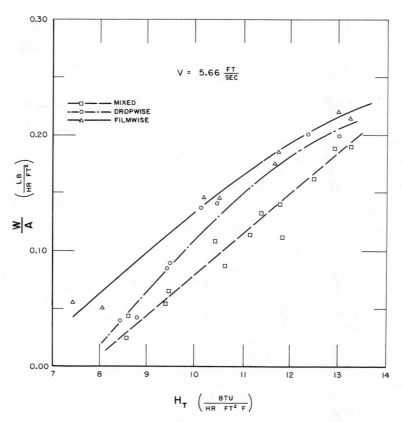

FIG. 8. Effect of rate of condensation on average heat transfer coefficients.

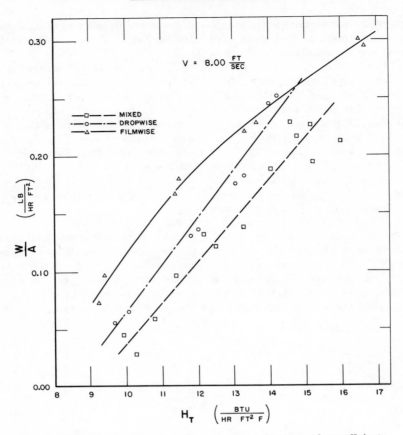

FIG. 9. Effect of rate of condensation on average heat transfer coefficients.

coils for approximately the same entering conditions, and consequently a greater total heat transfer (q_T). The effect also increases with an increase of air velocity through the coil. Figures 7, 8, 9 suggest that the heat transferred is related to the ratio of total heat to sensible heat, which, in fact, has been proposed by Tuve and McKeeman[4] and again demonstrated by Baker and Beatty.[1]

Colburn[5, 6] has suggested a dimensionless parameter (J) for a comparison of heat and mass transfer coefficients. Figure 10 is an attempt to correlate these data with the Colburn number plotted against the heat load ratio (q_T/q_s). A fairly reasonable correlation is observed for a given Reynolds number. Consequently, the J number is a function of both Reynolds number and heat load ratio. Baker and Beatty[1] report this same observation by presenting a similar correlation by using $Re^{0.8}$ instead of the Reynolds number.

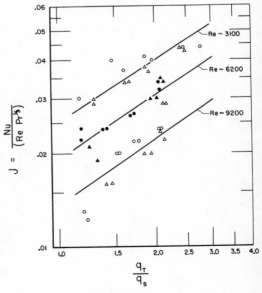

FIG. 10. Correlation of data.

While there appears to be no direct physical justification for it, a complete correlation for the data was found with computer studies to be:

$$J = Nu/RePr^{1/3} = \left(0.0138 - \frac{V}{476}\right)(q_T/q_s)^{0.60}$$

$$(4)$$

Overall inspection of the data indicate an advantage to filmwise condensation for dehumidification applications with an increase in condensation rate over an untreated coil of as high as 20 per cent at usual air-conditioning design conditions. There appears to be little advantage to the dropwise treatment.

NOMENCLATURE

A_1 = Heat transfer surface area of fins (ft²)
A_2 = Heat transfer surface area of tubes (ft²)
A = Heat exchanger total surface area ($A_1 + A_2$) (ft²)
η = Fin efficiency
A_e = Effective area of coil ($A_2 + \eta A_1$)(ft²)
D_e = Equivalent diameter of heat exchangers (ft)
M_a = Air flow (lb dry air/hour)
V = Maximum air velocity through heat exchangers (ft/sec)
q_T = Total heat transferred (Btu/hour)
q_l = Latent heat transferred (Btu/hour)

q_s = Sensible heat transferred (Btu/hour)
h_{fg} = Latent heat of vaporization of water (Btu/lb)
α = Thermal diffusivity of mixture (ft²/hour)
h_T = Average outside surface film coefficient (Btu/hour ft² °F)
ν = Kinematic viscosity of mixture (ft²/hour)
k = Thermal conductivity of mixture (Btu/hour ft °F)
Re = Reynolds number (VD_e/ν)
Pr = Prandtl number (ν/α)
Nu = Nusselt number ($h_T D_e/k$)
J = Colburn number ($Nu/RePr^{1/3}$)
W = Condensate flow rate (lb/hour)
T_1 = Air temperature through coil (°F)
T_3 = Average coil outside surface temperature (°F)

References

1. Baker, B. L., and Beatty, K. O., "Cooling and Dehumidification of Gases—Inside and Outside of Tubes," in "International Developments in Heat Transfer," ASME, Part IV, Sept. 1961.
2. Schneider, P. J., "Conduction Heat Transfer," Cambridge, Mass., Addison Wesley Publishing Co., 1955.
3. Zabronsky, H., "Temperature Distribution and Efficiency of a Heat Exchanger Using Square Fins on Round Tubes," *J. Appl. Mech.*, **22** (March 1955).
4. Tuve, G. L., and McKeeman, C. A., *HPAC*, **9** (1937).
5. Colburn, *A.I.Ch.E., Trans.*, **29** (1933).
6. Chilton and Colburn, *A.I.Ch.E., Trans.*, **26** (1934).

44. Dehumidification of Air over a Flat Plate and in a Plate-fin Heat Exchanger at Intermediate Reynolds Numbers

Suhas P. Sukhatme* and John C. Chato†

Massachusetts Institute of Technology, Cambridge, Massachusetts

ABSTRACT

The usual methods of determining the heat transfer coefficients for dehumidifying equipment require that wet tests be performed. This is a basically correct procedure, since condensation alters the conditions at the heat transfer surface. Analysis of the process of moisture removal from air, however, indicates that an intermediate range of flows could exist where the disturbance caused by the condensation is negligible. In such a regime the sensible heat transfer coefficient would remain essentially the same as that obtained from dry runs. The total heat transfer, of course, would be greater during dehumidification. Qualitatively, such a regime would occur above the very slow flow rates where the condensate is not carried away and can build up into a thick layer, but below such high flow rates where the condensate layer becomes extremely wavy and starts to tear off. In other words, if the condensate forms a relatively smooth layer on the cooling surface and if the film thickness is small compared to the channel dimensions, then the sensible heat transfer could remain essentially unchanged.

The existence of such regimes was proven experimentally over a flat plate and, by inference, in a plate-fin heat exchanger.

A series of experiments was conducted by dehumidifying air on top of an isothermal flat plate, which was cooled by chilled water. It was found that in the length-Reynolds number range of about 3×10^4 to 4×10^5, the sensible heat transfer coefficient was, indeed, the same for both dry and wet runs, provided the air boundary layer was turbulent.

Another series of experiments was performed with a plate-fin type heat exchanger, which was also cooled by chilled water. In order to predict the results, it was assumed that as the air entered the narrow passages of a plate-fin heat exchanger, it was first cooled to its dew point, then it followed the saturation line during dehumidification. The results showed that in the Reynolds number range of about 500 to 1200, which encompasses the usual operating conditions for such a heat exchanger, the predicted condition of the air leaving the heat exchanger agreed very closely with the measured condition. It was noted, however, that the friction factors did increase when dehumidification occurred.

INTRODUCTION

The performance of dehumidifying coils has hitherto been predicted in several ways. Goodman[1, 2] used the analogy between heat and mass transfer to integrate the equations for differential heat transfer. His method is based on the principal assumptions that the Lewis number for humid air is unity, that the relationship between the temperature and the enthalpy of saturation can be expressed in a linear form at each temperature, and that the heat transfer surface temperature is the same on both sides, i.e., the coil is made of a good

* Now with Dynatech Corp., Cambridge, Massachusetts.

† Now with University of Illinois, Urbana, Illinois.

conductor. The method is restricted to direct expansion coils with constant refrigerant temperature and to counter flow coils. Tuve and Seigel[3, 4] developed the Humidity Method. This is based on the good approximation that with dehumidification, the locus on the psychrometric chart of the exit air conditions for a heat exchanger, operating with decreasing surface temperature and constant condition of the entering air, coincides very closely with a line of constant relative humidity. Another method is to simply determine experimentally the characteristic *j*-curves for heat and mass transfer for any given configuration.[5]

All these methods either require or recommend that some wet tests be run when determining the performance of a particular heat exchanger. The necessity for these arises from the fact that the condensation changes the physical and heat transfer characteristics of a surface. Yet it seems possible that under certain circumstances such changes would have only negligible effects. Under such conditions, the wet performance of a heat exchanger can be predicted satisfactorily from dry tests alone. The purpose of this investigation was to determine what the conditions are under which dry tests are sufficient to determine both dry and wet performance of a heat exchanger.

THE EFFECTS OF CONDENSATION

Condensation affects both the flow of the moist air stream and the conditions at the walls. The first question to answer is where condensation actually takes place. If the mass transfer towards the wall is fast enough (relative to the heat transfer) to keep the local concentration level below that corresponding to saturation everywhere except at the wall, then condensation occurs only at the wall and no fogging takes place in the main stream. If the analogy between heat and mass transfer is employed, the relative "speed" of heat and mass flows may be expressed in terms of the ratio of Schmidt and Prandtl numbers. If this ratio is less than one, the heat transfer is relatively slow, and consequently all condensation occurs at the walls. This is indeed the case for air and water vapor mixtures in the usual regimes of applications.

Even if there is no condensation in the air, the diffusion of the water vapor towards the wall will affect the sensible heat transfer. The magnitude of this effect can be estimated by using the results obtained for heat transfer to ablating surfaces.[6] For the extreme case of 150°F saturated air being cooled and dehumidified to saturated condition at 50°F, this predicted effect is of the order of 1.5 per cent. Consequently, it may be assumed that the diffusion of water vapor does not significantly alter the sensible heat transfer rates within the operating range considered.

Depending on surface conditions the condensation on the walls can be either film-wise, drop-wise, or a mixture of both. At low air velocities, the orientation of the walls is important since on a vertical surface the liquid will run down, while on a horizontal one it will tend to collect into a relatively thick layer which will have to be moved by the gas alone. If the condensate can become thick in comparison to the air channel dimensions, then the liquid will seriously interfere with the air flow. In such a case the entire flow pattern, together with the heat transfer, will be altered by the condensation.

As the air velocity is increased, gravity becomes less important. The shear force exerted by the air stream drags the liquid film along and reduces its thickness. If the liquid quantities condensed are relatively small, which is the case for air and water vapor mixtures at ordinary temperatures, the condensed film remains thin in comparison to the channel dimensions and its surface is relatively smooth. Under such circumstances, it can be expected that the sensible heat transfer coefficient is not significantly influenced by the presence of condensation. This then, is the regime under investigation in this paper. For drop-wise condensation such a regime must be either extremely limited or possibly non-existent.

As the air velocity is further increased, the condensate film surface first becomes wavy, then, at even higher velocities, it breaks up and liquid droplets are entrained in the air stream. In this range, the condensation again significantly alters the heat transfer mechanism.

The preceding considerations indicate that there is a regime within which condensation occurring at the cooled boundaries does not significantly affect the sensible heat transfer coefficients. The existence of this regime, however, had to be proven experimentally also. For this purpose, the simple geometry of a horizontal flat plate was chosen. If such a regime was found to exist here, it could be assumed that it existed also in the case of heat exchangers with favorable geometries.

ANALYSIS OF THE PERFORMANCE OF A DEHUMIDIFYING HEAT EXCHANGER*

The intermediate Reynolds numbers at which the condensate on the surfaces forms a thin, smooth layer which does not significantly alter the sensible heat transfer characteristics, are likely to occur in the relatively narrow and long passages of a plate-fin heat exchanger. Based on the previous conclusions and on observation of the performance of such a device, the following assumptions can be made:

(1) For air and water vapor mixtures in the usual operating range, all moisture condensation occurs at the walls.

(2) The thermal resistance of the condensate film and the wall is negligible in comparison to that of the air and refrigerant boundary layers.

(3) The velocity of the interface between the condensate film and the air stream is negligible compared to the mean air velocity.

(4) The air entering the heat exchanger quickly becomes saturated. This means that the condition curve for the air moving through a passage can be accurately approximated by an initial sensible cooling to the saturation line, followed by sensible cooling and dehumidification along the saturation line until the air leaves the heat exchanger.

(5) In the operating range considered, the condensation does not significantly influence the sensible heat transfer mechanism. Consequently, heat transfer coefficients obtained from dry tests alone may be used to determine the sensible heat transfer.

From the third assumption, the temperature of the entire condensate film and the wall is the same, i.e.,

* This method was suggested by Dr. L. C. Hoagland, Vice President of Dynatech Corp., Cambridge, Mass.

$$T_i = T_{wa} = T_{wr} \qquad (1)$$

The sensible heat transfer is

$$q_s = h_a A_a (T_{ab} - T_i) = h_a A_a \Delta T_a \qquad (2)$$

The total heat transfer can be expressed in terms of the coolant side.

$$q_t = h_r A_r (T_{wr} - T_r) = h_r A_r \Delta T_r \qquad (3)$$

Both $h_a A_a$ and $h_r A_r$ can be made to include the effects of fins according to the standard methods either by using the concept of fin efficiency or by using experimental heat transfer coefficients which already include such effects.

The total temperature drop can be expressed as

$$\Delta T_t = q_s \left[\frac{1}{h_a A_a} + \frac{q_t/q_s}{h_r A_r} \right] \qquad (4)$$

The overall conductance, $U A_a$, may be defined in terms of the air side sensible heat transfer.

$$\frac{1}{U A_a} = \frac{\Delta T_t}{q_s} = \frac{1}{h_a A_a} + \frac{q_t/q_s}{h_r A_r} \qquad (5)$$

Since by the fourth assumption, the condition curve is known, q_t/q_s may be expressed in terms of the slope of this curve. For a differential small area, the sensible and latent heats can be expressed as follows:

$$dq_s = w_a c_{pa} dT_{ab} \qquad (6)$$

$$dq_l = w_a h_{fg} d\overline{w} \qquad (7)$$

Therefore,

$$\frac{dq_t}{dq_s} = 1 + \frac{h_{fg}}{c_{pa}} \cdot \frac{d\overline{w}}{dT_{ab}} \qquad (8)$$

Following the assumed condition curve, $d\overline{w}/dT_{ab} = 0$ and, correspondingly, $q_t/q_s = 1$ until the saturation line is reached. Afterwards $d\overline{w}/dT_{ab} =$ slope of the saturation line. This slope may be approximated by straight line segments. For the usual operating conditions, not more than two of these straight line approximations should be necessary. For a given mean value of $d\overline{w}/dT_{ab}$, Eq. (8) yields the corresponding mean value of q_t/q_s. This in turn can be used in Eq. (5) to determine the condition of the air leaving the corresponding section of the heat exchanger, either by the log mean temperature difference or the

Number of Transfer Units (NTU) techniques. For these calculations, a preliminary estimate of the exit air and coolant temperatures is required in order to determine the properties of the fluids and hence their Reynolds numbers. Fortunately, the solution is very insensitive to variations in this estimate and a deviation of $\pm 5°F$ from the true mean temperature can easily be allowed.

The advantage of this method of predicting performance in comparison to the Goodman technique, is its validity for any form of flow (i.e., parallel, counter, or cross flow) with a varying coolant temperature.

EXPERIMENTAL WORK

Description of the Apparatus

The overall setup is shown in Fig. 1. Air was circulated through the duct system by a fan driven by a variable speed DC motor. The air leaving the fan was brought to the desired conditions by two variable-input electric heaters and a steam-injection humidifier located between them. The conditioned air passed through mixers and straighteners before entering the test section which was the only part of the system that had to be altered for the two types of experiments. The air returned to the fan suction through a mixing section where the ratio of the recirculated to the fresh air could be controlled by a hand-operated damper.

Test Section for the Flat Plate

A wire-mesh screen was located in front of the test section to assure uniform air velocity. The test section had transparent side walls for visual observations.

The cooling surface was a horizontal copper plate 36 in. × 7 in. × $\frac{1}{4}$ in. Its leading edge was machined to a knife edge, which jutted into the flow about an inch above the bottom of the duct. Cooling of the plate was achieved

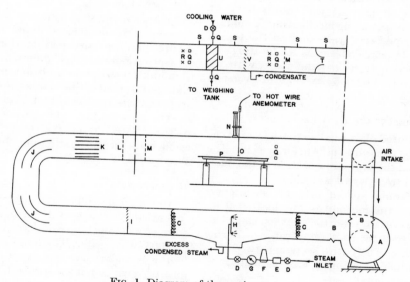

FIG. 1. Diagram of the equipment.

A	Fan	L	Wire mesh screen
B	Flexible connection	M	Perforated plate
C	Heater	N	Probe traversing mechanism
D	Valve	O	Hot wire probe or Pitot tube
E	Filter	P	Flat plate
F	Pressure regulator	Q	Thermocouples
G	Pressure gauge	R	Dew-point probes
H	Steam injectors	S	Pressure tap
I	Mixer	T	Flow measuring nozzle
J	Turning vanes	U	Heat exchanger
K	Straighteners	V	Mixer—water eliminator

by cold tap water flowing through four identical coils connected in parallel on the bottom side of the plate. The water flow rate was maintained at a relatively high value in order to keep the bulk temperature rise below 3°F. Five copper-constantan thermocouples embedded along the center line of the plate measured the surface temperatures. Because of the tapered leading edge, the first cooling coil had to be located about 3 in. from the edge. This arrangement caused the front 2 or 3 inches to heat up about 10°F above the rest of the plate. The magnitude of this temperature rise, however, was not objectionable since the temperature difference between the free stream and the plate was maintained around 100°F. The error involved could be estimated using the analysis of Furber.[7] If it was assumed that the first 2 in. of the plate were at the free stream temperature, the calculated error was at most 2 per cent.

The plate assembly was placed on three screw supports, which were isolated from the duct work to prevent the transmitting of vibration. A traversing mechanism for holding measuring probes was located on the top of the duct. It provided means for locating the probes anywhere above the plate with an accuracy of ±0.0005 in. in the vertical direction.

Test Section for the Heat Exchanger

A perforated plate was located in front of the test section to assure uniform air velocity. The section had the same cross section as the duct, but it had transparent walls.

A uniformly spaced grid of six copper-constantan thermocouples was located 9 in. before and 30 in. after the heat exchanger to measure the mean air temperature entering and leaving. The entire section between the thermocouple locations was insulated to minimize external losses.

The humidity of the air was determined from samples withdrawn near the two thermocouple locations before and after the heat exchanger. These samples were obtained through four-pointed probes located in the air stream. An Alnor Dew Pointer was used for these measurements.

The pressure drop across the heat exchanger was measured by an inclined manometer with a readability of 0.005 in. of water. The taps were located 4 in. before and 11½ in. after the heat exchanger. Although such distances are found in the literature,[8] some error might exist due to the relative proximity of these locations to the heat exchanger.

The heat exchanger used was supplied by the Hamilton Standard Division of the United Aircraft Company. Its specifications are given in Appendix I. The cooling medium was cold water. Its temperature rise was measured directly by two five-junction thermopiles. The water leaving the heat exchanger was mixed by a perforated copper strip inside the header before its temperature was measured. The water flow rate was determined by the weighing method.

A mixer was located downstream of the heat exchanger. This served the dual purpose of mixing the air stream and eliminating condensate drops carried along by the air. The condensate was collected in a container through holes in the bottom of the box. From here the condensate could be removed through a U-shaped air trap.

Another perforated plate was located after the downstream thermocouple location to assure uniform air velocity for the flow measuring nozzle which followed. This spun aluminum nozzle was built according to the National Bureau of Standards elliptical nozzle specifications, with a throat diameter of 4½ in. The pressure taps were located, according to the ASME Power Test Code.[9] Discharge coefficients for the nozzle were obtained from Wile's work.[10]

Measurements

Above the flat plate, the air velocity of the free stream was measured by a pitot tube using a micromanometer with an accuracy of ±.0005 in. of water. The temperature profile in the boundary layer above the plate was measured with a hot wire probe. This measurement was accurate to ±0.5°F. A new technique (see Appendix II) was developed, which increases the measuring sensitivity to such an extent that only a standard milliammeter and a standard millivoltmeter are necessary. Since this method of measuring temperatures is much simpler and subject to less error than the standard hot wire method for measuring velocities, within the boundary layer only the temperature profile was determined. Based on the experimental evidence of others,[11,12] it was assumed that the dimensionless velocity and temperature profiles were similar.

The accuracy of the EMF measurements for the thermocouples located before and after the heat exchanger was about ± 2 μV. This corresponds to about 0.1°F. The estimated maximum errors in the flow rate measurements were ± 1 per cent for air and 0.1 lb/min. (approximately .03 per cent of the minimum flow rate) for water. The Alnor Dew Pointer was capable of giving dew points within ± 0.5°F. It had the one limitation of not being able to measure dew points above room temperature. In such cases, the dew point was determined from the latent heat load, which was calculated by deducting the sensible heat loss from the total heat gained by the water. This was considered to be a reliable method because the heat balances always agreed to within 3 per cent.

Experiments with the Flat Plate

A few dry tests with a smooth leading edge were performed to determine the range of Reynolds numbers where transition from laminar to turbulent boundary layer occurred. For further experimentation, the leading edge was roughened to insure the formation of turbulent boundary layers from the start.

First a series of three dry tests were conducted at free stream velocities of 6.7, 12.0, and 21.0 fps. The temperature profiles at 11, 21, and 31 in. from the leading edge were measured. From these data, the heat transfer coefficients were calculated.

An identical series of three wet tests were conducted with the nearly saturated free stream air temperature around 150°F and the plate around 40°F.

Experiments with the Heat Exchanger

A series of dry tests were conducted first in order to obtain the "dry" heat transfer coefficients. Entering air temperature was varied from 60 to 120°F; air flow rate from 17 to 32 lb/min., corresponding to a variation in Reynolds number from 630 to 1200.

The wet tests were run approximately in the same Reynolds number range as the dry ones. The ratios of sensible to latent heats were varied between 0.5 and 2. The range of inlet air temperatures was from 75 to 120°F and the range of inlet dew points from 60 to 90°F. Visual observations were made during all these experiments.

Results with the Flat Plate

A set of typical measured temperature profiles for one particular run are shown in Fig. 2. From such temperature profiles, the average Stanton numbers were calculated

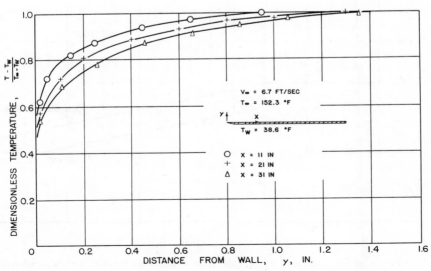

FIG. 2. Typical measured temperature profiles over the flat plate.

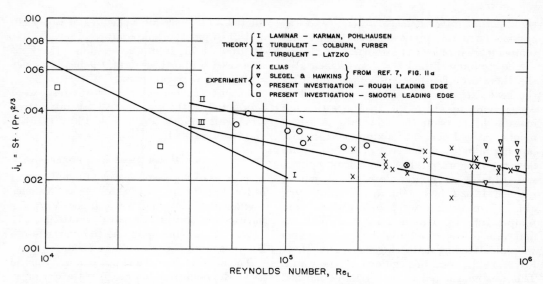

FIG. 3. Theoretical and experimental results for heat transfer to an isothermal flat plate without mass transfer.

from the following equation, which was numerically integrated for each case.

$$St_L = \frac{1}{L} \int_0^\delta \frac{V}{V_\infty} \left[1 - \frac{T - T_w}{T_\infty - T_w} \right] dy \quad (9)$$

The results of the dry tests are shown in Fig. 3 together with experimental and theoretical results of other investigators. It can be seen that transition occurs in the length-Reynolds number range of 10^4 to 3×10^4. Since 10^4 was actually the lowest Reynolds number obtainable, there is no data available in the laminar region. In the turbulent regime the results agree well with data of others. All these can be correlated within ± 10 per cent by the following relation.

$$j_L = 0.138 \, (Re_L)^{-0.32} \quad (10)$$

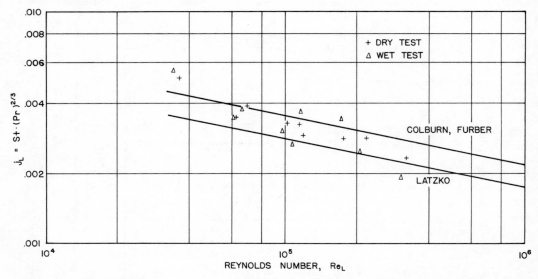

FIG. 4. Comparison of the average dimensionless heat transfer coefficients with and without condensation over a flat plate.

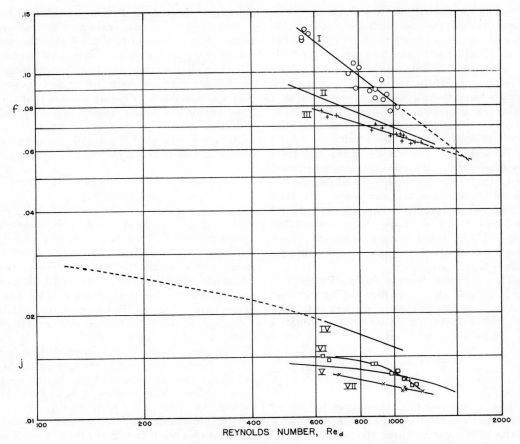

FIG. 5. Friction factors (f) and dimensionless heat transfer coefficients (j) for the plate-fin heat exchanger.

f curves for air side	j curves
I. Wet tests	Coolant side
II. Supplied by Hamilton Standard	IV. Supplied by Hamilton Standard
III. Dry tests	Air side
	V. Supplied by Hamilton Standard
	VI. Dry tests, $\Delta T_a = 13°F - 18°F$
	VII. Dry tests, $\Delta T_a = 5°F - 7°F$

In the wet tests, film condensation was obtained if the surface was well cleaned. However, considerable difficulty was experienced in obtaining a continuously joined film, largely because the rate of condensation was always relatively small. Ripples were observed only at the highest velocities of about 20 fps. This value and the observed appearance of the wavy film surface is in agreement with the report of Van Rossum.[13] The maximum velocity of the liquid was measured to be approximately 0.01 fps, and the maximum condensate film thickness

was found to be approximately 0.015 in.

Figure 4 shows a comparison of the experimentally obtained sensible heat transfer coefficients for both dry and wet tests. Within the experimental scatter, the Reynolds number dependence is identical for both. The range where such correspondence is expected to hold is about from 3×10^4 to 4×10^5.

Results with the Heat Exchanger

In calculating the heat transfer coefficients for the dry tests, the method of Smith[14] was used in conjunction with the coolant side *j*-curve supplied with the heat exchanger. The measured heat transfer coefficients and friction factors are shown in Fig. 5, together with the data supplied with the heat exchanger. The *j*-curves were found to be dependent on the mean temperature difference between the surface and the air stream. Since property values were calculated consistently at the average bulk temperature, this variation in the *j*-curves does not affect the results.

Table 1 gives the results of the wet tests together with the predictions calculated according to the method outlined previously, using the dry heat transfer coefficients. The maximum differences between the predicted and measured exit temperatures are $+2.0°F$ and $-1.6°F$. These deviations are extremely small in comparison with the overall temperature differences.

The measured friction factors for the wet tests are also shown in Fig. 5. The wet test data are consistently above the dry data. The two friction factor curves can be approximated by the following relations.

$$f_1 = 0.53 \, (Re_d)^{-0.3} \qquad (11)$$

$$f_2 = 20.5 \, (Re_d)^{-0.8} \qquad (12)$$

The Reynolds number range for these investigations was from 550 to 1200. The exact limits of the range where the basic assumptions hold cannot be ascertained. However,

since the two worst predictions occurred at the lowest Reynolds numbers and the friction factor curves intersect at about 1500, it seems reasonable that the range 500 to 1200 corresponds also to the range where dry heat transfer coefficients may be used for predicting wet performance. Another requirement is that the bulk air should follow closely the assumed condition curve. In general, compact heat exchangers with an L/d ratio of the order of 50 should satisfy this requirement.

CONCLUSIONS

It was shown that when condensation occurs from humid air flowing over a cooled, flat plate, there exists a Reynolds number range within which the heat transfer coefficients obtained from dry tests may be used to predict the sensible heat transfer when condensation occurs. The expected length Reynolds numbers for this regime range between 3×10^4 and 4×10^5.

A method was developed for predicting the wet performance of heat exchangers with the aid of the heat transfer coefficients obtained from dry runs. This method is valid for heat exchangers, such as the plate-fin type, where the air side length-diameter ratio is large and the Reynolds number is in the range from 500 to 1200.

TABLE 1

Test No.	Air Flow Rate (lb/min.)	Re_a	f_a	Inlet Temperature (°F)	Inlet Dew Point (°F)	Measured Exit Temperature (°F)	Measured Exit Dew Point (°F)	Predicted Exit Temperature (°F)	(Predicted Exit Temp) − (Measured Exit Temperature)
1	15.60	580	0.129	85.4	71.0	46.2	45.8	45.6	−0.6
2	21.62	805	0.103	77.9	58.2	43.4	42.8	43.1	−0.3
3	24.98	930	0.095	79.8	65.0	45.2	44.5	43.8	−1.4
4	27.98	1030	0.079	86.8	61.7	50.0	48.3	50.2	+0.2
5	15.33	555	0.124	113.5	72.0	48.4	48.1	49.4	+1.0
6	21.80	785	0.090	117.2	68.3	52.1	51.2	53.1	+1.0
7	24.80	890	0.084	119.4	73.4	55.9	54.6	55.9	+0.0
8	27.26	980	0.077	114.6	68.5	55.3	53.9	56.0	+0.7
9	15.30	565	0.133	87.3	82.7	49.0	48.3	50.7	+1.7
10	21.18	775	0.106	91.2	84.4	54.7	53.0	54.4	−0.3
11	24.64	895	0.089	95.7	90.0	60.8	60.6	59.8	−1.0
12	26.40	960	0.086	95.7	88.8	61.7	—	60.1	−1.6
13	15.36	555	0.126	113.9	83.8	51.4	50.3	53.4	+2.0
14	20.86	748	0.099	116.2	87.3	58.4	57.3	59.9	+1.5
15	24.08	860	0.088	115.6	90.0	63.0	—	62.8	−0.2
16	26.26	940	0.083	115.1	89.7	64.6	—	64.3	−0.3

LIST OF SYMBOLS

A = Heat transfer area
c_p = Specific heat
d = Tube diameter (or equivalent diameter)
e = Voltage across hot wire
f = Fanning friction factor, $(d/2L)(\Delta p \, g_0 \, \rho/G^2)$
g_0 = Conversion factor = 32.2 lbm ft/lbf sec^2
G = Mass velocity
h = Heat transfer coefficient
h_{fg} = Latent heat of vaporization
i = Current through hot wire
j = Nondimensional heat transfer coefficient, $St \, Pr^{2/3}$
L = Length of tube or passage
Pr = Prandtl number
Δp = Pressure drop across heat exchanger
q = Heat transfer rate
R = Hot wire resistance
Re_L = Reynolds number based on a characteristic length L
Re_d = Reynolds number based on equivalent diameter of passage.
St = Stanton number, $h/\rho V_\infty c_p$ for flat plate; $h/G c_p$ for heat exchanger
T = Temperature
U = Overall heat transfer coefficient
V = Velocity
w = Flow rate
$\bar{w}$ = Specific humidity of air-water vapor mixture
x = Distance along flat plate
y = Distance from plate surface
ρ = Density
δ = Boundary layer thickness

Subscripts

a = Air side
ab = Air side bulk value
i = Interface between air and condensate film
L = Average value over a length L
r = Refrigerant side
s = Sensible heat
t = Total (sensible and latent) heat
w = Wall
∞ = Free stream value (in the case of flat plate)
0 = Steady-state value
1 = Dry tests
2 = Wet tests

Acknowledgments. The work described in this paper was supported by the Hamilton Standard Division of United Aircraft Corporation. Thanks are due to Professors W. M. Rohsenow and A. L. Hesselschwerdt, Jr., of M.I.T., Professor R. J. Nickerson of Stevens Institute of Technology (previously at M.I.T.), and Dr. L. C. Hoagland of Dynatech Corporation for their help during various phases of the work.

References

1. Goodman, W., "Dehumidification of Air with Coils," *Refrig. Eng.*, **32**, 225 (1936).
2. Goodman, W., "Performance of Coils for Dehumidifying Air," *Heating, Piping Air Conditioning*, **10** (1938); **11** (1939).
3. Tuve, G. L., and Seigel, L. G., "Performance of Surface-Coil Dehumidifiers for Comfort Air Conditioning," *Trans. ASHVE*, **44**, 523 (1938).
4. Seigel, L. G., "Air Cooling Coil Problems and Their Solutions," *Trans. ASHVE*, **51**, 165 (1945).
5. Bryan, W. L., "Heat and Mass Transfer in Dehumidifying Extended Surface Coils," *ASHRAE J.*, **4**, 60 (1962).
6. Hidalgo, H., "A Theory of Ablation of Glassy Materials for Laminar and Turbulent Heating," *AVCO-Everett Research Laboratory Report No. 62*, 1959.
7. Furber, B. N., "Some Heat and Mass Transfer Experiments on Humid Air in Turbulent Flow Over a Plane Containing an Isolated Cooled Region," *Proc. Inst. Mech. Engrs.*, **168**, 847 (1954).
8. Kays, W. M., and London, A. L., "Heat Transfer and Flow Friction Characteristics of Some Compact Heat Exchanger Surfaces," *Trans. ASME*, **72**, 1075 (1950).
9. ASME Power Test Codes, Supplement, Chap. 4, Flow Measurement, 1959.
10. Wile, D. D., "Air Flow Measurement in the Laboratory," *Refrig. Eng.*, **53**, 515 (1947).
11. Hardy, J. K., and Mann, G., "The Condensation of Water on Refrigerated Surfaces," *DSIR Special Report No. 54*, Great Britain, 1951.
12. Elias, F., "The Transference of Heat from a Hot Plate to an Air Stream," *NACA Technical Memo. No. 614*, 1930.
13. Van Rossum, J. J., "Experimental Investigation of Horizontal Liquid Films," *Chem. Eng. Sci.*, **11**, 35 (1959).
14. Smith, D. M., "Mean Temperature Difference in Cross Flow," *Engineering*, **138**, 479 (1934).

APPENDIX I

Specifications of Plate-Fin Heat Exchanger Tested
Type: Cross flow
Air side: Herringbone, 18 fpi, 0.426 in. wide, thickness of fin 0.005 in.
Refrigerant side: $\frac{1}{16}$-in. serration, 8 fpi, 0.150 in. wide, thickness of fin 0.005 in.
Dimensions of heat exchanger: 9 in. × 7⅝ in. × 4⅜ in.
Heat transfer area on air side: $A_a = 61.3$ sq ft.
Heat transfer area on refrigerant side: $A_r = 15.29$ sq ft.
Free flow area for air: 40.5 sq in.
Average free flow area for refrigerant: 6.08 sq in.
Equivalent diameter of smallest passage on air side: 0.091 in.
Equivalent diameter of smallest passage on refrigerant side: 0.133 in.

APPENDIX II

Temperature Measurement Technique

In normal use, the hot wire probe is used as a "resistance thermometer" for measuring temperature. The technique adopted is to use a certain constant current and measure the voltage across the wire. It is a requirement here that the magnitude of the current be sufficiently low, so that the rise of temperature of the wire due to passage of the current is negligibly small.

In the present case, it was necessary to measure temperatures from about 50 to 160°F to a minimum accuracy of ±0.5°F. With a W-5 tungsten hot wire (diameter 0.0005 in.; resistance 0.7 Ω approx.; recommended current for no heating 3 mA) the sensitivity is 0.006 mV/°F.

Therefore, it was required to measure the voltage to an accuracy of ±3 μV and to be able to maintain the current constant within approximately ±3 μA (±0.1 per cent of its absolute value). Although this is experimentally possible, it was clear that a method involving measurements in millivolts and milliamps rather than microvolts and microamps would be useful and would require simpler instrumentation.

Consider a hot wire placed in a steady constant property flow in a region where the velocity and temperature are V and T respectively. Then, if radiation effects are negligible, the following equation relates the electrical power input to the wire to the heat dissipated:

$$i \cdot e = (T_0 - T) \cdot \text{function } (V)$$
$$= (T_0 - T) \cdot f(V) \tag{13}$$

where $f(V)$ is of the form $c_1 + c_2 V^n$ where $n \cong 0.5$. Also assuming a linear dependence between the temperature (T_0) of the wire and its resistance (R_0) yields:

$$R_0 = a + bT_0 \tag{14}$$

$$e = i(a + bT_0) \tag{15}$$

where a and b are constants.

Therefore,

$$T_0 = \frac{1}{b}\left(\frac{e}{i} - a\right) \tag{16}$$

Substituting this into Eq. (13) and rearranging the results, we obtain

$$e = \frac{i(a/b + T)}{1/b - i^2/f(V)} \tag{17}$$

The following qualitative observations can be made from Eq. (17):

(1) For fixed values of i and V, there exists a linear relation between the voltage e and the temperature T which is to be measured.

(2) When i is sufficiently small $1/b \gg i^2/f(V)$ and $T_0 = T$. Then $e = i(a + bT_0)$. Hence, the "resistance thermometer" application is a limiting case of Eq. (17).

(3) For a fixed value of V, the slope of the $e - T$ line increases (greater sensitivity) with increasing i.

(4) For a fixed value of i, the slope of the $e - T$ line decreases (lesser sensitivity) with increasing V.

The plot in Fig. 6 for a W-5 hot wire ($i = 35, 105, 155$ mA and V varying from 6 to 20 fps in each case) shows each of the above observations to be true.

The plot for $i = 155$ mA was used for the measurements in this report. At this value of current (which is close to the maximum safe value for the wire), the slope of the $e - T$ line is approximately 50 times that

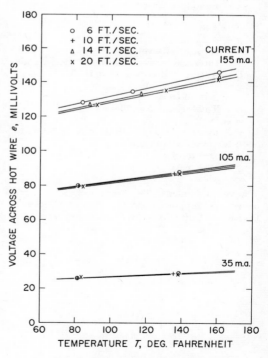

FIG. 6. Hot wire characteristics.

for $i = 3$ mA, the recommended value for no wire heating. Now, the sensitivity is 0.25 mV/°F. A milliammeter and millivoltmeter reading accurate to ± 0.1 mA and ± 0.1 mV respectively have yielded the required accuracy of measurement.

Also the velocity dependence decreases with decreasing current. Consequently, in a fairly uniform velocity field, a single straight line calibration for the maximum allowable current is satisfactory. However, in a strongly varying velocity field a lower value of the current may be preferable to strike a balance between increased sensitivity and increased dependence on velocity.

45. Chemical Dehumidification for Comfort Air-conditioning Systems

Will K. Brown, Jr.,* and John S. Hickman

Inland Steel Products Co., Milwaukee, Wisconsin

AND

Merl Baker*

The University of Missouri at Rolla, Rolla, Missouri

ABSTRACT

Liquid chemical air conditioners for building latent load control can be economically applied to comfort systems.

In comparison to conventional systems, the chemical air conditioner has these advantages:

(1) It will eliminate all wet coils in a system and thereby avoid the problems due to biological growth common in a conventional system.

(2) It will permit independent latent and sensible load control thereby eliminating costly reheat or bypass control.

(3) It is cheaper to operate because of a reduction in electrical demand and energy charges. The use of steam for regeneration is less costly than the electrical energy which would otherwise be required for mechanical refrigeration.

INTRODUCTION

The use of liquid chemical air conditioners for building latent load control can be one of the largest single factors which will revolutionize air-conditioning systems and technology. The present paper is intended to illustrate its advantages and show how the concepts can be economically applied to comfort systems.

* Formerly University of Kentucky, Lexington, Kentucky.

Chemical dehumidification in comfort systems offers many advantages, but in comparison to conventional systems the most significant are these:

(1) Biological control.
(2) Independent load control.
(3) Operating cost savings.

DESCRIPTION OF CHEMICAL DEHUMIDIFIER

To gain full appreciation of these advantages, the operation of a typical unit as illustrated in Fig. 1 will be described. This unit is divided into two basic sections—a conditioner for the removal of moisture and a regenerator to restore the concentration of the absorbent solution.

Moisture in the air passing through the conditioner is absorbed by the hygroscopic solution sprayed into the air stream. This transfer of moisture to the solution takes place by vapor pressure difference, the vapor pressure of the solution being less than that of the air in contact with it. The low vapor pressure of the absorbent solution in the conditioner is maintained by passing cooling tower water through the units' contact coils. This cooling tower water will remove directly the heat of condensation of the absorbed water, the heat of solution, and the regenerator

376

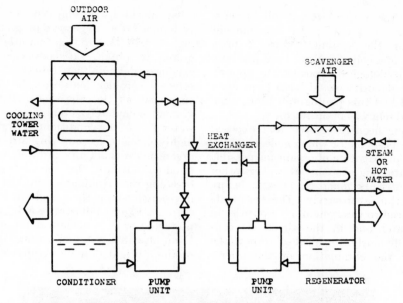

FIG. 1. Diagram of a typical chemical dehumidification unit.

dump back (that is, the additional load imposed on the unit due to concentrated solution returning to the conditioner at a temperature greater than that of the solution in the sump). The moisture removing capacity and the sensible cooling or heating of the air is dependent upon the initial solution concentration, the amount of heat transfer surface, and the quantity and temperature of the cooling tower water.

Generally speaking, only outside air is brought through the conditioner and consequently the entire latent load is handled with this air.

Regeneration is accomplished by heating the solution to a temperature where the vapor pressure of the solution is greater than that of the scavenging air, thereby driving off the moisture absorbed in the conditioner. This process is continuous, and consequently concentrated solution can be fed to the conditioner as required. In fact, control of the unit is achieved by regulating the concentration of the solution in the conditioner receiver in accordance with the amount of dehumidification desired. A dew-point controller located in the building supply air stream senses the humidity load. Economy of operation is improved with the heat exchanger located between the conditioner and regenerator.

SYSTEM ADVANTAGES

Biological Control

The chemical dehumidification unit is capable of combating biological problems which heretofore have been seriously neglected or minimized only by way of costly water treatment and extensive preventive maintenance programs.[1] Biological growth in spray coil dehumidifiers, wet coil dehumidifiers and air washers give rise to many common problems such as:

(a) Lack of cooling due to biological growth imparing heat transfer and restricting air flow on a heat exchanger coil. This biological deposit will continue to grow unless checked by some form of maintenance.[1]

(b) Foul odors which may be produced by the microorganisms in the system. Biological growth on coils is the principle source of these odors.[1]

(c) Corrosion which results from the direct action of the microorganisms themselves or indirectly by hindering the action of corrosion inhibitors added to the water.[1]

(d) Flaking or dusting which results from the accumulation of biological growths which break away from the coil in the supply air system and can eventually clog the various elements of the water circuit.[1] All of these problems are aggravated by intermittent operation of the system. Figure 2 is a photograph of a coil which has been partially clogged with biological deposits. The appearance of the deposits would have been more pronounced had this photograph been taken when the system was in operation.

It has long been recognized that exposed water is the basic factor which makes biological life and propagation of organisms possible in air-conditioning systems. However, other essential nutrients must be present before these living things can survive. These elements are introduced to the system as impurities in makeup water and in the air to be conditioned.[1] Obviously, the ideal solution to the problem is the elimination of the micro-organisms in the system. With a conventional system, a rather expensive program of cleaning, control, and routine maintenance is required to obtain satisfactory results. The chemical dehumidifier however, inherently solves the problem because of the LiCl solution employed as the absorbent. The chemical system completely eliminates all exposed water in the air-conditioning system and is highly efficient in removing airborne microorganisms without the addition of chemicals or odors to the air. Not only are the biological breeding sites eliminated, but the number of microorganisms in the outside air is drastically reduced. Figure 3 illustrates a dry cooling coil protected with a chemical air conditioner. Even after five years of service, the coil still retains a bright shiny new appearance.

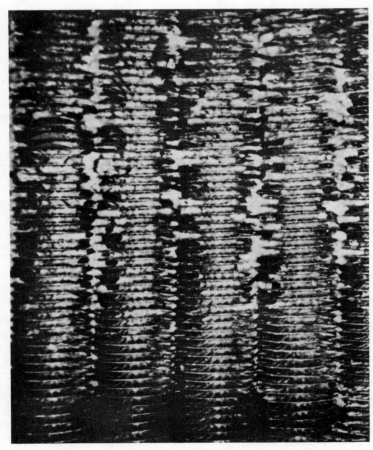

FIG. 2. Photograph showing biological growth on a coil in a conventional wet coil system.

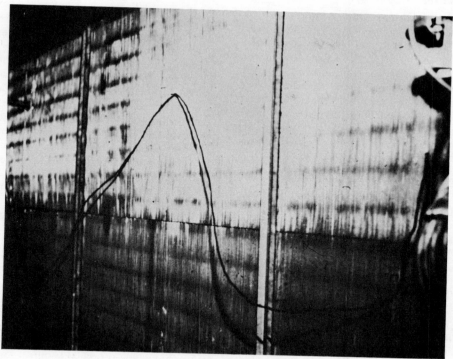

FIG. 3. Photograph of a clean cooling coil protected by a chemical dehumidification unit.

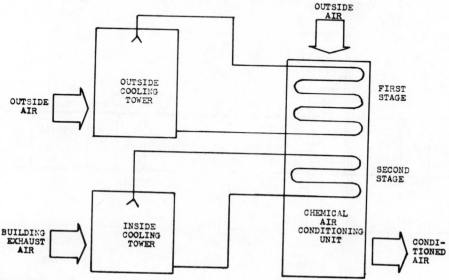

FIG. 4. Modification of basic chemical air conditioner with the second stage contact coil connected to an inside cooling tower.

Load Control

The chemical dehumidifier makes possible complete, independent control of latent and sensible loads which has been most urgently desired since the beginning of environmental control. All moisture is removed by the chemical air conditioner, and therefore every other central or terminal heat exchanger device operates dry. This advantage is most significant during part-load operation as the need for costly reheat or complicated bypass control is eliminated.

Operating Cost Savings

The chemical air conditioner properly applied can result in significant operating cost savings. In general, these savings result because:

(a) The humidity load and regenerator dump back is removed directly with cooling tower water.

(b) The unit is capable of sensible heat removal at other than near design conditions which would involve 85 to 90 per cent of the operating hours during the cooling season.

(c) Use of the chemical dehumidifier permits a reduction in the size of the refrigeration plant of 25 to 50 per cent depending on the ratio of latent to sensible load. This reduction will reduce demand charges in the case of electrically driven refrigerating equipment.

(d) Systems with chemical air conditioning can operate with 50°F chilled water instead of the 40 to 42°F water required with conventional systems. The higher suction pressure means a saving in the cost of electrical energy for refrigeration up to about 13 per cent. Further, since the size of the refrigeration plant is reduced, electrical energy is saved.

(e) Additional cooling capacity can be economically achieved by installing an additional cooling tower in the building exhaust air stream and thereby capitalize on the cooling potential of the relatively low wet-bulb air. For a given unit size, this technique increases the load removing capabilities of the equipment. This modification of the basic unit is illustrated in Fig. 4. Here, the contact coil of the unit is split into two sections, the second stage of which is connected to the inside cooling tower.

Because there are so many factors which affect operating costs, such as utility rates, climate, and the nature and size of a system, it is difficult to predict without an extensive analysis the magnitude or percentage savings for a particular installation. The variable demand and energy charges for each utility service have an appreciable effect on total costs and must be considered. However, a general feeling towards the savings which can be expected can best be illustrated by means of an example.

For purposes of analysis, consider a building

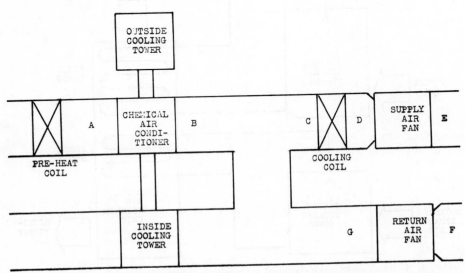

FIG. 5. Schematic diagram of an air handling system employing a chemical air conditioner.

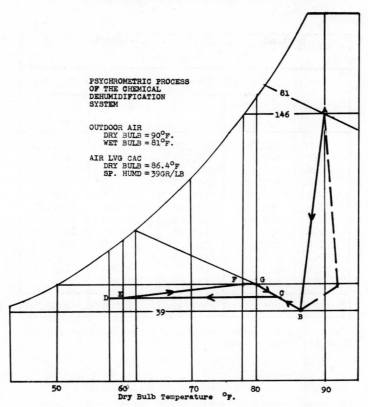

FIG. 6. Psychrometric chart showing the condition of air processed at design conditions for the example building.

100 × 100 ft and 5 floors in height with 25 per cent regular plate glass in the building facade. The wall U factor is .3 Btu/hour/ft²/°F and the roof U factor is .08. The building has an occupancy density of 1 person per 100 sq ft and the internal sensible load is 12.5 Btu/ hour/ft². The environment is maintained between 78°F in the summer to 72°F in the winter with radiant ceiling panels. Supply air introduced at 60°F is dehumidified to maintain a space dew point of 50°F maximum during the summer and 38°F minimum during the winter. The annual operating costs of two systems will be analyzed. These systems are identical in every respect except that one employs a chemical air conditioner and the other achieves moisture control with a conventional wet dehumidifying coil.

Figure 5 illustrates the air handling equipment for the chemical dehumidification system. The condition of air processed at design conditions is plotted on the psychro-

metric chart illustrated in Fig. 6. Note that the design point is characterized by the maximum dew-point condition and the concurrent dry bulb. The end states through the chemical air conditioner are indicated by points A and B, and the effective condition line connects these two points. However, the actual condition curve is shown as a dashed line and illustrates the contribution of the inside tower. The point at which the slope of the line changes is between the first and second stage of the unit.

With the aid of a computer, the cooling and heating loads were computed for the structure located in Houston. These loads are computed on an hourly basis for an average day of each month of the year 1961. A record of outdoor air conditions was obtained from the U.S. Weather Bureau in order to account for the daily and yearly periodic change of outdoor environment.[2] In addition, the computer was programed to calculate the position of the sun as a function of the time of day, time of year

ANNUAL COST OF CONVENTIONAL SYSTEM IN HOUSTON FOR THE YEAR 1961			
MONTH	TOTAL COST OF UTILITY SERVICE--DOLLARS		
	ELECTRIC POWER	GAS	WATER	TOTAL/ MONTH
JAN	438.70	186.95	81.33	706.99
FEB	541.53	172.21	87.87	801.62
MAR	618.62	150.71	92.63	861.97
APR	621.63	146.26	92.92	860.42
MAY	730.89	128.80	99.67	959.37
JUN	785.90	121.66	103.18	1010.75
JUL	800.67	117.58	104.85	1023.11
AUG	788.15	121.38	103.43	1012.97
SEP	770.19	126.27	101.40	997.87
OCT	665.84	146.33	95.71	907.89
NOV	552.34	167.75	88.53	808.63
DEC	511.05	178.02	86.12	775.20
TOTAL	7825.10	1763.92	1137.64	10726.59

Fig. 7. Table of annual operating cost for a conventional system located in Houston, Texas.

ANNUAL COST OF SYSTEM WITH CHEMICAL DEHUMIDIFICATION IN HOUSTON FOR THE YEAR 1961			
MONTH	TOTAL COST OF UTILITY SERVICE--DOLLARS		
	ELECTRIC POWER	GAS	WATER	TOTAL/ MONTH
JAN	413.31	143.26	81.06	637.63
FEB	466.98	160.57	92.64	720.20
MAR	489.39	165.87	97.38	752.65
APR	490.15	160.56	97.60	748.31
MAY	515.79	183.89	104.25	803.94
JUN	509.61	202.06	118.16	829.85
JUL	514.10	209.48	119.85	843.45
AUG	510.12	200.72	118.35	829.20
SEP	494.71	192.73	116.31	803.76
OCT	506.97	177.19	100.39	784.55
NOV	468.80	159.25	93.30	721.35
DEC	452.03	152.82	90.76	695.63
TOTAL	5832.96	2108.40	1230.05	9170.52

$$\text{OPERATING SAVINGS} = \frac{10727 - 9171}{50000} = 3.03\text{¢/SQ FT/ ANNUM}$$

Fig. 8. Table of annual operating cost for the system with chemical dehumidification for the example building located in Houston, Texas.

and latitude. In this way, the solar load can be computed for each building exposure at any time of the year. To obtain realistic cooling loads a solar diversity factor was taken as the ratio of the average daily radiation received on a horizontal plane to the theoretical maximum for each month.

The operation of each system was then simulated on the computer and with the load data determined, the total energy requirements can be computed. The various utility rate schedules for Houston were then applied to obtain the total monthly charges.[3-5] These results are summarized in Figs. 7 and 8.

For this particular system and structure the annual savings amount to $1,556 or $.03/ft². The monthly savings for the chemical air-conditioning system diminish during the winter. This decrease is related to the additional power usage to operate the chemical air-conditioner auxilaries during this period.

These operating costs do not include operating personnel or reflect any savings as a result of reducing the maintenance required over a conventional system.

CONCLUSION

The studies conducted show that even with present day chemical air-conditioning equip-

ment, remarkable advantages and savings can be realized, the most significant being:

(1) Biological control.
(2) Independent load control.
(3) Operating cost savings.

Further research and development will undoubtedly unveil additional savings.

Acknowledgment. The authors wish to express their appreciation to the Air Conditioning and Drying Division of Surface Corporation, Toledo, Ohio, for the use of the performance data on their Kathabar unit and for the photograph of the cooling coil shown in Fig. 3.

The photograph, Fig. 2, showing biological growth on a cooling coil was supplied with the courtesy of the Calgon Corporation.

Gratitude is also extended to the University of Kentucky Computing Center whose facilities were used to run the operating cost analysis.

References

1. Regutti, Carl W., "Problems Caused by Biological Deposits in Air Conditioning Spray Units," *Plant Engineering*, 127–132 (January 1963).
2. U.S. Department of Commerce, Weather Bureau, "Local Climalogical Data (Supplement) for Houston Texas," January–December 1961.
3. Houston Lighting and Power Company, Rate Schedule LGS.
4. Houston Natural Gas Corporation, Rate Sheet.
5. City of Houston, Water and Sewer Rates.

46. Developments in Adsorption Technology and How They Affect the Design of Drying and Dehumidification Equipment

Russell W. Harter

Desomatic Products, Division of Atlantic Research Corporation, Alexandria, Virginia

ABSTRACT

The objective of this presentation is to show how recent developments in adsorption technology aid the designers of drying and dehumidification equipment in establishing more efficient and satisfactory designs.

A description of the adsorption phenomena is presented first, following which the growth of adsorption design information is explained. This description traces the developments in the design thermodynamics from its initial concept to the presently existing technology regarding equilibrium and dynamic desiccant loading. The thermodynamic description is then applied in an example using static equilibrium data, and the analysis is further extended with hypothetical dynamic mass transfer information to develop the design of a desiccant bed.

It is concluded that established adsorption design information is available upon which specific formulations for actual equipment design can be established.

INTRODUCTION

Physical adsorption of liquids on solid desiccants is one of our oldest known methods of removing moisture from gas streams. This technique offers the particular advantage of being able to produce very low dew points (or water concentrations) in gas streams while working over a large temperature range. The problem of moisture freezing is not encountered with this process.

The objective of this presentation is to show how static and dynamic data, as normally obtained from the desiccant manufacturers, can be used in the design of dynamic drying and dehumidification equipment.

BACKGROUND

The following discussion pertains to both the continuous and cyclic desiccant machines. These types of machines require regeneration (or unloading) of the bed prior to an adsorption process. This operating sequence, regeneration, adsorption, regeneration, etc., is necessarily continuous and/or cyclic.

The art of designing desiccant adsorption equipment has gone through considerable change since its beginning and although there is still a long way to go concerning the ultimate in complete design information, we have, at the present time, sufficient data to approach this design work from a more intelligent and scientific view point.

Early designs of desiccant machines were based on very limited information. This usually amounted to only a number describing, for a particular desiccant, the amount of moisture each pound of that desiccant could hold.

This was our beginning, and a good one at that, for it started a thought process, i.e., just what is this adsorption phenomena and what are the logical governing factors? Additional study showed that this capacity of a desiccant was also affected by temperature and relative humidity. Consequently, some initial design rules were established relating useful capacity, temperature, and relative humidity. This was a big step in our science, but although this information was "necessary" it was not "sufficient". Fortunately, at this stage of development, the manufacturers of desiccants came to realize that this adsorption process provided them with a profitable business and that in order to promote this business they would need to supply the designers of adsorption equipment with better design information. They took the complete scientific approach to this concept and studied and defined adsorption as a stable thermodynamic system with finite controlling thermodynamic parameters.

This is where we are today. We have a defined thermodynamic system with information describing the controlling thermodynamic characteristics. This means we understand the magnitude of the problem; unfortunately, there isn't complete test information to cover the full range of the application of this adsorption process and, consequently, we are still designing with incomplete information. However, the information that is available is uniquely sufficient and in other cases where we are lacking information we at least realize the governing trends and the controlling factors.

DISCUSSION OF PHYSICAL ADSORPTION

The adsorption process depends upon:

(1) Desiccant type
(2) Desiccant pore size
(3) Adsorption temperature
(4) Adsorption vapor pressure
(5) Reactivation temperature
(6) Reactivation vapor pressure
(7) Dynamic loading characteristics.

Desiccant Characteristics

Physical adsorption is a surface phenomenon. The exact mechanism of the adsorption process is not fully understood, but certain generalizations about it have been established. One theory on physical adsorption states that the ability of a desiccant to adsorb a liquid (A) is proportional to the relative humidity or vapor pressure of the gas stream $(P_v)/(P_s)$ and

the surface tension (ρ) in the capillaries of the desiccant, i.e.,

$$A = K\rho\left(\frac{P_v}{P_s}\right) \qquad (1)$$

Of course when the vapor pressure of the stream (P_v) matches the vapor pressure of a saturated liquid (P_s) at the particular temperature, the condensation process starts. This, however, is not the case when drying unsaturated streams. At this point the unique characteristic of desiccants helps us out. The extremely tiny capillaries in the desiccant materials exert an additional suppressing force on the gas. This force, which is proportional to the surface tension* characterized by the diameter of the capillary, acts with the equilibrium vapor pressure to increase the suppression force on the kinetic gaseous molecules. The resulting increased force behaves as an increase in vapor pressure to the point where condensation occurs on the inner surface of the capillaries.

Now this suppressing surface tension force is considered to be inversely proportional to the diameter of the capillaries (d), i.e.,

$$\rho \approx 1/d \qquad (2)$$

Therefore, it can be seen that the smaller the capillary, the greater is the adsorption capability of a particular desiccant. (This minimum size, however, is directly related to the molecular size of the adsorbed fluid.)

This is one explanation of "how" and "why" a desiccant performs.

Equilibrium Characteristics

It has been stated that the adsorption and reactivation vapor pressures and temperatures affect the capacity of a desiccant. To clarify this, let it first be said that any desiccant is always in equilibrium with the particular thermodynamic system, the controlling factors being vapor pressure and temperature. That is, any desiccant, when in a system defined by a particular vapor pressure and temperature, will come to an equilibrium loading; i.e., a particular desiccant with a particular pore size will have a defined amount of liquid adsorbed on its surface which is in

---

* This is only one of several theories proposed to explain this adsorption phenomenon.

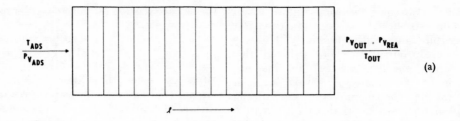

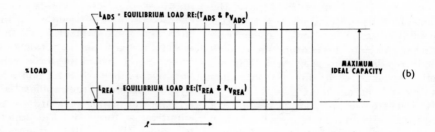

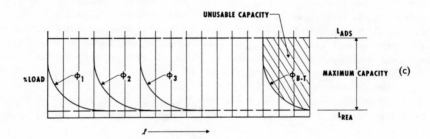

Fig. 1. Equilibrium loading characteristics.

equilibrium in a specific thermodynamic system.

This equilibrium phenomena is a physical fact and applies at all times—prior to adsorption, during adsorption, and during reactivation. Now let's build on this and see what it means.

Figure 1(a) represents a desiccant bed with horizontal flow through it. Figure 1(b) is an equilibrium loading plot for this same bed, the ordinate being per cent loading and the abscissa the bed length. The top horizontal line on Fig. 1(b) (L_{ADS}) represents the equilibrium bed loading under adsorption conditions. That is, in a thermodynamic system characterized by T_{ADS} and $P_{V_{ADS}}$, the temperature and vapor pressure of the adsorbing system, the particular desiccant

will become loaded to the equilibrium capacity (L_{ADS}).

Similarly, the lower horizontal line on Fig. 1(b), (L_{REA}) represents the equilibrium desiccant loading generated by the high temperature and low vapor pressure characterizing the reactivation process.

Both of these loadings (L_{ADS}) and (L_{REA}) are finite and they immediately tell us two things. First and most obvious, the *maximum ideal* capacity of the desiccant is indicated as shown on the Figures. We can't expect any *greater* capacity having once defined the adsorption and reactivation conditions.

The second fact that we determine is the effluent vapor pressure which is the equilibrium vapor pressure in the gas stream as it leaves the bed of desiccant. The equilibrium

loading of a desiccant is defined by a temperature and a vapor pressure, or, conversely, the
equilibrium vapor pressure characterizing a
stream is defined by the temperature of the
stream and the desiccant loading that the
stream is in equilibrium with. Therefore, from
Fig. 1(a) we know the effluent temperature,
and from Fig. 1(b) we know the equilibrium
loading of the desiccant generated during
reactivation. These two, then, rigidly define
the effluent vapor pressure (or dew point) until
the time one or the other is changed.

The author would like to point out that to a
limited degree, this equilibrium information
is available from desiccant manufacturers.

Dynamic Loading Characteristics

The foregoing discussion has described the
method to establish the ideally maximum
loading of a desiccant and the method to
establish effluent vapor pressure. Under
actual loadings in dynamic machines, however, this maximum loading cannot be
obtained. To explain why not, reference will
be made to Fig. 1(c).

The adsorption process is basically a mass
transfer phenomena (i.e., water being transferred from the gas stream to the desiccant)
representing a degree of both physical and
chemical inertia. A quantity of water vapor
in a gas stream must change phase and deposit
as a liquid on the surface of a desiccant. The
time for this mass transfer is in some proportion to the driving forces, i.e., temperature
and vapor pressure differentials. This is a very
complex mechanism and, rather than attempt
to explain it, let us say that it is basically a
residence function and examine its effects from
a design standpoint.

Figure 1(c) shows the hypothetical loading
gradients through the bed at various time
increments (ϕ_i). Visualize that when a wet
stream first comes in contact with a completely reactivated bed, the leading air front
is not instantaneously dried to the equilibrium
effluent condition on the very front edge of the
bed. Rather, since the stream has a finite
velocity and it takes a definite amount of time
to permit this mass transfer, moisture will be
adsorbed in different amounts at different
depths progressing through the bed until the
final equilibrium vapor pressure is established
in the stream. The resulting equilibrium

loading curve or mass transfer front *at a
particular time* is shown as curve ϕ_1 on Fig. 1(c).

The shape of this curve is determined by
many factors—gas velocity (or relative incremental residence time), instantaneous
vapor pressure differentials between the
stream and the bed, relative temperature rise
due to heat of adsorption, and bed geometry.
Mathematically relating these variables can
predict this curve, but this is a terribly complex and involved computation and we, as
designers, are more concerned with the results
than its method of determination. Let us just
suffice to say at this point that it can be done
experimentally and that gas velocity is an
important consideration.

We now have our mass transfer curve
established at some time ϕ_1. As the flow
continues, at some later time ϕ_2, the mass
transfer curve will have progressed to curve
ϕ_2 [Fig. 1(c)]. You will notice that at no time
does the maximum loading of the desiccant
exceed the adsorption equilibrium loading
(i.e., a function of purely T_{ADS} and $P_{v_{\text{ADS}}}$) nor
does the minimum or effluent loading become
less than the equilibrium loading (L_{REA})
established during the previous reactivation
period. This mass transfer curve will continue
to progress through the bed with some
velocity, v_P, until the bottom of the curve and
the reactivation equilibrium loading (L_{REA})
intersect at the leaving edge of the bed. At this
time, $(\phi_{B\text{-}T})$, we have what is called "breakthrough." At any time after this, the equilibrium loading of the leaving edge of the bed
(L_{REA}) will have increased and consequently
our effluent vapor pressure which is in
equilibrium with this (L_{REA}) will also have
increased. Generally, the adsorption period
should end at or prior to this time.

Referring again to Fig. 1(c) you will notice a
shaded area to the right of the final position of
the mass transfer front, $\phi_{B\text{-}T}$. This represents
the unusable portion of the desiccant bed if
breakthrough is not to be exceeded. Consequently, in the design of a bed. the total
capacity (ideal equilibrium capacity) of the
desiccant has to be decreased by this amount.

Sources of Design Information

We have discussed the basic types of information upon which the design of desiccant
machines can be based—equilibrium charac-

teristics and dynamic loading characteristics. The sources of the equilibrium data are the desiccant manufacturers. They present this information in the form shown on Fig. 2.[1] This type of presentation completely defines the equilibrium characteristics of a desiccant under any circumstance—adsorption to reactivation.

As an example, to describe the use of this type of data, assume that a bed of desiccant is reactivated at temperature (1) (i.e., 400°F) using a gas having a vapor pressure (2). This establishes the equilibrium reactivated bed loading at (3) to be 4 per cent. Now, with this residual 4 per cent loading [(3) to (5)] of the bed, suppose a stream of gas at temperature 70°F (4) is passed through the desiccant. Then

up until the time of breakthrough an effluent of −105° dew-point vapor pressure (6) is to be expected.

Extending this analysis further, having first established the minimum loading of the desiccant at (3) or (5), we can use the same approach to determine the maximum loading. That is, knowing our adsorbing stream is at 70°F temperature (4) and vapor pressure (2), we determine the maximum loading to be (7), i.e., about 21 per cent. The ideally maximum useful capacity is, of course, (7) minus (5) or 21 per cent − 4 per cent = 17 per cent.

The determination of the dynamic loading characteristics is more difficult but entirely practical. Experimental techniques are employed for this, and since so many variables

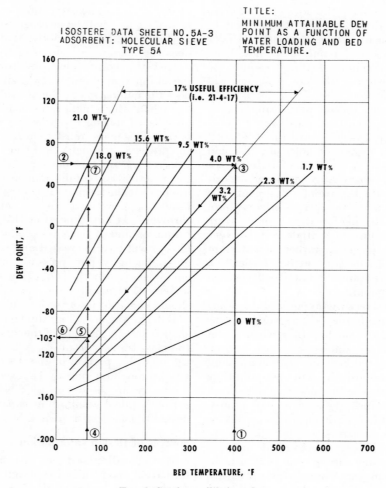

FIG. 2. Static equilibrium data.

have such an appreciable effect on the mass transfer front, only those conditions applying to a particular manufacturer's line of equipment are usually studied.

The basis of this determination is the old "velocity-time-distance" technique, i.e., $L_B = v_P \phi$; where

L_B = the distance traveled through the desiccant bed

v_P = the velocity of propogation of the mass transfer front through the bed, and

ϕ = the time increment.

Data are obtained by taking, at graduated time increments, vapor pressure (dew point) readings of the effluent stream from a desiccant bed which has been properly reactivated. Figure 3 shows a plot of such data for an isothermal system.

First of all you will notice two horizontal lines on the plot representing the equilibrium vapor pressures characterizing both the adsorption and reactivation loadings. Initially, and up to the time (ϕ_2), the effluent stream is in equilibrium with the reactivated equilibrium bed loading. At time ϕ_2 however, the reactivation equilibrium loading of the desiccant is exceeded and breakthrough is reached. Then between times ϕ_2 and ϕ_3 the vapor pressure characteristic of the effluent stream follows the increasing equilibrium loading of the bed and switches from the equilibrium reactivation loading to the equilibrium adsorption loading.

The length, $f_\phi(L_F)$, on Fig. 3 represents the length of the mass transfer front, and the form of the curve itself over this time increment ϕ_2 to ϕ_3 represents the profile of this front. Now referring again to the velocity-time-distance relation, we establish v_P, the velocity of propagation of the transfer front, as

$$v_P = \frac{L_B}{(\phi_2 - \phi_1)} \qquad (3)$$

Having determined this rate at which the transfer front moves through the bed we then can calculate the length of this front (L_F) using the time data of Fig. 3. The length of the mass transfer front is:

$$L_F = v_P(\phi_3 - \phi_2) \qquad (4)$$

Additional information available from this plot are: (a) the completely saturated bed length, $L_D = L_B - L_F$; (b) the maximum adsorption period (ϕ_2); and (c) a measure of the unusable capacity of the bed (which is the shaded area).

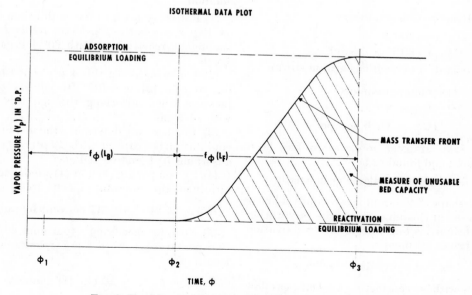

ISOTHERMAL DATA PLOT

FIG. 3. Experimental determination of mass transfer front.

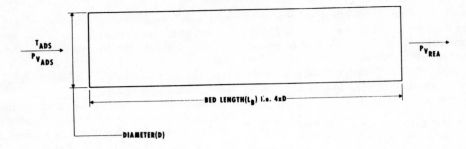

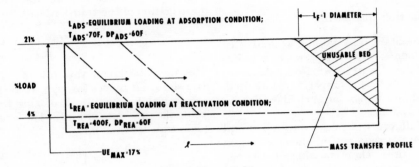

FIG. 4. Type problem.

SUMMARY

It seems that the best way to summarize and clarify what has been presented is to go through the type problem described on Fig. 4. Assume

(a) Reactivation conditions

$T_{REA} = 400°F$

$P_{v_{REA}} = 60°F$ dew point

Coolant = effluent adsorption stream

(b) Adsorption parameters

$T_{ADS} = 70°F$

$P_{v\ DS} = 60°F$ dew point

(c) Mass transfer information has been measured and found to be

$L_F = (1)$ tower diameter in length

The shape of the front is essentially a linear decrease in loading from the adsorption equilibrium loading line to the reactivation equilibrium loading line.

$v_P = 1$ tower diameter/hour

Now without considering a specific gas flow we can establish:

(d) Effluent dew point

(e) Useful capacity of the bed

(f) Adsorption period and bed depth relation.

Solution

(1) Referring again to the equilibrium data on Fig. 2, we get a *4 per cent residual* bed loading by reactivating with 60° DP gas at 400°F.

(2) Following down this 4 per cent isotere line we establish a *−105° DP effluent* vapor pressure when adsorbing through this bed with 70°F gas.

(3) Further, we determine the maximum equilibrium bed capacity to be *21 per cent* when adsorbing 70°F and 60° DP gas.

(4) By comparing (1) and (4) we define the ideally maximum useful capacity to be:

$$UE_{MAX} = 21 - 4 = 17 \text{ per cent by weight}$$

(5) Now, by specifying a four-hour adsorption period, (ϕ_A) ,we define a minimum bed length of:

$$L_B = \phi_A \times v_P = 4 \times (1) \text{ diameter}$$
$$L_B = 4 \text{ diameters}$$

(6) Since the last section of the tower has essentially a 45 degree mass transfer profile through it (i.e., $L_F = 1$ diameter), only half of this section of the bed is effective; therefore, the net useful capacity of the bed is:

$$UE_{\text{NET}} = \frac{3 \times 17 + 1 \times 17/2}{4} = 15 \text{ per cent}$$

This information is perfectly general, and by specifying the gas flow related to the mass transfer information, the following can easily be determined:

(1) Tower diameter:

$$D = \frac{(4 \times \text{cfm})^{1/2}}{\pi \times V_{\text{EL}}} \qquad (5)$$

(2) Bed length

$$L_B \geqq 4\,D \qquad (6)$$

(3) Bed weight (W_B)

$$W_B = \mu \times \frac{\pi D^2 L_B}{4} = \mu \pi D^3 \qquad (7)$$

where μ is the density of the desiccant,

(4) Water loading capacity

$$\text{Lb H}_2\text{O} = W_B \times UE_{\text{NET}} = .15 \times W_B \qquad (8)$$

CONCLUSION

From this presentation, it is hoped that two points have been made. The first is that there is a scientific approach to the design of adsorption equipment, and even though a great deal of design information is still lacking, a design approach in terms of controlling parameters is defined.

The second point is that, although the design approach is established and some data are available to describe equilibrium thermodynamic systems, there still exists a definite need for emperical dynamic loading data which can best be obtained through experimentation on specific pieces of equipment.

NOMENCLATURE

A	Measure of the capacity of a desiccant to adsorb moisture	arbitrary
cfm	Flow rate of adsorption stream	ft³/min.
D	Diameter of adsorption tower	ft
DP	Dew point	°F
K	Proportionality constant dimensionally consistent with other factors in equation	
L_{ADS}	Equilibrium loading of desiccant bed established by adsorption conditions	%
L_B	Distance traveled through desiccant bed, i.e., length of bed	ft
L_D	Length of completely saturated portion of desiccant bed at breakthrough	ft
L_F	Length of mass transfer front	ft
L_{REA}	Equilibrium loading of desiccant established by reactivation condition	%
P_S	Partial pressure of water vapor in a gaseous mixture saturated at some temperature	psi
P_V	Partial pressure of water vapor in a gaseous mixture	psi
$P_{V_{\text{ADS}}}$	Partial pressure of water vapor in stream prior to adsorption	°DP
$P_{V_{\text{REA}}}$	Partial pressure of water vapor in stream which is in equilibrium with reactivated bed at a particular temperature	°DP
T_{ADS}	Temperature of stream being dried	°F
T_{REA}	Temperature of reactivation stream	°F
UE	Useful adsorption capacity of desiccant bed	Lb H₂O/ Lb des.
V_{EL}	Gas velocity through adsorption bed	fpm
W_B	Weight of bed of desiccant	lb
d	Diameter of capillaries in desiccant	Å
$f_\phi(\ )$	Time function	
v_P	Propagating velocity of mass transfer front through bed	fpm
ρ	Surface tension of liquid on capillary surfaces	arbitrary
ϕ_i	Time	min.
$\phi_{B\text{-}E}$	Time elapsed until breakthrough is experienced	min.
μ	Specific weight of desiccant	Lb/ft³

Reference

1. Isotere Data Sheet No. 5A-3, "Adsorbent Molecular Sieves Type 5A," printed with permission of Linde Division of Union Carbide Corp.

47. Advantages of Humidity Control by Adsorption Dehumidifiers in Spaces Requiring Low Humidities

Gunnar C. F. Asker

Cargocaire Engineering Corp., New York, N.Y.

ABSTRACT

Increased use of automation has created a demand for compact air and gas moisture removal machinery.

This paper deals with design criteria, equipment development to meet criteria for a dry desiccant continuous duty automatic dehumidifier to maintain specific humidities or dew points, with or without other conditioning equipment, for air conditions where medium and low dew points or relative humidities are to be automatically maintained independent from temperature control in the space. The paper also highlights some typical applications and compares power requirements for low humidity air-conditioning systems.

The use of dry desiccant dehumidifiers for prevention of ice and frost formation on low temperature cooling coils is discussed.

CRITERIA FOR A CONTINUOUS DUTY DRY DESICCANT DEHUMIDIFIER

The increased demand for independent industrial humidity control equipment has created requirements for dehumidifiers to meet the following design criteria:

To be a dry permanent desiccant unit with the desiccant bound or imbedded in a hygroscopic material to prevent attrition and desiccant carry-over;

To have a continuously and automatically operated self-contained package unit, not requiring air switching valves;

To have automatic regeneration integral with the equipment for utilization of electric energy, steam or gas as power source;

To have a performance such that outlet temperature and humidity are constant without fluctuations for a given inlet condition;

To be able to provide a constant effluent dew point with a variable inlet condition by means of modulation of the heat source used for reactivation;

To be insensitive to dust and impurities;

To be compact and lightweight with few moving parts.

DEVELOPMENT OF THE HONEYCOMBE DEHUMIDIFIER

The well-known Swedish inventor and engineer, Carl Munters, foresaw in the late 1940's that automation would require new types of air-conditioning equipment and set about to analyze how more compact heat and moisture exchange media could be developed than what was available at that time.

He found that transfer media with narrow air passage channels made of fibrous heat-resistant materials, through which air would be forced in laminar air flow, would provide a compact exchange structure with a great internal surface exposed to the air stream. He also found that for given optimum channel widths with laminar flow that the heat transfer efficiency is as high as for turbulent flow in a wider channel.

As a result of this research in development of rotary gas-to-gas heat exchangers, he then

The HoneyCombe Wheel

View A

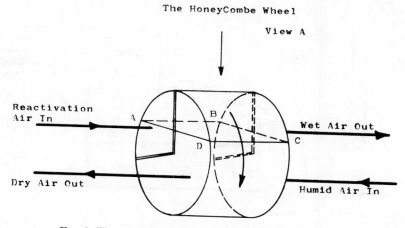

FIG. 1. Fixed desiccant structure dehumidifying wheel.

applied and modified the rotary heat exchanger design for moisture exchange purposes by impregnation of the transfer media with a stable desiccant material. The development, design, testing, production and marketing of the "Cargocaire HoneyCombe" industrial dehumidifiers constitute a joint international development by Carl Munters in Sweden, Hans Niemann in Germany, Peter Grant in England, Oliver Colvin and Kennard Bowlen in the United States, and many others. Figure 1, shows a structure arranged as a moisture exchange wheel assembly for passage of gas to be dehumidified through a larger sector of the

wheel assembly in one direction and simultaneous passage of gas in opposite direction through a smaller sector for desorption purpose.

Figure 2 shows a section through the wheel exposing the narrow air passage channels.

Water vapor flows towards the desiccant and the asbestos paper because of vapor pressure differential as driving force. Thin surface layer adsorption occurs in the boundary layer comprising contact surface area of the channel surrounding the air stream. This is in the adsorption sector. In the regeneration sector, air heated by electricity, steam or gas

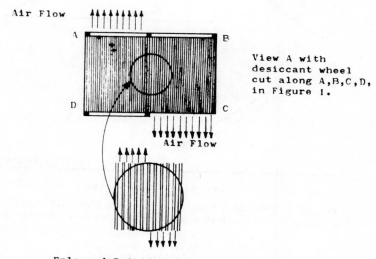

View A with
desiccant wheel
cut along A,B,C,D,
in Figure 1.

Enlarged Detail Within Circle

FIG. 2. Section through wheel exposing air passages.

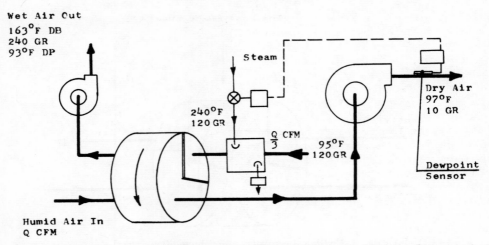

FIG. 3. "The HoneyCombe" dehumidifier flow diagram. Heat input modulation for constant effluent dew point. Conditions of air given are for adiabatic adsorption and desorption with constant enthalpy. Because of some sensible heat exchange, actual conditions are somewhat different.

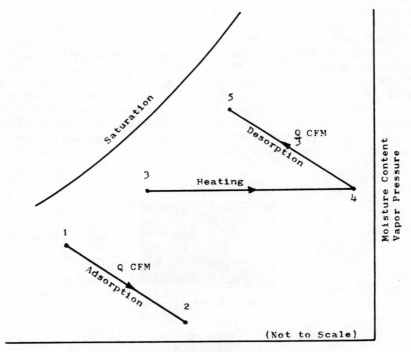

FIG. 4. "HoneyCombe" wheel psychrometrics. Change of conditions of air in the adsorption and reactivation air circuits plotted on psychrometric chart.

1. 70° DB, 50 GR
2. 97° DB, 10 GR
3. 95° DB, 120 GR
4. 240° DB, 120 GR
5. 163° DB, 240 GR

is passed counterflow to the adsorption air stream through the channels moving through the regeneration sector. The heated air heats the asbestos and the desiccant, which then is desorbed and gives up moisture to the heated air. If a hygroscopic stable chloride salt is used as desiccant, a change of state may occur chemically between the adsorption and regeneration cycles. Change of state may occur from anhydrous to monohydrate to saturation state, and back to original anhydrous, with the entire process automatic and reversible. The desiccant wheel assembly proper always remains in a fixed solid structure state.

One important feature of this design is complete separation between the two air circuits internally within the wheel, because of the longitudinal channels. This makes internal cross leakage impossible.

Figure 3 shows the two air circuits diagramatically and indicates how the heat input may be modulated from a dew-point sensor in the dry air outlet.

Refer now to Fig. 4, where the change of conditions in the two circuits is shown. In the example shown, the dehumidifier is at 70°DB and 50 grains and the outlet condition is 97° DB and 10 grains. On the reactivation side, with an outside weather condition of 95°DB and 120 grains, the air is heated to 240° and 120 grains. The air will then, at this temperature, have a lower relative humidity than that which corresponds to the leaving air condition on the dry air side, which is necessary for satisfactory reactivation.

The temperature conditions shown are for constant enthalpy on either side of the wheel. In actual operation, there is some heat carryover from the regeneration circuit, which causes a higher outlet temperature on the adsorption circuit side and a lowered effluent reactivation temperature.

The air velocity possible through this type of desiccant wheel is considerably higher than for a granular desiccant bed unit where consideration must be given to attrition of the desiccant and internal diffusion resistances within the desiccant particles. The contact area enclosing each channel in the corrugated "HoneyCombe" (R) wheel is readily exposed and immediate surface adsorption takes place. A 4500-dfm steam reactivated dehumidifier is shown in Fig. 5.

Fig. 5. A 4500-cfm "HoneyCombe" dehumidifier.

The effluent dew point obtainable is a function of inlet temperature, moisture content, contact time, contact area, reactivation temperature, and moisture content of reactivation air. Dew points down to −50°F are obtainable.

APPLICATIONS OF DRY DESICCANT DEHUMIDIFIERS

Applications are industry-wide in scope, but usage within a given industry group is somewhat limited.

The main applications are:

(1) For dry storage, with or without temperature control for preservation of materials in warehouses and caves;

(2) For process work, such as drying of heat sensitive materials, pharmaceutical tableting operations and packaging operations for highly hygroscopic materials;

(3) For independent humidity control in air-conditioning systems;

(4) For condensation control, in pumping stations, filtration plants, sewage lift stations, ice skating rinks, curling rinks, radomes, ship's cargo holds, containers, barges, boats, etc.

These dehumidifiers are also used in sewage lift stations, standby power plants and in cargo holds on ships to prevent both ship sweat and

SYSTEM 1.

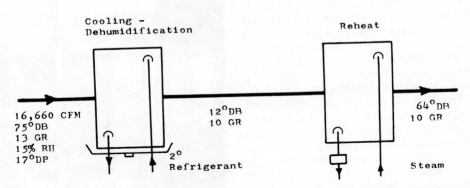

FIG. 6. Schematic arrangement for low humidity room using refrigeration and reheat for control.

cargo sweat. This also applies to refrigerated process areas such as brewery cellars, cheese curing rooms, etc.

Examples

Temperature and Humidity Controlled Low Humidity Room. Control condition: 75°DB, 10 per cent RH, 13 grains, 17° dew point; internal sensible load—120,000 Btu/hour; internal latent load—32 lb H_2O/hour.

The most common approach is to use a system as shown schematically in Fig. 6. All air is cooled by direct expansion refrigeration to such a level that the latent load can be handled. The air is then reheated to a point determined by the internal sensible load.

Because of the low dew point required, ice buildup on the cooling coil is rapid, and for a continuous system, two sets of coils must be used with air valves for switching flow from the iced-up coil which needs to be defrosted to a second cooling ice-free coil.

A more economical approach is to use a system as shown in Fig. 7, in which an adsorption-type dehumidifier is used in bypass and sized to handle the latent load with the cooling coil selected to handle only the sensible load.

The power requirements are listed in Table 1.

In evaluating System 1 against System 2, it is not enough only to glance at the hp and

SYSTEM 2.

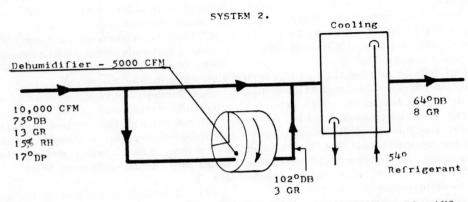

FIG. 7. Schematic arrangement for low humidity room using dry desiccant dehumidifier for latent load and refrigeration for the sensible load.

TABLE 1. COMPARISON OF REQUIREMENTS FOR A SYSTEM OF REFRIGERATION AND REHEAT (SYSTEM 1) WITH A SYSTEM OF ADSORPTION DEHUMIDIFICATION AND REFRIGERATION (SYSTEM 2)

	System 1	System 2
Air volume, cfm	16,600	10,000
Dehumidifier, cfm	None	5,000 of above 10,000
System fan, bhp	15	15
Refrigeration, tons	100	22
Refrigeration, bhp	180*	17.6
Dehumidifier steam btu/hour	None	165,000
Reactivation air fan, bhp	None	2
System reheat Btu/hour	1,225,000	None

* The refrigeration bhp may be reduced by using one compressor operating at 28°F suction temperature and one at 2°F suction temperature.

Btu/hour savings, as shown in Table 1. It should be recognized that System 1, must be operated continuously at all times when control is desired. A little thought on the difference in accomplishing control with System 2, will reveal additional savings. The dry desiccant dehumidifier will operate only as required by the latent load in the space as determined by a humidity or dew-point controller. The amount of refrigeration used is dependent on the internal sensible load as called for by the room thermostat. Very often, maximum latent loads do not coincide with peak cooling demand and vice versa.

The flexibility to adjust to load demands does not exist with System 1, which actually requires more reheat with low sensible loads.

The acquisition cost is less for System 2, so we will disregard first cost and look at operating costs during a five year period assuming year-round operation, 5 days a week, 8 hours per day.

System 1 will run continuously, and has a total operating time of 10,000 hours. We assume that System 2 will operate on the average with 50 per cent of maximum latent

	System 1	*System 2*
Total electric power demand, kwh	1,440,000	176,000
Cost at 2c/kwh	$28,800	$3,520
Total steam consumption, Btu	12,250,000,000	825,000,000
Cost at $1.20 per 1,000,000 Btu	$14,700	$990

load and 50 per cent of maximum sensible load, but with system fan operating continuously 40 hours per week.

Even if we assume that first cost is the same (System 2 is less costly), the operating savings for System 2 over System 1 would have paid for the entire installation in less than three years.

Dry Desiccant Dehumidifiers for Low-temperature Rooms. Low-temperature rooms are of two types:

(1) Those that are benefitted by low humidities, such as brewery cellars or other cold areas where condensation should be prevented, and where low humidities improve rather than harm the process.

(2) Those which require that humidities are maintained high to prevent product weight losses.

Let us look at a brewery cellar first. Usual practice in older installations has been to use bare unfinned cooling coils in the space. No effort is made to control humidity in the space. Moisture is added to the space from infiltration of moist outside air due to door openings and replacement of room air due to exhaust fans. This moisture will condense on the refrigeration coils which will ice up. It will also deposit on beer tanks and other internal room surfaces. Moisture is also added from water used for cleaning purposes.

What does dehumidification do in a brewery cellar? It prevents ice and frost formation in refrigeration coils, which increase heat transfer rates and makes defrosting unnecessary. It prevents condensation in the room, and thus reduces the cooling load as condensation releases heat. It prevents mold and bacteria growth in the space and thus makes frequent wash-downs of walls and ceilings unnecessary. It makes it possible to maintain lower cellar temperatures with no increase in refrigeration capacity.

Heat is added to the space from the desiccant dehumidifier as the vapor condensation in the dehumidifier converts latent heat to sensible heat, although total heat is changed very little.

The sensible heat added is offset by the following:

(1) Evaporation cooling by moisture vaporization from floor and other surfaces holding liquid moisture.

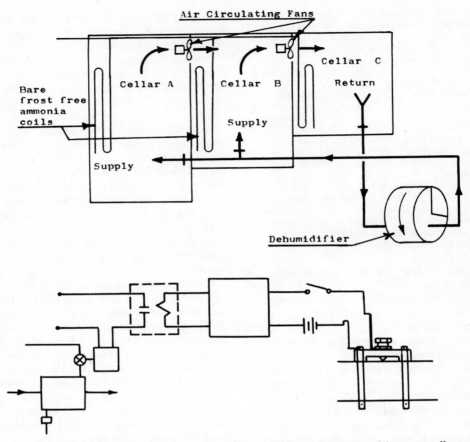

Fig. 8. Humidity control and condensation prevention in conventional brewery cellars and means for automatic defrosting of cooling coils with dry desiccant dehumidification.

(2) Increased efficiency of cooling coils operating without ice and only with a thin frost film (for maximum heat transfer).

(3) The fact that the surfaces are dry and free from condensation.

As mentioned above, we desire to maintain a thin frost film on the cooling coils, but we do not want ice to build up on the coils and accumulate. The heat flow is not reduced with only a thin frost film, but the effective contact area of the coil with the surrounding air is increased.

This makes it possible to adjust the degree of dryness of the dehumidified air to such a degree that this frost film is maintained. The author has, therefore, designed a control which automatically adjusts the heat input to the dehumidifier reactivation air circuit to a low level when the cooling coil is frost free. As the frost builds up to a predetermined thickness, a low voltage electrical circuit is closed and is amplified and energizes a relay coil. The relay contacts close the line voltage current to open the heat controlling valve for the heat source from low to high heat. With this type of control, we do not over dry the space, and the operation is automatically maintained at optimum efficiency (patent pending). See Fig. 8, for a schematic flow diagram. Figure 9, shows a 4500-cfm "HoneyCombe" dehumidifier for a brewery installation.

In new construction, refrigeration air handling units are usually used. Desiccant dehumidifiers are used also for these units to keep frost off the cooling coils and to maintain safe levels of humidity in the cellars.

Figure 10, shows schematically a 15,000-cfm air handling system using a 4500-cfm desiccant

Fig. 9. 4500-cfm "HoneyCombe" dehumidifier for a 30°F DB brewery cellar application.

dehumidifier in partial bypass of the main air stream.

Air at 14,100 cfm, with 32°F DB, 13.9 grains of moisture per pound of dry air and a dewpoint of 18°F, is recirculated from the space. Of this, 3600 cfm go to the dehumidifier inlet, and this air is mixed with 900 cfm of outside air of maximum condition 95°F DB, 124 grains/lb and 73°F DP. This mixture gives 4500 cfm to the dehumidifier of conditions 45°F DB, 36 grains/lb dry air and 40°F DP. Outlet air from dehumidifier is 75°F DB, 3 grains/lb and —11°F DP. This air is then mixed with the balance of the return air (10,500 cfm) for a total of 15,000 cfm. The dew point of the mixture is then 12.5°F DP, 1.5°F below the temperature of the 14°F ammonia in the flooded cooling coil of the air handling unit. Air of 15,000 cfm, 20°F DB and 10.6 GR grains/lb and 12.5°F DP is supplied to the cellar.

Operation of many low temperature rooms

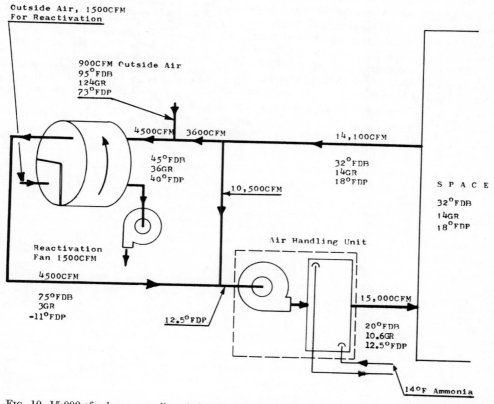

Fig. 10. 15,000-cfm brewery cellar air handling system using 4500-cfm desiccant dehumidifier air bypass with the main air stream.

require that the relative humidity is kept high to prevent weight loss of stored products.

Here again we want to operate the refrigeration coils ice free. The schematic layout is similar to that shown in Fig. 10, for a new type system for a brewery cellar. Moisture must then be added again downstream from the cooling coil. This moisture may be taken from part of the reactivation air outlet flow from the desiccant dehumidifier as the net space dehumidification load would be small.

CONCLUSION

The refrigeration and air-conditioning engineer has, until recently, been disinterested in adsorption equipment. Manufacturers of adsorption dehumidifiers, on the other hand, have tried to sell their equipment for applications where at least part of the moisture load should have been handled by other equipment.

With recent improvements in adsorption equipment technology and design, it is safe to predict more use of adsorption units in integrated air-conditioning systems which are capable of controlling temperature and humidity efficiently, accurately, and independently of each other and which will not require defrost cycles. Adsorption units will also find more use in low-temperature applications.

The design of this dehumidifier and some of the described control methods are covered by issued or pending patents.

References

1. Connell, André F. O., "Evolution des Moyens de Protection des Cargaisons Contre l'Humidité a bord des Navires," *Nouveautés Techniques Maritimes 1963, Le Journal de la Marine Marchande* (France).
2. Furman, Robert W., "Hold by Hold Climate Control," *Marine Engineering/Log* (November 1960) (USA).
3. Christensson, S., "Cargocaire Förbättringer och Nyheter," *Nautisk Tidskrift* (April 1960) (Sweden).
4. Norbäck, Per, "Värme och Fuktväxlare med trånga spalter," *Teknisk Tidskrift* (January 15, 1960) (Sweden).
5. Munters, Carl, "En ny utvecklingslinje för värme och fuktöverföring samt dess tillämpningsområden," *VVS*, Nr 3 (1959) (Sweden).
6. American Society of Heating and Air-Conditioning Engineers, Symposium Bulletin on Dehumidification, 63rd Annual Meeting of the Society, Chicago, Illinois, February 1957 (USA).
7. Colvin, O. D., and Duly, S. J., "Prevention of Moisture Damage to Cargoes in General Cargo Spaces," North East Coast Institution of Engineers and Shipbuilders in Newcastle on Tyne, *Institution Transactions*, **63** (February 28, 1947) (Great Britain).
8. Colvin, Oliver D., "Care of Cargo at Sea (Part 1) 1938 and (Part 2) 1941," *Transactions of the Society of Naval Architects and Marine Engineers* (USA).

SECTION V

PROCESS CONTROL

48. Indication and Control of the Moisture Content in Heat Treating Atmospheres with Temperature Regulated Humidity Sensors

WILLIAM J. KUNZ

Barber-Colman Company, Rockford, Illinois

ABSTRACT

An instrument has been developed which uses humidity sensors to determine the vapor state moisture content of protective gas atmospheres used in metal heat treating.

The sensors are located in a temperature controlled chamber. A filtered, pressure regulated gas sample is passed through the chamber. Sensor resistance is a function of the relative humidity in the chamber. The resistance varies inversely with respect to the gas moisture content and is measured at a constant chamber temperature. Resistance change is detected by a high-impedance AC Wheatstone bridge, electronically amplified and read out on a recorder in terms of degrees Fahrenheit dew point.

The instrument response time is measured in seconds and affords close control of the gas atmosphere moisture content. Methane to lower the dew point and air to raise the dew point are administered to the gas atmosphere through electrically operated solenoid valves and motor-operated proportioning valves.

Control to within $1°F$ dew point on short heat treating cycles and to within $.5°F$ dew point on extended cycles has been established in a number of field installations.

The use of dew-point measuring devices to indicate the moisture content of gas atmospheres used in heat treating furnaces and gas atmosphere generators has been well established. These gas atmospheres usually consist of H_2, N_2, CO, CO_2, CH_4, H_2O vapor and occasionally NH_3. Curves have been established which relate dew-point values to "carbon potential" as shown in Fig. 1. Carbon potential can be defined as the degree of carbon present in the gas atmosphere sufficient to cause the steel at a specific heat to take on carbon, lose carbon, or maintain a constant carbon level. Carbon potential is inversely proportional to the dew point. The dew point vs carbon potential curve is reliable provided the gas atmosphere generator produces a composite gas following a definite chemical equilibrium relationship. On this basis the dew-point method of determining carbon potential has been accepted.

Difficulties encountered with various dew-point controls in heat treating applications include: slow response times, need for refrigeration and pressurization and involved optical systems. In some cases it is necessary to condense the moisture from the gas to obtain dew points by optical and electrical measurement methods. Condensation of contaminants onto the measuring device at this point presents additional maintenance problems.

In an effort to minimize some of these problems, it was decided to adopt the method of measuring moisture content of the gas atmosphere in the vapor state using electrical humidity sensors at a constant temperature. An instrument was therefore developed which uses humidity sensors that change their resistance to indicate gas atmosphere moisture content (see Fig. 2). The sensors are located in a temperature controlled chamber and are

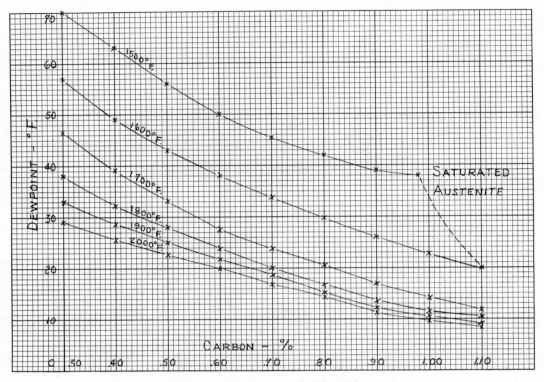

FIG. 1. Typical carbon potential *vs* dew-point curves.

FIG. 2. Dew-point recorder-controller instrument in operation.

FIG. 3. Temperature regulated chamber containing humidity sensors and copper wire temperature element.

situated so that a gas sample can easily flow over them as shown in Fig. 3. Incorporated in the rear of the chamber and separated from the humidity sensors are an electrical heating element, a thermistor, and a channel through which a small amount of cooling water may circulate. In Fig. 4, the gas sampling, filtering, regulating and moisture measuring components of the instrument are shown.

The thermistor measures the temperature of the chamber and through an electronic amplifier controls the chamber temperature by actuating either the electrical heater or the cooling water flow. A copper wire temperature sensing element adjacent to the humidity sensors allows the temperature of the immediate area to be measured and read out on an externally located meter. The chamber temperature is held to within .5°F. A constant flow of gas with a regulated positive pressure of 6.0 ounces S.I. is pumped past the humidity sensors and the temperature sensing element. The gas flow rate is 10 cfh and the pump used is a diaphragm type. The humidity sensor resistance is a function of the relative humidity in the chamber. At a constant chamber temperature, the resistance of the humidity sensors varies inversely as the moisture content of the gas varies. The per cent RH can be

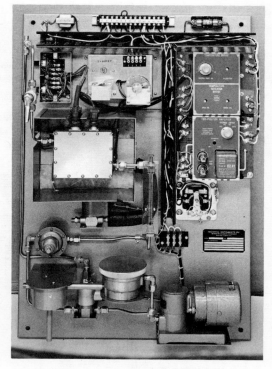

FIG. 4. Instrument interior containing gas pump, gas filtering system, temperature controls, regulated chamber, and sensor resistance bridge circuit.

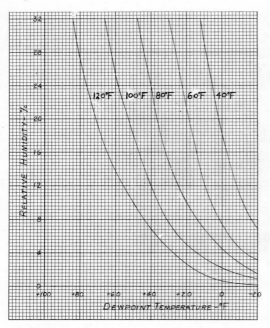

FIG. 5. Dew-point temperature *vs* per cent RH curves.

to 22 MΩ. The AC signal from the bridge is electronically amplified (see Fig. 6) and read out on a recorder chart. The recorder chart is calibrated in degrees Fahrenheit dew point and checked by an alternate method of dew-point determination, such as the dew cup test.

Several types of sensors operating on the resistance change principle were tested for use in the measuring circuit. One of the types selected utilizes a Kel-F base with platinum wire electrodes mounted on it. A salt solution of lithium chloride or lithium bromide together with an organic binder is deposited upon the Kel-F form. This is the Dunmore-type hygrometer. Another sensor selected consists of a plastic wafer constructed from a copolymer of styrene. The wafer is impregnated with lithium salt, and gold grid type electrodes are mounted on the plastic sensor.

Using two Dunmore-type lithium salt sensors in the bridge circuit, dew points of from −50°F DP to +140° DP can be determined at chamber temperatures of 45 to 150°F. Use of pairs of sensors having various relative humidity ranges results in a dew-point span as wide as 50 to 55°F when using chamber temperatures of from +40 to +120°F. Measuring higher dew points with chamber temperatures up to 150°F can result in dew-point spans as narrow as 10°F. The response time of the instrument to a change in the gas atmosphere dew point is under ten seconds. The stainless steel sample gas line in this case is 30 ft long. Reducing the chamber tempera-

converted to degrees Fahrenheit dew point as shown in Fig. 5. Sensors with the desired resistance *vs* relative humidity curves can be selected to establish the instrument dew-point range for a specific chamber temperature. In Fig. 6, the sensors are incorporated in a 60-cycle AC Wheatstone bridge which will null balance at sensor resistances of from 22,000 Ω

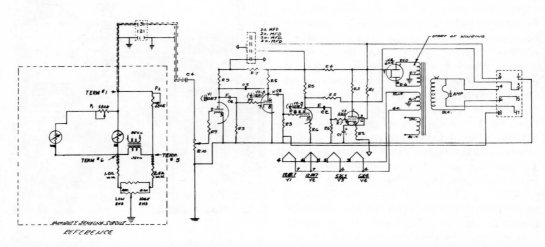

FIG. 6. High impedance, 60-cycle Wheatstone bridge circuit and AC amplifier in dew-point recorder.

ture to zero degrees Fahrenheit and pressurizing the chamber to 95 psi extends the lower dew-point limit of the instrument to $-60°F$ DP. At the lower temperatures, the response time of the sensors is slower. A thermoelectric cooling device installed in the chamber cover is used to maintain lower chamber temperatures.

Using a single polystyrene wafer with gold grid electrodes, the dew-point range obtained is from $+10$ to $+60°F$ DP at an 85°F chamber temperature and from $+20$ to $+70°F$ at 95°F chamber temperature. Below 32°F chamber temperature, a loss of sensitivity for this type of sensor is experienced. These sensors were not used at elevated temperatures. In many heat treating applications, a dew-point range of from $+10$ to $+60°F$ is adequate.

Certain conditions must be maintained when sampling the moisture content of the gas in the vapor state. The chamber temperature must always be maintained higher than the maximum dew point to be encountered. This is to avoid condensation of water onto the sensor and consequent "washoff" of the lithium salt or damage to the electrodes of the plastic sensor. When sampling gas with a high dew point, the entire instrument cabinet is maintained at an elevated temperature with the gas sample lines externally heated electrically or with steam tracer lines. A constant gas flow is always pumped to the instrument, and by means of a 3-way valve the gas is admitted to the sensing element chamber or bypassed either to the outside air or returned to the furnace. Provision is made for electrically switching the gas flow away from the chamber for a timed interval whenever the furnace door is opened. A switch is located in the recorder, and if the highest dew-point indicated on the instrument scale is exceeded, the sample gas flow is passed around the sensing element chamber for a timed interval.

There has been no problem in sampling gases from furnaces as hot as 2000°F with respect to cooling the gas sample. The gas line cools to room temperature a few feet from the furnace. Sample lines as short as 4 ft and as long as 100 ft have been used. Mechanical filtering of the carbon particles in the gas sample line is accomplished with two stages of filtering. A glass wool filter is at the furnace and a .25-μ fiber-glass disc filter is located at the instrument.

It has been decided in some instances that aromatic hydrocarbons, esters and ketones present in the gas atmosphere contaminate the humidity sensors resulting in a slow increase in sensor resistance. No adverse effect has been observed upon the copper wire temperature indicator. Filtering techniques used here included the use of acrylic plastic and polystyrene chips which are attacked by the contaminants, resulting in a filtering action. These filters have resulted in extended sensor life. Freedom from sensor resistance change due to contaminations has been experienced over periods as short as one month and as long as 18 months. Oil traces in the gas atmospheres have remained in vapor form and have presented little problem. No satisfactory filter has been found to enable the sensors to operate when ammonia is present in the gas. All sensors tested to date experienced a rapid permanent increase in resistance within 8 hours of exposure to ammonia vapors. It is assumed that displacement of particles of salt in the sensors has taken place.

In the event of undesired sensor resistance change, the original calibrations over at least a portion of the dew-point range may be restored by changing the temperature of the chamber. This feature can also be used to advantage in compensating for batch-to-batch variations in the initial sensor resistance when manufactured. When greater tolerance, lower cost sensors are used, resistances in series and parallel with the sensors in the bridge circuit help to produce the desired dew-point scale.

To prevent direct current polarization of the sensors, 1.0 V AC is applied to the bridge circuit. This low voltage allows the sensors to operate well below their maximum power dissipation ratings with sensor resistances as low as 22,000 Ω and with a high dew point indicated on the recorder chart. At low dew points, the sensor resistance can reach 22 MΩ. It is necessary to shield and ground all bridge circuit and amplifier wiring. Electrical lead placement is also critical when using a high-impedance Wheatstone bridge in this manner. Conventional shielding and common grounding techniques appeared adequate in all but a few instances where electrically powered furnaces and poorly grounded plant systems were involved. Complete physical isolation of the bridge circuit and amplifier from the

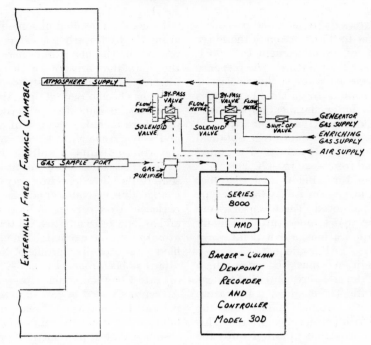

FIG. 7. Dew-point control system for a heat treating furnace atmosphere.

instrument panel proper was required in these cases.

The gold-grid wafer-type sensor had a high capacity effect when used in the AC bridge circuit. This was compensated by balancing the opposite arm of the bridge with a capacitor. It was found that the sensor could be made to appear purely resistive at a resonant frequency

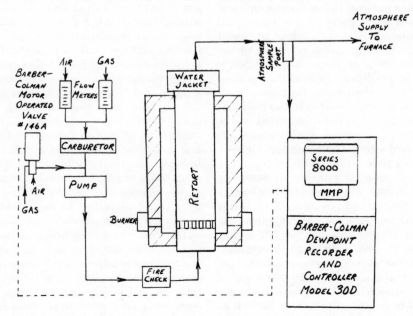

FIG. 8. Dew-point control system for a heat treating atmosphere generator.

Fig. 9. Control panel showing recorders and 3-function controllers for furnace atmosphere and temperature control.

of several hundred cycles. The AC bridge in use was the only one considered because of its compatibility with the existing product line.

Referring to Fig. 7, in response to an electrical signal from the 100 Ω recorder slidewire, electrically operated solenoid valves can be actuated. Through these valves, control of the dew point of the gas atmosphere is achieved by addition of natural gas to the atmosphere to lower the dew point and the addition of air to raise the dew point. As shown in Fig. 8, a proportioning valve is also available which will deliver gas or air to the atmosphere in amounts which range from a fraction of a cubic foot per hour to 20 cu ft/ hour or more. One mode of control incorporates control switches in the recorder which will activate the gas or air solenoid valves as the recorder pointer deviates a prescribed distance from the set control point. More sophisticated control includes two and three function controllers including proportioning positioning, rate action and reset action (see Fig. 9). Zone control of furnaces is achieved by sampling the gas and controlling air or gas additions to each zone in turn during a programmed time interval. This technique can also be applied to measurement and control of several furnaces and gas generators using a single instrument. The indicating, recording, and controlling functions of the instrument may be divorced from the gas sampling, filtering, and moisture measurement functions for centralized control room applications.

The instrument control system is extremely sensitive to dew-point changes in the gas atmosphere. Speed of response of the sensors has been on the order of a few seconds, quite adequate for dew-point control requirements in heat treating applications. Changes in dew point of a gas generator at a distance of 75 ft have been detected and corrective control action begun in less than 30 seconds. Within ten minutes, the dew point of a short cycle heat treating furnace can be restored to $+30°F$ dew point after the furnace atmosphere has been raised to above $+70°F$ dew point by the loading process. Usually the desired control point can be approached before the furnace temperature has reached equilibrium and the carbon potential activity has begun. Control is possible to within $1°F$ dew point on furnaces where the heat treating cycles are of 15 to 30 minutes duration. Where the heat treating cycle extends from 30 minutes to several hours or more, control is to within $0.5°$ dew point.

49. Differential Temperature Control

D. R. Massie, G. C. Shove and E. F. Olver

Agricultural Engineering Department, University of Illinois, Urbana, Illinois

ABSTRACT

An application of the use of a differential temperature control is for controlling the wet- and dry-bulb temperature of air used for drying grain. The difference between these two temperatures, the wet-bulb depression, is related to the equilibrium moisture content of a particular grain at a given dry-bulb temperature. The wet-bulb depression corresponding to an equilibrium moisture content varies with the dry-bulb temperature necessitating a control which will maintain a varying temperature difference.

An electronic differential temperature control consists of two thermistors, each of which is in the arm of a Wheatstone bridge circuit. The bridge is operated as a balanced bridge controller. The signal generated by the unbalance resulting when the temperature difference departs from the design value is used to actuate controls for correcting the temperature difference.

This paper discusses the procedure for determining the values of the resistors to be used in a bridge circuit with thermistors to obtain a balanced bridge controller. The control of the wet-bulb depression of air used for drying was selected as an example for explaining the procedure; however, the method can be applied to developing a circuit for the control of any temperature difference.

Thermistors having equal resistance are used in two arms of a bridge circuit so that a difference in temperature between the two thermistors will cause their resistance to differ sufficiently to cause an elecrtrical unbalance in the bridge. To obtain a balanced bridge, additional resistance must be added to one or both of the bridge arms containing the thermistors. The additional resistances are of such values and so arranged that the effective resistance of each arm containing the thermistors is equal for all values of the temperature difference.

In brief, the values of the resistors to be used in the bridge arms are determined by: (1) finding the relationship between the resistance of the dry-bulb temperature sensing thermistor and the resistance of the wet-bulb temperature sensing thermistor for the desired temperatures; and (2) altering this relationship is such a way that the effective resistance of each arm is equal.

In this paper, an example completely worked out, and a discussion of the accuracy of such a control is presented with data obtained from drying shelled corn.

INTRODUCTION

The final or equilibrium moisture content of air-dried grain will depend on the temperature and relative humidity of the drying air. The concept of equilibrium moisture content for hygroscopic materials such as grains has been discussed in detail by Henderson [1] and Hall [2], and considerable data on equilibrium moistures for agricultural products have been published [3]. An empirical equation for defining equilibrium moisture content curves is

$$1 - rh = e^{-cTM_E^n} \qquad (1)$$

where

rh = equilibrium relative humidity, expressed as a decimal

M_E = equilibrium moisture content, per cent dry basis

T = absolute temperature, degrees Rankine

c, n = constants varying with hygroscopic materials.

Suggested values of c and n for shelled corn are 1.10×10^{-5} and 1.90 respectively. These values can be used to calculate the equilibrium relative humidities corresponding to a particular shelled corn moisture content for various dry-bulb temperatures. The relationship between the wet- and dry-bulb temperatures corresponding to the chosen equilibrium moisture content can then be plotted (Fig. 1).

If the wet- and dry-bulb temperatures of the air used for drying corn are maintained at the respective values represented by the curve of Fig. 1, the corn will dry to 12 per cent moisture

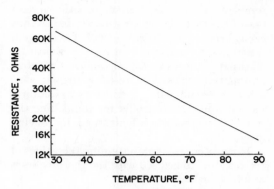

FIG. 2. Resistance-temperature characteristics for 1R173 General Electric thermistors.

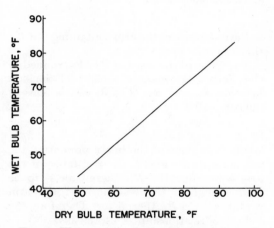

FIG. 1. Wet- and dry-bulb air temperatures in equilibrium with 12 per cent moisture content, wet basis, shelled corn.

content, wet basis. The temperature difference between the wet- and dry-bulb temperatures, the wet-bulb depression, suggests the use of a differential temperature control for controlling the temperature of the drying air. The basic electrical circuit of an electronic differential temperature control consists of two thermistors, each of which is in an arm of a Wheatstone bridge circuit.

Haynes and Longo[4] described the use of two thermistors in a bridge circuit for controlling the ventilation of potato storages. Thermistors having equal resistance were used so that a difference in temperature between the two thermistors caused their resistances to differ sufficiently to produce an electrical unbalance in the bridge. Yung and Soderholm[5] stated

that electronic differential thermostats had the desirable features of flexibility of installation, ruggedness of construction, good sensitivity, and moderate cost that made them potentially suitable for grain and hay drying.

DISCUSSION OF THEORY

If equal resistance thermistors are used in a balanced bridge to sense two different temperatures, such as the dry- and wet-bulb temperatures corresponding to a particular equilibrium moisture content (Fig. 1), the

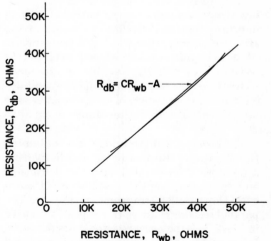

FIG. 3. Relationship between the resistance of the dry-bulb temperature sensing thermistor and the resistance of the wet-bulb temperature sensing thermistor for air temperatures corresponding to 12 per cent equilibrium moisture content, wet basis, shelled corn.

temperature-resistance characteristic curve of one of the thermistors must be altered so that each arm of the bridge will have equal resistance for all temperature combinations. This paper discusses the procedure for determining the values of the resistors to be used in a bridge circuit with thermistors to obtain a balanced-bridge controller for controlling the wet-bulb depression of air used for drying grain.

The procedure for determining the values of the resistors to be used with the thermistors is as follows, where:

R_{db} = resistance of the dry-bulb temperature sensing thermistor.

R_{wb} = resistance of the wet-bulb temperature sensing thermistor

P = resistance of a resistor in parallel with R_{wb}

S = resistance of a resistor in series with R_{wb} or R_{db}

The relationship between R_{db} and R_{wb} is determined by referring to the temperature-resistance characteristic curve for the thermistors (Fig. 2) and plotting R_{db} versus R_{wb} (Fig. 3) for the temperature combinations corresponding to the desired equilibrium moisture content.

If the resistances of the bridge arms containing the thermistors are to be equal, Fig. 3 indicates that the effective resistance of the arm containing the wet-bulb temperature sensing thermistor must be less than the actual resistance of the R_{wb} thermistor. In other words, the resistance of the bridge arm containing the R_{wb} thermistor must be altered in such a way that the altered resistance is equal to R_{db}.

The resistance of the bridge arm containing the R_{wb} thermistor can be altered by placing a resistor, P, in parallel with the thermistor and by placing another resistor, S, in series with the parallel arrangement (Fig. 4). The parallel resistor changes the slope of the curve in Fig. 3, and the series resistor shifts the curve to the right. If the series resistor were placed in the arm containing the R_{db} thermistor, the curve in Fig. 3 would shift to the left. Proper selection of the resistance of each of the resistors, P and S, will make the resistance of the arm containing the R_{wb} thermistor equal

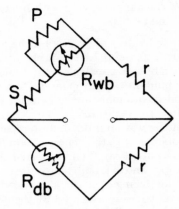

FIG. 4. Arrangement of thermistors and resistors in a balanced bridge circuit.

to the resistance of the arm containing the R_{db} thermistor.

The value of the resistor P is determined in the following manner. The relationship between R_{db} and R_{wb} (Fig. 3) can be closely approximated by

$$R_{db} = CR_{wb} - A \qquad (2)$$

where C = slope of the line representing the relationship. In Fig. 4, the resistance of the arm containing the R_{wb} thermistor is to be made equal to the resistance of the arm containing the R_{db} thermistor. Therefore, the following relationship is established :

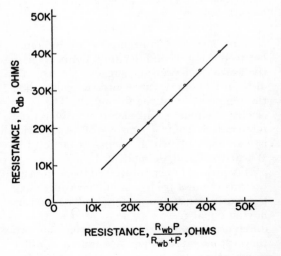

FIG. 5. Relationship between R_{db} and $\dfrac{R_{wb}P}{R_{wb}+P}$.

$$R_{db} = \frac{R_{wb}P}{R_{wb} + P} + S \qquad (3)$$

or

$$R_{db} = C\,R_{wb} - A = \frac{R_{wb}P}{R_{wb} + P} + S \quad (4)$$

The derivative with respect to R_{wb} is

$$\frac{dR_{db}}{dR_{wb}} = C = \frac{(R_{wb} + P)P - R_{wb}P}{(R_{wb} + P)^2} \qquad (5)$$

Solving for P by use of the quadratic formula and selecting the sign which will make the multiplier on R_{wb} positive:

$$P = \frac{C + \sqrt{C}}{1 - C}\,R_{wb} \qquad (6)$$

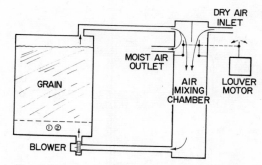

FIG. 7. Schematic of the drying system showing the louvers used to maintain the desired relationship between the wet- and dry-bulb air temperature.

1 — Wet-bulb thermocouple and thermistor
2 — Dry-bulb thermocouple and thermistor

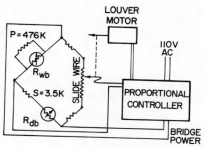

FIG. 6. Schematic of the electrical circuit of a differential temperature control used to maintain the desired relationship between the wet- and dry-bulb air temperatures for drying grain.

the R_{wb} thermistor must be decreased in relation to the resistance of R_{db} by an amount S for balanced bridge operation. This can be done by placing the series resistor, S, in the arm containing the R_{db} thermistor. If the value of S is positive, the series resistor, S, is placed in the arm containing the R_{wb} thermistor.

To evaluate P, the temperature condition under which the system will generally be operating is selected and the corresponding value of R_{wb} is determined. The relationship between R_{db} and $R_{wb}P/(R_{wb} + P)$ can now be plotted (Fig. 5); this relationship can be closely approximated by a straight line having a slope of 1. The value of the series resistor, S, is determined by writing the equation for this line. The equation of the line is

$$R_{db} = \frac{R_{wb}P}{R_{wb} + P} + S \qquad (7)$$

or

$$S = R_{db} - \frac{R_{wb}P}{R_{ub} + P} \qquad (8)$$

If the value of S, as determined by Eq. 8, is negative, the resistance of the arm containing

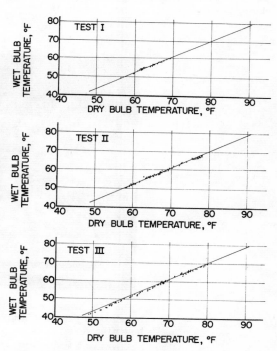

FIG. 8. Hourly wet- and dry-bulb air temperatures compared with the line representing the wet- and dry-bulb air temperatures in equilibrium with 12 per cent moisture content, wet basis, shelled corn.

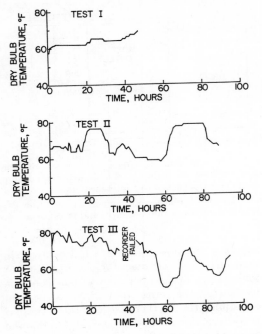

The effectiveness of the differential temperature control was tested by constructing a system to dry shelled corn to 12 per cent moisture, wet basis. A resistance of $30K\Omega$ was selected for R_{wb} by assuming a general operating wet-bulb temperature of about $60°F$. The slope C of the line in Fig. 3 was found to be 0.885. The value of the parallel resistor, P, was computed as:

$$P = \frac{0.885 + \sqrt{0.885}}{1 - 0.885}\ 30K = (15.88)\ 30K$$
$$= 476K\Omega$$

The relationship between R_{db} and $R_{wb}P/(R_{wb} + P)$, as shown in Fig. 5, was plotted by using values of R_{db} and R_{wb} from Fig. 3.

The equation of a straight line representing the points in Fig. 5 was found to be

$$R_{db} = \frac{R_{wb}\ 476K}{R_{wb} + 476K} - 3.5K \qquad (9)$$

where $S = -3.5K\Omega$. The negative sign indicates that the $3.5K$ series resistor should

Fig. 9. Variation in the dry-bulb air temperature during the tests.

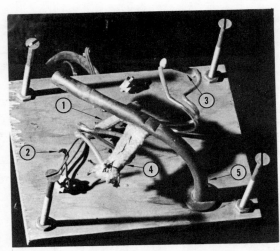

Fig. 10. Wet- dry-bulb temperature sensing elements mounted on panel for installation in the plenum chamber under the grain.

1 Wet-bulb temperature sensing thermocouple.
2 Dry-bulb temperature sensing thermocouple.
3 Dry-bulb temperature sensing thermistor.
4 Wet-bulb temperature sensing thermistor.
5 Water supply tube for wetting wicks.

be placed in the arm of the bridge containing the R_{db} thermistor.

The arrangement of the $476K$ and $3.5K\Omega$ resistors in a Wheatstone bridge circuit is shown in Fig. 6. The unbalanced bridge signal was fed into a proportional controller. The output from the proportional controller actuated a louver motor which changed the position of louvers in the air duct and re-balanced the bridge.

The arrangement of the louvers in the air duct is shown in Fig. 7. The louvers operated by the louver motor were positioned to control the quantity of moist air recycled. The mixing of the moist air with the dry air maintained the desired relationship between the wet- and dry-bulb temperatures of the drying air.

The results of the tests are shown in Fig. 8. The lines represent all combinations of the wet- and dry-bulb air temperatures in equilibrium with shelled corn containing 12 per cent moisture, wet basis. The plotted points are hourly air temperatures recorded during the tests on the strip chart of a temperature recorder. The differential temperature control maintained accurate control of the relationship between the wet- and dry-bulb air temperatures as indicated by only slight scatter of the points from the desired wet-dry bulb temperature line. Control of the relationship between the wet- and dry-bulb air temperatures was maintained even though there was considerable variation in the dry-bulb temperature (Fig. 9).

SUMMARY

An electronic differential temperature control consisting of two equal resistance thermistors in a balanced bridge circuit can be used to control the relationship between two different temperatures. The temperature-resistance characteristic of one arm of the bridge is altered so that each arm of the bridge will have equal resistance for all the desired temperature combinations. One application of

FIG. 11. Physical arrangement of the drying system used for testing the differential temperature control. Components left to right: grain drying chamber, air mixing chamber with louver motor, and proportional controller (see Fig. 7).

the differential temperature control is to control the final moisture content of grain in a drying system by maintaining the proper relationship between the wet- and dry-bulb temperatures of the drying air.

References

1. Henderson, S. M., "A Basic Concept of Equilibrium Moisture," *Agr. Eng.*, **33**, 29–32 (January 1952).

2. Hall, Carl W., and Rodriguez-Arias, Jorge H., "Equilibrium Moisture Content of Shelled Corn," *Agr. Eng.*, **39**, 466–470 (August 1958).

3. Hall, Carl W., "Drying Farm Crops," Agricultural Consulting Associates, Inc. Reynoldsburg, Ohio, 1957.

4. Haynes, B. C., and Longo, C. V., "Packaged Electronic Ventilation Control," *Agr. Eng.*, **34**, 827, 830 (December 1953).

5. Yung, F. D., and Soderholm, L. H., "Differential Thermostats for Agricultural Applications," *Agr. Eng.*, **33**, 205–206 (April 1952).

50. Moisture Sensing and Control in Drycleaning Solutions

ROBERT H. GASCH, JR.

Honeywell Inc., Minneapolis, Minnesota

ABSTRACT

Drycleaning of fabric requires a solvent, detergent, and moisture. The solvent is used to remove grease type soil. The detergent and water combine to remove water-soluble soil. The amount of detergent is small, amounting to about 2 per cent by volume and the water to about 1/10 per cent or less by volume.

The solvent can be either Stoddard solvent or perchlorethylene. Usually the detergent used is a non-ionic synthetic material. Some soaps are still used.

Water is very important to the action of the detergent. Too little water results in poor removal of water-soluble soil. Too much water causes wrinkling of the fabric. The excess water also causes loss of creases and pleats, guide lines in the pressing of the fabric. Larger amounts of water will cause shrinkage of fabrics.

In the past the water content of the bath has been controlled by hand addition of water. This method was very inaccurate since it did not take into account the amount of moisture in the fabric or in the solvent system.

During the past thirty years, various investigators have found that the relative humidity of the air in equilibrium with a cleaning bath was a measure of the amount of water in the solvent and fabric. This discovery prompted the use of relative humidity sensors as controls for addition of water to the bath. Dunmore sensors of lithium chloride-polyvinyl alcohol type were found to be particularly suitable for this use providing that they were made of the proper materials. These sensors are stable over long periods of time in the vapor phase over either Stoddard solvent or perchlorethylene solutions. A small but reproducible and permanent calibration shift is found when the elements are used in the perchlorethylene vapor phase, but this does not interfere with the application.

This paper describes the application of the humidity sensors, and also covers certain problems encountered and solutions to these problems. The control system and water addition mechanism are also discussed.

INTRODUCTION

Water has long been considered the most nearly universal solvent. While it does remove most dirt and thus cleans, it also can cause damage. For example, in the cleaning of clothes water can cause undesirable damage to some fabrics and dyes. This is especially true for shrinkage damage to fabrics containing wool.

To overcome these undesirable cleaning results, the cleaning of wool and other water damaged fabrics is done with other solvents. The most popular are Stoddard solvent (a petroleum based solvent) and perchlorethylene (a chlorinated hydrocarbon). Either of these solvents can be used with the water sensitive fabrics and dyes with no harmful effects. Both of these solvents suffer one major defect—they will not readily dissolve or remove water-soluble soil or stains.

Various additives have been used in an attempt to improve the ability of these organic solvents to remove water-soluble soil. The most successful additives are detergents

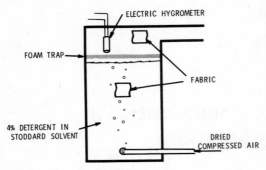

FIG. 1. Method of fabric moisture pick-up determination.

human error. However, no control system seemed possible until work at the National Institute of Drycleaning showed that the identical fabrics in solvent vapor and the solvent picked up the same amount of moisture. The tests were conducted generally as shown in Fig. 1.

The solvent is placed in an enclosed container. Dried compressed air is piped to a fritted glass bubbler and allowed to bubble through the solvent. The vapor in passing through the solvent picks up moisture from the solvent and conditions the vapor space above the solvent.

A foam trap is used above the solvent to prevent any liquid or bubbles from contacting the electric hygrometer.

One sample of similar fabric was placed in the solvent and one in the vapor space. Moisture measurements made on both fabrics showed equal amounts of moisture in both fabrics. These results were reported in the National Institute of Drycleaning *Service Bulletin* **T290** dated September 30, 1952.

including natural soap and synthetic detergents. It was found rather early in the history of detergent dry cleaning that better soil removal was obtained when the ambient relative humidity was high. This led to the addition of water to the solution or preconditioning of the garments in humidity chambers. Water addition proved the most successful and was widely adopted.

CORRELATION OF AIR AND FABRIC MOISTURE

Methods and systems were devised to add water to the solvent-detergent agent to get the best cleaning. Methods were crude and open to

SOLVENT WATER CARRYING ABILITY

Further, it was shown that as the concentration of the detergent was increased, the solvent system could hold more water at the same relative humidity. (See Fig. 2.) The knee

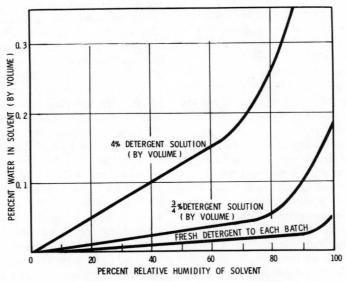

FIG. 2. Per cent RH over solvent *vs* per cent moisture in solvent.

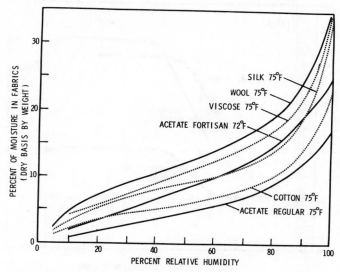

FIG. 3. Per cent RH around various fabrics *vs* per cent moisture in fabrics.

in these curves is very helpful, for if fabrics are placed in the solvent with excess moisture, the solutions can hold increasing amounts of moisture without increasing the solvent relative humidity greatly.

FABRIC WATER CARRYING ABILITY

Figure 3 is a presentation of the amount of moisture in various fabrics at various ambient equilibrium relative humidities. Fabrics can hold about 500 times as much water on a weight basis as can the solvent-detergent system. However, the total weight of the solution greatly exceeds that of the fabric at any one time so that the water distribution between these two components is more nearly equal.

Figures 4 and 5 point out the desirability of holding a cleaning system in close control. The best cleaning occurring at about 75 per cent RH in equilibrium with the solvent in the washer.

SHRINKAGE

Figure 6 presents data covering shrinkage showing that 75 per cent RH is about the top limit of moisture without excessive wrinkling.

All curves shown point out the importance of maintaining an internal system ambient equilibrium relative humidity of 75 per cent for best cleaning and least wrinkling.

MOISTURE SENSING

In order to maintain this moisture at an optimum figure, various moisture sensors have been used. They have included membrane materials, solution conductivity devices and electrical relative humidity sensors. The latter devices have proven the most practical and reliable. The "Honeywell" lithium chloride element, a variation of the original Dunmore sensor, has proven reliable and accurate for this application and has been used throughout the industry since 1955.

The "Honeywell" sensor has shown from various tests and numerous installations that it can be used in either perchlorethylene or petroleum vapors. The sensor is connected to an electronic relay that responds to element resistance changes as the element resistance changes in response to relative humidity.

MOISTURE CONTROL SYSTEM

A typical system shown in Fig. 7 includes the "Honeywell" lithium chloride sensor, electronic relay, timer, sensor housing with fan and water injection equipment.

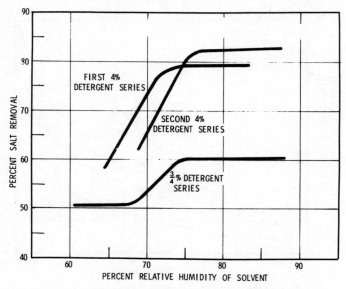

FIG. 4. Per cent RH over solvent *vs* per cent salt removal.

The sensor housing with fan—labeled "Vapo-Lator"—is used to insure that a representative sample of washer atmosphere is drawn from the washer and sampled by the element. The housing also maintains the element and vapor sample at the same temperature as the solvent in the washer. A short piece of pipe is used to close-couple this housing to the washer. Two 90-degree elbows are usually employed to prevent solvent splashing on the sensor. The vapor sample is always returned to the washer to insure that sampling does not create a vacuum in the washer; this also reduces the possibility of drawing room air in through any cracks in the washer, either of which can prevent a representative sample

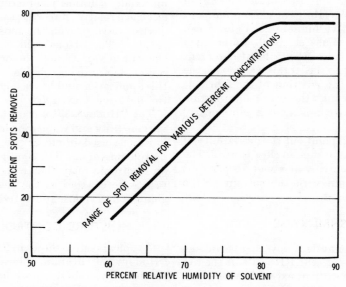

FIG. 5. Per cent RH over solvent *vs* per cent spot removal.

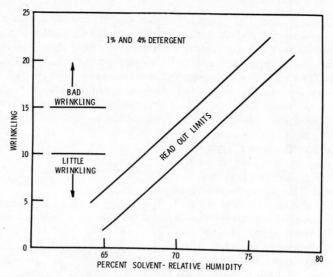

FIG. 6. Per cent RH over solvent *vs* wrinkling.

from reaching the element. A small portion of solvent is routed to the jacket of the housing to keep the housing at approximately the same temperature as the solvent in the washer. The portion of solvent is returned to the washer. The "Honeywell" lithium chloride element is located in this housing and is wired to the control station.

An electronic relay and a timer are located in the control station to provide control of the water injection cycle and control of the amount of water to be injected into the washer. A push button in the panel provides a manual starting means. The timer limits the time for water injection and, in addition, provides an initial delay before water can be added. This delay serves to allow the solvent, fabrics and vapor in the washer to come to moisture equilibrium before any water is added.

A per cent RH adjustment is also in this control station to adjust the per cent relative humidity to be maintained in the washer air space. This adjustment can be used to set the relative humidity to the optimum 75 per cent or any other value as required by various fabrics or types of soil. The adjustment can also be set to add only a minimum of water.

The water injection assembly is used as

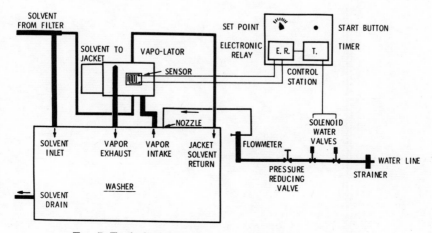

FIG. 7. Typical washer relative humidity control system.

the final control of the water. The assembly includes a water pressure regulator, a flow meter and flow nozzle to limit the rate of water addition. Two water valves are usually used in each system. The valves are connected in series in the water line. In the event that some dirt passes the water strainer—also included in the injection assembly—and lodges on one valve seat, the second valve will close the water line. The water is normally added to the washer by spraying it on the outside of the rotating washer wheel near the vapor sampling point. This allows the moisture to be sensed quickly and to be added in small amounts. The total moisture in the system is only allowed to increase slowly to prevent overshooting of the desired relative humidity.

The use of the above-described system has taken much of the guesswork out of the cleaning of fabrics. The machine operator is in complete control of the washing process.

OTHER USES

In addition to the use of the lithium chloride sensor for moisture control in dry-cleaning washers, this same approach can be used in other similar areas. Moisture can be detected in hydrocarbons such as fuel oil and in degreasing compounds such as trichlorethylene. If moisture is desired in these fluids, it can be added automatically to a desired concentration. Also, if moisture is undesirable, an alarm signal can be given on high moisture.

References

1. National Institute of Drycleaning, Silver Springs, Md., *Bulletin Service*. Bulletins **T268** (October 29, 1951); **T290** (September 30, 1952); **T292** (October 30, 1952); **T294** (November 28, 1952); **T296** (December 31, 1952); **T307** (June 30, 1953); **T310** (August 12, 1953); **T341** (May, 1955); **T342** (June, 1955); **T343** (July, 1955); **T350** (March, 1956); **T351** (April, 1956).
2. "Why the Charge System Wetcleaning?" *National Cleaner and Dyer* (April, 1953).
3. *Textile Res.*, **10**, 357–71 (1939).
4. Miner and Seastrone, "Handbook of Engineering Materials," 1st ed., New York, John Wiley & Sons, Inc., 1955.

51. An Actuating System for Condensation Control Equipment

Robert H. Gasch, Jr.

Honeywell Inc., Minneapolis, Minnesota

ABSTRACT

Condensation which forms on cold surfaces may cause considerable economic loss. Examples are the rusting of finished steel surfaces, the "white rust" of galvanized sheets, the deterioration of packages and labels of commodities, the water logging of the insulation of water cooled electrical generating equipment and damage to building structures.

Methods of condensation control used to prevent this sort of damage are: (1) heating of air or surfaces, (2) drying the ambient air, and (3) control of water temperature or flow to water cooled equipment.

An instrument is described which compares the dew point of the ambient air with the temperature of surfaces which may be damaged by condensation. When these temperatures approach each other within a predetermined differential, a relay may actuate any of the desired condensation control measures. The control system has an adjustable differential because some products are affected by humid air which is less than saturated and because the desired degree of protection from damage may vary in different applications.

INTRODUCTION

A most important problem in the steel distribution industry is the tendency toward surface deterioration of products during storage for further processing. Many attempts have been made to determine what conditions favor the rusting of steel. Experience indicates that the greatest contributor toward this problem is moisture, aided by ionic materials such as sulfur compounds and airborne salts.

It has been found that clean steel will begin to rust at 65 per cent RH even in the absence of accelerating ionic materials. When thses are present it is possible for rusting to occur at 35 per cent RH. Below this humidity level, steel is commonly regarded as safe from damage.

Organic protective materials are commonly used to protect finished steel from corrosion in storage, and these do decrease the possibility of damage. However, high humidity damage is still possible at cut edges or abraded surfaces, and water which condenses on the steel surface often penetrates the coating to damage areas selectively. Actual water condensed on materials not only can damage steel, but can ruin the finish of galvanized products, aluminum and copper alloys. Condensation on packaged goods spoils containers, labels and often the product itself. Steel storage is thus probably the largest but by no means the only area where protection from high atmospheric moisture is important.

HEATING AND DRYING

The product damage problem is most severe in temperate climates during the fall and spring periods where cold dry air alternates with air of high moisture content. It is severe during the entire year in tropical climates. In the cool periods, the steel is cooled, and the lag in temperature when the warmer moist air appears results in high relative humidity or

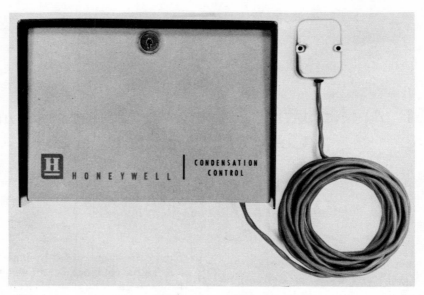

FIG. 1. Condensation control—external.

actual condensation on the product surface.

In the past 15 years, there has been an increasing tendency to prevent this meteorologically induced moisture damage by heating the product when periods of possible damage occur. Infrared heating appears to have certain advantages for this sort of application, but other forms of heating are also used. In tropical climates the use of air dryers may be indicated because additional heat may not be practical. The application of either air dryers or heating systems depends upon the use of a control system which will predict the possibility of damaging conditions and will control the counteracting equipment so that it operates only when required. Continuous operation of the counteracting equipment is unnecessarily expensive, and manual operation is ordinarily unreliable and requires the use of predicting instrumentation of considerable complexity. Manual control is useful on shipboard where competent supervision is available on the bridge during the entire 24-hour period. The cost of duplicating this type of care in land-based warehouses is almost prohibitively expensive.

Control of counteracting measures for moisture damage in warehouses requires a continuous record or continuous manual monitoring of ware temperature and of air dew-point temperature. Switching decisions are based on the data obtained. These decisions may utilize the trends of the observed temperatures or may be based only on the differential between the dew-point temperature and the ware temperature. The latter is the basis of the development of the "Honeywell Condensation Controller" (Fig. 1).

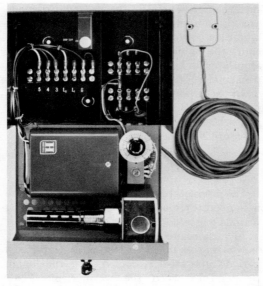

FIG. 2. Condensation control—internal.

CONDENSATION CONTROLLER

This controller compares the dew point of the ambient air with the temperature of the surface of the steel or other ware and switches on counteracting equipment if the differential decreases to a predetermined level. The differential is adjustable over a range of 4 to 35°F. No recording or indication instrumentation is provided or necessary although it may be fitted if desired.

The controller shown open in Fig. 2 utilizes a lithium chloride dew-point sensor of the self-heating type ("Honeywell DewProbe"). A special resistance thermometer in this dew-point sensor is operated in a bridge circuit to balance against the external resistance thermometer which is used for determining the surface temperature of the ware. A potentiometer in the bridge permits adjustment of the differential to the desired level.

SETTING THE DIFFERENTIAL

Many stored materials are injured by condensed water which may cause corrosion, injure the appearance of the commodity, its package or label, or initiate bacterial action. When prevention of condensation damage is important, the controller may be set near the minimum differential. However, since steel products do not require the presence of liquid water for damage to occur, it is necessary to control the counteracting equipment when the relative humidity reaches a "dangerous" level.

Consideration of Fig. 3 indicates that the condensation controller can also approximate a relative humidity controller if the differential is widened. For example, if a constant differential between the steel surface and the dew point is maintained at $13\frac{1}{2}$°F, the equivalent relative humidity will vary from 65 to 60 per cent over the temperature range 85 to 50°F. If the differential is maintained at $31\frac{1}{2}$°F. the equivalent relative humidity will vary from 35 to 25 per cent over the temperature range 85 to 50°F. This order of control accuracy is satisfactory for the protection of steel.

In temperate climates where the possibility of loss is severe but is limited to short periods each year, the control differential should be set to maintain 35 per cent RH or less at the steel,

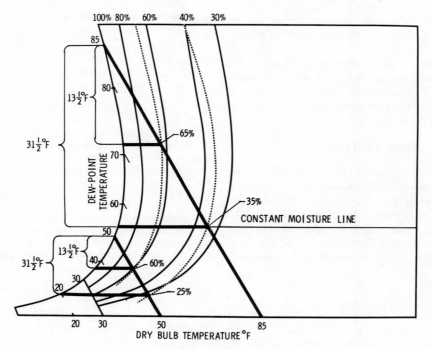

FIG. 3. Skeleton psychrometric chart.

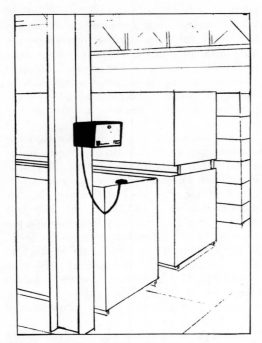

FIG. 4. Typical installation of condensation control.

as the cost of doing this will be relatively low during the short period of damaging weather. In tropical climates where protection is needed each day, it may be necessary to search out a more economical setting or to zone the storage areas so that different settings can be used depending on the properties of each material. Figure 4 shows the unit set up for steel storage; the temperature sensor is held to the steel.

DRIP PREVENTION

In some warehouses, on shipboard, or in various types of field house buildings, damage results primarily from the dripping of condensed water from ceilings or girders. The condensation controller may be used to prevent this type of damage. In this case the resistance thermometer must be fastened to the offending structure.

References

1. "Corrosion of Steel in Warehouses," *J. Appl. Chem.*, 8, 270–2 (April 1958); 8, 469–71 (August 1958).

2. "Influence of Insulation on Moisture Condensation Aspects of a Steel-Framed Cold Storage Warehouse Structure," *Refrig. Eng.*, 66, 39–44 (January 1958).

3. "Application of Humidity Control," *Instruments & Automation*, 31, 1208–9 (July 1958).

4. "Effects of Sunlight on Corrosion of Steel," *Corrosion*, 17, No. 6, 93–4 (June 1961).

5. "Investigation of Mild Steel Corrosion Rate in San Diego Harbor," *Corrosion*, 17, No. 4, 112–4 (April 1961).

6. "Are Hydrogen Ions Culprits that Cause Metal Corrosion?" *Iron Age*, 186, No. 5, 107–9 (August 4, 1960).

7. "Rust Preventitives Tested for Stainless Qualities," *Steel*, 147, No. 5, 92–3 (August 1, 1960).

8. "Note on the Anomalous Behavior of Ammonium Chloride Particles on the Corrosion of Steel in Humid Atmospheres," *Chem. & Ind.*, 1953, No. 38, 995–7 (September 19, 1953).

9. "Influence of Temperature on Corrosion Fatigue," *Corrosion*, 15, No. 5, 58–64 (May 1959).

10. "Atmosphere Corrosion of Steel," *Ind. Eng. Chem.*, 51, 79a–80a (September 1959).

11. "Corrosion Mechanisms in the Reaction of Steel with Water and Oxygenated Solutions at Room Temperature and 316°C," *J. Electrochem. Soc.*, 107, 73–9 (February 1960).

12. "Atmospheric Corrosion of Iron," *Heating and Ventilating*, 42, 110 (October 1945).

13. "Effect of Combined High Temperature and High Humidity on the Corrosion of Samples of Various Metals," *ASME Trans.*, 66, 624–32 (1944).

14. "Corrosion Control by Dehumidification," *Corrosion Prevent. & Control*, 5, 46–7 (December 1958).

15. "Corrosion of Steel in the Atmosphere of a Steel Mill," *J. Appl. Chem. USSR*, 31, 1770–2 (November 1957).

16. "The Study of Effect of Atmospheric Environment on Corrosion Rates of Steel," *Am. Paint J.*, 43, 68–84 (August 10, 1959).

17. "Corrosion of Steel in Moist Air," *J. Appl. Chem.*, 8, 270–2 (April 1958).

18. "The Protection of Structural Steelwork Against Atmospheric Corrosion," *Intern. Assoc. for Bridge & Structural Engrs. Publications*, 16, 185–230 (1956).

19. "Controlling Factor in Atmospheric and Immersed Corrosion," *J. Sci. Instr.*, 22, 226–30 (1945).

20. "Relation of the Moisture in Rust to the Critical Corrosion Humidity," *Trans. Faraday Soc.*, 27, 277–83 (1931).

21. "Rust, The Destroyer," *Paint Ind.*, 64, 287–90 (1949).

22. *Trans. Faraday Soc.*, 31, 2 (1935).

23. *Trans. Faraday Soc.*, 23 (1927).

24. *Corrosion*, 7, 335 (1951).

25. *Corrosion*, 9, 259 (1953).

26. *Proc. ASTM*, **46**, 652 (1946); **45**, 554 (1945); **48**, 591 (1948).

27. Proceedings of the Symposium on Preservation for Mobilization Requirements, U.S. Naval Civil Engineering Research and Evaluation Laboratory, Port Hueneme, Calif., 1956.

28. "Humidity and Temperature Effects on Atmospheric Corrosion Rates," Literature Report, Rock Island Arsenal Laboratory, PB No. 171547, AD256597.

29. Brasunas, Anton de, "Symposium on Corrosion Fundamentals,"

30. Friend, "Corrosion of Iron and Steel,"

31. Speller, Frank N., "Corrosion Causes and Prevention," New York, McGraw-Hill Book Co., Inc.,

52. The Use of Relative Humidity Sensors to Monitor the Atmosphere within Hermetically Sealed Electronic Modules

Elias J. Amdur and Harold C. Lofgren

Minneapolis-Honeywell Regulator Co., Minneapolis, Minnesota

ABSTRACT

High relative humidity is often the cause of failure of electronic components and assemblies. One way of overcoming this danger is to mount these components within a container which is subsequently evacuated and heated, then back filled with dry inert gas, and then hermetically sealed.

Experience has indicated that modules processed in this way may not be free of moisture. Humidity sensors may be enclosed in such packages during preliminary stages of development so the processing steps may be worked out and the desired moisture-free condition achieved, or they may be enclosed permanently in each such module so that they may be given 100 per cent inspection at any time.

A special humidity sensor of the lithium chloride PVA type was developed for this type of service, and has been used in approximately 30,000 modules of a military computer system. It was found in early experiments that a major source of moisture was that which diffused from the interior of enclosed plastic materials such as nylon. This diffusion of moisture was found to continue for several months.

A procedure was worked out with the manufacturer of these modules whereby the plastic parts were predried in an oven and other process details were improved. Subsequent operational checks proved that both the modules and the humidity sensing system were highly satisfactory.

Sensors used for this service have an oper-ational alarm range of 3.5 to 16 per cent RH and a drift of calibration of less than ½ per cent RH per year under these conditions.

INTRODUCTION

High relative humidity is often the cause of failure of electronic components and assemblies which are not specifically designed to be resistant to this condition; it may cause difficulties even in assemblies which are so designed. Consequently, a humidity warning or control system is often a part of important electronic installations such as computers.

A recent trend in the computer field and in the design of other electronic devices required to have a long reliable life, is to install sub-assemblies in individual hermetically sealed packages (modules) in which an inert dry atmosphere is maintained. These modules are built as plug-in units which may be replaced if they are found defective. This system substantially reduces the number of components and connections which are exposed to the ambient atmosphere, resulting in improved reliability of the completed system. It is often possible with this modular design to use inexpensive standard components rather than premium sealed units within the packages. This cost reduction may equal or exceed the additional cost of the container and processing.

Examples of the use of hermetically sealed computer modules are found in the Athena missile guidance computer developed by

428

Remington Rand Univac and in a similar computer developed by the Burroughs Corporation. In these units the printed circuit boards and components are mounted on the base of the container which carries glass insulated feed throughs. The remaining part of the container is a metal shell which is soldered to the base by means of induction heating. This process is carried out in a very rapid cycle so that the contents of the package do not rise to a temperature harmful to germanium transistors. After the module is assembled it is evacuated through a seal-off tube for several hours at moderate temperatures of 120 to 130°F. It is back filled with a dry gas composed of 5 per cent helium and 95 per cent nitrogen to a pressure of 2 to 4 psig. The seal-off tube is then pinched off and solder-sealed.

Experience has shown that modules processed in this manner may not be initially moisture free, or slow leaks may allow entrance of moisture after a period. It is therefore essential to include a moisture indicator in every package. Visual indicators, observed through a glass port, have been tried but have not been satisfactory. Electrical resistance humidity sensors have been found to be particularly well adapted to this service. A resistance sensor is assembled as an additional component within the module, and connection is made through two additional glass insulated leads in the base of the module. During processing and storage the moisture content of the package may be determined by testing with an AC ohmmeter, contact being made directly to these leads. In service in a computer, the humidity sensors are connected through a panel board to a motorized selector switch and warning system. As part of the daily computer check, the moisture content of each module is tested. If a defective unit is found, the selector switch stops at this position and a warning light attracts attention to the failure. Computers with 800 to 1200 modules have been successfully operated with this warning system.

HUMIDITY SENSORS

Minneapolis-Honeywell has manufactured electrical resistance humidity sensors since 1950. The "MH Q229A" element which has

been available since that time has proved to be a stable and reliable device in many applications. While this sensor is suitable for computer applications, space and other design considerations did not permit its use in the Univac and Burroughs' Computers. For the Univac application the "Q422A was developed. This sensor differs from the "Q229A" element in size and shape, but has the same electrical characteristic. It is useful in the range 3.5 to 16 per cent RH, the exact limits varying with the resistance range of the measuring instrumentation used with it. The mount and electrical connections, and the automatic scanning readout meter were supplied by Univac. The "Q464A" sensor is a more recent device, for which Honeywell supplies mounts and readout equipment. These sensors are shown in Fig. 1. The electrical characteristic curve is shown in Fig. 2.

The "Q229A", "Q422A" and "Q464A" sensors are not affected by the heat and flux fumes of the soldering operation in assembly of the cans. They are unaffected by evacuation and by the final atmosphere within the modules. A small drift in characteristic occurs with time, this being less than 1 per cent per year. It is easy to compensate for this change by sampling modules after several years of service. This should not be necessary more often than at intervals of three to five years.

PROCESSING OF HERMETICALLY SEALED PACKAGES

When the first humidity sensors were installed in hermetically sealed modules, it was found that processing methods used for these units were unsatisfactory. As a result of intensive cooperative efforts of Minneapolis-Honeywell and the computer design personnel, a satisfactory procedure was developed. This procedure and precautions are discussed below.

An important consideration in the selection of components for inclusion in a module is that none of the materials used in their construction should be hygroscopic. For example, nylon may hold as much as 6 per cent of water and should be avoided if possible. If such plastics must be used, they should be preprocessed in a vacuum oven for an extended period before assembly. The time required will depend upon

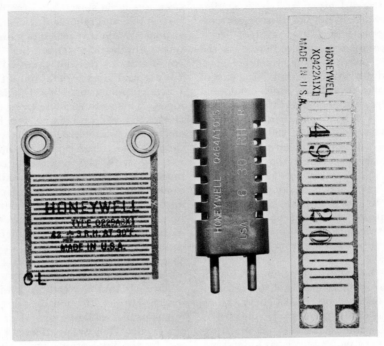

Fig. 1. Humidity sensors, Q229, Q464 and Q422, from left to right.

section thickness. The moisture absorbed from the atmosphere during assembly usually presents no problem as it does not penetrate deeply during the period that the part is exposed to the atmosphere. This surface water may then be removed in the evacuation step. Assembly in a dry atmosphere is a practical solution if resorption is felt to unduly burden the evacuation equipment with a long drying period.

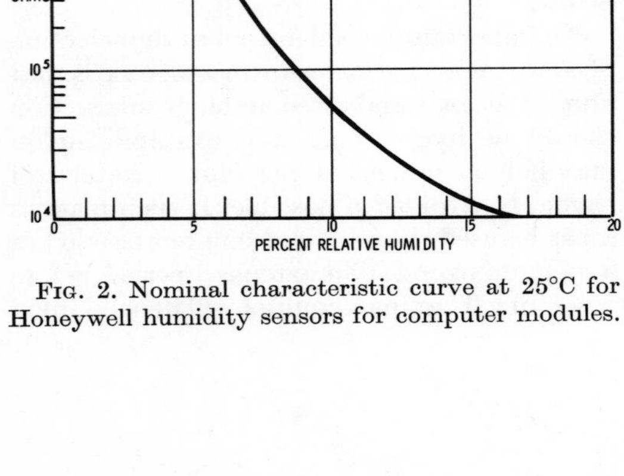

After completion of assembly and inspection, the metal shell is induction soldered to the connector end. The unit is then checked for large leaks by evacuation on a mass spectrometer leak tester, and testing with a helium jet or atmosphere around the exterior.

The drying of the sealed computer modules is accomplished by evacuation equipment capable of achieving 0.1 to 1 μ of pressure within the module. The modules are connected to fittings from the pumping equipment mounted on removable oven doors and are then placed in the oven. They are pumped for 4 to 8 hours at 120 to 130°F. The progress of the drying can be checked by sealing off the oven manifold and observing the rate of rise of pressure in the module. When the modules are dry, the manifold is back filled with a gas mixture of 95 per cent nitrogen and 5 per cent helium which has a dew point below −40°F. A positive pressure of 2 to 4 psig is maintained in the manifold and modules. The individual modules are then sealed off by pinch sealing

Fig. 2. Nominal characteristic curve at 25°C for Honeywell humidity sensors for computer modules.

and cutting of the copper tube suction connection. Dip soldering assures a tight pinch seal. The modules can be rechecked for leaks by a helium leak detector sniffer used around the exterior of the shell and pinch seals.

This procedure was evolved after a long series of trials using ordinary oven drying for short periods before sealing in the can, and a variety of rapid evacuation and back filling procedures. While the recommended procedure is a rather involved one, the necessity of each step and condition has been thoroughly proven.

HOW DRY SHOULD THE MODULES BE?

Even after a reasonable length of experience with hermetically sealed modules no single value of humidity has been accepted as adequate and standard. While most of these computers are operated at constant temperature, they are likely to be stored or transported under less favorable conditions. If a module had a relative humidity of 20 per cent at 77°F, water would condense in it if it were suddenly cooled to 32°F. As corrosion may occur at humidities well below saturation, it is desirable that relative humidity values below 10 per cent at 77°F be used. Then the relative humidity will be only 50 per cent at 32°F.

Aside from leakage, the most common source of excessive moisture within the hermetic package is the hygroscopic plastic which may form part of its insulating or structural material. Other factors may dictate the use of such materials even though they may require special care in processing. If these materials are not adequately dehydrated, the vapor pressure within the processed modules may build up to undesirable values after a few weeks. Vacuum predrying of these components at maximum safe temperatures for an extended period should precede assembly. The procedure of pumping the completed package at the maximum safe temperature of 130°F for eight hours will then bring the contents to a low humidity, and safety will be assured. Remington Rand Univac processed to an initial relative humidity of less than 2 per cent at 77°F. Some rise in relative humidity was observed in the following weeks of storage. When proper care had been taken at all stages

of the processing, the module reached equilibrium at a safe relative humidity level. The humidity sensor thus performs a valuable function in monitoring the entire drying process, and it can be said to be an essential inspection tool for hermatic sealing operations.

The primary purpose of the humidity sensor, nevertheless, is to serve as a means of detecting modules which develop leaks in service. Frequent automatic scanning of the humidity sensors with the warning limit set at just above the reading of the module with the highest relative humidity in the computer will detect units failing suddenly. Periodic logging of the individual sensors while close temperature control is maintained will detect units which are slowly drifting up toward unsafe conditions.

EFFECT OF AGE ON THE TOLERANCE HUMIDITY SENSORS

All humidity sensors of the resistance *vs* relative humidity type show some change in calibration with time. Elements of the Dunmore type are the most stable humidity sensors which are available. They may change in calibration about $\frac{1}{2}$ per cent RH per year in the sealed packages. In order to insure that element resistance readings can be adequately interpreted at all times, Honeywell has undertaken to offer recalibration service for elements taken from modular packages. A sample lot of such elements is thus recalibrated to give data from which a new calibration curve may be constructed for the remaining units.

Module safeguard elements are sold with an initial guaranteed tolerance of $\pm$ 3 per cent from the standard curve (Fig. 2). As actually made, they have proved to be almost 100 per cent within a tolerance of $+ 1$ and $- 3$ per cent RH. Since the calibration shift which occurs is toward higher relative humidity values, the elements when new are all at least 2 per cent below the upper tolerance limit. Thus the elements will require up to four years for any to age outside the original tolerances, and up to eight years for any to age outside the five-year tolerance of $+5$ per cent RH. These elements thus have a rated life of five years, and by means of the recalibration procedure, this may be extended with confidence to a ten-year period or longer.

SUMMARY OF APPLICATIONS

The use of relative humidity sensors can yield information at several stages of the manufacturing operation. In the design and development stage, the sensors can be used to evaluate the choice of materials and components and the design of the module case. In the process stage, they can evaluate production processing equipment and processing schedules. In the production stage, the sensors serve as a qualtiy control tool for maintaining adequate processing conditions, and for final inspection of modules. Finally, in the operational stage of the computer, they supply a signal to the warning system for indicating failure of seal of the module case.

The enclosure of one sensor in each module is the most reliable procedure and a necessity for certain military computers. For commercial computers, where this extreme reliability may not be required, the humidity sensors can monitor production processing conditions even when installed on a small fraction of the modules. Or, even if no sensors are sealed into the final modules, periodic processing of simulated modules containing sensors will aid in the development of adequate processing techniques.

In some types of equipment, the modules are large semi-hermetically sealed units with gaskets and are designed to be recharged with a desiccant or reprocessed with dry gas periodically. If economics preclude the use of one sensor per module, a method of withdrawing a sample of the atmosphere and measuring its condition by an external sensor could be devised.

53. An Unusual Nylon-actuated Humidistat

GORDON GUSTAFSON

Honeywell Inc., Minneapolis, Minnesota

ABSTRACT

This paper describes the selection, examination, and application of nylon film as an actuator for a humidistat.

The work covering the initial examination of the nylon material is discussed in some detail. Figures showing the difference between nylon 6-10 and nylon 6-6 are included.

Two preliminary humidistat designs with nylon 6-6 are considered in some detail.

The properties of tensile strength and modulus, creep, time constants of sorption and desorption and how they affect humidistat design are discussed. The effect of switch energy requirements are considered.

A "final" design of nylon actuated humidistat and the development work leading to this design is included. Nylon type 6 is applied to this design.

Nylon is an excellent actuator for a humidistat if carefully applied. Attention must be given to film thickness and mounting. Consideration must be given to maximum and normal operating stresses. The material must be properly conditioned for best results.

It is recommended that a specific lot of nylon be ordered and sampled for any given application. The design may then be modified to provide optimum results.

Using homogeneous readily available film as a sensing element was considered when the need for an inexpensive yet dependable, humidistat for controlling humidity appliances became evident. Classic hygroscopic materials such as animal membranes and cellulose products have one or more characteristics which make them undesirable as humidistat elements. These include long-term instability, lack of resistance to normal environments, small dimensional change with change in relative humidity, excessively long response time, processing difficulties, and high cost.

For satisfactory service a humidistat must have these minimum characteristics:

(1) Low cost,

(2) Reasonable maintenance-free reliability,

(3) Durability to withstand storing, shipping and installation in a wide range of environments, and

(4) Ability to switch the required electrical load in response to nominal relative humidity changes around a preset control point.

A preliminary survey of materials for an actuator turned up extensive research on hygroscopic materials made by engineers at Honeywell's Wabash (Indiana) plant in the early 1930's. Additional research was done by Dr. E. J. Amdur, Research Director of Honeywell's Special Sensor Products Group in 1954. These studies indicated that of all the possible useful hygroscopic materials, nylon showed the most promise.[2]

Several samples of nylon material in filament and film form were investigated (Fig. 1). The samples of nylon 6-10 showed less than 1 per cent change in length from 0 to 80 per cent relative humidity, while the sample of nylon 6-6 showed a change slightly less than 1.75 per cent for the same relative humidity change. The results were found to be reproducible within a very small margin.

The tensile-elastic modulus of nylon 6-6 was known to be approximately 250,000 psi in the 50 per cent RH range, greater at lower relative

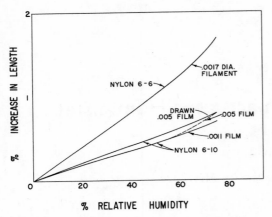

FIG. 1. Length change with per cent RH of preliminary nylon samples.

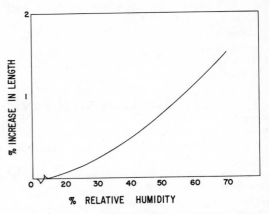

FIG. 2. Length change with per cent RH. Type 6-6 nylon film (first designs).

humidity levels, and somewhat less at higher relative humidities.

Samples of nylon 6-6 in the form of films were further investigated as elements for experimental humidistats. The length change of nylon 6-6 film with varying relative humidities (Fig. 2) was checked by experiment. The length change with relative humidity of this material is slightly greater than the sample filament of Fig. 1. This is typical of nylon material.

Problems to be solved included adjusting the stress to a level where creep[4] or long-term stability and the time constant of sorption and

desorption would be at useful levels. Element contamination was an unknown factor.

Two designs were developed and produced using nylon film ½ in wide and .002 in. thick. These sensors operated snap-action switches with approximately .0002-in. differential travel and 1-ounce operating force differential.

The first device was designed to have approximately equal tension on the element at all times when the relative humidity was at or below the switching point (Fig. 3A). However, load switching requirements dictated larger changes in switching force, and a second design (Fig. 3B) was produced. This design would

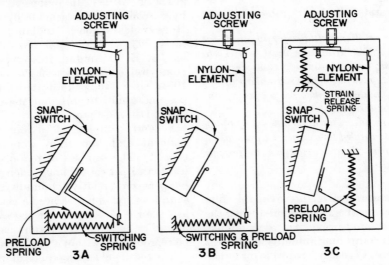

FIG. 3. Three designs with ½ in. wide × .002 in. thick elements of nylon type 6-6.

operate at a maximum sensor stress level of approximately 300 psi when the relative humidity was below the control point. At this stress level, the creep or loss of control point would reach approximately 5 per cent relative humidity after 24 hours and proceed to drift at the rate of 0.5 per cent relative humidity a month. The original control point was restored upon removal of the stress.[4] The stress while cycling the switch was approximately 100 psi; when the RH was above the control point, the stress was 0 psi.

Requirements for larger switch ratings prompted a dual-element design (Fig. 3C). This design would switch larger loads because it could apply force to the switch beyond the internal switch effort. Still larger switch loads were obtained by raising the energy input to the switches. The effect on device differential

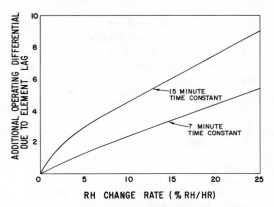

FIG. 5. Additional operating differential due to element lag.

entials was a lag due to a time constant of 15 minutes. The effect of this time constant on operating differential is shown in Fig. 5. Since most residential humidity apparatus is of relatively small capacity, a rate of rise or fall of 5 per cent RH per hour is "normal." This time constant would add 3 per cent RH to the cycling differential. Larger equipment or a smaller space would produce a greater rate of rise or fall and add more to the differential.

Ordinary dust and residential atmospheres do not affect the performance adversely. Relatively heavy coatings of grease or oil will slow the element response to RH changes. After cleaning with naphtha or ether the element will perform at its original efficiency. Production elements, which may become oily, are degreased with trichloroethylene with no adverse effect. Chemicals described as polar,

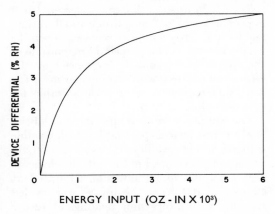

FIG. 4. Device differential and switch energy for the design of Fig. 3C.

vs energy input for this design is shown in Fig. 4. (In passing, switching ability of snap-action switches in a given device is not proportional to the energy input. The device in Fig. 3C would switch a 6-A motor load with the .0002 in.-ounce switch while the device with the .006 in.-ounce switch could only handle 10 As. The reason is that the maximum element stress is the same for a given design. This limits the overtravel or contact-opening ability more severely for a switch of higher energy level. With careful switch design, however, a higher energy switch will deliver more switching ability).

Superimposed upon the operating differ-

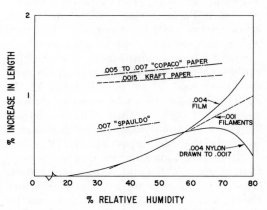

FIG. 6. Length change with relative humidity for miscellaneous materials.

such as glycols and alcohols, will simulate the presence of water and should be avoided.

Other materials—drawn nylon monofilament, drawn nylon film, thicker nylon film, high-grade papers—were checked to see if they might be more suitable (Fig. 6, Table 1.)

TABLE 1

Material	Time Constant
.004 Nylon film	90 min.
.001 Dia. drawn and annealed filaments	5 min.
.007 "Spauldo" paper	9 min.
.005–7 "Copaco" paper	4 min.
.0015 "Kraft" paper	3 min.

Results show that high-grade papers have low time constants while the length change is so small that they are of little practical value. The thicker (.004-in.) nylon film could carry a heavier load, but it has an exceedingly long time constant. The nylon monofilaments have both reasonable length change and time constant, but they also have additional problems: the length change is approximately 50 per cent that of the standard nylon element and the material must be stress-relieved to eliminate the characteristic shown by the drawn film (Fig. 6), and this results in unequal shortening of the filaments. Then the stress-relieved filaments are subject to the same creep as the extruded film. Drawn film was of no value as a possible humidistat element without further conditioning.

Another investigation established the relationship between element stress and control point shift. Two materials were included in this investigation—.002-in. thick and half-inch wide samples of nylon type 6-6 and type 6.

Samples were mounted in humidistats with calibrated springs providing the load. Ambient conditions were 50 per cent RH and 75 °F. Drift readings were taken by removing the load to the switching level of approximately 50 psi. This data was compared with results obtained by Marin, Webber, and Weissmann (Fig. 7).[4]

The findings indicate nylon film creeps more than Marin, Webber and Weissmann predict. Some of the discrepancy may have been from the difference between molded samples and the extruded film examined in this test. Mounting conditions of the films may introduce some

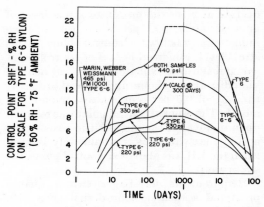

FIG. 7. Control point shift with time for nylon 6-6 and nylon 6 at various stress levels.

error, and differences in the periodic reading may have caused error.

The results do show that nylon elements drift in proportion to load magnitude and duration, and have a nearly complete recovery when the load is removed. The shape and magnitude of the curves were probably influenced by the relaxation required while taking readings. The drift was measured on a scale suitable for type 6-6 nylon.

Test samples were also exposed to humidities varying from 20 to 80 per cent RH to determine stability or repeatability of these elements over a long period of time. For the test, the elements were mounted in humidistats calibrated at 42 per cent RH. Then the devices were cycled 10 times with intervening readings at 42 per cent. The total elapsed time was 140 days with

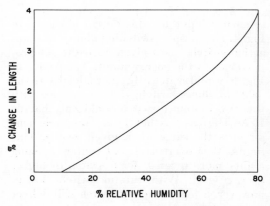

FIG. 8. Length change with per cent RH for a sample of type 6 nylon.

7 to 21 days elapsing between successive readings.

Results showed a maximum deviation at the calibration point of 1 per cent RH for the type 6-6 elements and 2.8 per cent for the type 6 elements—excellent for this type humidistat.

In addition, elongation of the type 6 nylon was much greater than that of type 6-6 (Fig. 8). The total length change of nearly 4 per cent over the relative humidity range of 20 to 80 per cent is a tremendous improvement over the less-than-2 per cent change for type 6-6 material, for it means that linkage accuracy and stiffness, switch energy input and calibration accuracy may be relaxed for a given quality of device. Conversely, the quality of a given device will be upgraded by changing to the more active material.

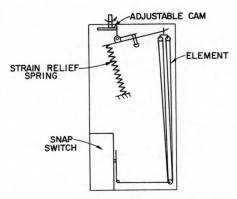

FIG. 9. A humidistat design with an element of type 6 nylon .75 in. wide × .001 in. thick.

The problem of obtaining faster response to humidity changes was solved by reducing the material thickness from .002 to .001 in. Cheney[3] indicates that nylon suffers from oxidation when exposed to high temperatures and sunlight. However, observation of elements several years old showed no measurable shifts from this condition. Cutting the film thickness in half reduced the time constant to approximately 7 minutes (Fig. 5).

One more device was designed to take advantage of this additional elongation (Fig. 9). Four parallel ribbons .001 in. thick, .75 in. wide, and 2.9 in. long drive a switch with .001-in. travel and 1-ounce force change. Maximum element stress is below 300 psi and

stress at switching is approximately 50 psi. The device has a differential of approximately 2 per cent RH and will swtich a 7-A motor load.

With an untreated element under maximum stress, the device is conditioned at a temperature and RH above normal service conditions for three reasons:

(1) The nylon conforms to any inclination of the rollers and each ribbon carries its share of the load.

(2) The nylon assumes the radii of the rollers, with a resulting greater axial stiffness.

(3) While the nylon creeps during the process, it will not continue to creep nor reverse or recover this creep under normal operating conditions. The unit then has a more stable control point and is not dependent on a drop in stress to restore original calibration.

Nylon from different manufacturers—and even the same material in different lots from a given manufacturer—will have different properties. For a given purpose, enough material of the same lot should be accumulated to cover the purpose intended. The material should be tested for the characteristics important to the design, and any needed corrections should be made.

Strip nylon film, with the exceptions noted, has good long-term stability, is uniform, readily available in continuous strip, durable in normal environments, and easily fabricated into humidistat elements. Nylon was chosen as the most satisfactory plastic film due to its relatively large change in length with relative humidity and high modulus in tension. Other plastic films were considered but discarded as less desirable than nylon for one or more of the reasons mentioned.

References

1. Magner, Philip G., A report covering work on hygroscopic materials directed by Paul F. Shivers and Mark C. Honeywell at the Wabash (Indiana) Plant of Minneapolis-Honeywell Regulator Company, 1932–1934.
2. Abbott, N. J., Note on the Construction of Fiber Hygrometers, *Textile Res. J.*, **24**, 59 (1954).
3. Cheney, A. J., "Designing with Nylon," *Machine Design*, **28**, 95–102 (February 1954).
4. Marin, J., Webber, A. C., Weissmann, G. F., "Creep-time Relations for Nylon in Tension, Compression, Bending and Torsion," *A.S.T.M. Proc.*, **54**, 1313 (1954).

5. Kline, G. M., Martin, A. R., Crouse, W. A., "Sorption of Water by Plastics," *Mod. Plastics*, **18**, 119–23, 152–4 (1940).

6. Quistwater, J. M. R., Dunell, B. A., "Dynamic Properties of Nylon 6-6 and the Plasticizing Effect of Water Vapor on Nylon," *J. App. Polymer Sci.*, **1**, 267–71 (1959).

7. Abbott, N. J., and Goodings, A. C., "Moisture Absorption, Density, and Swelling of Nylon Filaments," *J. Textile Inst.*, **60**, 232–46 (1949).

8. Eckstein, B. H., Olson, E. H., Ames, W. F., "Responses to Environmental Changes and an Equation of State for Nylon Yarn," *Textile Res. J.*, **28**, 701–7 (1958).

9. Riley, M. W., "New Look at Modern Plastics," *Mater. Design Eng.*, **48**, No. 7, 94–9 (1958).

SECTION VI

METEOROLOGY

54. State-of-the-art Survey on the Application of Hygrometry to Meteorology

Albert K. Showalter

U.S. Weather Bureau, Washington, D.C.

ABSTRACT

Hygrometric problems unique to meteorology are discussed. Moisture occurs in all three of its forms—vapor, liquid and solid—in the atmosphere, and the exchanges of latent heat accompanying changes in state have direct effects on atmospheric circulation. The frequent occurrence of subcooled water droplets makes it very difficult to predict changes of state.

Typical demands for information and general requirements for accuracy are reviewed. Emphasis is placed on the need for precision of measurement as the relative humidity nears the saturation value. This precision is difficult to attain if the moisture content is determined from a direct-reading dew-point indicator scaled in whole degrees. At low relative humidity, dew points to the nearest degree Celsius may be adequate.

The limitations of some well-known hygrometers are itemized, and specific requirements for more ideal sensors are outlined for both surface and upper air observations. Accuracy criteria are listed as 0.3°C for surface dew points and 1.0°C for upper air dew points. An additional objective is that the instrument should indicate at least 95 per cent RH when exposed in a saturated calibration chamber.

BASIC PROBLEMS

Meteorology has exacting, unique and sometimes puzzling requirements for measurement of humidity and moisture content of the atmosphere.

Water occurs in the atmosphere in all three of its phases and is the only major constituent of the atmosphere which varies markedly in time and space.

The state of the atmosphere is controlled to a large degree by the content and form of water within it.

Each change of state is accompanied by some exchange of latent and sensible heat.

Changes from the liquid to the solid state or from the vapor to the solid state are not expressly determined by the ambient air temperature. Liquid water has often been observed at temperature well below −30°C. Kobayashi[1] detected direct condensation of liquid droplets at temperatures well below −50°C.

The reverse process of changing from the solid to the liquid state apparently is uniquely determined by the wet-bulb temperature of the ambient air, and melting invariably begins as soon as the wet-bulb temperatures exceed 0°C.

TYPICAL DEMANDS

In his function of describing, recording and forecasting the state of the atmosphere, the meteorologist must have a wide variety of moisture measurements. Such measurements are not for his science alone but to meet the requirements of the many customers he serves. Prominent among these requirements are:

(1) The oceanographers, hydrologists and the agriculturalists must know the rate of moisture loss or gain over oceans, lakes, snow

surfaces, forests, prairies and other land surfaces.

(2) The aviation interests must know the vapor content of the air in order to anticipate the formation of fog, clouds, vapor trails and carburetor icing. Pilots, in effect, need to know the 3-dimensional distribution and the liquid and solid water content of fog, and clouds and precipitation because of the associated implications of poor visibility, icing and turbulence. New high-speed jet aircraft flying through zones of excessively high liquid water content are exposed to possible flame-out and serious skin damage.

(3) Radar and microwave communication rays are subject to refraction and attenuation by moisture layers and liquid and solid forms of water.

(4) Exploration and air travel in the space, missile and supersonic-transport age have introduced new problems of air sampling requiring the detection of moisture at levels above 30 km. Because nearly all airborne carriers, including parachutes, move at relatively high speeds at levels of 50 km and above, a special type of very accurate, sensitive and fast response detector is required to measure the very low quantities of moisture in the upper stratosphere.

ACCURACY REQUIREMENTS

One of the major problems of meteorologists is the forecasting of the occurrence of condensation in the form of fog or clouds. Because of impurities in the atmosphere which may serve as nuclei of condensation, fog may begin to form well before the relative humidity reaches 100 per cent. To anticipate clouds, it is necessary to have high accuracy of humidity measurements when the true relative humidity. is greater than 80 per cent. Temperature, dew point and relative humidity are interrelated functions of saturation vapor pressure which is uniquely determined by temperature. A temperature of 20°C and a dew point of 10°C indicate a relative humidity of 52.5 per cent regardless of the pressure. With this combination, an error of 1°C in dew point would result in an error of 3.5 per cent in relative humidity. As saturation is approached at the same temperature an error of 1°C in dew point would cause an error of 6 per cent in relative humidity.

At temperatures of −30°C, an error of 1°C in dew point near saturation would cause 10 per cent error in relative humidity. However, with an air temperature of −30°C and a dew point of near −50°C, an error of 1°C in dew point would produce only about 1.5 per cent in relative humidity.

Because of the fact that forecasting condensation is so important, the greatest requirement for precision must be placed in the near-saturation zone. Unfortunately at all ranges of temperature, small changes in dew point are associated with relatively large changes in relative humidity in the near-saturation zone. If precise methods were available for measuring relative humidity directly to 1 per cent accuracy this would be the best criteria for a calibration standard. Relative humidity would also serve as a more precise unit than any we now have for transmission of moisture data to computers or data processing centers. However, for identification of air masses, as a tracer and for geographical comparisons of moisture distribution, the dew point is a much better index. Relative humidity changes with any change in temperature, whereas dew point is conservative with respect to non-adiabatic heating or cooling and is relatively conservative with respect to small changes in pressure. For most meteorological purposes, an accuracy of 1°C in dew point is sufficient. However, when the relative humidity goes above 80 per cent the need for precision increases, and calibration tests must incorporate criteria for better definition of the nearness to saturation.

AVAILABLE TECHNIQUES

A review of presently available techniques points up problems and inadequacies:
(A) Meteorologists have traditionally used the wet- and dry-bulb psychrometer as a basic humidity measuring device in making surface observations.

Difficulties in its use include:
(1) Automation and telemetering are complicated.
(2) Use at below-freezing wet-bulb temperatures requires special techniques and care. The result is that data obtained at low temperatures are erratic and at times very inaccurate.
(3) Under extremes of relative humidity

special techniques are required and, in the case of high humidity at least, required accuracy is difficult if not impossible to achieve.

(B) The infrared hygrometer is an instrument currently under development by instrument engineers of the Weather Bureau and others. (Mr. Foskett and his colleagues report on this instrument in Volume I). It is a sensitive and accurate instrument, but its routine use in meteorology presents problems:

  (1) The intricacy of the instrument may result in unfavorable cost and maintenance demands if its output is to be directly converted to dew-point temperatures.

  (2) Weight and power demands may be high.

  (3) The form of the measurement (i.e., absolute humidity) is not conservative with respect to adiabatic compression and expansion and is therefore not commonly used by meteorologists. To convert the output of the infrared hygrometer into dew point requires complicated calculation or precise graphical computation. These computations require knowledge of the ambient air temperature.

  (4) For high relative humidities at moderate and high temperatures, the accuracy of measurement may not be adequate.

  (5) Since the instrument has instantaneous response (i.e., no lag), the read-out must have an integrator to obtain representative meteorological measurements and filter out the higher frequency variations which, for the purpose of most meteorological measurements, constitute meteorological noise.

(C) The Lyman-Alpha humidiometer shows interesting possibilities but is still a laboratory type instrument and requires further development.

(D) With developments in Peltier cooling, the technique based on the change of light reflectivity of a mirror as it is cooled to the dew-point temperature is being tested by meteorologists. However,

  (1) Until the tests are completed it will not be possible to assess the value of this type of sensor.

  (2) For some meteorological applications (upper air measurements), weight is too great and power requirements are too high.

(E) The dewcell has been adopted as an interim standard for automated humidity measurements at the surface by the U.S. Weather Bureau, the U.S. Air Force and the U.S. Navy.

  (1) This device converts a lithium chloride "dew-point" temperature to a direct-reading equivalent water vapor dew-point temperature.

  (2) The dewcell does not have satisfactory accuracy for many meteorological purposes, and its range is completely inadequate.

  (3) The instrument may become unstable and may, without prior indication, begin giving completely erroneous measurements.

  (4) Power requirements, weight and its highly critical ventilation rate preclude the use of the sensor for upper air measurements.

(F) Tests are being conducted on organic sensors which change physical form or dimensions with changes in humidity. Sensors included in this classification include the hair hygrometer, the Frankenberger hair, gold-beater's skin, the xerometer, etc.

  (1) All sensors of this class have accuracy and reproducibility limitations that make them unsatisfactory for precise meteorological purposes. They are most useful as trend indicators at temperatures well above freezing.

  (2) There are also problems with automation of these sensors since an intermediate transducer to convert motion (produced by change of length or form) to an electrical parameter is necessary. This characteristic also complicates the use of such sensors in upper air measurements by a balloon-borne radiosonde.

  (3) In these sensors the lag is a function of temperature and becomes intolerably large especially for radiosonde work at low temperatures.

(G) Humidity to electrical resistance transducers have common problems of accuracy and reproducibility.

(1) The lithium chloride strip has unsatisfactory accuracy, particularly with very high or very low humidity. It has excessive lag at low temperatures. If it is washed by rain its accuracy is completely destroyed.

(2) Aluminum oxide sensors (Jason Hygrometers) have been found to have unsatisfactory accuracy at high relative humidities.

(3) Ion-exchange sensors have not yet demonstrated sufficient accuracy for many meteorological purposes.

(4) The carbon element which is still under development responds well at high humidities, but it appears difficult to mass-produce units with stable calibration properties.

(5) The potassium metaphosphate hygrometer is highly temperature sensitive and has unsatisfactory lag and accuracy characteristics at low temperatures.

(6) The barium fluoride has good accuracy and very satisfactory lag characteristics but will not hold calibration more than a few days.

(7) In all sensors of this class, the lag is a function of temperature and, as is true of sensors which depend on deformation or change of dimensions, the lag becomes intolerably large for upper air work at low temperatures.

(8) Sensors of this type have a limited range when used in conjunction with available readout devices. For example, it is impossible for the radiosonde using the lithium chloride sensor to measure relative humidities less than 40 per cent at temperatures of $-40°C$ or less.

FUTURE OPERATIONAL REQUIREMENTS

The operational needs of the meteorological profession could be met by three new sensors having capabilities beyond the present state-of-the-art. One would be for use in the surface observational program, the second for use in the radiosonde program and the third for use in the rocketsonde program.

(A) The sensor for the surface observational program should:

(1) Have an overall accuracy equivalent to less than 0.3°C error in dew-point temperatures.

(2) Be stable in calibration and remain within the above specified accuracy for periods of several months. This must include immunity to common atmospheric contaminants.

(3) Be capable of continuous unattended operation for weeks or even months.

(4) Have lag independent of temperature.

(5) Read directly in terms of dew-point temperature.

(a) The dew point is independent of temperature changes if pressure is constant.

(b) It varies only slightly with pressure changes which might occur at the earth's surface. For example, assume $P = 1010$ mb, $T = 10°C$ and $DP = 5°C$. Assume further that the pressure falls under adiabatic conditions to $P = 960$ mb, then $T = 6°C$ and the dew point then becomes 4.5°C.

(6) Have a lag coefficient of not less than 30 seconds.[2]

(7) Have a dew-point range of $+30$ to $-65°C$ with temperature between $+50$ and $-60°C$.

(8) Have few or no moving parts and have complete temperature compensation.

(9) Have an output form satisfactory for use as input to an automatic data acquisition system.

(B) The sensor for the radiosonde program should:

(1) Readout as a function of relative humidity or dew point.

(2) Have an overall accuracy equivalent to less than 1°C error in dew point with the additional requirement to indicate at least 95 per cent RH during saturation calibration tests.

(3) Cost less than $20.00 when procured in quantity.

(4) Have a fast response (lag coefficient less than 2 seconds) which is independent of temperature.

(5) Weigh less than 300 grams.

(6) Have an electric power requirement less than 2 watts.

(7) Be able to measure a range of dew points from +30 to −100°C at all temperatures encountered in the atmosphere (+50 to −90°C).

(8) Provide an electrical output for ease in telemetering measurements to the ground.

(C) The sensor for the rocketsonde should:

(1) Readout in dew point.

(2) Have an overall accuracy equivalent to less than 1°C error in dew point.

(3) Have a very fast response (lag coefficient less than ½ second) which is independent of temperature.

(4) Weigh less than 150 grams.

(5) Be able to withstand a loading of 100 g's at launch.

(6) Have an electric power requirement less than 100 milliwatts.

(7) Be able to measure a range of dew points from +30 to −100°C at all temperatures between +50 and −90°C.

(8) Contain no plastic or other material which would act as a moisture source to cause inaccuracies in the measurements of the very small amounts of water present at altitudes of 100,000 ft and above.

(9) Provide an electrical output for ease in telemetering.

(D) Even these highly idealized sensors would not meet all the requirements of the meteorologist—only those involved in making the frequent routine measurements of the atmosphere which he requires. Additional specialized sensors are badly needed for special measurements made as part of research efforts.

(E) For uses B and C it must be pointed out that the ideal sensor would be a remote sensor which could measure humidity at a considerable distance. Ideally, it should be possible to make such measurements from the ground and to localize the measurement to a segment of 10 per cent or less of the distance from the ground based sensor to the segment being measured.

CONCLUSIONS

Finally, in conclusion it is pointed out that in spite of the ingenuity, skill and technical know-how which has gone and is still going into meteorological instrumentation, present day sensors are far from ideal and in most instances something short of satisfactory. Future progress in meteorology will be dependent to a large degree on the obtaining of better and more representative data on the state of the atmosphere and in particular the moisture content of the atmosphere.

The objectives of this paper have been to emphasize the needs for rugged reliable mass-produced units for field operations. There is also a need for a smaller number of secondary standard measuring devices which can be used for field calibration checks. To complete the program, there must be continued emphasis on basic theoretical studies and development of precision laboratory instruments to serve as base controls.

References

1. Kobayashi, J., "Investigations on Hygrometry," *Papers Meteorol. Geophys.*, (*Tokyo*), **11**, Nos. 2–4, 244–245 (1960).
2. Middleton, W. E. K., and Spilhaus, A. F., "Meteorological Instruments," pp 63–66, 3rd Edition, University of Toronto Press, 1953.

55. Stratospheric Moisture Measurements using Infrared Spectroscopy

David M. Gates

National Bureau of Standards, Boulder, Colorado

ABSTRACT

The occurrence of strong absorption lines in the pure rotation spectrum of water vapor makes it possible to observe extremely small amounts of water vapor in the stratosphere under low pressure conditions using infrared spectroscopic techniques. From the computed theoretical spectrum which is degraded by means of a slit factor, it is possible to show that a spectral resolution of 1 cm^{-1} is required in order to unambiguously record the amount of water vapor above an altitude of 32 km. There is increasing evidence for a dry upper stratosphere rather than a wet one; however, the water vapor content may be highly variable. A far infrared spectrometer and sunseeker which is being flown by balloons is described.

INTRODUCTION

Infrared radiation passing through water vapor is absorbed by numerous discrete bands and lines at various frequencies. Because the water molecule possesses a permanent dipole moment, it gives rise to a pure rotation spectrum in addition to numerous vibration-rotation bands. The pure rotation spectrum is characterized by an irregular distribution of single lines throughout the intermediate and far infrared and extending to microwave frequencies. In the vicinity of 303 cm^{-1} or 33.0 μ there are several very strong lines which would be useful for observing the quantity of water vapor in a given path length of radiation. These lines are shown in Fig. 1.

Because of the great strength of these lines it was decided that stratospheric water vapor could be measured using high resolution spectroscopy at far infrared wavelengths. The technique would be to use the sun as a source, to image the solar disc on the entrance slit of a spectrometer, to scan a limited region of the spectrum and to record in these lines the strength of the absorption of solar radiation. The use of high resolution spectroscopy permits the detection of very small amounts of water vapor along the absorbing path. This is illustrated in Fig. 1 where the theoretical spectrum is shown for two different zenith amounts of stratospheric water vapor. The quantity of water vapor along a given path will be measured in terms of the thickness of liquid water which would be formed if all of the water vapor were condensed out. This measure is termed "precipitable water". The theoretical absorption spectrum is shown, and degraded absorption spectra are given for various spectral slit widths. The degraded spectra represent the theoretical spectrum multiplied by an instrument factor in the form of a triangular slit function. It is clear from Fig. 1 that if the amount of stratospheric water vapor above 32 km is relatively large (10^{-3}cm ppt H$_2$O), then a spectral slit width as large as 2.0 cm^{-1} will be adequate for observing the absorption due to the closely spaced pair of lines near 303 cm^{-1}, but not adequate to easily discern single line absorption. If the water vapor amount in the stratosphere above 32 km is small (10^{-4} cm ppt H$_2$O), then a spectral slit width of 2 cm^{-1} is entirely too large. If the

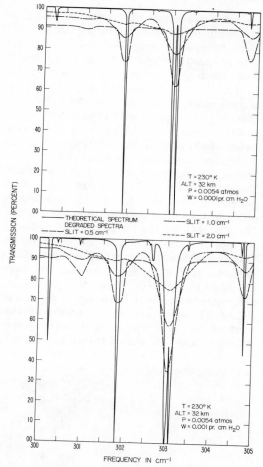

FIG. 1. Computed line absorption in the purse rotation band of water vapor for the highly resolved theoretical spectrum and for degraded spectra for water vapor in the stratosphere above an altitude of 32 km. The upper curves represent the expected absorption if the upper stratosphere is relatively dry and the lower curves represent the expected absorption if the upper stratosphere is relatively wet.

spectral slit width is 1.0 cm⁻¹, then single line absorption is readily discernable even at a zenith water vapor amount as low as 10^{-4} cm of precipitable H_2O. It is also evident from Fig. 1 that an even narrower slit width is desirable.

PROBABLE STRATOSPHERIC WATER VAPOR

Most of the observations of stratospheric water vapor concentrations have been reviewed by Gutnik[1] who shows a dry region in the

neighborhood of 15 km, where the mixing ratio is about 10^{-5}, and shows an increasing mixing ratio with altitude above this height. At 30 km the mixing ratio would appear to be about 10^{-4}. Since spectroscopic observations are more readily represented in terms of the total precipitable water vapor along the path, it is desirable to present the relationship between this and the mixing ratio if the water vapor is distributed with a constant mixing ratio above a given altitude. Considering the photo-dissociation of water vapor to take place at a height of 75 km, Table 1 lists the amounts of precipitable water vapor in the zenith direction above various altitudes for different mixing ratio values.

TABLE 1. ZENITH AMOUNTS OF PRECIPITABLE WATER VAPOR IN MICRONS ABOVE VARIOUS ALTITUDES FOR UNIFORM MIXING RATIOS

Altitude (km)	Mixing Ratio			
	10^{-5}	5×10^{-5}	10^{-4}	5×10^{-4}
15	12.4	62	124	620
20	5.7	29	58	290
25	2.6	13	26	130
30	1.2	6.0	12	60
35	0.6	2.9	5.8	29
40	0.3	1.5	3.0	15

Table 1 would indicate that if the mixing ratio above 32 km was uniform at 10^{-4}, the zenith amount of precipitable water vapor would be about 10μ. This is the amount used for the calculation of the lower curves in Fig. 1. If, on the other hand, the upper stratosphere is dry and the mixing ratio above 32 km is uniform at 10^{-5}, then the zenith amount of precipitable water vapor would be 1.0μ. The upper curves of Fig. 1 were calculated on this basis.

Recently some new high resolution spectroscopic data has been obtained at an altitude of 45,000 ft (13.7 km) over Florida by Cumming[2] of the Canadian Armament Research and Development Establishment. This observation represented a high resolution scan of the 2.7μ region of the water vapor spectrum. In this wavelength region, the absorption is caused by the ν_1, $2\nu_2$, and ν_3 vibration-rotation bands of the water vapor molecule. From the quantum mechanics of the water vapor molecule, we have recently computed the line positions, strengths and half widths for all the absorption lines within these bands. These are tabulated by Gates, Calfee, Hansen, and Benedict[3] and were used for the determination of the expected transmission of solar radiation for a given water vapor concentration above 15 km. The transmission at any given frequency was calculated by summing the wing effects of all the water lines in the band and simultaneously including the Lorenz profile of each line as any given line is approached in the spectrum. In order to match the observed spectrum by Cumming, the theoretical spectrum had to be degraded using a triangular slit function and a full slit width of 1.75 cm^{-1}. Using half the pressure at 15 km and a temperature of 217°K, the calculated degraded spectrum agrees precisely in every detail with the observed spectrum if the amount of precipitable water vapor along the path to the sun is 30 μ. Since the observations were made with a solar zenith angle of 71 degrees, this gives the zenith water vapor concentration above 15 km to be 9 μ of precipitable water vapor. This can only amount to a very dry upper stratosphere with a mixing ratio of about 0.8×10^{-5}. If the upper stratosphere is more moist at 30 km, then it must have been drier than this in the region just above 15 km.

Murcray, Murcray, Williams, and Leslie,[4] using an infrared prism spectrometer for the 6.3μ band of water vapor, obtained values of the mixing ratio above 92,000 ft (28.0 km) of between 1.5 and 3.4 $\times$ 10^{-4} or a total precipitable water of at least 20 μ. A later report by Murcray, Murcray, and Williams[5] on more recent flights with the same instrumentation gives 11 μ of precipitable water vapor above 95,000 ft (29.0 km) or a mixing ratio of somewhat less than 10^{-4}.

The conclusion to be drawn from this discussion is that the upper stratosphere may be quite dry at certain times of the year and that any spectroscopic observations which may be made from balloons at 30 km or above should use slit widths of about 1.0 cm^{-1} or better.

INSTRUMENTATION

In order to make spectroscopic observations in the stratosphere from balloons, a portable high resolution spectrometer and a sunseeker

are required. A first experiment of this type was conducted by Gates, Murcray, Shaw, and Herbold[6] in 1955 using a low resolution prism type of spectrometer in the very near infrared from which the amount of water above 42,000 ft (12.8 km) was about 80 μ or a uniform mixing ratio of 5×10^{-5}. It was recognized that a prism spectrometer would not give sufficient resolution to measure the water vapor absorption above an altitude of 32 km with any degree of precision and that a grating spectrometer was probably required. The decision was made to design and build a grating spectrometer for the far infrared in order to take advantage of the strong single line absorption in the vicinity of 30 μ due to the pure rotation spectrum of water vapor. The present equipment which is being flown is shown in Fig. 2. The sunseeker has been described by Edwards, Goddard, Juza, Maher, and Speck[7] and is seen in the upper portion of Fig. 2. The spectrometer is a grating instrument of the Ebert type, using a thermocouple detector. The AC signal from the thermo-

FIG. 2. Balloon-borne far infrared spectrometer and sunseeker as used in attempts to observe the amount of water vapor above various altitudes in the stratosphere.

couple is amplified and recorded on an FM tape recorder. Originally, the plan was to use filters to eliminate scattered radiation and higher order radiation from the grating spectrometer. This scheme did not work as well as hoped for, and it unduly reduced the signal at the detector to too low a level. A predispersing prism (CsBr) monochromator is now being added to the spectrometer in order to eliminate higher order radiation. It is sandwiched between the sunseeker and the grating spectrometer. The entire monochromator and spectrometer can be evacuated in order that water vapor be eliminated from the instrument. Rather extreme precautions must be taken in order to assure the absence of water vapor trapped within the spectrometer.

Originally the instrument was designed to scan the far infrared spectrum from 25 μ to beyond 35 μ in approximately 4 minutes. In order to improve the signal-to-noise ratio, a shorter span has had to be used. It is now planned to scan an interval of about 6 cm^{-1} or about 0.63 μ centered on 303 cm^{-1} or 33.0 μ in a time interval of 2 minutes. This will include some of the strong lines shown in Fig. 1 and will permit a spectral slit width of about 1.0 cm^{-1} to be realized.

Several flights of the instrument were made during 1961 and 1962. Various difficulties were encountered with the sunseeker which have caused us to redesign it drastically. A new version of the sunseeker will be flown in the future. It was decided to take advantage of the delays caused by the sunseeker to improve the performance of the spectrometer. Therefore the spectrometer has been im-proved, with the monochromator added, in order to get higher resolution. Although previously a resolution of about 2.0 cm^{-1} was achieved for the spectrometer, it is now expected that a resolution of 1.0 cm^{-1} can be realized.

Although low resolution prismatic spectroscopy can give some useful information at lower elevations in the atmosphere, it is now felt that only high resolution (1 cm^{-1} or better), such as can be achieved by grating instruments, will yield definite information concerning the water vapor content of the stratosphere above an altitude of 35 km.

References

1. Gutnick, M., "How Dry is the Sky?", *J. Geophys. Res.*, **66**, 2867–2871 (1961).
2. Cumming, C., Private communication (1963).
3. Gates, D. M., Calfee, R. F., Hansen, D. W., and Benedict, W. S., "Line Parameters and Computed Spectra for Water Vapor Bands at 2.7μ," NBS Mono. No. 71 (1964).
4. Murcray, D. G., Murcray, F. H., Williams, W. J., and Leslie, F. E., "Water Vapor Distribution above 90,000 Feet," *J. Geophys. Res.*, **65**, No. 11, 3641–3649 (1960).
5. Murcray, D. G., Murcray, F. H., and Williams, W. J., "Distribution of Water Vapor in the Stratosphere as Determined from Infrared Absorption Measurements," *J. Geophys. Res.*, **67**, No. 2, 759–766 (1962).
6. Gates, D. M., Murcray, D. G., Shaw, C. C., and Herbold, R. J., "Near Infrared Solar Radiation Measurements by Balloon to an Altitude of 100,000 Feet," *J. Opt. Soc. Am.*, **48**, 1010–1016 (1958).
7. Edwards, H. D., Goddard, A., Jr., Juza, M. J., Maher, T., and Speck, F., "Balloon-Borne System for Tracking the Sun," *Rev. Sci. Instr.*, **27**, 381–385 (1956).

56. Field Tests and Calibration of the Total Atmospheric Water Vapor Hygrometer

Robert L. King and H. Dean Parry

U.S. Weather Bureau, Washington, D.C.

ABSTRACT

This paper describes the field tests of a total atmospheric water vapor hygrometer and analyzes the results of these tests. Objectives of the field tests were: (1) to establish the calibration curve, (2) to analyze the operational characteristics of the hygrometer, (3) to evaluate its usefulness to the forecaster, and (4) to determine the usefulness of data from this instrument to meteorological analysis and research. Under the first objective, a suitable calibration curve for the Tucson instrument was produced. Under the second objective the principal desirable characteristics of the instrument were absence of lag and economy of making observations. Undesirable characteristics included limited sensitivity to smoke and a shift of the calibration with changes in elevation at which the instrument is used. With regard to objectives three and four, it was concluded that the instrument's negligible lag and its ability to make continuous and economical measurements make it invaluable to the forecaster as a means of monitoring atmospheric processes; the instrument has several important potential uses in meteorological research including the ability to measure the full spectrum of total water vapor variation and the ability to contribute to our knowledge of hydrodynamics by indicating certain atmospheric motions using water vapor as a tracer.

INTRODUCTION

In 1912, F. E. Fowle[1] used an infrared spectrophotometer to measure atmospheric water vapor above Mount Wilson. Kimball and Hand[2,3] published descriptions of a scheme for measuring total atmospheric water vapor during the mid 1930's. The need of synoptic meteorology for such a device and the feasibility of building an operational instrument were established in 1940, during informal discussions between A. K. Showalter and Norman B. Foster, the latter then of the Weather Bureau's Instrumental Engineering Division (IED). The device was developed into its present form by staff members of the Physical Science Laboratory and Instrumental Division of the U.S. Weather Bureau. Details of this development are reported in a paper by Foster, Volz, and Foskett.[4] This paper reports the field test of the total atmospheric water vapor hygrometer. Basically, the instrument is a spectrophotometer which compares the intensity of sunlight received at two wavelengths, .935 and .880 μ. The first wavelength is heavily absorbed by water vapor, while the second one is attenuated so slightly that it can be used as a reference. These two frequencies are directed upon a pair of silicon photovoltaic cells. The ratio of the output of these two cells is recorded by a suitably designed recorder.

PURPOSE OF TEST

This numerical ratio does not provide an absolute measure of total water vapor in the path. The ratio must be compared with absolute measurements of the moisture to numerically calibrate the instrument. Establishment of this calibration was the first purpose of this test. The second purpose of the test was to analyze the operational characteristics and peculiarities of the instrument and its output when used under field conditions. A third purpose was to evaluate the usefulness to the weather forecaster of measurements made by the instrument. We pause to point out that no purely observational technique from star gazing to satellite meteorology can per se "improve forecasting". The very best it can do is to supply additional data to the forecaster who must use his own skill and/or data processing techniques to project the current weather measurements forward to some future point in time.

The fourth and final purpose of the test is to determine the usefulness of data from the instrument to meteorological analysis and research.

DESCRIPTION OF TEST SITE AND ITS CLIMATIC CONDITIONS

The test site is situated at the Weather Bureau Airport Station, Tucson, Arizona Municipal Airport, which is 6 miles from the center of Tucson and has an elevation of 2,584 ft. Climatologically, the Tucson area may be classified as low latitude desert. The air at the surface is very dry throughout most of the year. Most of the annual precipitation occurs in two "rainy" periods. The primary maximum occurs during the latter part of the summer when southeasterly or monsoon flow aloft brings in tongues of moist (Tg) air from the Gulf of Mexico. These influxes of moist air produce scattered showers and thunderstorms which account for more than 50 per cent of Tucson's annual rainfall between July 1 and September 15. A secondary maximum in the annual precipitation cycle occurs during the period December through March. Conditions in Tucson during the primary precipitation maximum are nearly ideal for the operational test of the total water vapor measuring device. The sun, which must be visible in order to obtain a measurement from the device, normally continues to shine, intermittently at least, after an influx of moisture. The precipitation occurs as convective showers which are the result of the total water vapor in the column. Warm front or up-glide precipitation, in contrast to this, is ordinarily preceded by sun-obscuring clouds and may be generated by

the interaction between alternate wet and dry layers so that this type of precipitation may not be related to the total moisture in the air column. In short, one of the most promising uses of the device under test is as a data source for forecasting the summer afternoon (convective) showers which are typical of the Southwest and the Intermountain area. Tucson was chosen as one of the first test sites. A second instrument has been under test at Salt Lake City since the fall of 1960 and a short test was carried out using a third instrument at Missoula for a short period during the summer of 1960. At Tucson the total amount of water vapor in the atmosphere represents a minimum for the latitude except during July, August and September when a secondary maximum appears over the interior southwest. Average and maximum values of total atmospheric water vapor for Tucson are shown in Table 1.

TABLE 1. TOTAL ATMOSPHERIC WATER VAPOR (IN.) AT TUCSON

Mean Values For Period 1946–1956			
January	0.4	July	1.3
February	0.4	August	1.3
March	0.4	September	1.0
April	0.5	October	0.7
May	0.6	November	0.5
June	0.7	December	0.5
Maximum Values From June Through September 1961 As Computed From Radiosonde			
June	1.39	August	1.69
July	1.73	September	1.57

* After Reitan.[5]

ESTABLISHMENT OF THE CALIBRATION CURVE

Observed data for the scatter diagram used in defining the calibration curve for the hygrometer were obtained as follows: On test days, using the early morning and afternoon radiosondes the total water vapor value for each sounding was computed using standard radiosonde evaluation techniques[6-8].

For the rather numerous layers for which the radiosonde gave no humidity data, statistical values were used. Many hygrometer readings were not made at the same time as the radiosonde ascent. To overcome this difficulty a linear change between morning and afternoon soundings was assumed, and linearly

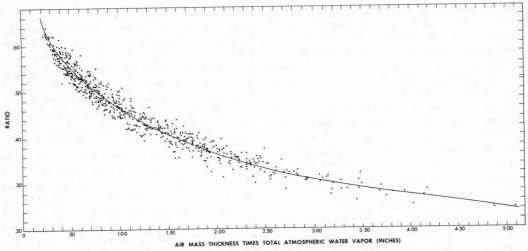

FIG. 1. Calibration curve—ratio of the energy received by the two silicon cells *vs* the product of air mass thickness and total atmospheric water vapor.

interpolated values were ascribed to the times at which hygrometer readings were obtained. A number of the readings fell within one hour of the 1630MST radiosonde time. Both types of observations were plotted using easily distinguishable marks on a large sheet of cross-section paper. This was the working diagram and the curve finally drawn was fitted to all available data.

Figure 1 shows this curve which was drawn from all these data. Because of drafting problems, only those points for which the readings fell within one hour of the time of the radiosonde were reproduced on the Figure. The curve is based on a total of some 3,000 observations of the hygrometer which were compared with concurrent or interpolated values of the total water vapor as computed from the radiosonde data. Even the points shown on Fig. 1, though they represent nearly concurrent observations by radiosonde and hygrometer, show considerable scatter. This scatter is by no means unexpected and is largely attributable to:

(1) Imperfect humidity measurements by the radiosonde. The radiosonde humidity measurements of low humidities at all temperatures are unsatisfactory. Figure 2 shows the cutoff curve for humidity measurements and the lag characteristics of the humidity sensor. At −40°C the typical lag of the radiosonde humidity sensor is about ten minutes. Under the most favorable circumstances, radiosonde humidity measurements are no better than ±10 per cent RH.

(2) Hygrometer and radiosonde measurements along different paths and at slightly different times under conditions of small scale variations in moisture amount. Existence of such variations will be discussed later.

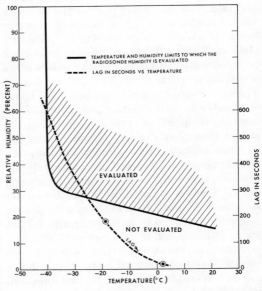

FIG. 2. Characteristic curves of the radiosonde humidity sensor.

(3) Errors inherent in the spectrophotometric technique. The effect of pressure, and unwanted differential attenuation are the principal offenders here. These will also be discussed later.

(4) Simple instrumental or hardware error. This is estimated to be only a few per cent.

Thus, in spite of the rather appreciable scatter, calibration errors are largely compensating and the curve obtained provides an adequate calibration of the instrument. This curve has been accepted for operational use by the Tucson Weather Bureau Airport Station.

INSTRUMENTAL CHARACTERISTICS AND PECULIARITIES

One of the unusual features of this humidity measuring technique is that it can continuously measure total water vapor from the surface to the top of the atmosphere with virtually no instrumental lag. This capability is unique to this instrument and is most significant and desirable. A second characteristic of the instrument, dictated by theory at least, is that smoke, haze, air pollution, etc., do not upset the accuracy of the measurements. This follows from the fact that the instrument senses *difference* of attenuation, and any equal attenuation of both wavelengths should not degrade accuracy. The correctness of this theory for the average atmospheric pollution which prevails in Tucson in the winter time was shown by an experiment which consisted of dividing the calibration data into two sets and drawing independent calibration curves for each set of data.

One set was for the period March 22 to September 21 (high sun elevation angles) and the other for the period September 22 to March 21 (low sun elevation angles). In order to provide a graphic comparison of the annual curve and those for the shorter periods, all three curves have been drawn on Fig. 3. There

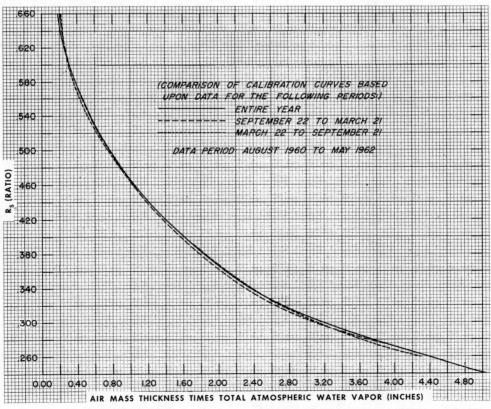

FIG. 3. Comparison of calibration curves for winter situations and summer situations with the combined annual curve.

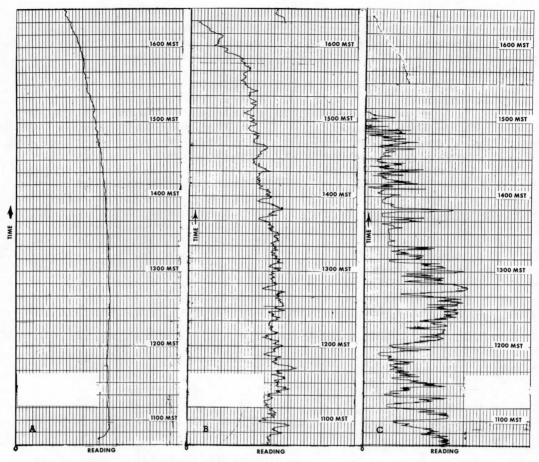

FIG. 4. Section A—a typical hygrometer trace for a clear day. Section B—a typical trace for a day with strong winds at or near the surface. Section C—a typical trace for a day with scattered to broken high thin clouds.

seems to be no significant differences in these curves. It is inferred that air pollution of the average winter day in Tucson and the longer path length in winter have little effect, hence the theory is supported.

In the Salt Lake tests, the effect of pollution was not always negligible. Mr. Arlo Richardson who with Mr. Wayne Harrell is testing the Salt Lake instrument reported that with heavy air pollution and low sun angles, early forenoon readings indicated too little moisture. As the sun angle increased and the smoke over the city to the east decreased due to diffusion and advection, the indicated moisture gradually increased to an amount consistent with the air mass thickness and the radiosonde measurement of the total water vapor. The

instrument then followed the usual diurnal pattern showing minimum moisture at local noon and the normal increase as the air mass thickness increased during the afternoon. The effect of smoke under the extreme conditions prevailing early in the day is just opposite to that produced by clouds since clouds shift the pen all the way to the left—the "wet" side of the chart. (See Fig. 4C). It follows, if the failure under thin clouds is due to nonlinear response with low light intensity, that the too dry indication under smoky conditions results from stronger attenuation of the reference band by some component of the atmospheric pollution.

A third characteristic of the instrument is its response to pressure. The instrument used in Salt Lake was calibrated in Washington before shipment. In order to make Washington and Salt Lake data follow the same calibration curve, Richardson and Harrell found that Salt Lake data had to be multiplied by P_0/P where P_0 is sea level, and P Salt Lake City station pressure. This result suggests that total attenuation due to water vapor is proportional to surface pressure. If this is the case an instrument calibrated at sea level, if located at 10,000 ft will measure $7/10$th of the water vapor and if located at 18,000 ft will measure half of the water vapor.

THE USEFULNESS OF TOTAL WATER VAPOR MEASUREMENTS TO THE FORECASTER

A statistical comparison between total atmospheric water vapor values computed from the radiosonde and values measured by the hygrometer has been made. This comparison shows that the two values fall within 0.05 in. of each other 65 per cent of the time and within 0.10 in. of each other 90 per cent of the time. Differences have a Gaussian distribution around zero difference. It is therefore apparent that the hygrometer capability to measure total atmospheric water vapor is at least equivalent to that of the radiosonde. This measurement of total atmospheric water vapor which is sometimes called precipitable water is directly applicable to a number of forecast problems. The late Dr. Gilman[9] and Mr. Peterson[9] used this value in a system they developed foremaking quantitative precipitation forecasts. Sabine,[10] Williams[11] and King[12] found this quantity a good index of the likelihood of shower precipitation. As has been suggested in our discussion of the test site, there may be some situations in which rain may occur because of a moist layer of air being superimposed over a dry layer. In spite of these exceptions, total water vapor in the atmosphere is directly and intimately related to both the tendency to rain and the amount of rain which the atmosphere can produce. Total atmospheric water vapor computed from the radiosonde ascent is generally available only twice a day. A major advantage of the hygrometer is that it is not limited to two-a-day observations but provides a con-

tinuous record of total water vapor. Every forecaster has had the unpleasant experience of basing a forecast on the early morning radiosonde observations only to have rapid changes in atmospheric moisture (i.e., water vapor) during the day completely invalidate his forecast. This device can continuously monitor such moisture and inform the forecaster of changes. Table 2 shows examples of moisture changes which were caught by the Tucson hygrometer and which were sufficiently large to warrant an advisory message to the forecast offices concerned.

TABLE 2. TYPICAL CHANGES IN MOISTURE REQUIRING A MESSAGE TO THE FORECAST OFFICE

Date	Computed TAWV 0500 Raob	Measured Time	TAWV Value
12/3/60	0.48	1030M	0.74
12/12/60	0.35	1400M	0.51
4/18/61	0.45	1400M	0.72
6/13/61	0.74	1330M	0.53
6/21/61	0.76	1400M	0.95
7/17/61	1.41	1430M	1.15
8/5/61	1.28	1430M	0.96
5/25/62	0.23	1420M	0.50

Another major advantage that this instrument has is the economic feasibility of making many observations. Cost of ground equipment, expendables and manpower required for radiosondes sharply limit the number of observations of this type which can be made with the economic resources available. On the other hand, it is quite feasible economically to render a major service to the forecaster by filling in time and space gaps in the radiosonde net through the use of this hygrometer which has a relatively low initial cost, uses no expendables and requires only about one minute of observer time per observation.

APPLICATION OF HYGROMETER DATA IN RESEARCH

This device because it records continuously and without lag, provides information on total atmospheric water vapor not available up to now. Figure 4B shows high-frequency variations in water vapor usually associated with strong winds at or near the surface and probably due to small scale clear air turbulence.

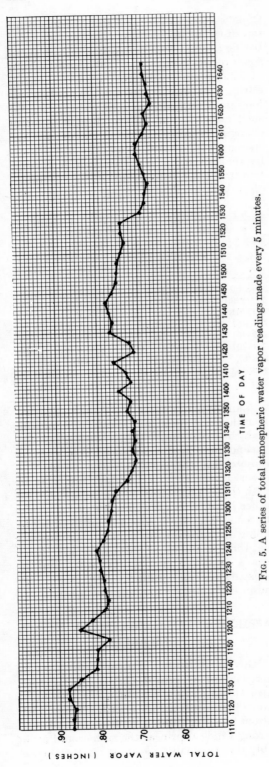

FIG. 5. A series of total atmospheric water vapor readings made every 5 minutes.

Figure 5 shows variations having frequencies of 15 minutes to a few hours as indicated by measurements made every 5 minutes. Table 3 shows variations on several days on which observations were made every half hour.

TABLE 3. HALF HOURLY SPECTROMETER OBSERVATIONS, TUCSON, ARIZONA, 1962

Solar Time	Total Water Vapor (In.)					
	May 16	May 17	May 21	May 26	May 28	June 1
1000						
1030		.44			.58	
1100		.43	.29	.67	.59	
1130		.41	.27	.66	.58	.60
1200		.41	.30	.69	.56	.57
1230	.42	.42	.28	.66	.54	.55
1300	.41	.46	.29	.69	.53	.55
1330	.37	.41	.26	.65	.54	.51
1400	.38	.40	.27	.63	.52	.50
1430	.40	.43	.29	.67	.49	.39
1500	.41	.40	.29	.66	.52	.40
1530	.35	.40	.28	.73	.51	.47
1600	.40	.38	.40	.68	.51	.56
1630	.34	.35	.36	.60	.51	.56
1700	.34	.40	.30	.60	.53	.60
RAOB TAWV 1630MST	.34	.37	.32	.63	.52	.63

These half hourly observations show variations having frequencies of one cycle per several hours. A day-to-day record of total water vapor shows variations of one cycle per several days corresponding to the passage of major circulation systems. Finally, the annual cycle of total atmospheric water vapor is apparent from the means shown in Table 1. A complete spectrum of frequencies of water vapor variation is obtainable using this instrument and as a consequence the instrument can enhance our knowledge of water vapor variation and distribution in the atmosphere.

Water vapor in addition to being of prime importance as a weather maker is an excellent tracer. Consequently, the hygrometer is an effective tool in studying atmospheric motions including some forms of clear air turbulence. Under the assumption of identical flow at all levels, one may determine, as suggested by McMurray,[13] the size of bubbles of homogeneous air which pass across the instrument and from this infer the size of the circulation cells involved in the prevailing atmospheric motion. Properly interpreted, measurements from this hygrometer should contribute materially to our knowlegde of the hydro-dynamics of the atmosphere.

CONCLUSIONS

(1) Measurements of total atmospheric water vapor by the hygrometer equal in accuracy and repeatability those computed from radiosonde data.

(2) The instrument's negligible lag and its ability to make continuous and economical measurements make it invaluable to the fore-caster as a means of monitoring atmospheric processes.

(3) The instrument has several important potential uses in meteorological research including the ability to measure the full spectrum of total water vapor variation and the ability to contribute to our knowledge of hydrodynamics by indicating certain atmos-pheric motions using water vapor as a tracer.

Acknowledgment. The authors wish to ack-nowledge the significant contribution to this paper provided by the field tests of the hygrometer at Salt Lake City. This test was conducted by Messrs. Arlo Richardson and Wayne Harrell of the U.S. Weather Bureau. We also thank Messrs. Charles M. Lennahan and David T. Volz who read and criticized the manuscript and Mrs. Gladys Fifer who typed the manuscript and prepared it for publication. Finally, we wish to acknowledge the assistance rendered to us by Mr. Earl W. McMurray during our preparation of tables for computing air mass thickness.

References

1. Fowle, F. E., "The Spectroscopic Determination of Aqueous Vapor," *Astro-phys. J.*, **35**, 149 (1912).

2. Kimball, H. H., and Hand, Irving F., "The Use of Glass Color Screens in the Study of Atmos-pheric Depletion of Solar Radiation," *Monthly Weather Rev.*, **61**, 80–83 (1933).

3. Kimball, H. H., "Determinations of Atmospheric Turbidity and Water Content," *Monthly Weather Rev.*, **64**, 1–6 (1936).

4. Foster, N. B., Volz, D. T., and Foskett, L. W., "A Spectral Hygrometer for Measuring Total Precipitable Water," "Humidity and Moisture," Vol. I, New York, Reinhold Pub. Corp., 1964.

5. Reitan, Clayton H., "Distribution of Precipitable Water Vapor Over The Continental United States," *Bull. Am. Meteorol. Soc.*, **41**, No. 2, 79–87 (1960).

6. Solot, S. B., "Computation of Depth of Precipit-able Water in a Column of Air," *Monthly Weather Rev.*, **67**, 100–103 (1939).

7. Showalter, A. K., "Precipitable Water Tem-plate," *Bull. Am. Meteorol. Soc.*, **35**, 129–131 (1954).

8. Peterson, K. R., "A Precipitable Water Nomo-gram," *Bull. Am. Meteorol. Soc.*, **42**, 119–121 (1961).

9. Gilman, C. S., and Peterson, K. R., "Notes on a Procedure for Quantitative Precipitation Forecasting," Manuscript of the U.S. Weather Bureau, 1960.

10. Sabine, W. L., "Forecasting Thunderstorms at Phoenix, Arizona," Unpublished manuscript, undated.

11. Williams, Phillip, Jr., "Forecasting Summer Shower Activity at Salt Lake City, Utah," Manuscript of the U.S. Weather Bureau, 1961.

12. King, R. L., "A Graph Showing Relation Occurrence and Nonoccurrence of Summer Showers and Thunderstorms *vs* Precipitable Water and Stability Index," Unpublished, 1962.

13. McMurray, "Measurement of Atmospheric Water Vapor by a Spectrometric Technique," Uni-versity of Arizona, Institute of Atmospheric Physics, Scientific Report No. 19, ONR Con-tract No. 2173(02), September 21, 1962.

57. Adsorption Technique for the Collection of Water Vapor in the Upper Atmosphere

Sheldon Steinberg and S. F. Rohrbough*

Applied Science Division, Litton Systems, Inc., St. Paul, Minnesota

ABSTRACT

A technique has been developed for collecting and quantitatively determining the water vapor in the stratosphere. The sampling devices used can be flown on balloons to an altitude of about 42 km. They work on the principle of adsorption of water vapor on synthetic zeolites. At the conclusion of a flight, the exposed adsorbent is returned to the laboratory for regeneration and quantitative analysis of adsorbed water vapor and carbon dioxide.

Considerable laboratory experimentation has been performed to develop this method. The laboratory experimental data on adsorption, regeneration, and breakthrough characteristics of the adsorbent for water vapor and carbon dioxide are presented here. In addition, thermodynamic and kinetic data for adsorption of dry, CO_2-free air on zeolite are given.

Two different sampling devices for use at two different altitudes have been developed using this adsorption technique. One sampling unit can be flown to an altitude of approximatley 30 km, while the other is useful for altitudes above 30 km. Both types have been flown and mixing ratios obtained were 0.031 g H_2O/kg air at 21.9 km and 0.32 g H_2O/kg air at 36.4 km**.

* Presently with Honeywell, Military Products Group, Minneapolis, Minnesota.

** The question has been raised as to the possibility of contamination during our flights that would give results indicating a relatively wet middle stratosphere. Although some contamination may exist, the sampling devices used and the precautions taken to prevent contamination (described in the paper) would keep to a minimum the influences due to contamination. We know that a controversy exists concerning the moisture content of the atmosphere. If one automatically eliminates all data that suggest the existence of a "wet" atmosphere, he eliminates the controversy. No one, to date, has shown that the data compiled by Gutnick are erroneous because of contamination. The ring cloud photographed over Arizona at about 80 km (*Science*) and the rocket sampling data of noctillucent clouds published by Soberman (*Scientific American*) indicate high local concentrations of moisture in the upper atmosphere. Although there is some question as to the validity of the Japanese data, the fact remains that the Japanese obtained different frost points north and south of the jet stream under the *same operating conditions*. This shows that the atmosphere does vary; this subject is discussed in Paper 62 of this volume. Recent unpublished flight data (November 1963) obtained by Ballinger (Honeywell) show that there was very little difference in results during ascent, float and descent. Differences in ascent and descent values have in the past been described as evidence for contamination. Ballinger's results, obtained during a night flight on which all equipment had been demoisturized and sealed prior to flight, do not show the extremely low frost points indicated in Paper 60 of this volume.

INTRODUCTION

Various instruments have been used to determine the water vapor content of the atmosphere, and most of these are described elsewhere in this book. At present there are only two types of instruments that both collect and quantitatively determine water vapor in the stratosphere. One of these is the liquid nitrogen, cooled-vapor trap designed, built and flown by Goldsmith and his associates.[1] The other type consists of sampling devices designed, fabricated and flown by this laboratory,[2,3] which utilize the principle of adsorption of water vapor on synthetic zeolites. Although both are gravimetric devices, the latter have the advantage of sampling large air volumes and are thus less susceptible to large error due to local contamination. In both types, carbon dioxide and water are collected simultaneously.

Two different sampling devices for use at two different altitude regimes have been developed using this adsorption technique. One sampling unit, which can be flown to an altitude of approximately 30 km, has a blower that draws ambient air through two beds of zeolite. The other sampling unit, which is useful above 30 km, has a Cryogenic Adsorbent Pump that draws air through a bed of zeolite. This pump may also be used as a whole-air sampler. This paper mainly describes the laboratory experimentation which developed the adsorption techniques and, briefly, the sampling devices, and it reviews the results of experimental flights utilizing these devices.

WATER ADSORPTION CHARACTERISTICS

A series of laboratory experiments were performed to establish the proper preparation and regeneration parameters and to further determine the water adsorption characteristics of the synthetic zeolites. At the present time, Type 13X Molecular Sieve (sodium alumino silicate) in $\frac{1}{8}$-in. diameter pellets—each pellet contains 20 per cent inert binding material—is used in our sampling units. Although research was performed on Types 4A, 5A, and 13X, the discussion below is mainly limited to Type 13X.

The material on page 461 contains all temperature citations in degrees Fahrenheit; the remainder of this paper cites temperatures in degrees Centigrade. This is due to our laboratory regeneration furnace having a scale reading in degrees Fahrenheit. It appeared more convenient to leave the "round" temperature increments in degress Fahrenheit.

Sieve Preparation and Regeneration

Seven-liter batches of Type 13X Molecular Sieve were heated under vacuum conditions to 1400°F in the following manner. Each batch was first brought to 1000°F with the desorbed water discarded. The temperature was then raised to 1100°F and kept at this temperature until the pressure in the system, observed by a vacuum thermocouple gauge, remained stable. The water desorbed during this interval

was collected and measured. The temperature was then raised to 1200°F, and the procedure was repeated. This procedure was repeated at 100°F intervals until a temperature of 1400°F was obtained. It should be noted that the sieve was allowed to cool overnight between each 100°F temperature rise. Table 1 shows the amount of water collected from one of these batches during each 100°F interval from 1000 to 1400°F. The results given are typical of all batches.

TABLE 1. WATER COLLECTED DURING HEAT TREATMENT OF TYPE 13X MOLECULAR SIEVE (7 LITERS)

Temperature Interval (°F)	Water Collected (g)
1000–1100	4.97
1100–1200	3.19
1200–1300	2.32
1300–1400	2.02

These batches were subsequently used in the water-introduction and recovery studies discussed below. At the conclusion of these studies, the batch of Table 1 was further heated under vacuum conditions at temperatures above 1400°F. The zeolite was regenerated repeatedly on successive days at 1400°F with no further water collected; the temperature was then increased in 25°F increments to 1550°F and finally to 1600°F. The water recovered was determined at each temperature interval and the zeolite was allowed to cool overnight between increments. In addition, the apparent damage to the zeolite was determined by its adsorption capacity for dry, CO_2-free air. Results are given in Table 2.

TABLE 2. RELATIONSHIP OF REGENERATION TEMPERATURES, WATER COLLECTION, AND ZEOLITE DAMAGE—TYPE 13X MOLECULAR SIEVE

Temperature Interval (°F)	Water Collected (g)	Apparent Damage
1400–1425	0.2294	No
1425–1450	0.1132	No
1450–1475	0.1434	No
1475–1500	0.1725	Yes
1500–1525	0.2452	Yes
1525–1550	0.0544	Yes
1550–1600	Negligible	Yes
Total	0.9581	

Data indicate that, although most water is removed at 1400°F, approximately 1 gram of residual water still remains in 7 liters of Type 13X Molecular Sieve. Further, there is no apparent damage to the zeolite up to a regeneration temperature of 1475°F, after which there is progressive deterioration.

Studies of Type 4A (sodium alumino silicate) indicate that about 0.25 gram of residual water remains above 1400°F and that the zeolite is apparently damaged at temperatures above 1450°F. The results of studies on Type 5A (calcium alumino silicate) differ markedly from those of Types 13X and 4A. In the case of Type 5A, the zeolite is damaged at a regeneration temperature slightly above 1400°F, and no water is recovered after the zeolite indicates adsorption damage.

Water Introduction and Recovery

A series of tests were performed to determine the feasibility of recovering a known quantity of introduced water sample from Type 13X Molecular Sieve. In order to determine whether the recovered water sample was the same as that introduced, the sample contained 54 per cent by weight of deuterium oxide (D_2O).

To the batch discussed in the previous section, a 3.19-gram water sample containing 54 per cent by weight D_2O was introduced under vacuum conditions after its heat treatment at 1400°F. Upon regeneration 3.17 gram were collected with a D_2O concentration of 38.5 per cent by weight. Here, the sample recovered was 99.4 per cent by weight and 100.9 per cent by number of moles introduced.

A second D_2O-H_2O sample (2.36 grams) was introduced into this batch. In this case, 2.33 grams were recovered and the D_2O concentration was 47.9 per cent, or 98.7 per cent by weight and 99.3 per cent by number of moles.

Next, a 3.23 gram sample of distilled water was added to the same batch, and the batch regenerated. Here, 3.25 grams were collected which contained 16.5 per cent D_2O by weight, giving a recovery of 100.9 per cent by weight and 99.4 per cent by number of moles.

Further studies of the recovery of water samples introduced into other batches of Type 13X gave recoveries within ± 2 per cent of the amount of sample introduced. Exchange of introduced D_2O for zeolite water and recovery of D_2O in seeded zeolite for introduced distilled water were again observed.

If an equilibrium exchange is assumed and the experimental data for the batch given above are used, calculations show that approximately 1 gram of water is intimately associated with the 7 liters of the zeolite and that this water is not removed at 1400°F. Results in the previous section showed that, after heating this same batch to 1600°F, an additional 0.96 gram of water was obtained in excess of that recovered at 1400°F. This water sample contained 19.7 per cent D_2O. Thus, it appears that there is an equilibrium exchange between D_2O and water in the zeolite.

Storage Contamination Tests

To determine the results of varying durations of storage on prepared adsorbents, a series of Type 13X Molecular Sieve samples were regenerated at 1400°F under vacuum conditions. These samples were carefully transferred to clean, dry Dual Molecular Sieve Unit canisters, which were then pressurized to 2 psig with dry nitrogen and allowed to stand for varying periods. After storage, the zeolite samples were transferred to the heating vessel and again heated to 1400°F under vacuum conditions. The amount of regenerated water was measured. Storage contamination test results are given in Table 3.

The canisters failed to retain pressurization in the first two tests, and it is thus apparent that leakage and/or diffusion occurred. Further evidence of leakage is the presence of carbon dioxide and water in the zeolite. In the two succeeding tests the canisters still remained pressurized upon transfer. In each test, water was collected even though the adsorbent had not been exposed to the atmosphere. Tests 5, 5a, and 5b (Table 3) were conducted to determine whether the regeneration temperature or the handling technique caused the contamination.

For Test 5, the zeolite was prepared at 1425°F and handled the same as in Tests 1 through 4. The result was the same. The sample was next prepared at 1425°F and left in the regeneration flask for 11 days. The amount of contamination was slightly smaller, but still significant. Test 5b was prepared at 1475°F and left for 5 days in the regeneration flask. This temperature is just below the adsorbent's

TABLE 3. STORAGE CONTAMINATION TEST RESULTS

No.	Time Stored (days)	Preparation and Regeneration Temperature (°F)	Storage Conditions	Material Collected	Remarks
1	76	1400	Stored in canister pressurized to 2 psig.	0.412 g H_2O 6 cc CO_2	Container was found not pressurized upon transfer for regeneration.
2	59	1400	Stored in canister pressurized to 2 psig.	0.390 g H_2O 7 cc CO_2	Container was found not pressurized upon transfer for regeneration.
3	10	1400	Stored in canister pressurized to 2 psig.	0.191 g H_2O	Container still pressurized.
4	10	1400	Stored in canister pressurized to 2 psig.	0.168 g H_2O	Container still pressurized.
5	14	1425	Stored in canister pressurized to 2 psig.	0.160 g H_2O	Container still pressurized.
5a	11	1425	Kept in regeneration flask at 1 atm dry CO_2-free air.	0.118 g H_2O	No opportunity for leakage into adsorbent.
5b	5	1475	Kept in regeneration flask at 1 atm dry CO_2-free air.	0.082 g H_2O	No opportunity for leakage into adsorbent.
6	31	1400	In canister 25 days. 0.971 g H_2O added. Pressurization to 2 psig for 31 days.	1.016 g H_2O less 0.971 g added equals 0.045 g	Container still pressurized. Amount of unknown H_2O smallest of all tests.
7	7	1400	Kept in regeneration flask at 1 atm dry CO_2-free air.	0.162 g H_2O	No opportunity for leakage into adsorbent.
7a	11	1400	In regeneration flask for 7 days at 1 atm dry CO_2-free air; 1.183 g distilled H_2O added. Kept 4 days more.	1.228 g H_2O less 1.183 g added equals 0.045 g	Required two regenerations. First gave 1.096 g H_2O, second 0.132 g H_2O.
7b	2	1400	In regeneration flask; 1.216 g added first day, regenerated next day.	1.223 g H_2O less 1.216 g added equals 0.007 g	Required two regenerations. First gave 1.093 g H_2O, second 0.130 g H_2O.

destruction temperature. The amount of water collected from this test was smaller than in any of the previous tests. However, storage time in this test was short relative to that of the others, and the initial total amount of associated water was less.

Although it may be possible for leakage and/or diffusion to occur (1) while the zeolite is being transferred, (2) while the zeolite is cooling in the furnace, or (3) during periods in the heating vessel between transfer, the probability is small. A possible explanation for this water is that after regeneration at 1400°F, the intimately associated water not originally removed at 1400°F migrates during a period

of storage, and a new equilibrium is established between the zeolite and water. This new association may then give up water when heated further to 1400°F. This seems to be substantiated by recently reported research[4] which indicates that two types of water bonding do occur in Molecular Sieve X. Infrared spectra show that a very small amount of water, <0.05 molecule per large cavity, is strongly held in a hydrogen-bonded configuration, while the rest is adsorbed close to a cation, with one hydrogen free and one bonded to a surface oxygen.

In order to simulate actual flight conditions more closely, Test 6 was prepared. The adsorbent was regenerated at 1400°F and transferred to a canister. The canister was pressurized to 2 psig and stored for 25 days. At the end of this period, 0.971 gram of water was added to the adsorbent, and the canister was again pressurized. Six days later the adsorbent was regenerated and 1.016 grams of water were recovered. An additional 0.045 gram of water contaminant was recovered in addition to the injected sample. This value is much smaller than that of other tests for similar or shorter storage times.

Test 6 results show that the addition of a water sample, as for example during a collection flight, may either retard migration of the adsorbent's intimately associated water or fill vacancies in the zeolite left by this water. Tests 7, 7a, and 7b were performed to confirm Test 6 results. In test 7, a freshly prepared 7-liter batch of zeolite was allowed to remain in the regeneration flask for 7 days. At the end of this time, 0.162 gram of water was recovered. The adsorbent (Test 7a) was then held in the regeneration flask under atmospheric pressure of dry, CO_2-free air for 7 days. Then, 1.183 grams of distilled water were added to the adsorbent. The adsorbent was regenerated 4 days later. However, regeneration was for a shorter period than normal due to indicated low pressure readings. The collection of 1.096 grams of water upon regeneration was less than the amount introduced. A second regeneration produced an additional 0.132 gram of water to give 1.228 grams, or 0.045 gram more than introduced.

This adsorbent remained in the oven (Test 7b), and 1.216 grams of water were added. The adsorbent was regenerated the following day.

Again, the low pressure over the adsorbent was used to terminate regeneration sooner than usual. Collection of only 1.093 grams of water indicated that regeneration had not been complete. A second regeneration one day later yielded an additional 0.103 gram of water, or 100.6 per cent of the amount introduced into the adsorbent.

These data, in addition to confirming Test 6 results, indicate that the duration at temperature is the most important criterion in determining when regeneration is complete.

Water Breakthrough Tests

A series of tests were performed to determine the water adsorption efficiency of Type 13X Molecular Sieve. A schematic diagram of the apparatus used in the breakthrough tests is shown in Fig. 1. In this apparatus, air is pulled through the system by means of a 100-cfm fore pump. The air first passes through a flowmeter, then through a cooling coil immersed in ice water. The latter holds the mixing ratio of the air at a dew-point of 0°C. Next, the air flows through a 2-in. bed of prepared adsorbent. The adsorbent bed is pre-cooled by a dry ice-alcohol bath. The air temperature and pressure directly above the adsorbent are measured. After passing through the adsorbent, the air then passes through a liquid-nitrogen-cooled collection trap. Any water vapor or carbon dioxide not adsorbed by the adsorbent is removed here. Later, the water vapor and carbon dioxide are separated by means of differential distillation and are quantitatively measured.

Test conditions and the results of the series of breakthrough tests on a 2-in. deep bed of

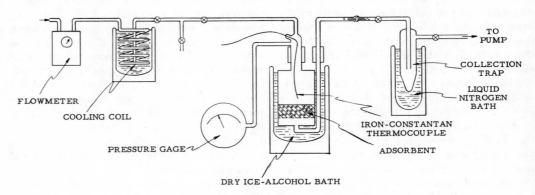

FIG. 1. Water breakthrough test apparatus.

TABLE 4. WATER BREAKTHROUGH TESTS
(2-IN. BED—TYPE 13X MOLECULAR SIEVE)

Test Conditions	Flow Rate (m/min.)	Length of Run (min.)	Pressure (mm)	Mixing Ratio of Inlet Air (g/kg)	Water Collected at Breakthrough	Remarks
Air and adsorbent at 23°C	29	30	21.5	6.19	Negligible	No breakthrough
Air and adsorbent at 23°C	30	60	21	6.19	Negligible	No breakthrough
Inlet air at 0°C—air at adsorbent −55°C	26	60	19.5	3.56	Negligible	No breakthrough
Inlet air at 0°C—air at adsorbent −41°C	37	120	20	3.56	0.003 g (0.013 l CO_2)	0.05 per cent H_2O breakthrough
Inlet air at 0°C—air at adsorbent −35°C	41	120	20	3.56	0.004 g (0.032 l CO_2)	0.06 per cent H_2O breakthrough

Type 13X Molecular Sieve, previously regenerated at 760°C (1400°F), are given in Table 4. The data clearly indicate that there is negligible breakthrough of water from the zeolite even under adverse conditions, i.e., uncooled air and warm zeolite.

Carbon Dioxide Breakthrough Tests

A test was made to determine the carbon dioxide adsorption efficiency of Type 13X Molecular Sieve. A schematic diagram of the test apparatus is given in Fig. 2. In this test, the pressure in the system was maintained at 33 mm Hg and the airstream was cooled to −28°C. The air had a flow rate of 38 m/min. through a 2-in. bed of prepared adsorbent. The system initially has two airstreams. The first airstream is dried and passed through a cooling coil while the second airstream is passed through a water bath to saturate the air. Immediately in front of the adsorbent bed, the two airstreams are combined, with excess moisture condensing on the walls of the mixing tube. This design results in a 100 per cent RH at the adsorbent inlet. Since the zeolite has a greater adsorbent affinity for water than carbon dioxide, this test was performed under "worst-case" conditions. The carbon dioxide concentration at the bed inlet is approximately 310 ppm. The air temperature and pressure directly above the adsorbent bed is measured. After passing through the adsorbent, the air goes through the fore pump and is monitored by a carbon dioxide infrared analyzer. The data from the analyzer is recorded on a strip chart recorder.

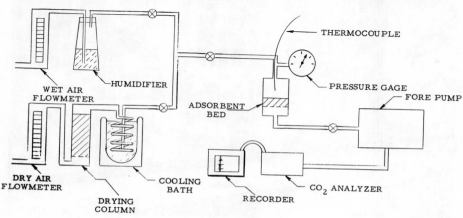

FIG. 2. Schematic diagram of CO_2 breakthrough determination apparatus.

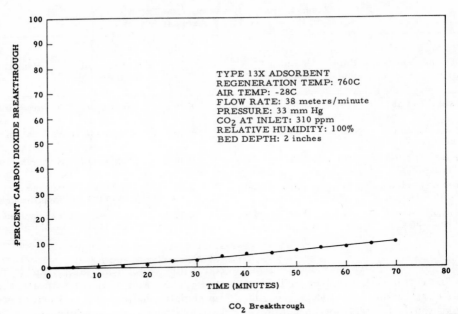

TYPE 13X ADSORBENT
REGENERATION TEMP: 760C
AIR TEMP: -28C
FLOW RATE: 38 meters/minute
PRESSURE: 33 mm Hg
CO_2 AT INLET: 310 ppm
RELATIVE HUMIDITY: 100%
BED DEPTH: 2 inches

CO_2 Breakthrough

FIG. 3. CO_2 breakthrough.

The results obtained from a 2-in. bed of Type 13X Molecular Sieve, previously regenerated at 760°C (1400°F), are plotted as per cent breakthrough *vs* time in Fig. 3. From the breakthrough curve, it is clear that even under conditions of a 100 per cent RH, the total quantity of carbon dioxide that has broken through the 2-in. bed is less than 5 per cent.

FIG. 4. Volumetric adsorption apparatus.

AIR ADSORPTION CHARACTERISTICS

A series of experiments were performed to determine the thermodynamic and kinetic characteristics of the adsorption of dry, CO_2-free air on synthetic zeolites at cryogenic temperatures. The results of these experiments were later used as design parameters in the fabrication of a Cryogenic Adsorbent Pump.

Thermodynamic Studies

Adsorption isotherms and calorimetric heats of adsorption were determined simultaneously in a volumetric adsorption apparatus (Fig. 4) at a sample temperature of $-195°C$. This was accomplished with a combined adsorption-calorimeter sample cell (Fig. 5), which consists of two chambers, one within the other. The inner chamber contains the adsorbent under study and the other liquid nitrogen. The heat produced during adsorption vaporizes the liquid nitrogen, and the escaping gaseous nitrogen is measured. From this value, and the known heat of vaporization of liquid nitrogen, one calculates the calorimetric heat of adsorption.

In addition, adsorption isotherms were determined at $-183°C$ (with liquid oxygen used as refrigerant) and $-78°C$ (dry ice-alcohol mixtures as refrigerant). Isosteric heats of adsorption were calculated from the Clausius-Clapeyron equation using the -195 and $-183°C$ isotherm data.

The adsorbents were Type 5A Molecular

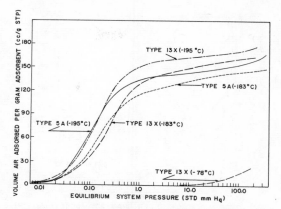

FIG. 6. Adsorption isotherms of dry, CO_2-free air on Type 13 X and Type 5A molecular sieve ⅛-in. diameter pellets.

Sieve (calcium alumino silicate) and type 13X Molecular Sieve (sodium alumino silicate) in ⅛-in. diameter pellet form; each pellet contains 20 per cent, by weight, inert binding material. Prior to sealing the adsorbent in the adsorption apparatus, the pellets were evacuated at 760°C, while between adsorption determinations of the same sample, the pellets were evacuated at 320°C.

Room air, previously treated to remove its water and carbon dioxide content by passage through beds containing "Drierite," "Ascarite" and zeolite, was the adsorbate.

Figure 6 gives the adsorption isotherms of dry, CO_2-free air on Type 13X and Type 5A Molecular Sieves at -195 and $-183°C$, and on Type 13X at $-78°C$. Each isotherm shown is the result of at least two determinations. The isosteric (q_i) and calorimetric (q_c) heats of adsorption are given in Fig. 7.

The isotherms of Type 13X and Type 5A at both -195 and $-183°C$ exhibit a similar "foot" which ends at about 0.02 mm with an adsorbed air volume of 6 cc/g adsorbent. Initially, above 0.03 mm, Type 5A exhibits greater adsorption capacity than Type 13X; however, after approximately 95 cc/g has been adsorbed, the situation is reversed. This crossing over takes place at 0.17 mm at $-195°C$ and at 0.35 mm at $-183°C$. This may be explained by slight differences in active surfaces of the two types of adsorbent.

From 1 mm and above, Type 13X exhibits about a 13 per cent higher adsorbing capacity than Type 5A at both -195 and $-183°C$. This

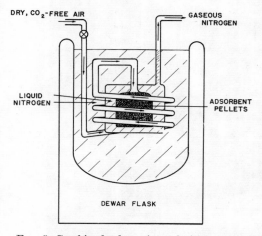

FIG. 5. Combined adsorption-calorimeter sample cell.

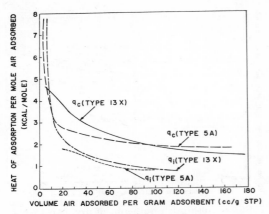

FIG. 7. Calorimetric (q_c) and isosteric (q_i) heats of adsorption; q_c determined at $-195°C$ and q_i calculated from $-195°C$ and $-183°C$ adsorption isotherms.

is understandable since the void volume of the zeolite is 13 per cent greater for the former than the latter.[5]

The effect of temperature on adsorption appears to be the same for both types of adsorbent. This is illustrated by the percentage difference of adsorbing capacity due to temperature at -195 and $-183°C$. For example,

Type 13X gives 17 per cent difference at 1.0 mm and 6.3 per cent at 50 mm, and Type 5A gives 16 per cent and 6.4 per cent at the same respective pressures. Above 100 mm at $-195°C$, the isotherm also indicates the effects of condensation of unadsorbed air.

At $-78°C$, Type 13X exhibits practically no adsorption up to a pressure of about 6 mm. Above this pressure there is a slow increase to an adsorbent capacity of 23 cc/g at 170 mm.

The heats of adsorption of Type 13X, q_i and q_c, appear to be only slightly higher than Type 5A up to an adsorbed volume of about 95 cc/g. Above this volume, there is a crossing over of curves, which may be coincidental or possibly related to the previously discussed change in adsorption isotherms. However, this cross-over relationship appears to be opposite from what might be expected. The curve average of q_i for Type 13X is 1.54 kcal/mole adsorbate and q_c is 2.33 kcal/mole, while for Type 5A curve average q_i is 1.16 kcal mole and q_c is 2.26 kcal/mole.

Kinetic Studies

The rates of adsorption were measured in a gravimetric adsorption apparatus (Fig. 8) at

FIG. 8. Gravimetric adsorption system.

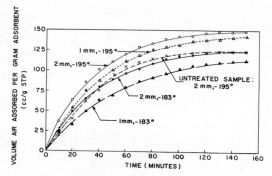

FIG. 9. Rate of adsorption of dry, CO_2-free air on Type 13X molecular sieve ⅙-in. pellets.

sample temperatures of $-195°C$ (liquid nitrogen bath) and $-183°C$ (liquid oxygen bath) and constant system pressures of 1 and 2 mm Hg. This apparatus utilizes a quartz helical spring balance of the McBain and Bakr[6] type, which was adapted with a linear differential transformer wired to a carrier preamplifier in a Sanborn Recorder. Thus, changes in weight were automatically recorded. Design of the gravimetric apparatus provides for maintaining a constant pressure in the adsorption system.

The adsorbent was Type 13X Molecular Sieve (sodium alumino silicate) in ¹⁄₁₆-in. diameter pellet form; each pellet contains 20 per cent of inert binding material. In all determinations except one, the pellets were evacuated in the apparatus at $450°C$ before a rate determination was made. The exception was evacuated at room temperature.

Room air, previously treated to remove its water and carbon dioxide content by passage through beds containing "Drierite," "Ascarite," and anhydrous magnesium perchlorate, was the adsorbate.

Figure 9 gives the rates of adsorption of dry, CO_2-free air on Type 13X adsorbent at -195 and $-183°C$ at both 1-mm and 2-mm constant system pressure. Included is a curve giving the rate for untreated pellets at $-195°C$ and 2 mm.

Data indicate that the effect of temperature is greater than the effect of pressure on the rate of adsorption, within the range of the experiments. For example, after 60 minutes at $-195°C$, the 2-mm pressure system gives an 8.5 per cent greater adsorption than 1 mm, and at $-183°C$ the former is 21.6 per cent greater than the latter. For the same time period at 1

mm, the colder system $(-195°C)$ gives a 39.2 per cent higher adsorption than the $-183°C$ system, and at 2 mm the former is 24.2 per cent better than the latter. Equilibrium adsorption data (discussed above) give a temperature effect at 1 mm of 17 per cent greater adsorbing capacity and at 2 mm 14 per cent, while pressure effect at $-195°C$ is 4 per cent and at $-183°C$ 7 per cent.

The pellets as received from the manufacturer contain adsorbed water and carbon dioxide. Since water and carbon dioxide are preferentially adsorbed over the other constituents of air and are adsorbed at room temperature, they would occupy adsorption sites and reflect a lower adsorbent capacity for the Molecular Sieve. Data clearly show this lower capacity. After 60 minutes at 2 mm and $-195°C$, the regenerated adsorbent is 18.5 per cent greater than the untreated material. The latter appears to have about the same rate of adsorption at $-195°C$ as the former at $-183°C$.

SAMPLING DEVICES

From the results of the laboratory experimentation, the adsorption technique was incorporated into two different sampling devices for use at two different altitude regimes.

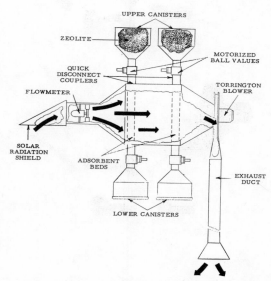

FIG. 10. Dual molecular sieve unit (schematic diagram).

One device, known as the Dual Molecular Sieve unit, utilizes a blower and can only be flown to altitudes of approximately 30 km; the other utilizes a Cryogenic Adsorbent Pump and is useful above 30 km. The present altitude limit of balloons is 42 km. This state of the art is the present limit on the height at which the Cryogenic Adsorbent Pump can operate. Although both of these units have been described elsewhere,[2, 3] a brief description here is appropriate, not only for completeness, but also for a better understanding of the results obtained with these units.

Dual Molecular Sieve

The Dual Molecular Sieve is shown schematically in Fig. 10 and pictorially in Fig. 11. There are two upper canisters and two lower canisters, each having a volume of 6.8 liters. The ball valves which seal the canisters have a $1\frac{1}{4}$-in. port and are actuated by a DC drive mechanism. The canisters are connected above (and below) the adsorbent beds by quick-disconnect couplers. The two adsorbent beds

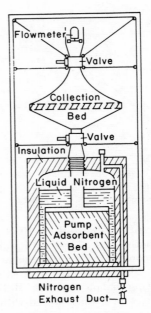

Fig. 12. Cryogenic adsorbent pump system (schematic diagram).

are connected in series; each presents a 1-sq ft surface of adsorbent to the airstream. The beds are 2 in. deep, and each has a stainless steel screen to hold adsorbent pellets in place. These beds are held in a vertical position approximately 1 ft apart by an airtight duct. A $\frac{1}{10}$-hp Torrington blower, with its outlet connected to an exhaust duct, is the air mover. At the intake of the device is an aluminum solar radiation shield followed by a propeller-type flowmeter.

Prior to flight, freshly prepared adsorbent is placed in the upper canisters, and these canisters are pressurized to 2 psig with dry nitrogen in the laboratory. The lower canisters are prepared for flight in the laboratory by being cleaned, evacuated, flushed with dry nitrogen, evacuated, and pressurized to 2 psig with dry nitrogen. The canisters are later connected to the sampling unit in the field. When the unit reaches the desired sampling altitude, the blower is turned on to exhaust water vapor trapped at lower altitudes.

After a 5-minute flushing, the ball valves on the upper canisters are opened and the adsorbent drops into the adsorbent beds to start the sampling period. At the end of the sampling period, the blower is turned off, valves on the upper canisters are closed and valves on the

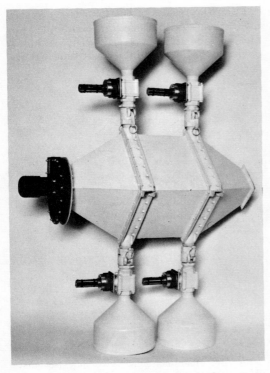

Fig. 11. Dual molecular sieve unit.

lower canisters are opened. This permits the adsorbent to drop from the adsorbent beds into the lower canisters. After a 5-minute delay, valves on the lower canisters are closed, sealing the exposed adsorbent, and the sampling is complete. After recovery of the Dual Molecular Sieve, the lower canisters are removed from the unit and are sent to the laboratory for regeneration and sample analysis.

Cryogenic Adsorbent Pump System

The system containing the Cryogenic Adsorbent Pump is shown schematically in Fig. 12 and pictorially in Fig. 13. This collecting device consists essentially of a propeller-type flowmeter, a collection adsorption bed,

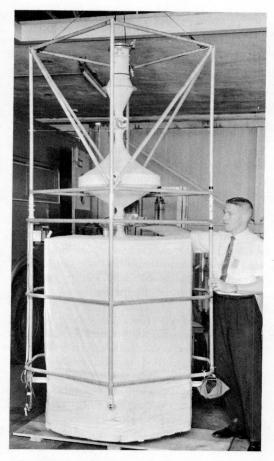

FIG. 13. The complete cryogenic pump system and gondola.

and the Cryogenic Adsorbent Pump. The collection bed, containing specially prepared Type 13X Molecular Sieve pellets, is 2-in. deep and 22 in. in diameter. This bed is sealed by two ball valves, one each at the inlet and outlet of the airstream. The adsorbent here is always at ambient temperature. The pump's adsorbent bed is designed to keep the adsorbent (Type 13X Molecular Sieve) at the temperature of liquid nitrogen throughout the sampling period. A pressure relief valve on the liquid nitrogen chamber keeps the nitrogen from either building up to high pressures or solidifying at the reduced pressures of high altitude.

In operation, the two valves on the collection bed are opened when the balloon system reaches float altitude. The inlet valve allows ambient air to enter the collection bed chamber, while the outlet valve, which is the inlet to the pump proper, allows air in the collection chamber to pass into the pump, where it is adsorbed. It is the adsorption process which pulls the ambient air through the collection bed. The water vapor and carbon dioxide are removed from the ambient air in the collection bed. The valves are closed at the end of the sampling period. Upon recovery of the system, the entire device is returned to the laboratory for analysis.

EXPERIMENTAL FLIGHTS

Since some of the laboratory experimentation on the water adsorption characteristics of Type 13X Molecular Sieve were preformed after the results of our experimental flights were reported,[2, 3] it is appropriate to review these flights at this time taking into consideration the new laboratory data.

Dual Molecular Sieve Flight

The Dual Molecular Sieve described in the previous section was flown from San Angelo, Texas, on 15 March 1961. The sampling unit was actuated at 9:45 AM CST at a float altitude of 21.9 km and the sampling period lasted 60 minutes. To minimize contamination, the sampling units were suspended 150 ft below the balloon. In addition, the instruments, batteries, etc., were completely enclosed in polyethylene. A drying agent was placed inside the polyethylene with the instrument package.

A breakdown of the laboratory analysis and results of this flight are given in Table 5.

TABLE 5. DUAL MOLECULAR SIEVE FLIGHT DATA

Location	San Angelo, Tex.
Date	15 March 1961
Sampling altitude	21.9 km
Ambient air temperature	−61°C
Sampling time	60 min.
Flowmeter air volume sampled*	19.2×10^3 l (STP)
Carbon dioxide collected (STP)	
Bed A	6.06 l
Bed B	0.14 l
Total	6.20 l
% Carbon dioxide (by flowmeter volume)*	0.032%
Water collected	
Bed A	0.783 g
Bed B	0.437 g
Total	1.220 g
Mixing ratio*	
Based on total water collected	0.049 g H_2O/kg air
Based on Bed A water only	0.031 g H_2O/kg air

* Based on flowmeter readings and calculations, there is a possible ±5% error in this determination.

Due to the method of calibration and instrument uncertainty, there is at least a possible combined error of ± 5 per cent in the pressure, temperature, and flowmeter measurements. This possible error is reflected in the flowmeter calculations and all determinations dependent on flowmeter volume. On this basis, the amount of carbon dioxide recovered, 0.032 per cent by volume, is within experimental error of the generally accepted value of 0.031 per cent.

In a previous paper,[2] we reported the mixing ratio obtained was 0.049 g H_2O/kg air. Since then, the laboratory experimental studies discussed under Water Adsorption Characteristics, p. 459, were performed. It is apparent from these studies that Type 13X Molecular Sieve holds or bonds the water in at least two different ways. After heat treatment at 760°C under vacuum conditions, Type 13X Molecular Sieve still contains intimately associated water. If water is added to this zeolite and then heat treated in a similar fashion, one recovers within 2 per cent the amount introduced, though it may not be the same water as that added. However, if no water is added and the zeolite is reheat-treated under vacuum conditions, some of the intimately associated water is collected. From water breakthrough data, it is known that only a negligible amount of water goes through a 2-in. bed of adsorbent even under adverse conditions. Therefore from the above experimental data, it would appear that the total water collected on the flight is not the sum of the water regenerated from both beds of zeolite but rather only from the first bed (Bed A). Thus, the mixing ratio obtained on this flight is really 0.031 g H_2O/kg air. This type of error will not occur on any future flights since we have set up a control procedure (see p. 471, Summary and Recommendations).

For comparison with data from other investigators, this corrected value is placed in Fig. 14 on a graph containing mixing-ratio data compiled by Gutnick.[7] Our value appears to agree quite favorably with those obtained by other investigators.

Cryogenic Adsorbent Pump Flight

The Cryogenic Adsorbent Pump system, described in a previous section, was flown from Minneapolis, Minnesota, on 2 May 1962 to a sampling altitude of 36.4 km. To eliminate balloon-borne contamination, the system was located 150 ft below the balloon. At the end of a 180-minute sampling period, the Adsorbent Pump descended for recovery. A flowmeter was used to determine flow rate and total volume flow during the sampling period. As with the Dual Molecular Sieve, this flowmeter volume is subject to a possible ±5 per cent error. In addition, all of the sampled air retained by the Adsorbent Pump was subsequently measured. Flight results are given in Table 6.

The flight results obtained appear to be in good agreement with each other and with those found by other investigators. The calculated values of carbon dioxide mixing ratio (0.030 per cent and 0.032 per cent by volume based on flowmeter and desorbed air volumes, respectively) agree within experimental error with the previously stated generally accepted value of 0.031 per cent .Since only one adsorbent bed is used in this sytem, no correction is needed for the total volume of water collected. Although no measurements have been re-

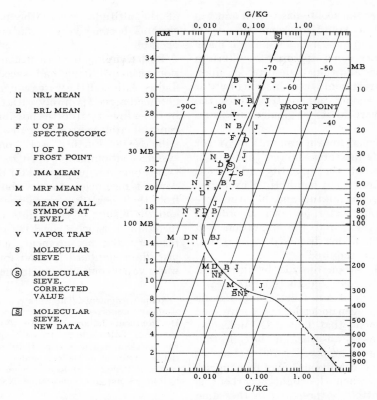

Fig. 14. Comparison of flight data with mixing ratios obtained by other investigators.[7]

TABLE 6. CRYOGENIC ADSORBENT PUMP SYSTEM FLIGHT DATA

Location	Minneapolis, Minn.
Date	2 May 1962
Sampling altitude	36.4 km.
Sampling time	180 min.
Total volume air sampled	
Flowmeter readings*	3.3×10^3 1 (STP)
Desorbed air	3.6×10^3 1 (STP)
Carbon dioxide collected	1.07 1 (STP)
Per cent Carbon dioxide	
Flowmeter readings*	0.032%
Desorbed air	0.030%
Water recovered	1.448 g
Mixing ratio	
Flowmeter readings*	0.34 g H_2O/kg air
Desorbed air	0.31 g H_2O/kg air

* Based on flowmeter readings and calculations, there is a possible $\pm 5\%$ error in this determination.

ported to date for altitudes above 31 km, the water vapor mixing ratio obtained (0.34 and 0.31 g H_2O/kg air based on flowmeter and desorbed air volumes, respectively) appears to agree well with an extrapolation of the mixing ratio-data compiled by Gutnick[7] (see Fig. 14). The value 0.32 g H_2O/kg air, reported in a previous paper,[3] is a weighted average of the mixing ratios calculated from flowmeter readings and desorbed air volumes.

SUMMARY AND RECOMMENDATIONS

Various synthetic zeolite characteristics for water vapor adsorption were investigated. These included zeolite preparation and regeneration, introduction of known quantities of seeded water and their recovery, storage contamination, and possibility of water and carbon dioxide breakthrough under various conditions.

Results show that, although most water is removed from the zeolite, Type 13X retains some residual, intimately associated water when heat-treated under vacuum conditions at 760°C. After the zeolite has cooled and has been allowed to stand for some time, this water migrates in some manner and/or is made available under some apparent equilibrium condition for additional desorption upon further heat treatment. Introduction of water to prepared zeolite apparently causes the zeolite to revert to its original equilibrium condition.

Introduction of known amounts of 54 per cent D_2O-H_2O mixtures showed that within ±2 per cent of the quantity added are recovered. There is an equilibrium exchange between the seeded mixture and the intimately associated zeolite water, however. In order to more fully understand the migration and exchange mechanisms discussed, a great deal more research is required.

Water and carbon dioxide breakthrough tests indicate clearly that there is practically no breakthrough of water or carbon dioxide from the zeolite even under adverse conditions.

We recommend that Type 13X Molecular Sieve be used as the adsorbent in the collection beds and that it be prepared at 760°C (1400°F) under vacuum conditions. We recommend further, that, when the flight adsorbent is prepared, controls be prepared in the same manner from the same lot. These controls should be stored in containers similar to the flight containers. At the conclusion of a flight, the adsorbent from both the flight and the controls, respectively, should be regenerated at 875°C (1600°F) under vacuum conditions and total water and carbon dioxide determined. The amounts of water collected from the controls should then be subtracted from the flight-collected water. This technique would then hold the possible error in the determination of water vapor to within 5 per cent. In addition, the isotopes containing deuterium, tritium and carbon-14 can be determined and would rule out any error due to the exchange phenomenon.

The series of thermodynamic and kinetic experiments on the adsorption of dry, CO_2-free air on zeolites indicated the feasibility of using the adsorption principle in a pump for use at high altitudes. These data were eventually used in the design and fabrication of a Cryogenic Adsorbent Pump utilizing Type 13X Molecular Sieve for use at altitudes above 30 km. The Cryogenic Adsorbent Pump is most suitable at the altitudes where the normal blower systems become very inefficient or are not operable.

Both sampling devices utilizing the adsorption principle have had successful balloon flights. Although the water vapor mixing ratios obtained agree favorably with those reported by other investigators the possibility of system contamination contributing to water collection still exists. Further work on eliminating system contamination must be performed.

Although one experimental flight for each device is insufficient to prove out a technique, from the laboratory experience reported here and the results of the flights, this sampling technique, which consists of collection, recovery, and measurement, can nevertheless provide a standard method for determining water vapor concentration in the stratosphere.

Acknowledgments. The work reported is based on studies supported partially by Meteorological Development Laboratory, Air Force Cambridge Research Laboratories; partially by the Atomic Energy Commission; and partially by an agency of the Department of Defense under a U.S. Air Force contract. Type 13X Molecular Sieve is manufactured by Linde Company, Tonowanda, New York.

References

1. Barclay, F. R., et al., "A Direct Measurement of the Humidity in the Stratosphere Using a Cooled-vapour Trap," *Quart. J. Roy. Meteorol. Soc.*, **86**, 259–64 (1960); Brown, F., et al., "Measurements of the Water Vapor, Tritium, and Carbon-14 Content of the Middle Stratosphere Over Southern England," *Tellus*, **13**, 407–16 (1961).
2. Steinberg, S., and Rohrbough, S. F., "The Collection and Measurement of Carbon Dioxide and Water Vapor in the Upper Atmosphere," *J. Appl. Meteorol.*, **1**, 418–21 (1962).
3. Rohrbough, S. F., "Determination of the Mixing Ratios of Water Vapor and Carbon Dioxide in the Stratosphere," *Science*, **137**, 599–600 (1962).
4. Bertsch, L., and Habgood, H. W., "Infrared Spectra of Water and Carbon Dioxide Adsorbed on Molecular Sieve X," American Chemical Society Abstracts of papers presented at Atlantic City, N.J., p. 1, Sept. 9–14, 1962.
5. Linde Co., Bulletin 9947-A, "Physical Properties of Linde Molecular Sieves—Types 4A, 5A, 13X."
6. McBain, J. W., and Bakr, A. M., "A New Sorption Balance," *J. Am. Chem. Soc.*, **48**, 690–95 (1926).
7. Air Force Cambridge Research Laboratories, Air Force Surveys in Geophysics No. 147, "Mean Annual Mid-latitude Moisture Profiles to 31 km," by M. Gutnick, AFCRL-62-681, p. 25, July 1962.

58. A Stratospheric Humidity Experiment

T. Y. PALMER*

Air Force Cambridge Research Laboratories, Bedford, Massachusetts

S. ROHRBOUGH

Minneapolis-Honeywell, Minneapolis, Minnesota

AND

S. STEINBERG

Applied Science Division, Litton Systems, Inc., St. Paul, Minnesota

ABSTRACT

A comparison of alpha radiation dew-point hygrometers and a Goldsmith Vapor Trap was made at Minneapolis, Minnesota on 17 October 1962. Values obtained over an interval from 28 to 78 mb gave good agreement between the two devices.

The sample was obtained in a region of pronounced vertical descent, and it is postulated that the high values of mixing ratio may be a result of this motion.**

It is suggested that similar measurements be made in a region of sudden stratospheric

warming to investigate the distribution of water vapor to elevations presently out of reach of balloon soundings.

* Present affiliation, The Boeing Co.

** In replying to a question raised by the reviewer about the possibility of contamination by the wake of the balloon, Mr. Palmer has written (personal communication to editor) that he has prepared a paper for publication elsewhere in which he shows that:

"Contamination within the wake of a balloon from desorbing water is sufficient to give almost any dew point from completely dry to $-70°C$. However, at the dew point which we measured it would be physically impossible, granting the measured characteristics of polyethylene, for sufficient moisture to be carried aloft to give the integrated values observed.

This, plus the care taken in remoting the sample tube and the fact that the descending values agreed with the ascending values force us to reject the comments of the reviewer."

On October 17, 1962 a balloon flight to a pressure of 28 mb was conducted at Minneapolis, Minnesota for the purpose of comparison of various types of humidity sensitive devices.

The flight had two Minneapolis-Honeywell "alpha" dew-point hygrometers, two Bendix microwave refractometers, a Ballistic Research Laboratories optical dew-point hygrometer, and a Bendix optical dew-point hygrometer. In addition, a Goldsmith Vapor Trap and a dual molecular sieve unit were carried. These two gravimetric measuring devices were aboard to furnish standards of comparison and to provide an intercomparison between the two devices.

The instruments were at a distance of 500 ft below the balloon and parachute assembly, while the individual instruments and the air intake for the gravimetric measurements were on outriggers a distance of 8 ft from the center of the package as shown in Fig. 1.

Since laboratory tests conducted just prior to the assembly of the flight package had shown that styrofoam insulation absorbed and desorbed water readily, its usage was held to a minimum. Several other materials were tested,

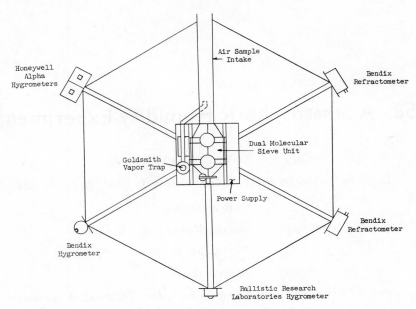

Fɪɢ. 1. Arrangement of instruments.

such as closed cell polyethylene, and were also found to have this undesirable characteristic. In addition, desiccating materials were placed in the power supply box to absorb any water vapor given off by the batteries. Aluminum surfaces (whose oxide is hygroscopic) over which air would flow and exposed styrofoam surfaces were well coated with paint or glyptol.

All instruments were tested together in an altitude-pressure chamber on a progammed flight to simulate the expected conditions; they compared quite well with each other.

Due to an unfortunate launch accident, the Bendix hygrometer, the Ballistic Laboratories Hygrometer, and the radiosonde transmitting the information on one Bendix refractometer were rendered inoperative.

After the launch at 0917 CST, the flight progressed to its float altitude of approximately 25 km as planned. After 30 minutes at this level, the balloon developed a slow leak and commenced a slow descent, finally impacting 185 miles east of Minneapolis near Merrill, Wisconsin. The surface winds were quite strong, which resulted in extensive damage to much of the equipment.

A relay on the Dual Molecular Sieve unit failed to operate so that stratospheric data was obtained only from the two "alpha" hygrometers and the Goldsmith Vapor Trap.

The measured frost points followed a relatively normal distribution with altitude, with values ranging from -75 to $-78°$C between 140 to 45 mb as would be expected based on past observations. At the 45-mb level, a relatively sharp increase in dew point to $-71°$C was observed. The dew point continued to rise above this level reaching $-63°$C at 30 mb and $-60°$C at 28 mb. This last value is believed to be erroneous because the temperature of the heat sink increased rapidly due to insufficient ventilation as the balloon decelerated near the float altitude. The temperature difference between the indicated dew point and the heat sink was then greater than the Peltier cooler could generate. For this reason, the dew-point data was extrapolated linearly for the last few hundred feet of the flight.

After the float altitude had been reached, the Goldsmith Vapor Trap began sampling, but due to the slow descent which began after 30 minutes at altitude, it actually sampled over the interval from 28 to 78 mb. This sample yielded an average mixing ratio of 0.09 ± 0.01 g/kg. One hygrometer yielded a time weighted average value of 0.10 ± 0.01 g/kg while the other provided 0.12 ± 0.01 g/kg over this interval. Since the hygrometer giving the value of 0.10 g/kg had been test flown extensively and in addition had been checked in the Minneapolis-Honeywell two-pressure humidity simulator, while the other had not, it is believed that this hygrometer provided the most realistic and reliable data.

During the descent the air flow to the dew-point hygrometers had to pass over the instruments' styrofoam insulation, and in addition because the "delta T" remained greater than or near the maximum capabilities of the Peltier cooler, the descent data was rejected as erroneous. Aircraft and ground visual tracking indicated that the balloon was almost completely stationary near Eau Claire, Wisconsin during the gravimetric sampling.

It is apparent that the instruments gave comparable results within the limits of error of the experiment.

These relatively high dew points and mixing ratios were sufficiently unusual that is seemed desirable to seek an explanation of their origin in the associated meteorological conditions.

During the period from the 10th to the 18th of October a strong, persistent, west/east

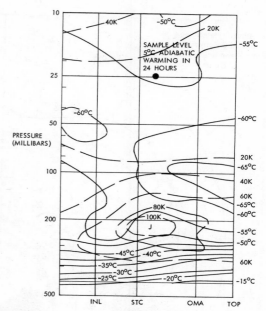

FIG. 3. Cross-section of circulation at 1200 GMT (October 17, 1962).

jetstream with maximum speeds near 100 knots existed over this region with only minor day-to-day changes. As a matter of fact, this jet stream had consistently delayed the flight due to the danger of the associated extreme shears damaging the balloon. However, it finally became necessary to launch and the test was made. For these reasons, it is believed that this flight is unique in that no measurements of stratospheric humidity have been made above a strong jetstream. A cross section through this circulation is given in Figs. 2 and 3.

The stratospheric circulation as indicated by Figs. 4 to 6 of the 30-mb level charts from the first to the 23rd of October was characterized by a continuous movement of a high pressure ridge to more northern latitudes. During the period from the 7th of October to the 16th, a high pressure cell migrated from the coast of western Europe across the United States to the Hawaiian Islands.

On the day of the flight, a minor trough of low pressure in the stratosphere moved across Minnesota and Wisconsin. Associated with this trough was pronounced downward motion between $\frac{1}{2}$ and 1 kilometer per day which was determined by the adiabatic method. This probably underestimates the magnitude of the

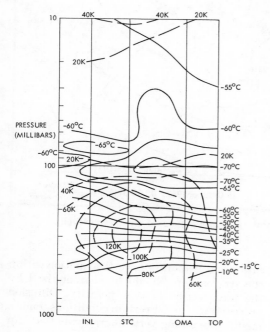

FIG. 2. Cross-section of circulation at 1200 GMT (October 16, 1962).

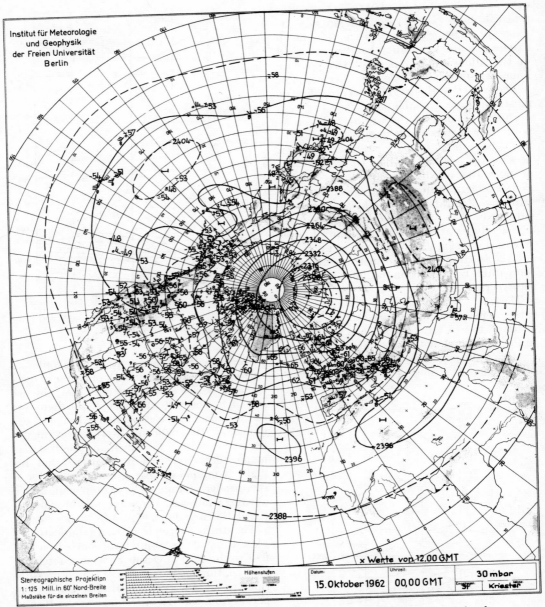

FIG. 4. Stratospheric circulation at 0000 GMT, October 15, 1962, at the 30 mb level.

motion because of the radiational losses that would occur with the observed humidity distribution. The kinematic method gives much greater values but is unreliable in this case due to the scarcity of data.

Since the mixing ratio is a conservative property of the air in the absence of conden-sation and evaporation, vertical motion within the stratosphere should be characterized by the preservation of this quantity. Diffusion processes will under certain conditions tend to modify the strong vertical gradients that can be established by such descent.

Gutnick has extensively studied the distribution of water vapor in the stratosphere. After incorporation of the observation of the mixing ratio of Rohrbough at 35 km into his data, it was found that the mean data between 18 and 35 km fit a curve

$$w = 2457/p^{1.22}$$

where w is the mean mixing ratio in milligrams per kilogram and p is the pressure in millibars.

The sounding under consideration can be reconstructed approximately from Gutnick's mean data by lowering the mean curve 20 mb. Use of the maximum mixing ratios he obtained would give downward motion over pressure increments on the order of 17 mb. This effectively gives the observed maximum.

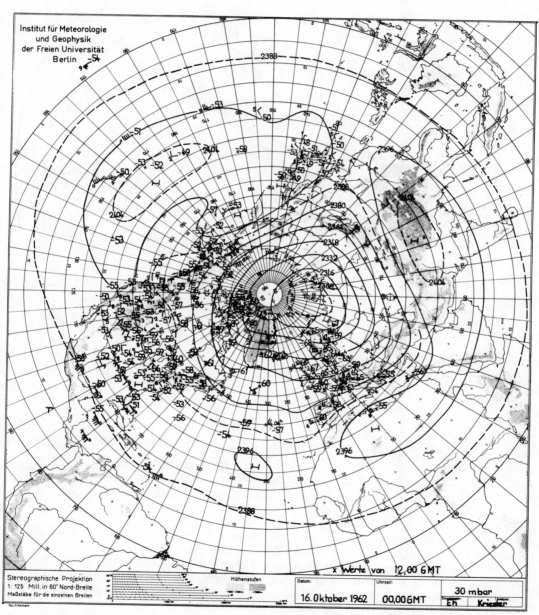

Fig. 5. Stratospheric circulation at 0000 GMT, October 16, 1962, at the 30 mb level.

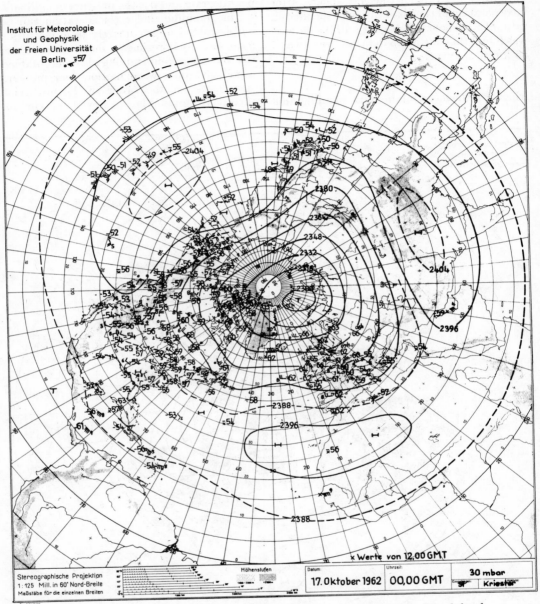

FIG. 6. Stratospheric circulation at 0000 GMT, October 17, 1962, at the 30 mb level.

Motions over this pressure increment are indicated from the observed rates of motion and the periods of time over which they occurred. The shear at 45 mb would advect drier air below this moist layer, and diffusive mixing would act to smooth out the gradient near this level especially in the time interval of days with which we are concerned. This is shown in Fig. 7.

Thus, the essential features of the curve of mixing ratio *vs* pressure for this flight can be accounted for from the associated meteorological conditions.

Further, inferences can be made about the

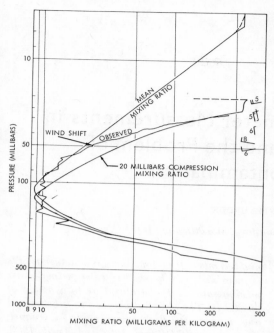

FIG. 7. Mixing ratio *vs* pressure.

than about 0.3 g/kg at pressures less than 8 mb. Since the Schumann Runge band disassociates water vapor as well as molecular oxygen, the mixing ratio would become even less above 90 km or 1.3×10^{-3} mb.

Under conditions of extremely strong and rapid descending motions, such as are observed in the sudden stratospheric warmings, it should then be possible to infer the distribution of humidity to high levels from measurements currently possible. Further information could be obtained about the relative strength of the sources (or sinks) such as the solar wind hypothesis of de Turville that may exist in the upper levels of the stratosphere.

Also within the range of possibility is the determination of stratospheric vertical motions from direct observations of the water vapor distribution.

References

1. Rohrbough, S. A., "Study of High Altitude Water-Vapor Detectors," Scientific and Final Report Contract AF 19(628)-483, March 31, 1963.
2. Gutnick, Murray, "Mean Annual Mid-Latitude Moisture Profiles to 31 km," *A F Surveys in Geophysics*, No. 147, July 1962.
3. Rohrbough, S. F., "Determination of Mixing Ratios of Water Vapor and Carbon Dioxide in the Stratosphere" *Science*, **137**, 599–600 (August 24, 1962).
4. de Turville, C. M., "Terrestial Accretion of the Solar Wind," *Nature*, **190**, 156 (April 8, 1961).

distribution of the mixing ratio at levels above 35 km or 5.8 mb from the temperature distribution above 28 mb. Since the St. Cloud, Minnesota sounding reached a level of 10 mb with a temperature of −53°C and since no clouds were observed, it seems likely that the mixing ratio in this case was not much greater

59. Frost-point Hygrometer Measurements in the Stratosphere and the Problem of Moisture Contamination

H. J. MASTENBROOK

U.S. Naval Research Laboratory, Washington, D.C.

ABSTRACT

One of the principal problems associated with the use of the frost-point hygrometer as a vertical sounding instrument is that of excluding extraneous moisture from the sample. Balloon-borne instrumentation must be prepared in the moist region of the lower troposphere; within an hour after launching, the instrumentation is at stratospheric levels where the moisture content is five or six orders of magnitude lower. Moisture is carried into the stratosphere by the instrumentation, the balloon and associated equipment; accurate measurements can be made only to the extent that this moisture can be excluded from the sample.

A number of frost-point hygrometer soundings have been made to study the effects of moisture contamination as it relates to various sampling procedures. Emphasis has been placed upon data collection during the descent portion of flight with sample collection at the lowest point in the flight train. Location of the sample inlet beneath the instrument resulted in higher moisture values during the ascent and lower values during the descent of a daytime flight. Moisture values measured while floating at 90,000 ft were also higher than values obtained after initiating descent. A night flight, also with a bottom inlet duct, yielded much lower moisture values during ascent than the equivalent day flight, but yielded comparable values to the day flight during descent. Comparison of ascent and descent observations for the night flight shows somewhat higher values for the ascent at the upper layers.

Using only the descent data for the day and night flights with bottom ducts, a moisture profile is obtained which shows water vapor-to-air mixing ratio in the stratosphere to a height of 90,000 ft. The observed values range between 1 and 4 ppm; the flights were made in August, September, and October, 1962 and April, 1963.

The first measurements in quantity of the water vapor content in the stratosphere were obtained through the British Meteorological Research flights[1] in the period 1952 through 1955. The measurements were made using a manually operated frost-point hygrometer and provided data to a height of approximately 50,000 ft. These observations showed the lower stratosphere to be very dry with a nearly invariant water vapor-to-air mixing ratio of about 2 ppm.

In the years following the Meteorological Research Flights, several independent investigators have measured moisture distributions to higher stratospheric levels using balloon-borne instrumentation and a variety of observational techniques. The total available data from all sources[2] considered without qualification suggest two characteristics of the stratospheric moisture distribution: First, there is a general trend of increasing mixing ratio with altitude; and second, the moisture content is highly variable at all levels. A selective consideration of the data, however, reveals systematic differences which require explanation. There is the comparison between balloon and aircraft observations; where the aircraft observations show an average mixing ratio of 2 ppm and a small variance, the balloon observations range

480

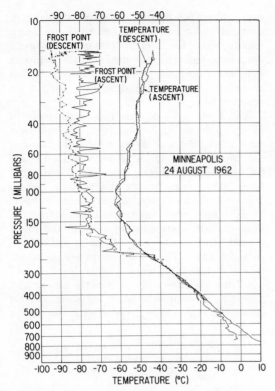

FIG. 1. Frost point and ambient temperature for flight 8-24-62, Minneapolis.

to much higher values with a large variance. Considered in somewhat different terms, the minimum mixing ratios observed by balloon, regardless of altitude, have a higher magnitude and are more variable than the minimums observed by aircraft. Considering next the mean vertical distributions of mixing ratio of independent investigators, it is found that the individual distributions show the same general trend of mixing ratio increases with height at stratospheric levels; however, the distributions are displaced one from the other in a quantitative sense.

The systematic differences between the observations of independent investigators has not been satisfactorily explained in terms of atmospheric behavior; nor has any generally accepted hypothesis been advanced to account for an increase in mixing ratio with altitude. In attempting to resolve these differences, it seems significant that the aircraft provided the lowest, and least variable observations of stratospheric moisture content. It might be

argued that extraneous moisture from the observation platform has entered more significantly into the observations of those using balloon systems than has been the case for the aircraft observations. Certainly the aircraft offers greater opportunities for minimizing sample contamination and for dilution of contamination arising within the sampling ducts.

Balloon flight assemblies which start their ascent in the moist troposphere rise in a matter of 30 to 40 minutes to stratospheric levels where the absolute humidity is 4 to 5 orders of magnitude lower. There can be little question but that large amounts of moisture are carried into the stratosphere with the flight assembly, and evolve as the flight continues. The extent to which this extraneous moisture enters into the observations of water vapor from a balloon-borne platform has been a matter of conjectures, and more definitive experiments are needed to resolve the question.

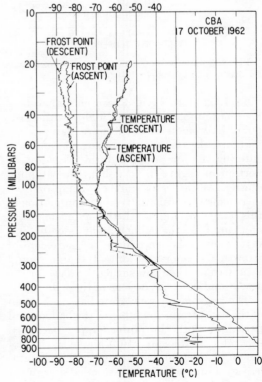

FIG. 2. Frost point and ambient temperature for flight 10-17-62, Chesapeake Bay Annex (near Washington, D.C.).

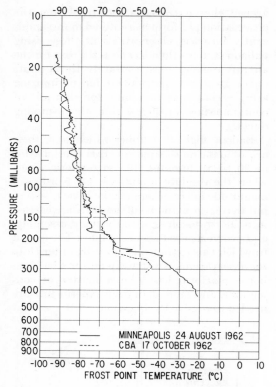

FIG. 3. Comparison of descent curves of frost point for flights 8-24-62 and 10-17-62.

In 1962, the Naval Research Laboratory made a number of balloon flights with frost-point hygrometers which were designed to minimize the amount of moisture contaminant entering the air sampled during the descent portion of flight. In so doing, the sampling during ascent was further compromised, increasing the probability of contamination in this stage of flight. If the evolvement of moisture from the balloon flight assembly is a matter of consequence in the measurement of stratospheric moisture content, than it should be apparent when comparing the data for the ascent and descent portions of these flights.

The hygrometer was located at the bottom of the flight train, 900 ft below the balloon and parachute with the power supply packaged separately and located 10 ft above the hygrometer. The sensor was located within a stainless steel duct which was extended downward to place the inlet below all other components of the flight assembly. The air sample was drawn past the sensor at an approximate rate of 0.2 cubic meter per minute using an exhaust fan, and particular care was taken to eliminate all leakage along the duct. A 7000-gram neoprene sounding balloon was used as the support vehicle for both the ascent and descent flights in order that the sounding rates might be comparable.

The first flight of this type was made in Minneapolis on 24 August 1962. The stainless steel inlet duct was 20 in. long and extended downward at an angle of 45 degrees. There were no visible cloud forms other than scattered fairweather cumulus in the surface layers. Figure 1 shows a plot of frost-point temperature which was constructed by extracting data at half-minute intervals from the flight record and connecting these points with straight lines. The data points are instantaneous values. At tropospheric levels, good agreement is observed between the ascent and descent curves of frost point. At stratospheric levels the two curves diverge with the ascent

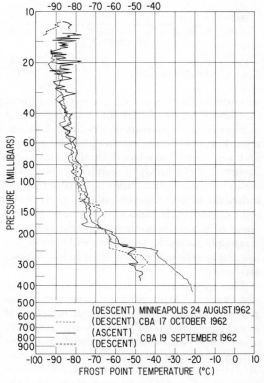

FIG. 4. Ascent and partial descent curve of frost point for flight 9-19-62 compared with descent frost point curve for flights 8-24-62 and 10-17-62.

providing the higher and more variable record of frost point. Turn-around of the balloon occurred at 93,000 ft and was followed by a 15-degree drop in the observed frost point during the first 3000 ft of descent. Thereafter, a trend of frost-point increase was observed for the remainder of the stratospheric descent.

On October 17, 1962, a similar flight was made at night from the Chesapeake Bay Annex of the Naval Research Laboratory, a facility 35 miles southeast of Washington, D.C. For this flight the inlet duct of the hygrometer was extended directly beneath the instrument with the blower positioned ahead of the sensor. The plot of frost point (Fig. 2) shows excellent agreement between the ascent and descent curves at all levels below 70,000 ft. At the higher levels the curves diverge with higher frost points observed for the ascent.

The descent curve of frost point for the night flight is next compared (Fig. 3) with the descent curve for the day flight. The agreement is quite good, and shows a decreasing frost-point temperature with height at the stratospheric levels. The ascent curves for these two flights show lower frost points at night for the upper levels by some six degrees.

On September 19, 1962, a flight was made which provided an extended period of flight at 100,000 ft. Data was obtained for the ascent, the period of level flight, and the initial part of the descent. The inlet duct of the hygrometer in this case extended beneath the instrument with the blower on the exhaust side of the sensor.

The ascent and descent frost-point curve is compared (Fig. 4) with the descent curves for the other two flights. The ascent curve is in general agreement with the two descent curves up to 70,000 ft, though representing somewhat higher frost points. Above this level, the curve ceases to follow the trend of the two descent curves and becomes extremely variable. The descent is characterized by a large decrease in frost point in the first few thousand feet, as was observed for the other two flights.

Considering now the collective data for the three flights, it is seen that there is a pattern to the frost-point observations which relates to the manner of data collection. In the troposphere and lower stratosphere there is general agreement between the ascent and descent observations of frost point. In the upper stratosphere, consistently higher values of

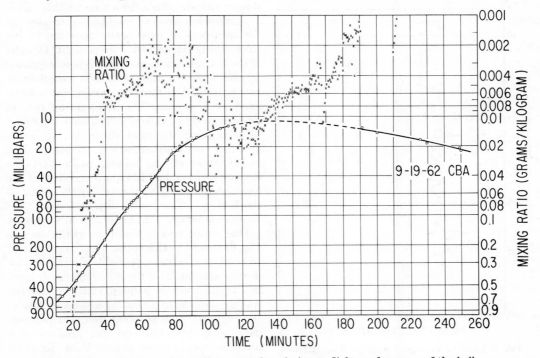

FIG. 5. Time variations of frost point and the relation to flight performance of the balloon.

frost point are observed during the ascent than during descent, and the separation between the ascent and descent curves of frost point increases with altitude.

The higher frost points observed during ascent may be reasonably explained in terms of the evolvement of moisture from the flight assembly and the inclusion of this moisture in the sample collected at the lowest level of the flight train. During descent, the wash from the flight assembly is not encountered, and moisture from sources external to the sampling duct can reach the inlet only through a diffusion process.

The interrelation between the observed moisture content and flight performance is more evident when the flight of 19 September is considered (Fig. 5) as a time function. Of particular interest is the increase in mixing ratio with decreasing ascent rate in the last 10,000 ft of ascent. In this 60-minute period the mixing ratio increased an order of magnitude and was extremely variable, reflecting perhaps a decreasing volume of air comprising the wash of the flight train as the ascent rate decreases and a continuing evolvement of

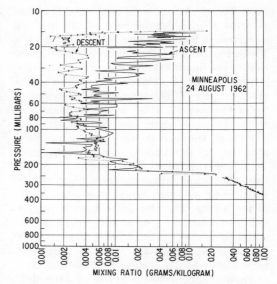

FIG. 7. Water vapor-to-air mixing ratio distribution for flight 8-24-62.

moisture into this volume which does not decrease to the same degree.

As the balloon came to rest at the top of the flight, the mixing ratio decreased to about 6 ppm and stabilized for a time at this value.

A diffusion process would have to account for transport of extraneous moisture to the inlet during this period of level flight. Descent of the balloon commenced slowly, accompanied by a decrease in mixing ratio. When the descent rate reached 130 fpm, the mixing ratio stabilized at $1\frac{1}{2}$ ppm. The accelerating rate of descent could be considered to have the effect of advancing the inlet down the diffusion gradient of contaminating moisture. The stabilization of the mixing ratio after the descent rate reached 130 fpm suggests that the amount of contaminant reaching the inlet had reached a value substantially under the natural moisture content of the atmosphere.

One other recent flight is available (see Fig. 6) to add to this series which were instrumented to minimize probable contamination during descent. This flight was made on April 26, 1963. Due to balloon rupture, descent was by parachute providing a descent rate at the highest levels of 9000 fpm. No pressure data was obtained, and the pressure-time relation was reconstructed from previous balloon flight characteristics. The pressure-

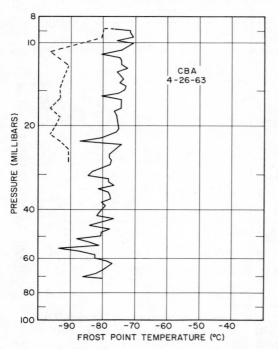

FIG. 6. Frost-point temperature for flight 4-26-63, Chesapeake Bay Annex.

time relation for the parachute descent was determined from the estimated burst altitude and the change in elevation angle of the tracking antenna. The height error is estimated not to exceed 10 per cent. The resulting distribution again shows higher frost points for the ascent than for the descent, and the overall distribution is very similar to that obtained at Minneapolis in August, 1962. For this particular flight, the readjustment of frost point to the lower value, after balloon burst, occurred in a period of 30 seconds, a much shorter adjustment period than was observed with the slower turn-arounds. This is a further indication of a relation between descent rate and the amount of contaminating moisture reaching the inlet.

It is of interest now to examine this series of flights in terms of the vertical distribution of moisture at stratospheric levels as determined by the descent data. For the August, 1962 Minneapolis flight (Fig. 7) the mixing ratio ranges between 2 and 4 ppm in the height interval 50,000 to 90,000 ft. The night time flight (Fig. 8) for October, 1962, near Washington, gives mixing ratios of 3 to 4 ppm for the stratospheric range. The prolonged high altitude flight of September 1962 (Fig. 5) gave 10 minutes of stabilized frost-point data after attaining a descent rate of 130 fpm. The mixing ratio ranges between 1 and 2 ppm in the

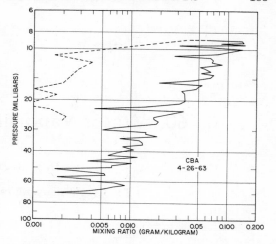

FIG. 9. Water vapor-to-air mixing ratio distribution for flight 4-26-63.

general height interval 94,000 to 96,000 ft. The parachute descent for April, 1963 (Fig. 9) shows mixing ratios between 1 and 4 ppm in the interval 80,000 to 100,000 ft.

Collectively, the flights indicate a vertical distribution of water vapor in the stratosphere which approximates a constant mixing ratio of about 1 to 4 ppm.

This distribution is in marked contrast to earlier observations from balloon platforms which show trends of increasing mixing ratio with altitude with substantially higher mixing ratios for the upper levels.

Whether the lower mixing ratios result entirely from the measures taken to minimize the inclusion of extraneous moisture in the measurements cannot be said for certain. What can be said at this time is that the range of the accumulated observations of stratospheric water vapor has been extended to include much lower mixing ratios at the higher levels and that vertical distributions of mixing ratios have now been observed which do not show the increase with height which has characterized the earlier balloon observations.

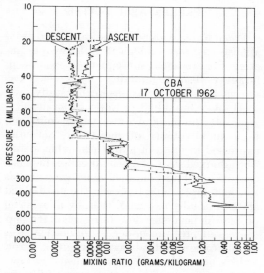

FIG. 8. Water vapor-to-air mixing ratio distribution for flight 10-17-62.

References

1. Tucker, G. B., "An Analysis of Humidity Measurements in the Upper Troposphere and Lower Stratosphere over Southern England," Meteorological Research Paper 1052, Air Ministry, Meteorological Research Committee, 1957.
2. Gutnick, M., "Mean Annual Mid-Latitude Moisture Profiles to 31 Km," *Air Force Surveys in Geophysics*, No. 147, Air Force Cambridge Research Laboratories, 1962.

60. Water Vapor in the Atmosphere

D. C. HUTCHERSON

LTV Vought Aeronautics Division, Dallas, Texas

ABSTRACT

Radiation at virtually all wavelengths in the infrared (IR) region of the electromagnetic spectrum is attenuated to some degree by water vapor in the atmosphere. This study attempts to obtain an estimate of atmospheric moisture content in a form consistent with the needs of analysts concerned with evaluation of infrared detection devices operating within the atmosphere. Profiles of absolute humidity for both standard and nonstandard days are presented along with tabulations of precipitable water for these conditions. Results are valid for the middle latitudes and for altitudes between sea level and 100,000 ft.

INTRODUCTION

The most common measure of attenuating water vapor between an IR source and an IR sensor is precipitable water (W). Precipitable water may be defined as the depth of water that would result should all vapor along an IR path be condensed and accumulated in a layer. In essence, therefore, precipitable water is an optical thickness of water which must be penetrated by IR radiation.

In penetrating this layer of precipitable water, each IR wave length is attenuated to some degree. The fraction of incident radiation transmitted through the layer is the transmission coefficient. Tables and graphs presenting values of the transmission coefficient as functions of wavelength and precipitable water are widely available.[1, 2]

Any estimate of atmospheric moisture content intended for wide application in IR sensor analyses should therefore be an estimate of atmospheric precipitable water. Several other important requirements for an effective estimate are:

(1) The altitude region under consideration should be as extensive as possible.

(2) The estimate should be valid for any geographical location;

(3) Provisions for estimating unusual IR attenuation conditions such as abnormally wet or dry days should be included;

(4) Data forming the foundation for the estimate should be of sufficient quantity and quality to insure reasonable accuracy. Previous studies have failed to satisfactorily meet all these requirements.

PRECIPITABLE WATER

Precipitable water may be calculated from almost any meteorological moisture parameter. For reasons subsequently explained, however, absolute humidity (A), is selected as a basis for the calculations in this study.

Absolute humidity, or water vapor density, is simply the mass of water vapor contained in a unit volume of moist air, normally expressed in units of grams per cubic meter. The admixed state of moist air causes dependence of absolute humidity upon pressure, as well as temperature; however, the unadmixed state is usually assumed, thereby alleviating pressure dependence. For the ranges of temperature and pressure under consideration, this simplification introduces negligible error. Tables of unadmixed vapor density *vs* dew-point or frost-point temperature (T_d) are available.[3]

If absolute humidity is a function of position along the radiation path, the following expression mathematically defines precipitable water:

$$W = 0.3048 \int_{r_0}^{r} A \, dr \qquad (1)$$

where

A = absolute humidity in g/m³,
r_0 = one end of the radiation path,
r = any arbitrary position along the radiation path (the distance between r and r_0 is measured in feet),
W = precipitable water between r_0 and r measured in microns ($1\mu = 10^{-6}$m).

Should absolute humidity be independent of position, the integral reduces to a simple product, and

$$W = 0.3048 \, A \, (r - r_0) \qquad (2)$$

In a vertical path extending from an altitude h_0 upward to an arbitrary altitude h, where absolute humidity is a function of altitude, precipitable water is related to absolute humidity by an expression similar to the general case:

$$W_z = 0.3048 \int_{h_0}^{h} A \, dh \qquad (3)$$

Path length here is altitude difference between h_0 and h in feet.

For any other path at an angle (θ) to the vertical, between altitudes h_0 and h,

$$W_\theta = \frac{W_z}{\cos \theta} \qquad (4)$$

where W_θ is precipitable water in the inclined path and θ is less than 90 degrees. A flat earth is implicitly assumed in this equation, introducing negligible error.

As stated previously, charts and tables are available which present transmission coefficients as functions of wavelength and precipitable water. These tabulations are valid only for standard conditions of pressure and temperature, however.

While changes produced by temperature deviations are often negligible, variations in pressure bring about rather complex and significant changes in the coefficients due to spectral line broadenings. Hence, some correction is necessary before precipitable water can be used to enter the tabulations when pressure is other than standard. A "reduced absolute humidity," defined as $A\sqrt{p/p_0}$ is often used to correct precipitable water for pressure deviations.[4] This modification, introduced into the equations presented previously, gives rise to a pressure corrected precipitable water (W'), thus:

$$W' = 0.3048 \int_{r_0}^{r} A \sqrt{p/p_0} \, dr \qquad (5)$$

$$W' = 0.3048 \, A \sqrt{p/p_0} \, (r - r_0) \qquad (6)$$

$$W'_z = 0.3048 \int_{h_0}^{h} A \sqrt{p/p_0} \, dh \qquad (7)$$

and

$$W'_\theta = \frac{W'_z}{\cos \theta} \qquad (8)$$

Values of W' obtained in this manner may be used to enter the standard condition coefficient tabulations directly.

WATER VAPOR PROFILE

By far the most difficult task associated with obtaining an accurate estimate of atmospheric precipitable water is that of specifying the expected amount of moisture at any altitude. Early attempts at this task were certainly less than satisfactory.[5, 6]

The principal cause of this difficulty is the relatively small moisture data sample which is available, especially in the upper troposphere and in the stratosphere. The radiosonde humidity element normally used to collect tropospheric humidity data ceases to function at temperatures below −40°C or when the humidity is very low. Consequently, specialized gear such as electronic or spectrographic hygrometers are required if altitudes in excess of approximately 23,000 ft are to be sampled. Use of such equipment necessitates an expensive platform such as an airplane or a "skyhook" class balloon. Consistent effort to obtain high altitude data has, therefore, been very rare. Two notable exceptions are the British effort in over 400 data gathering flights to approximately 50,000 ft in aircraft, and Japanese Meteorological Agency balloon ascents during the IGY.[7-12] Other high altitude moisture data have been collected by a few sporadic investigations over the past two decades.

Data for altitudes below 23,000 ft are available on a routine basis through the extensively reported efforts of the United States Weather Bureau.[13]

All data, even those collected on a consistent basis, are subject to errors introduced by instrumentation and method of measurement; often these errors are difficult, if not impossible, to correct or eliminate. Coupled with inherent lack of data, these errors make the task of preparing an estimate of atmospheric moisture content one of subjective analysis.

The original intent in this study was to prepare an estimate of moisture content from data which are available. After an extensive search of meteorological literature, however, it appears that such an effort would be somewhat wasted, for an excellent estimate has already been prepared by Gutnick of the Cambridge Research Center.[14] Gutnick has isolated most of the independently reported data and has applied good judgement in selection of data to be used in his analysis. Certainly, the estimate is open to revision once new data become available or new theories are developed, but any attempt at improving the estimate at present would merely involve personal choice.

Gutnick's estimate, as prepared, consists of two independently derived vertical moisture profiles; one of these being a vertical profile of mean annual mixing ratio (mass of water vapor per unit mass of air), the other being a vertical profile of mean annual dew-point or frost-point temperature ($\overline{T}_d$). The former profile is considered to be the more accurate of the two, but absolute humidity is derived more directly from the latter profile. Since absolute humidity is the parameter of interest in this study, the $\overline{T}_d$ profile is selected as a basis of analysis. Figure 1 is a presentation of this profile. It is valid only for the middle latitudes due to data limitations.

Absolute Humidity Profile

In the discussion of precipitable water, the point was made that a profile of frost-point or dew-point temperature leads directly to a profile of absolute humidity through the use of tables. There is a range of temperature, however, for which this statement is not strictly valid. For the range of temperature between zero and −40°C, there is always some question as to whether absolute humidity should be measured with respect to ice or with respect to water. Considerable differences exist in the two

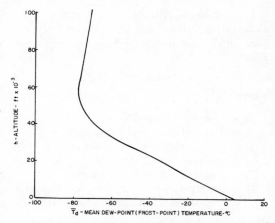

FIG. 1. Mean annual dew-point (frost-point) temperature as a function of altitude for the middle latitudes.

values at the lower end of this temperature range.

Some analysts have arbitrarily assumed that absolute humidity should be measured with respect to ice for all temperatures below 0°C, while other analysts have selected the −40°C temperature as the transition point. The first method excludes the possibility of any super-cooling while the second method results in a discontinuous absolute humidity profile. An ideal compromise appears to be one which

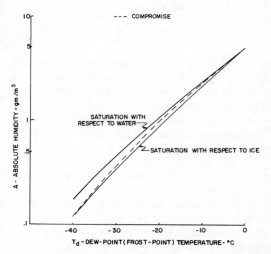

FIG. 2. The difference between saturation water vapor density (absolute humidity) measured with respect to water and with respect to ice as a function of temperature. The compromise adopted to alleviate this difference is shown.

allows some supercooling while eliminating the discontinuity.

Figure 2 shows the compromise adopted for this study. To obtain this compromise, it is assumed that the probability of supercooling is a linear function with temperature between 0°C and −40°C. In other words, absolute humidity is measured with respect to water at 0°C, with respect to ice at −40°C, and it changes linearly from one state to the other for temperatures between these values. The absolute validity of this assumption is certainly open to question, but not any more so than other arbitrary practices. As may be seen from Fig. 1, this compromise involves a 20,000 ft range of altitude.

Figure 3 presents the mean annual vertical absolute humidity profile derived from Fig. 1 using data from Fig. 2. It is valid for all altitudes between sea level and 100,000 ft in the middle latitudes.

Abnormal Attenuation Conditions

Designers concerned with infrared detection devices are usually interested in a range of conditions under which their devices must operate in order to account for as many contingencies as possible. Hence, in addition to an estimate of mean atmospheric moisture content, some method of predicting the probability of occurrence of abnormal attenuation introduced by such conditions as unusually wet or dry days is highly desirable.

At this writing, the exact distribution assoc-

iated with absolute humidity is not known, although data indicates a highly skewed distribution at all altitudes. Dew-point or frost-point temperature, however, has been shown to be normally distributed.[5] Since A is obtained directly from T_d (under proper assumptions), reasoning dictates that a mean value of T_d represents a median value of A. Furthermore, a standard deviation (S) of T_d may be calculated whereby tolerance limits of the T_d data may be established. Since a one-to-one mapping relation exists between T_d and A, these tolerance limits also apply to the associated absolute humidity data.

The proper procedure, therefore, is to calculate S of T_d at each altitude from data used to drive the mean T_d profile. The validity of this procedure, however, is directly dependent upon the degree to which the T_d distribution may be established and upon the confidence limits associated with the estimate of the mean for T_d.

Difficulty in exactly implementing the procedure under discussion is encountered on two fronts. First, all the data used by Gutnick in establishing the mean T_d profile are not readily available. Second, calculating S of T_d at all altitudes of interest is a very tedious and time-consuming project. The procedure of reference 5, therefore, is followed to alleviate these difficulties.

In an analysis of data from Southern England taken at the 300-, 200- and 125-mb levels, Gutnick found that S of T_d is correlated

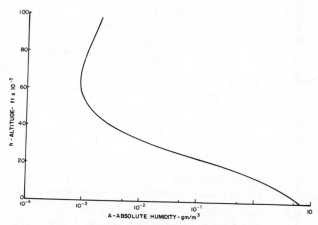

FIG. 3. Mean annual absolute humidity as a function of altitude for the middle latitudes.

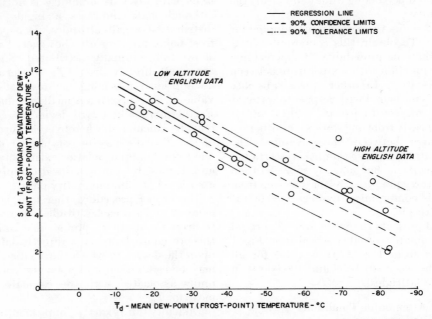

Fɪɢ. 4. Comparison between regression analyses of low and high altitude English $\overline{T}_d$ and S of T_d data showing regression line and 90 per cent tolerance and confidence limits.

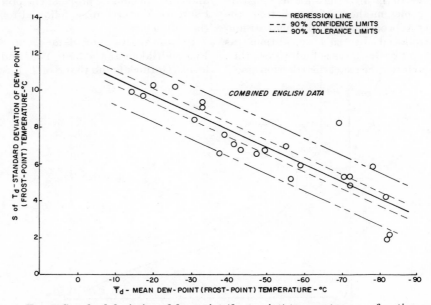

Fɪɢ. 5. Standard deviation of dew-point (frost-point) temperature as a function of mean dew-point (frost-point) temperature. Results of regression analyses of combined low and high altitude English data showing regression line and 90 per cent tolerance and confidence limits.

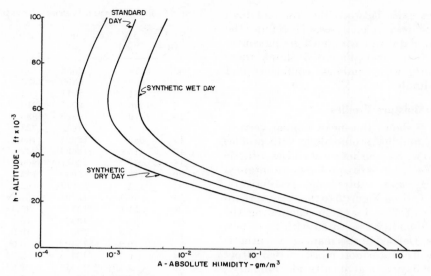

FIG. 6. Absolute humidity as a function of altitude for the middle latitudes and for standard, wet, and dry days.

with $\overline{T}_d$. A best-fit straight line was obtained through a regression analysis, thereby establishing a unique value of S of T_d for every value of $\overline{T}_d$. Rather than risk extrapolation of Gutnick's line to lower altitudes, a similar analysis of 700-, 500- and 400-mb data was undertaken along with re-analysis of the 300-, 200- and 125-mb data. Figure 4 shows a comparison of the two analyses.

Rather than compute correlation coefficients for the data, the slopes of the regression lines were used as tests of correlation. For the low altitude data, correlation was found to be significant at the 0.01 level, and for the high altitude data significant correlation was found at the 0.10 level. Confidence and tolerance limits associated with each set of data are also shown in Fig. 4. As may be seen, no significant

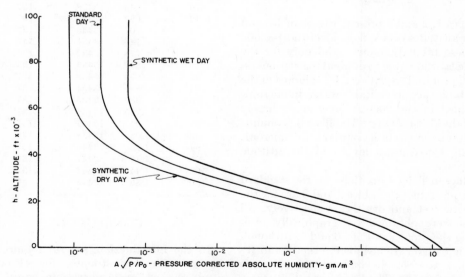

FIG. 7. Pressure corrected absolute humidity as a function of altitude for the middle latitudes and for standard, wet, and dry days.

differences exist between the low and high altitude regression analyses. Therefore, the two sets of data were combined giving correlation at 0.01 level. Figure 5 shows these results along with combined confidence and tolerance limits.

Synthetic Moisture Profiles

Figure 6 shows the mean annual vertical absolute humidity profile along with profiles associated with a synthetic wet and a synthetic dry day. These latter two profiles were obtained by adding and subtracting, respectively, $1.282S$ of T_d from Figure 5 to the mean vertical T_d profile of Fig. 1 and by computing the absolute humidity associated with these new T_d values. Defined in this manner, a synthetic wet day will contain more moisture than 90 per cent of all days at a given altitude. Similarly, a synthetic dry day will contain less moisture than 90 per cent of all days at a given altitude. In this light, the mean absolute humidity profile represents a standard day.

Figure 7 presents the mean and synthetic profiles of the "reduced absolute humidity" parameter required in W' calculations. The definitions of wet and dry day are the same. Values of $\sqrt{p/p_0}$ were obtained from the Revised United States Standard Atmosphere, 1962.

RESULTS

Tables 1, 2 and 3 present values of W_z and W_z' for altitudes between sea level and 100,000 ft. These tabulations are valid only for the middle latitudes due to original restrictions on the $\overline{T}_d$ profile. The ΔW or $\Delta W'$ columns in the three tables are precipitable water, in microns, contained in the 2000 ft layer immediately below the altitude entry. The W or W' columns are total precipitable water, in microns, existing between sea level and the altitude entry.

Values in Table 1 are those for the standard day while values in Tables 2 and 3 are for the synthetic wet and dry day respectively. All values were obtained by graphically integrating the profiles in Figs. 6 and 7. Although up to five digits are included in the W and W' columns, accuracy beyond the third digit is probably lacking. The additional digits were included only for purposes of consistency.

TABLE 1. PRECIPITABLE WATER—STANDARD DAY

h (ft $\times 10^{-3}$)	ΔW (μ)	W (μ)	$\Delta W'$ (μ)	W' (μ)
2	3538	3538	3488	3488
4	2662	6200	2533	6021
6	2011	8211	1804	7825
8	1496	9707	1310	9135
10	1119	10825	996	10131
12	814	11639	723	10854
14	582	12221	466	11320
16	415	12635	307	11627
18	277	12912	200	11827
20	178	13090	133	11960
22	122	13212	82.3	12042
24	79.1	13291	51.8	12094
26	51.6	13342	32.4	12126
28	31.6	13374	19.2	12145
30	17.6	13392	10.9	12156
32	10.2	13402	5.96	12162
34	6.50	13408	3.34	12166
36	4.40	13413	2.04	12168
38	2.95	13416	1.31	12169
40	2.12	13418	.880	12170
42	1.54	13419	.664	12171
44	1.28	13421	.516	12171
46	1.02	13422	.397	12172
48	.873	13422	.310	12172
50	.719	13423	.254	12172
52	.655	13424	.213	12172
54	.582	13424	.183	12173
56	.532	13425	.162	12173
58	.510	13425	.146	12173
60	.510	13426	.141	12173
62	.536	13426	.138	12173
64	.560	13427	.137	12173
66	.588	13428	.137	12173
68	.618	13428	.137	12174
70	.649	13429	.137	12174
72	.680	13430	.137	12174
74	.707	13430	.137	12174
76	.746	13431	.137	12174
78	.778	13432	.137	12174
80	.817	13433	.137	12174
82	.853	13433	.137	12174
84	.890	13434	.137	12175
86	.939	13435	.137	12175
88	.985	13436	.137	12175
90	1.04	13437	.137	12175
92	1.08	13438	.137	12175
94	1.13	13440	.137	12175
96	1.19	13441	.137	12175
98	1.24	13442	.137	12176
100	1.30	13443	.137	12176

CONCLUSIONS

In the introduction, several requirements for an effective estimate, for IR design purposes, of atmospheric moisture were discussed. The requirements are:

TABLE 2. PRECIPITABLE WATER—SYNTHETIC WET DAY

h (ft $\times 10^{-3}$)	ΔW (μ)	W (μ)	$\Delta W'$ (μ)	W' (μ)
2	6995	6995	6913	6913
4	5128	12123	5034	11947
6	3834	15956	3563	15510
8	2847	18803	2533	18043
10	2099	20902	1816	19859
12	1590	22492	1276	21135
14	1138	23630	880	22015
16	861	24491	635	22649
18	631	25122	444	23094
20	442	25564	308	23402
22	312	25876	204	23605
24	211	26087	136	23741
26	138	26225	84.8	23826
28	81.7	26307	53.2	23879
30	50.0	26357	32.8	23912
32	29.0	26386	19.6	23932
34	18.0	26404	11.6	23943
36	11.5	26416	6.91	23950
38	7.67	26423	3.77	23954
40	5.86	26429	2.38	23956
42	4.27	26433	1.69	23958
44	3.24	26437	1.26	23959
46	2.55	26439	.980	23960
48	2.11	26441	.779	23961
50	1.80	26443	.641	23961
52	1.60	26445	.522	23962
54	1.39	26646	.438	23962
56	1.28	26447	.376	23963
58	1.23	26449	.343	23963
60	1.22	26450	.331	23964
62	1.25	26451	.324	23964
64	1.37	26452	.326	23964
66	1.45	26454	.326	23964
68	1.52	26455	.326	23965
70	1.59	26457	.326	23965
72	1.67	26459	.327	23965
74	1.75	26460	.328	23966
76	1.84	26462	.329	23966
78	1.93	26464	.329	23966
80	2.02	26466	.329	23967
82	2.12	26468	.330	23967
84	2.23	26470	.330	23967
86	2.34	26473	.332	23968
88	2.45	26475	.333	23968
90	2.58	26478	.333	23968
92	2.71	26481	.334	23969
94	2.85	26483	.335	23969
96	2.98	26486	.335	23969
98	3.12	26489	.335	23970
100	3.27	26493	.336	23970

TABLE 3. PRECIPITABLE WATER—SYNTHETIC DRY DAY

h (ft $\times 10^{-3}$)	ΔW (μ)	W (μ)	$\Delta W'$ (μ)	W' (μ)
2	1815	1815	1747	1747
4	1345	3160	1266	3013
6	980	4140	893	3906
8	709	4848	622	4528
10	524	5373	483	5011
12	378	5750	338	5349
14	270	6020	234	5583
16	192	6212	159	5742
18	134	6347	105	5847
20	91.8	6438	68	5915
22	60.7	6499	41	5956
24	37.2	6536	25	5981
26	21.5	6558	14	5995
28	12.5	6582	7.0	6002
30	6.73	6589	3.3	6005
32	3.96	6593	1.9	6007
34	2.32	6595	1.3	6008
36	1.53	6597	.79	6009
38	1.08	6598	.52	6009
40	.811	6599	.36	6010
42	.628	6600	.26	6010
44	.500	6600	.20	6010
46	.402	6600	.15	6010
48	.341	6601	.13	6010
50	.295	6601	.11	6011
52	.259	6601	.095	6011
54	.234	6602	.078	6011
56	.219	6602	.070	6011
58	.216	6602	.061	6011
60	.216	6602	.057	6011
62	.221	6602	.055	6011
64	.230	6603	.055	6011
66	.240	6603	.056	6011
68	.250	6603	.056	6011
70	.261	6603	.056	6011
72	.272	6604	.056	6011
74	.285	6604	.055	6011
76	.298	6604	.055	6011
78	.311	6605	.055	6011
80	.325	6605	.054	6011
82	.340	6605	.054	6011
84	.355	6606	.054	6012
86	.371	6606	.054	6012
88	.386	6606	.054	6012
90	.402	6607	.053	6012
92	.419	6607	.053	6012
94	.438	6608	.053	6012
96	.456	6608	.053	6012
98	.475	6609	.053	6012
100	.495	6609	.053	6012

(1) The estimate should be in the form of a precipitable water profile for a wide range of altitude;

(2) The estimate should be valid for any geographical location;

(3) Unusual IR attenuation conditions such as abnormally wet or dry days should be included;

(4) Data forming the foundation of analysis should be of sufficient quantity and quality to yield reliable results.

Examination of this list of requirements

reveals that the only requirements completely neglected by this study concerns the estimate's validity regardless of geographic location.

Comparison of the results with other studies of precipitable water reveals no glaring discrepancies. For example, Peixoto[15] tabulates yearly averages of W for several latitudes in 1950. At 50°N, a value for W of 1.33 cm corresponds almost exactly with the value of W for a standard day found in this study.

RECOMMENDATIONS

Future studies of atmospheric precipitable water should concentrate on improving the basic moisture profile. At present, data available for constructing moisture profiles are far from adequate, both in quantity and in quality. It is hoped that more concentrated effort will be devoted to sampling stratospheric regions. More data for a wider range of latitudes should be obtained so that some estimate of moisture content for latitudes other than those considered in this study might be obtained.

It is suggested that future studies of abnormal attenuation conditions pursue a more rigorous treatment of moisture parameter distributions at all altitudes. The simplifications made in this study may have introduced unnecessary errors in the final synthetic profiles.

Acknowledgments. The author wishes to acknowledge the invaluable assistance provided by numerous personnel of LTV Vought Aeronautics Division. Miss Charlotte Vinson of the technical library helped secure large amounts of meteorological literature. Miss Ruth Huffman and Dr. W. W. Hoy provided helpful statistical consultation as well as critical comment and aid in applying computer techniques to the analysis. Mrs. L. P. Slayton and Mrs. R. G. Brittain prepared the manuscript, and Mr. J. D. Louthan provided editorial assistance. Appreciation is also expressed to Mr. Murray Gutnick of the Cambridge Research Center and to Mr. H. J. Mastenbrook of the Naval Research Laboratory for supplying some of the data used in this report.

References

1. "Handbook of Geophysics for Air Force Designers," Geophysics Research Directorate, AFCRC, 1957.
2. Mallow, R. D., "Atmospheric Water Vapor Transmission Coefficients for the Infrared Spectrum," 2-58000/3TM-1, Chance Vought Corporation, April 2, 1963.
3. "Smithsonian Meteorological Tables," Sixth Revised Edition (1951).
4. Elasser, Walter M., "Heat Transfer by Infrared Radiation in the Atmosphere," Harvard Meteorological Studies No. 6, Harvard University Blue Hill Meteorological Observatory, 1942.
5. Gutnick, Murray, "An estimate of Precipitable Water Along High-Altitude Ray Paths," *AF Surveys in Geophysics No. 120*, Geophysics Research Directorate, AFCRC (March 1960).
6. Hutcherson, D. C., "A Model Wet Atmosphere for Use in Infrared Range Calculations," AER-EOR-12907, Chance Vought Corporation, June 3, 1960.
7. Murgatroyd, R. J., Goldsmith, P., and Hollings, W. E. H., "An Interim Report on Measurements of Humidity from Aircraft to Heights of About 50,000 Feet Over Southern England," *MRP No. 877*, Great Britain Meteorological Research Committee, September 1954.
8. Murgatroyd, R. J., Goldsmith, P., and Hollings, W. E. H., "Some Recent Measurements of Humidity from Aircraft Up to Heights of About 50,000 Feet Over Southern England," *Quarterly J. Royal Meteorol. Soc.*, 81, 533–537 (October 1955).
9. Helliwell, N. C., MacKenzie, J. K., and Kerley, M. J., "Further Observations of Humidity Up to 50,000 Ft. Made from an Aircraft of the Meteorological Research Flight in 1955," MRP No. 976, Great Britain Meteorological Research Committee, April 1956.
10. Helliwell, N. C., MacKenzie, J. K., and Kerley, M. J., "Some Further Observations From Aircraft of Frost Point and Temperature Up to 50,000 Ft.," *Quarterly J. Royal Meteorol. Soc.*, 83, 257–262 (April 1957).
11. Tucker, G. B., "An Analysis of Humidity Measurements in the Upper Troposphere and Lower Stratosphere Over Southern England," MRP No. 1052, Great Britain Air Ministry, Meteorological Research Committee, May 1957.
12. Japanese Meteorological Agency, "IGY Data on Upper Air (Radiosonde) Observations During World Meteorological Intervals," March 1960.
13. Ratner, Benjamin, "Upper-Air Climatology of the United States," Technical Paper No. 32, Part 1, Office of Climatology, United States Weather Bureau, June 1957.
14. Gutnick, Murray, "Mean Annual Mid-Latitude Moisture Profiles to 31 Km," *AF Surveys in Geophysics No. 147*, Geophysics Research Directorate, AFCRC (July 1962).
15. Peixoto, Jose' P., "Hemispheric Humidity Condition During the Year 1950," Scientific Report No. 3, Department of Meteorology, Massachusetts Institute of Technology, October 1958.

61. Reevaluation of the Mid-latitude Moisture Profiles

Murray Gutnick and Henry A. Salmela

Air Force Cambridge Research Laboratories, Bedford, Massachusetts

ABSTRACT

Previously published tentative mean annual mid-latitude moisture profiles to 31 km are reevaluated in the light of new data. Up to 400 mb, these profiles were derived by an indirect procedure. Above that level the profiles were based upon subjectively selected and weighted experimental stratospheric moisture ascents. The reevaluation, up to 400 mb, utilizes a direct and conventional approach contrasted to the indirect method used previously. This direct approach reveals that up to 400 mb, the profiles are slightly moister than were the original ones.

At higher levels the reevaluation is, of necessity, still based upon judiciously selected, but more recent, stratospheric ascents. These new data reveal no valid reason for changing the stratospheric portions of the mean annual moisture profiles. However, much more data are needed before definite conclusions can be made.

INTRODUCTION

In July 1962, Gutnick[1] published a paper which presented tentative average annual moisture profiles, both dew point and mixing ratio up to 31 km for the middle latitudes. Since dew point is not a linear function of mixing ratio, the average of one does not give the average of the other. Hence the profile of average mixing ratios is not the same as the profile of average dew points. Up to 400 mb (about 7 km), the profiles were derived from radiosonde observations using an indirect

method. Briefly, the average yearly precipitable water above the surface, 850, 700 and 500 mb, was extracted at 45N from recent maps by Bannon and Steele[2]. Then it was reasoned that if one or more stations could be found that had similar vertical distributions of precipitable water as that at 45N, the mixing ratios and dew points at this station, or stations, should in practice be similar to the mixing ratios and dew points at 45N. Accordingly, such stations were found and the mean mixing ratios and dew points for these stations were used to establish the profiles up to 400 mb. Above 400 mb, the moisture profiles are based upon experimental humidity ascents of various types. These ascents were subjectively selected and weighted and, as such, reflect the personal opinion, experience and prejudices of the selector. Admittedly, such an arbitrary procedure leaves much to be desired, but until enough data of proven reliability becomes available, it appears to be the only way of obtaining a stratospheric moisture profile. The mixing ratio profile is shown in Fig. 1. The symbols shown in this Figure are:

BRL—Mean of two hygrometric ascents by U. S. Army Ballistic Research Labs;

NRL—Mean of three hygrometric ascents by USN Research Labs;

U of D—One hygrometric and one spectroscopic ascent by University of Denver;

JMA—Means of the Japanese Meteorological Agency hygrometric ascents, 100 of which reached or exceeded 300 mb, and two of which reached 10 mb;

MRF—Means of the British Meteorological

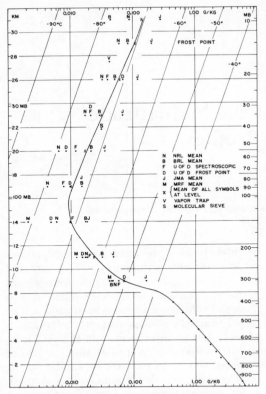

FIG. 1. Mean annual mixing ratio for the mid-latitudes.

Research Flight hygrometric ascents, about 400 of which reached or exceeded 300 mb;

Vapor Trap—Mean of seven ascents of the United Kingdom Atomic Energy Authority's water vapor absorption device;

Molecular Sieve—A single ascent of the General Mills, Inc., water vapor absorption device.

All but the MRF and JMA data were taken on a nonsystematic basis and were more or less randomly distributed with respect to time of year. The MRF data were well-distributed in time while the JMA data was for September, December, March and June. All of the NRL ascents were made near Washington, D.C.; the BRL ascents were taken on the eastern coast of the U. S. near 40N. All British soundings were taken around 52N. While the U of D ascents were taken at Alamorgordo (33N). The molecular sieve was taken at 31N in Texas. The mean JMA sounding comprised an average of Sopporo (43N) Tateno (36N),

Kagoshima (32N) and Hachijojima (33N).

It was realized that using stations below, say 35N, might introduce a latitudinal error if a latitudinal variation does indeed exist. However, it was deemed preferable to use the lower latitudinal stations rather than eliminate much scarce and valuable data.

Figure 2 shows the equivalent dew point profile. This profile was constructed by exactly the same procedure as the mixing ratio profile, and the symbols have the same connotation. However, in a few cases the dew points had to be estimated using standard atmospheric pressure because the actual pressure was not given; all the mixing ratios were given and required no approximations.

NEW DATA AND RESULTS ABOVE 400 MB

Let us now examine the new data which has become available since the publication of the mean moisture profiles. First there was a flight made with the molecular sieve at Minneapolis, Minnesota (44° 53N, 43° 13W) on 2 May 1962.[3] The air was sampled at 36.4 km. The amount of ingested air was determined by three methods, all of which closely agreed. The observed mixing ratio at 36.4 km was

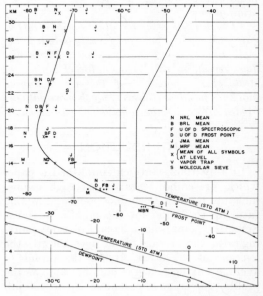

FIG. 2. Mean annual dew point – frost point for the mid-latitudes.

measured as 0.320 g/kg. Now if we extrapolate the mean mixing ratio profile to 36.4 km we obtain 0.420 g/kg. Extrapolating the mean profile much further is, of course, absurd since it would imply enormous quantities of water in short order. However, the molecular sieve observation does confirm that there is a relatively moist stratum in the middle stratosphere, and the extrapolation of the mean mixing ratio profile gives gratifyingly reasonable agreement between the two results.

If we assume ARDC standard atmosphere pressure for 36.4 geometric km we obtain a frost point with respect to saturation over ice of $-70.3°C$. Extrapolating the mean annual frost-point profile to 36.4 km gives a value of $-68.6°C$. Again a surprisingly good agreement!

The Japanese Meteorological Agency (JMA) has recently published the results of numerous systematic frost-point ascents made in 1959 and 1960.[4, 5] The ascents were made at the same four stations as previously. The published raw data were hand-reduced in the same manner as in the previous study. That is, all twice-a-day or more ascents at any one station were averaged and counted as one observation. Frost points were recorded to the nearest whole centigrade degree, and the mixing ratio was computed. All obvious errors in the published data were eliminated.

As was mentioned previously, all four stations were used in the previous study despite the fact that two of the stations were located at latitude south of 35N. It now became apparent that if the previous data were combined with the new data, for Tateno (36N) and Sopporo (43N) only, there would be sufficient data, relatively speaking, so that only those two stations need be used; and the other two lower-latitude stations could be omitted. This was done, giving 148 observations at the 300-mb level decreasing to 96 observations at 50 mb and two observations at the 10-mb level. This procedure posed some difficulties.

(1). Tateno had more observations than had Sopporo.

(2). Although all months except May, August and November were now represented, not all the months had the same number of observations. For example at 300 mb there were 59 observations in winter, 18 in spring,

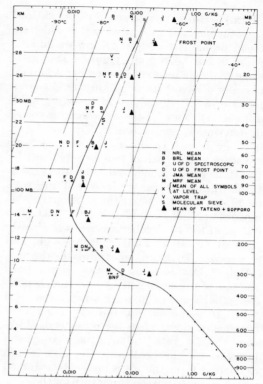

FIG. 3. Mean mixing ratio for Tateno plus Sopporo compared to the mean annual profile.

34 in summer and 37 in autumn. It would have been desirable to weight everything equally, but the small numbers of observations in some months precluded using this approach. Instead, the conventional method of averaging was used. That is, all the observations were pooled and given the same weight; the resulting values were then considered the mean of Tateno and Soporo, although it was realized that they were biased toward Tateno and winter. The results were plotted, and the values were extracted from the graph at the same nine levels as shown previously. The results are given in Fig. 3. Figure 3 is the same as Fig. 1 except mean of Tateno plus Sopporo values are also plotted. As can be seen from Fig. 3, the mean of the Tateno plus Sopporo values are fairly close to the old JMA values except as 31 km where there were only two observations. Actually the mean of Tateno plus Sopporo results would change the mean profile very little. For example, if we take the largest variation in mixing ratio (excepting

31 km) between the two sets of values (26 km), then the mean of all symbols (upon which the mean profile is based) at 26 km would shift from .062 to .056 g/kg. Figure 4 shows the same results in terms of frost point. Again the mean of all symbols at 26 km would change from −73.3°C to only −74°C—a negligible difference in view of the smoothing involved in determining mean profile. The last bit of new evidence we have on stratospheric moisture is the mean of two ascents made by the Minneapolis-Honeywell "Alpha" hygrometers. One ascent was made over Minneapolis on 17 October 1962 and the other over Alamogordo, N. M., on 17 January 1963. The details of the 17 October ascent have already been discussed by Palmer, Rohrbough, and Steinberg.[6] To briefly recapitulate, the two "Alpha" hygrometers on the Minneapolis balloon were unaffected by the launch accident; they appeared to work satisfactorily and the moisture profile from one hygrometer was practically identical to the other one. Moreover, the integrated value of the mixing ratio between 28 (the peak altitude) and 78 mb calculated from the hygrometer data agreed closely with that of the vapor trap for the same layer.

The 17 January 1963 ascent carried aboard 2 of the older models "Alphas," a new light-

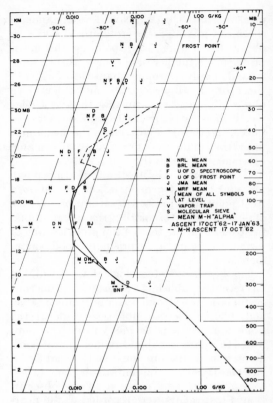

Fig. 5. Mixing ratios for the "Alpha" ascents compared to the mean annual profile.

weight "Alpha," a deluxe lab model "Alpha" and an infrared solar spectrometer. Release of the hypsometer antenna caused radio-frequency interference which affected 3 of the hygrometers; moreover command capability was lost at about 19 km. Thus the only clean trace was from the deluxe lab model "Alpha" and this only to 64 mb. However, the infrared solar spectrometer values were in reasonable agreement with the "Alpha" hygrometer up to this level.

The mean mixing ratio of these 2 flights is presented in Fig. 5. Actually since the 17 January flight reached only 19 km the higher portions (dashed line) represent only the 17 October ascent. The equivalent dew-point plot is shown in Fig. 6.

Both "Alpha" soundings exhibit peculiar characteristics in their respective upper portions. For example, the 17 January ascent had steadily decreasing relative humidities at 90, 80 and 70 mb of 38, 36 and 34 per cent; yet

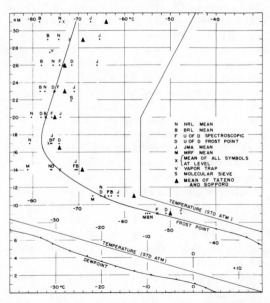

Fig. 4. Mean frost points for Tateno plus Sopporo compared to the mean annual profile.

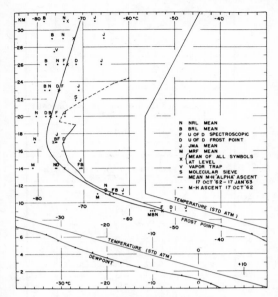

FIG. 6. Frost points for the "Alpha" ascents compared to the mean annual profile.

the relative humidity suddenly jumps to 53 per cent at 64 mb (an increase of 19 per cent in only 500 meters). In fact, with but one exception, relative humidities from 13.7 km upwards exceed 38 per cent (unusually high values at this altitude). The upper portion of

the 17 October sounding is definitely anomalous. The dew point of −60°C at 28 mb approaches, if not exceeds, a world high dew point for so high an altitude. Also, this dew point was associated with a temperature which produced a relative humidity of 67 per cent, a virtually unheard of value at this high altitude. Moreover the relative humidity some 500 meters lower was 44 per cent. A series of hypothesis was set forth to explain the abnormally high dew points; after thorough investigation, all were rejected. For instance, it was thought the leak in the balloon might have contaminated the air and in some way produced the high dew points. However, it was subsequently found out that very dry bottled helium having a dew point of −80°C had been used, so this could not have been the cause. Also the synoptic situation did not appear so unusual to account for the high dew points. Thus it would appear that the large deviations of the "Alpha" curve from the mean annual profiles at the higher levels can be attributed to highly abnormal features in one or both of the respective "Alpha" soundings.

Be that as it may, we can draw two conclusions from the new stratospheric data presented here:

(1) The existence of a moist upper layer

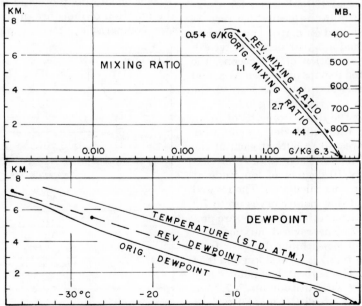

FIG. 7. Revised mixing ratio and dew-point profiles up to 7.2 km as compared to the original profiles to the same level.

appears confirmed; that is, all of the new data point to an increase of mixing ratio with height several kilometers above the tropopause. However, this point is still far from settled. Some authorities believe the increase in moisture is the result of contamination. They argue that the balloon picks up moisture on its skin or on the packaging of the instruments while it is in the troposphere; this moisture is subsequently evaporated aloft. There are plans underway to experimentally test this hypothesis.

(2) There appears to be no valid reason for changing the stratospheric portion of the mean annual moisture profiles. However further valid data is needed before definite conclusions can be made. Unfortunately it will take several years to obtain such data if the current rate of stratospheric moisture ascents is continued.

DATA AND RESULTS OBTAINED UP TO 400 MB

The method used to verify the moisture profiles up to the 400-mb level was straightforward and direct in contrast to the indirect approach used previously. That is, the mean annual mixing ratios and dew points at 1000-, 850-, 700-, 500- and 400-mb levels for a network of about 50 stations located between 40 and 50N were plotted on maps. The majority of the stations had a 5-year period of record. Also, with the exception of the oceans, the sparsely inhabited regions of eastern Asia, and the 400-mb level (where data was scanty), the spatial coverage was relatively good.

After plotting the data, isopleths of mean annual mixing ratio and dew point were drawn for the area 40 to 50N at each of the aforementioned levels. Then values were extracted for every 10 degrees of longitude at 45N, and a mean was calculated. The revised mixing ratio and dew-point curves up to 7.2 km, together with the original curves, are presented in Fig. 7. The revised mixing ratio shows an almost logarithmic decrease from 6.3 g/kg at 0 km to 2.7 g/kg at 3 km and 0.54 g/kg at 7.2 km. The revised dew-point curve decreases linearly with altitude up to 7.2 km with a lapse rate of $-5.83°C/$ km; at 0 km, the dew point is 4.8°C.

Since there is little likelihood of obtaining

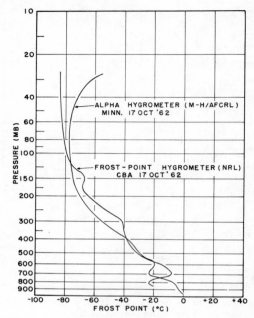

FIG. 8. Comparison of the frost points of two soundings on October 17, 1962.

satisfactory data from areas having sparse coverage, the mean annual mixing ratios and dew points to 7.2 km thus derived will probably not be revised in the foreseeable future.

As a bit of a footnote and commentary on the question of moisture in the stratosphere, two comparisons of stratospheric humidity

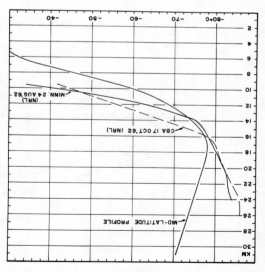

FIG. 9. Frost points for the latest two NRL soundings compared to the mean annual profile.

based on some material which Mastenbrook of NRL kindly shared with us are quite striking.

Fig. 8 shows the frost-point profiles of two specially instrumented flights made on 17 October 1962. The Minneapolis flight carried an Alpha radiation frost-point hygrometer and the NRL Chesapeake Bay flight an optical frost-point hygrometer. The frost point spread between 400 and 125 mb, mainly in the troposphere, is no doubt due to hurricane Ella off the coast of Florida. More pertinent to our interests are the two divergent profiles above 100 mb.

The stratospheric humidity controversy is graphically illustrated here. The dry profile shows the typically nearly constant low frost point, while the other indicates humidity increasing with altitude. If the observations approximate the true state of affairs, then the stratosphere is both wet and dry. This view is slowly gaining support and is diplomatically advantageous. If the stratosphere is wholly dry or moist then one or the other set of observations is incorrect.

Fig. 9 compares the upper portion of the mid-latitude frost-point profile with the two new NRL soundings which were not available for the preparation of the early part of this paper. One is the Chesapeake Bay, 17 October sounding shown in Fig. 8, and the other was made at Minneapolis on 24 August 1962.

Both of these show the typically dry stratosphere as compared to the mid-latitude frost-point profile and would have resulted in moving the profile slightly to the left if they had been available.

The questions are still far from answered.

References

1. Gutnick, M., "Mean Annual Mid-Latitude Moisture Profiles to 31 km," *Air Force Surveys in Geophysics*, No. 147, AFCRL, Bedford, Mass. (July 1962).
2. Bannon, B. A., and Steele, L. P., "Average Water-Vapor Content of the Air," Meteorological Office, Air Ministry, Geophysical Memoirs No. 102, 1960.
3. Rohrbough, S. F., "Determination of the Water Vapor and Carbon Dioxide in the Stratosphere," *Science*, **137**, 599–600 (August 24, 1962).
4. Japan Meteorological Agency, "IGC Data on Upper Air (Radiosonde) Observations During World Meteorological Intervals," March 1961.
5. Japan Meteorological Agency, "Post-IGC 1960 Data on Upper Air (Radiosonde) Observations During World Meteorological Intervals," March 1962.
6. Palmer, T., Steinberg, S., and Rohrbough, S. F., "A Stratospheric Humidity Experiment," in "Humidity and Moisture," Vol. II, p. 473, New York, Reinhold Publishing Corp., 1964.
7. Mastenbrook, H. J., "Frostpoint Hygrometer Measurements in the Stratosphere and the Problem of Moisture Contamination," in "Humidity and Moisture," Vol. II, p. 480, New York, Reinhold Publishing Corp., 1964.

62. Hemispheric Water Vapor Balance during 1958

Alfred Renato Crisi

United States Air Force, Headquarters Air Weather Service, Scott Air Force Base, Illinois

ABSTRACT

A study of the atmospheric water vapor over the northern hemisphere during the International Geophysical Year (IGY) covering the mean conditions for the calendar year 1958 is presented. The study includes analyses of precipitable water vapor and water vapor transport for the entire northern hemisphere. The relation of the divergence of water vapor transport to the water balance of evaporation and precipitation at the earth's surface is pointed out. Significant features of the precipitable water vapor and water vapor transports for 1958 are discussed. It is shown that the analyses of mean yearly precipitable water vapor and zonal and meridional transports of water vapor are meteorologically meaningful and physically significant for studying the general circulation of the atmosphere. The average water storage in the atmosphere is found to be small. A need exists for more accurate and complete observations of atmospheric humidity and motion over many portions of the equatorial regions and over all areas at the higher altitudes above 20,000 ft.

INTRODUCTION

The water balance at the earth's surface has been the subject of many investigations during the past 50 years. Until the mid-1930's most of the investigations considered only the (land-ocean) earthbound branch of the water cycle. Over land surfaces, the balance of precipitation, evapotranspiration, run-off above and below the ground, and the change in ground-water storage formed the basis for investigation. This type of investigation often produced results which were not widely accepted and which, at best, were representative of the water budget of only limited areas or watershed regions. Over the oceans, the situation was made even more difficult by the lack of basic quantitative measurements or computed values of evaporation and precipitation. Sverdrup[15] discussed (1) the unreliability of observations of evaporation from pans on board ships as compared to the actual evaporation at the sea surface, (2) the limitations of computations of evaporation over the oceans based upon energy considerations, and (3) the widely divergent results obtained by computing evaporation rates and the vertical flux of water vapor from the sea surface based upon theoretical considerations involving assumptions as to the character of the eddy diffusion and transfer processes near the sea surface. Jacobs[5] found that data on precipitation amounts over the oceans were very scarce and unreliable. He was able to prepare a new chart of the annual precipitation over the oceans based upon available published regional precipitation data. However, to this date, actual precipitation values over the oceans are still rather scarce and difficult to interpret.

In view of the difficulties involved in studying the water balance at the earth's surface by considering the earthbound branch of the hydrologic cycle, a number of studies in recent years have approached the problem by evaluating the atmospheric branch of the hydrologic cycle. This approach relies on the principles of continuity and mass conservation in the atmosphere rather than at the earth's surface. Such an approach was not feasible until recent years when the quantity and quality of aerological observations became more nearly adequate to the task of making reliable computations of the atmospheric branch of the hydrologic cycle and its part in the water balance at the earth's surface.

Benton, Blackburn, and Snead[1] discussed the role of the atmosphere in the hydrologic cycle and clarified the relation of this cycle to air masses over the Mississippi River watershed. From aerological data, they determined the total flux of moisture in maritime and continental air over the watershed and then prepared a complete balance of the hydrologic cycle for the watershed. Their study showed that, although only a small percentage of the maritime moisture advected over the continent is precipitated, most of the precipitation occurring is from maritime air and is derived directly from oceanic sources. This result contradicted earlier views which minimized the flux of water vapor in the atmosphere to and from the oceans and held almost exclusively to a concept of land-derived sources of precipitation.

Benton and Estoque[2] computed the transfer of water vapor by the atmosphere over the North American continent for the year 1949. They used all available aerological data and geostrophic winds scaled from copies of constant pressure charts for 850, 700, and 500 mb and corresponding mixing ratio humidity data to compute the water vapor transfer and divergence field of atmospheric water vapor transfer in the layer from the earth's surface to 400 mb. One conclusion of this study was that there need not be a high correlation between monthly water-vapor transfer and precipitation; precipitation is more directly associated with the net convergence rather than with the transfer of atmospheric moisture. Another conclusion was that atmospheric winds and mixing ratios have a definite place in hydrologic research and that the divergence field of atmospheric water vapor transfer can be used to evaluate accurately the monthly or seasonal water balance of large continental areas.

The modern approach of Starr[11] to studies of the general circulation of the atmosphere resulted in several investigations[10,12-14] of northern hemisphere water vapor and its relation to the general circulation. Peixoto[10] provided the most complete, comprehensive, and extensive observational study of atmospheric water vapor ever attempted up to this date. Lufkin[6] carried on in great detail the discussion of the field of divergence of atmospheric water vapor flux which was first presented by Starr and Peixoto.[13] All of the above-mentioned studies were based upon aerological data for the year 1950 and included various evaluations of daily data for some 90 upper-air sounding stations at several levels up to 500 mb over the entire northern hemisphere. These studies proved the merit of treating problems associated with the terrestrial hydrologic cycle on a hemispheric basis; they made possible the averaging of various properties of atmospheric moisture over particular areas of interest or over the entire hemisphere for comparison with hydrologic and oceanographic measurements, such as runoff, evaporation, precipitation, ground storage, and salinity.

Encouraged by the results of the atmospheric water vapor studies for the year 1950 and by the continuing growth of the hemispheric network of upper-air sounding stations, the author of this paper has extended the water vapor studies to include the year 1958 (a part of the IGY). This paper will review briefly the procedures and some of the more important results of the new study for 1958.

DATA

The basic data used in this study were aerological observations taken during the calendar year 1958, the last 12 months of the recent IGY. An extensive coverage of 321 selected weather stations provided representative data over the entire northern hemisphere. Where a choice was possible, the most reliable and meteorologically significant stations were selected; in areas where observations were sparse, all available data were used. The quantity and quality of the IGY data used in this study were superior to those used in any other northern hemisphere study for a similar time period. Figure 1 shows the index numbers and locations of all the stations.

The primary stations used in this study were 285 rawinsonde observing stations. The upper-air data for these primary stations were

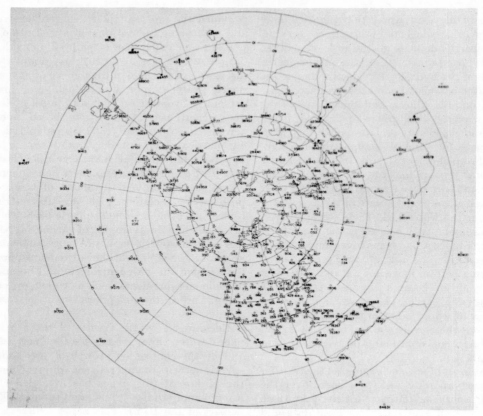

FIG. 1. Index numbers and locations of stations.

on punched cards or magnetic tape; all these data were checked and processed by electronic computer. All rawinsonde data available for each primary station were used; rawinsonde data for most stations were available at least once each day, a majority of stations provided two soundings each day, some three and even four. Statistical computations were based upon all the data available at each station. These data were made available to the M.I.T. General Circulation Project under Contract Number AF 19(604)-6108 with the Air Force Cambridge Research Laboratories, Office of Aerospace Research, United States Air Force at Laurence G. Hanscom Field, Bedford, Mass. The data handling and machine processing were accomplished in a superior manner by the Department of the Air Force, Air Weather Service Climatic Center, Data Control Division, at Asheville, N.C.

The 36 secondary stations used in this study were principally those in critical areas not covered by the primary station network and also a few stations chosen to fill in gaps at the equatorial border. The data from these stations were obtained with either radiosonde, radiowind, pilot balloon, rawinsonde or a combination of these methods; only seven stations used the pilot balloon (theodolite) method for observing upper winds. In general, the data from these stations were not so reliable or numerous as those from the primary stations. These data were tabulated from the IGY microcards and were processed by the very capable staff of the M.I.T. General Circulation Project.

In spite of generally excellent coverage of data over the northern hemisphere and near the equatorial border in the southern hemisphere, there were some rather disappointing areas of little or no data: the Amazon River Basin in South America; the east-central Pacific Ocean from Panama to Christmas Island and from Central America to the

Hawaiian Islands; and the Indian Ocean. That such interesting and critical areas were deficient in meteorological data coverage represents a serious shortcoming in the value of the IGY data for basic research of the general circulation of the earth's atmosphere.

Nevertheless, the overall coverage of reliable data over the arctic and middle latitudes in the northern hemisphere was excellent. The data from arctic stations were fairly complete north to 80 degrees latitude. The coverage over North America was complete and especially dense over the United States; all stations in this area were used except a few superfluous ones. The coverage over China, Mongolia, and especially the Tibetian plateau was most helpful and, perhaps the first data of its kind to be used in a hemispheric research study.

It might be interesting to note some facts on the number of observations used in the computation of data from the primary set of stations. The maximum was 1427 observations from Sault Ste. Marie, Michigan (WMO Number 72734), the minimum was 48 observations from Benina, Libya (WMO Number 62053). Most stations had somewhere between 200 and 700 observations for the year 1958; a large number of stations had between 500 and 700 observations, representing just about two rawinsonde observations per day during the year. Only four stations had less than 100 observations: Tura, USSR (WMO Number 24507) had 94; Nunchiang (CPR Number 50557) had 96; Yinchwan (CPR Number 53614) and 97; and Benina, Libya (WMO Number 62053) had 48. Twelve stations had over 1000 observations; Thule, Greenland (WMO Number 04202) had 1346; Lages Field, Azores (WMO Number 08509) had 1400; Osan Air Base, Korea (WMO Number 47122) had 1351; Eglin Air Force Base, Florida (WMO Number 72221) had 1422; Laughlin Air Force Base, Texas (WMO Number 72261) had 1356; Oklahoma City, Oklahoma (WMO Number 72353) had 1254; Sault Ste. Marie, Michigan (WMO Number 72734) had 1427; Stephenville Air Force Base, Newfoundland (WMO Number 72815) had 1374; Goose Bay Air Base, Labrador (WMO Number 72816) had 1285; Resolute Bay, NWT (WMO Number 72924) had 1148; Kindley Air Force Base, Bermuda (WMO Number 78016) had 1347; and Wake Island (WMO Number 91245) had

1003. Complete details on station names, index numbers, exact geographical locations, heights above sea level, periods of record, number of observations, and all the processed data parameters used in this study will be published later in a comprehensive report to be prepared at M.I.T. by the Planetary Circulations Research Project.

ASSUMPTIONS, DEFINITIONS, DATA PROCESSING AND FORMULAS

The particular meteorological parameters treated in this study were the specific humidity q, and the components of the actual wind, u and v; these parameters were derived from the basic upper-air meteorological measurements of pressure, temperature, humidity, and wind made at the stations shown in the chart in Fig. 1 with rawinsonde, radiosonde, radiowind, or pilot balloon, or combinations of these types of equipments.

The parameters u and v are the horizontal components of the wind vector, $\mathbb{V}$, such that $\mathbb{V} = \vec{i}\,u + \vec{j}\,v$, where $\vec{i}$ is the unit vector in the west-to-east direction and $\vec{j}$ is the unit vector in the south-to-north direction. Thus, u is the zonal (west-to-east) wind component taken in meters per second (m/sec) with west wind positive; and v is the meridional (south-to-north) wind component taken in meters per second (m/sec) with south wind positive.

The parameter q is the specific humidity in grams per kilogram; the simplified expression $q \approx 622\,(e/p)$ given in Haurwitz[4] and Brunt[3] was used to compute q from the values of temperature and relative humidity at each of four standard pressure surfaces: 1000, 850, 700 and 500 mb. Given the temperature, TT, at any atmospheric pressure, p, the saturation water vapor pressure, e_s, is uniquely defined at that temperature, TT. Then knowing the relative humidity, UU, the actual water vapor pressure, e, can be obtained from the relation $UU = e/e_s$ or $e = UU \times e_s$, where e_s is the saturation water vapor pressure at the given air temperature, TT. Thus, at each station and for each separate upper-air observation the specific humidity, q, can be obtained easily for each pressure surface and the accompanying wind components, u and v, can be obtained for each corresponding pressure surface.

This is a research study on the general circulation of the northern hemisphere, and the time averages of the meteorological parameters covered a summary period of one year.

The following quantities were computed separately for the 1000-, 850-, 700- and 500-mb standard pressure surfaces at each station when available:

(1) Mean q, $\quad\quad \overline{q}$

(2) Mean $q \times u$, $\quad \overline{qu}$

(3) Mean $q \times v$, $\quad \overline{qv}$

The usual statistical definitions are implied in the above quantities with the "bar ($\overline{}$)" denoting a time average over the period summarized, in this case, one year.

At each station the mean specific humidity, $\overline{q}$, for the year at any given pressure surface is simply a measure of the mean amount of water vapor at that surface and station for the yearly period. At each station the values, $\overline{qu}$ and $\overline{qv}$, represent the components of the mean horizontal transport of water vapor, $\overline{q\mathbb{V}}$, for the year at any given pressure surface, where the horizontal wind vector $\mathbb{V}$ is defined as given in the second paragraph of this section: $\mathbb{V} = \vec{i}\,v + \vec{j}\,v$. Using the geographical (spherical) coordinate system $(\lambda,\ \phi,\ p,\ t)$ where λ is longitude measured positive to the east ($\vec{i}$ unit vector), ϕ is latitude measured positive to the north ($\vec{j}$ unit vector), p is the pressure in mb (positive and increasing downward through the atmosphere) and t is the time, the respective zonal (λ) and meridional (ϕ) components of the mean horizontal transport of water vapor at any station are thus represented by the quantities, $\overline{qu}$ and $\overline{qv}$, for any given pressure surface and for the yearly period.

The fields of mean specific humidity and water vapor transport for all the stations at each of the four standard pressure surfaces make for interesting studies in themselves. This study will treat only the vertically integrated values of the quantities $\overline{q}$, $\overline{qu}$, and $\overline{qv}$ computed for the year 1958 at each station shown in Fig. 1. The development of the vertical integration technique follows that used by Peixoto.[10] The total mean horizontal transport of water vapor above a point on the earth's surface for a time interval defined by the bar (in this case, one year) may be represented by a two-dimensional vector field. $\overline{Q}(\lambda,\phi)$

$$\overline{Q}(\lambda,\phi) = \frac{1}{g} \int_0^{p_0} \overline{q\mathbb{V}}\ dp$$

where g is the acceleration of gravity, assumed constant and equal to 9.8×10^2 cm/sec^2, and p_0 is the mean value of the surface pressure in mb; q and $\mathbb{V}$ have deen defined in preceding paragraphs. The zonal and meridional components of the vector field, $\overline{Q}$, are given by

$$\overline{Q}_\lambda = \frac{1}{g} \int_0^{p_0} \overline{qu}\ dp$$

Units of $\overline{Q}$ = gm m sec^{-1} cm^{-2}

or $\overline{Q}$ = 10^2 gm cm^{-1} sec^{-1}

$$\overline{Q}_\phi = \frac{1}{g} \int_0^{p_0} \overline{qv}\ dp$$

Similarly, if $\overline{W}$ is defined as the mean precipitable water vapor content in a column of air of unit (one cm^2) area above a given point on the earth's surface over the yearly period taken in this study, then

$$\overline{W}(\lambda,\ \phi) = \frac{1}{g} \int_0^{p_0} \overline{q}\ dp$$

Units of $\overline{W}$ = gm/cm^2 or cm of water

All these formulas incorporate the hydrostatic equation

$$\delta p = -\rho g\ \delta z$$

where ρ is the density and z the geometric height, because the atmosphere is in a state of hydrostatic equilibrium, or very nearly so, most of the time; this is a valid assumption and certainly can be used with extremely small error in a study of the general circulation such as this one. By means of the hydrostatic equation, the geometric height variable, z, has been replaced by the pressure, p, as the vertical coordinate in the vertical integrals used in this study.

Actually, in performing the vertical integrations of the yearly mean quantities $\overline{q}$, $\overline{qu}$, and $\overline{qv}$, it is not feasible to integrate from a truly representative mean value of the surface pressure, p_0, to the top of the atmosphere ($p = 0$) at each station; it is feasible and generally acceptable to assume some reasonable boundary conditions which are suitable.

Following Peixoto,[10] contributions to the vertical integrals above 500 mb and between 1000 mb and the surface were disregarded.

The values of specific humidity are very small above 500 mb, and although the wind speeds are generally high, the total water vapor transport remains relatively small. Therefore, it is reasonable to assume that the errors introduced by setting the upper boundary of the vertical integrals at 500 mb are small; these errors are likely to be greater in the equatorial regions and over extensive areas of high terrain such as the Rocky Mountains (western United States) and the Himalayan Mountains and plateaus (Tibet and central Asia); an estimate of the error in these cases will probably be attempted in a later study. In the meantime, the upper boundary of the vertical integrals was set at 500 mb in this study.

The lower boundary of the vertical integrals was set at the standard 1000-mb pressure surface. In cases where the mean surface pressure, p_0, for the yearly period is greater than 1000 mb, this procedure underestimates the total vertically integrated values. Peixoto[10] found that with the exception of tropical areas, the contribution of the thin layer between 1000 mb and the surface was of little relative significance for the total integrated values. The largest errors probably occur over the trade wind regions, where low-level humidities are high, winds are strong, and the mean surface pressure exceeds 1000 mb. In cases where the mean surface pressure is less than 1000 mb or where the surface topography normally extends above the 1000-mb surface, the actual surface values of humidity and wind were used and substituted for the 1000-mb surface; hence, no fictitious values were introduced into the vertical integrals for these cases.

As a result of the foregoing assumptions in setting the boundary conditions for the vertical integrals, the magnitudes of the mean horizontal transport of water vapor and the mean precipitable water vapor content above the earth's surface for the year 1958 were probably slightly underestimated; however, the underestimation was very likely confined chiefly to extensive areas of high terrain and to the trade wind regions.

The vertical integrations of $\overline{q}$, $\overline{qu}$, and $\overline{qv}$

were computed numerically, applying the trapezoidal rule to the yearly mean values of these quantities at the four standard pressure surfaces of 1000, 850, 700, and 500 mb and using the boundary conditions at 1000 and 500 mb.

In all computations, when 1000-, 850- or 700-mb data were missing due to station elevation, surface data were substituted for the missing level. The following elevation limits were used in selecting levels for the vertical integrals.

Station Elevation	*Levels Used*
Sea level to 2500 ft	1000, 850, 700, and 500 mb with surface substituted if 1000 mb missing
2501 to 6900 ft	850, 700, and 500 mb with surface substituted if 850 mb missing
Above 6900 ft	700 and 500 mb with surface substituted if 700 mb missing

ANALYSIS OF PROCESSED DATA

The representative yearly mean values of $\overline{W}$, $\overline{Q}_\lambda$, and $\overline{Q}_\phi$ for each station were plotted on three separate charts. The plotting chart used was a polar stereographic projection, scale approximately 1 : 40 million, of the northern hemisphere as shown in Fig. 1. The data were analyzed for the best possible fit; all values were carefully studied in relation to terrain and geographical features before the final analysis was computed.

The analysis of the mean precipitable water vapor content, $\overline{W}$, for the year 1958 was carried out first (Fig. 2). No major difficulties were encountered; the data were quite sufficient for the task, and the patterns relatively smooth; isolines were drawn for every 0.5 gm/cm^2 (or cm) of water vapor content. The analyzed $\overline{W}$ field shows, perhaps better than any other, the essence of significant water vapor distribution in the atmosphere. With few exceptions, the analysis shows a continuous decrease of precipitable water vapor content from the equator to the north pole. The effects of maritime influences and continentality are evident. The Sahara, the desert areas of the Middle East south of the Caspian Sea, and the desert region north of Tibet are dry. In addition, the effects of high

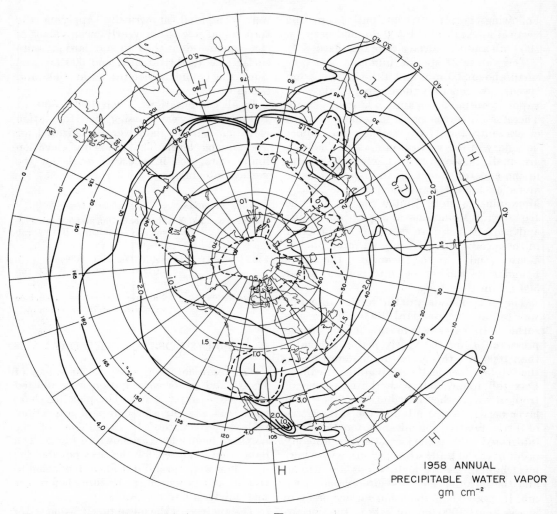

FIG. 2. Mean precipitable water vapor content, $\overline{W}$, for 1958. Isoline spacing every 1.0 gm/cm².

terrain on moisture distribution are illustrated by the very dry areas (less than 1.0 gm/cm²) over the Rockies in the western United States, over central Mexico, and over the Himalayan Mountains and plateaus of Tibet and central Asia; the possibility that the values of $\overline{W}$ over the high terrain areas have been underestimated was discussed, earlier in this study. Until this possibility can be fully explored and checked, it would seem reasonable to assume that the underestimation, if any, is small, and that the atmosphere over these areas is, in fact, relatively dry.

Over the western portions of the subtropical oceanic anticyclones, the water vapor content is generally higher than over the eastern portions; this fact is especially evident in the Pacific and agrees with the concept of general convergence and divergence, respectively, in the western and eastern portions of these semipermanent, large-scale features of the general circulation. The moist areas of highest water vapor content are the equatorial region of South America, the equatorial eastern and western Pacific Ocean, Indian Ocean (especially south and east of India, including the Bay of Bengal), and equatorial west Africa. The driest area is in the Arctic, where the yearly mean precipitable water vapor content is less than 0.5

gm/cm² north of 80°N. The 1.0-gm/cm² isoline enclosing the Arctic regions is found generally at or near the latitude of 60°N; it dips south of 60°N over the regions of most frequent outbreaks of cold, dry polar continental air in eastern Siberia and the Bering Sea and eastern Canada and Hudson Bay; it extends north of 60°N and even slightly north of 70°N over Jan Mayen and northeast of Iceland, very probably showing the effects of the warm North Atlantic Drift current and warm, moist air masses frequently carried northeastward across the North Atlantic Ocean toward the Arctic Ocean. The 0.5 gm/cm² isoline encloses the area between

80°N and the North Pole and also dips slightly southward toward eastern Siberia, over Ellesmere Island, and over Greenland. As a concluding remark, it is obvious from the analysis and important to note that the mean water vapor storage in the atmosphere is very small.

The analyses of the zonal $(\bar{Q}_\lambda)$ and meridional $(\bar{Q}_\phi)$ components of the mean horizontal transport of water vapor for the year 1958 were completed as shown in Figs. 3 and 4. These analyses were more complex than the analysis of the $\bar{W}$ field and, were especially difficult over areas of sparse data coverage. In areas where data coverage was sparse or

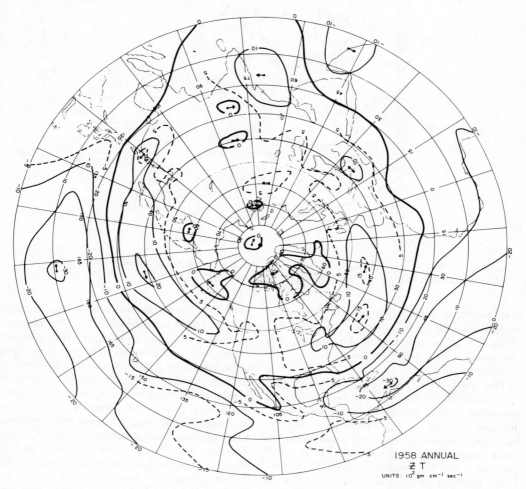

FIG. 3. Zonal component of the mean horizontal transport of water vapor, $\bar{Q}_\lambda$, for 1958. Isoline spacing, full curves, every 10×10^2 gm cm⁻¹ sec⁻¹.

FIG. 4. Meridional component of the mean horizontal transport of water vapor, $\overline{Q}_\phi$, for 1958. Isoline spacing, full curves, every 4×10^2 gm cm^{-1} sec^{-1}.

completely lacking, such as the equatorial eastern Pacific Ocean, careful attention was given to the analyzed $\overline{W}$ field together with the mean wind field[7, 8, 16] in preparing the final analyses.

The analysis of the field of zonal $(\overline{Q}_\lambda)$ transport of water vapor (Fig. 3) shows consistency with the mean zonal wind field. Isolines are drawn for every 10×10^2 gm cm^{-1} sec^{-1} values of the zonal transport with some areas filled in with every 5×10^2 gm cm^{-1} sec^{-1} to show significant details. Large positive (west-to-east) centers of zonal transport are found in the mid-latitudes where westerly winds are predominant, especially

over the North Pacific and North Atlantic Oceans between 30 and 50°N. Large negative (east-to-west) centers of zonal transport are found in low latitudes where strong, persistent easterly winds prevail; the two centers of largest zonal transport are found in these low latitudes, one between 10 and 15°N over the Central North Pacific Ocean near the Marshall Islands and one over the Caribbean Sea between the northern coast of South America and Puerto Rico. A series of four small centers of negative zonal transport are found along the southern fringes of the Arctic regions; two very small negative centers, one over the Sea of Okhotsk and one near the Gulf of Ob in north central Siberia may be questionable, but two fairly large and definite areas are evident over western Alaska and over the Arctic Archipelago of Canada and over portions of Greenland. North of these negative areas are found small positive values of zonal transport girdling the Arctic Ocean around 70 to 80°M.

The analysis of the field of meridional ($\overline{Q}_\phi$) transport of water vapor (Fig. 4) is somewhat more complex than the field of zonal transport of water vapor. Isolines are drawn for every 4×10^2 gm cm^{-1} sec^{-1} values of the meridional transport with some areas filled in with every 2×10^2 gm cm^{-1} sec^{-1} to show significant details. Large centers of positive (northward) transport are found generally over the regions of mid-latitude storms, especially in the vicinity of the mean positions of the Pacific and Atlantic Polar Fronts. Large centers of negative (southward) transport are found generally over low latitudes, especially near 20°N over the eastern North Pacific and North Atlantic Oceans where trade winds prevail. Other centers of northward and southward transports are scattered throughout the northern hemisphere. Around the Arctic regions there are both northward and southward transports. These appear to be very small.

An interesting strong positive (northward) transport area, found over the lower Rio Grande Valley, extends northward in a narrow band over the "tornado alley" of Texas, Oklahoma, and Kansas; this rather striking feature and other generally north-south oriented bands in the field of meridional water vapor transport over the United States (where there are detailed data) are reminiscent of the moist and dry tongues found in mean isentropic charts by Namias[9]. Along the equator there seem to be more positive areas than negative, but since the analysis of large equatorial regions of sparse data relied heavily on the mean wind field, these results may not be representative; Peixoto[10] found positive and negative areas balancing each other over the equator and concluded that the net moisture flow across the equator was practically zero. This conclusion can certainly be justified in the long-period averages, but it may not necessarily be valid for any particular one-year period.

DIVERGENCE OF WATER VAPOR TRANSPORT

Assuming that the analyzed fields of zonal and meridional components of transport of water vapor shown on Figs. 3 and 4 are representative of the total mean horixontal transport of water vapor above the earth's surface for the year 1958, the divergence of the water vapor transport can be calculated. This has been done using finite-difference methods on a basic five-degree, latitude-longitude grid, except north of 80°N latitude, where a ten-degree grid was used. It can be shown that the divergence of the water vapor transport is directly related to evaporation and precipitation at the earth's surface. These matters will be discussed by Dr. Barnes, of the Air Force Cambridge Research Laboratories, in the following paper.

CONCLUDING REMARKS

The analyses of the mean yearly precipitable water vapor and zonal and meridional transports of water vapor are meteorologically meaningful and physically significant for studying the general circulation of the atmosphere. From the analysis of precipitable water vapor, we note that the average water storage in the atmosphere is small. We can compute the divergence from the fields of zonal and meridional transport of water vapor in the atmosphere; this divergence can then be related to the large-scale features of the water balance (evaporation and precipitation) at the earth's surface.

There is a need for more accurate and complete observations of atmospheric humidity and motions in the data-sparse regions of equatorial South America, the east-central Pacific Ocean from Panama to Christmas Island and from Central America to the Hawaiian Islands, and the Indian Ocean. Over all areas we need more accurate humidity measurements at the higher altitudes (above 20,000 ft) in the atmosphere. Further hemispheric or regional studies of atmospheric water vapor for other years, seasons, and possibly even individual months should be undertaken to improve our basic understanding of the planetary circulation and water balance at the planetary interface.

Finally, the author would like to suggest the use of mean specific humidity analyses at standard pressure surface in the atmosphere as "first guess" fields in areas of sparse data for moisture analyses in dynamical numerical weather prediction and cloud forecasting schemes.

Acknowledgments. Much help has been received from many people and sources during this study. The author first wishes to express his sincere appreciation for the encouragement, advice, and assistance of Professor Victor P. Starr, Director of the Planetary Circulations Project at the Massachusetts Institute of Technology, whose keen and enthusiastic interest in this study was a constant source of inspiration to carry on in spite of unexpected difficulties. The expert counsel and direct assistance of Dr. Jose P. Peixoto, University of Lisbon, Portugal, was most helpful and is greatly appreciated. The cooperation and assistance of many individuals associated with the United States Air Force in procuring and machine processing the basic IGY data used in this study was a vital factor in making such an extensive, hemispheric research undertaking possible; those chiefly responsible for success in this important aspect of this study include Major David J. Eddleman,* Staff Meteorologist, Electronic Systems Division, Air Force Systems Command; Mr. R. H. Ferrell and Lt Col G. W. Moxon, Deputy Director and Director respectively of the Air Weather Service Climatic Center; Dr. Adam Kochanski** and Mr. William Spreen,† of the Air Weather Service Climatic Center; Dr. Ralph Shapiro of the Air Force Cambridge Research Laboratory; and members of the staff of the Air Weather Service Data Control Division at Asheville, N.C., and of the M.I.T. Planetary Circulations Project.

The author must also mention other individuals associated with M.I.T. who helped in various ways with typing, hand computation and plotting of data and drafting: Mrs. Jane McNabb; Mr. Henry Cochran;‡ Misses Ellen C. Fetter, Ruth Birtwell, Isabelle Kole, and Barbara Stieglitz; Mrs. Barbara Goodwin and Mrs. Oneda Pruehsner.

References

1. Benton, G. S., Blackburn, R. T., and Snead, V. O., "The Role of the Atmosphere in the Hydrologic Cycle," *Trans. of Am. Geophys. Union*, **31**, 61–73 (1950).

* Now Lt. Col. David J. Eddleman, Hq USAF.
** Now with the U.S. Weather Bureau.
† Now with N.A.S.A.
‡ Now with The Travelers Research Center, Inc.

2. Benton, G. S., and Estoque, M. A., "Water Vapor Transfer over the North American Continent," *J. Meteorol.*, **11**, 462–477 (1954).
3. Brunt, David, "Physical and Dynamical Meteorology," 2nd ed., London, Cambridge University Press, 1944.
4. Haurwitz, Bernhard, "Dynamic Meteorology," 1st ed., New York, McGraw-Hill Book Company, Inc., 1941.
5. Jacobs, Woodrow C., "Large-Scale Aspects of Energy Transformation over the Oceans," in "Compendium of Meteorology," pp. 1057–1070, Boston, American Meteorological Society, 1951.
6. Lufkin, D. H., "Atmospheric Water Vapor Divergence and The Water Balance at the Earth's Surface," Scientific Report No. 4, General Circulation Project, M.I.T., (Victor P. Starr, Director), 1959.
7. Mintz, Y., "The Observed Zonal Circulation of the Atmosphere," *Bull. Am. Meteorol. Soc.*, **35**, No. 5, (1954).
8. Mintz, Y., and Dean, G., "The Observed Mean Field of Motion of the Atmosphere," *Geophysical Research Papers*, No. 17, Air Force Cambridge Research Center, Cambridge, Mass., 1952.
9. Namias, Jerome, "Air Mass and Isentropic Analysis," Milton, Mass., The American Meteorological Society, 1940.
10. Peixoto, J., "Hemispheric Humidity Conditions During the Year 1950," *Scientific Report, No. 3*, General Circulation Project, M.I.T. (Victor P. Starr, Director), 1958.
11. Starr, V. P., "The Physical Basis for the General Circulation," in "Compendium of Meteorology," pp. 341–50, Boston, American Meteorological Society, 1951.
12. Starr, V. P., and Peixoto, J., "On the Global Balance of Water Vapor and the Hydrology of Deserts," *Tellus.*, **10**, 189–194 (1958).
13. Starr, V. P., Peixoto, J., and Livadas, G. C., "On the Meridional Flux of Water Vapor in the Northern Hemisphere," 124–143, Final Report II, General Circulation Project, M.I.T., 1957.
14. Starr, V. P., and White, R. M., "Direct Measurement of the Hemispheric Poleward Flux of Water Vapor," *J. Marine Res.*, **14**, 217–225 (1955).
15. Sverdrup, H. U., "Evaporation from the Oceans," in "Compendium of Meteorology," 1071–1081, Boston, American Meteorological Society, 1951.
16. Wiederanders, C. J., "Analyses of Monthly Mean Resultant Winds for Standard Pressure Levels over the Pacific," Hawaii Institute of Geophysics Report No. 13, 1961.

63. Atmospheric Water Vapor Divergence: Measurements and Applications

Arnold A. Barnes, Jr.

Air Force Cambridge Research Laboratories, Bedford, Massachusetts

ABSTRACT

Maps of water vapor divergence as determined from actual atmospheric soundings are presented for the Northern Hemisphere. The yearly mean divergence maps for 1950 and 1958 are compared to show the similarities and differences between the two years. Applications of this part of the hydrological cycle are considered.

Effects of damming the Mediterranean at the Strait of Gibraltar and filling the Qattara Depression in Egypt are investigated in terms of altering local precipitation and weather modification.

INTRODUCTION

This paper contains discussions of the maps of annual mean moisture divergence over the Northern Hemisphere for the years 1950 and 1958. Applications of knowledge gained from such maps are explored with consideration of the analysis of two proposals for changing climatic conditions.

The Planetary Circulations Project, Department of Meteorology, Massachusetts Institute of Technology was first drawn to the study of water vapor in the earth's atmosphere by the importance of the latent heat in the energy balance of the earth's atmosphere. Benton[3] and others approached this topic through consideration of the hydrological cycle. Before World War II, hydrological research was directed toward the determination of the water budget of large regions (e.g., watersheds, continents) from precipitation and stream-flow measurements. From series of such estimates, numerous authors derived equations which sought to relate the total evapotranspiration of a region to various observed meteorological quantities or to the observed evaporation from pans, weighed boxes of earth, porous water-filled globes and the like. None of these investigations, however, produced results which were widely accepted by other workers.

A second approach to the water balance problem is that of applying the restrictions of continuity and mass conservation to the atmosphere rather than to the surface of the earth. In 1937, Holzman[7] suggested the use of airplane soundings for the determination of the total water content at a station and the moisture divergence of a region. Divergence calculations were first made by Wundt[14] and later by Benton *et al.*[2, 3] and others, but only for restricted areas.

Holzman's[7] findings have been reconfirmed by many authors in the past twenty-six years. Briefly, he showed from aerological soundings that (1) the principal sources of moisture for the United States are derived from maritime air masses whose principal water vapor content is obtained by direct evaporation from oceanic provinces; (2) although a major portion of the precipitation is returned to the atmosphere, only a small part is available for reprecipitation the rest being robbed by dry air masses; (3) the absolute quantity of moisture in the atmosphere has no immediate or direct relation to the process of precipitation. A striking example of this last statement can be seen by comparing Death Valley, which has around 4 in. of rain a year and an annual mean precipitable water content of over 1.1 gm/cm², and Northern Canada with over 10 in. of precipitation a year and an annual mean precipitable water content of under 0.7 gm/cm².

One very important point which must be emphasized over and over again is that cooling of the moist air is necessary for precipitation. In other words, high precipitable water content is a necessary but not a sufficient condition for high precipitation amounts. The cooling can be brought about by upslope, orographic motions or by dynamic ascending motions in the atmosphere such as one air mass overriding another or convective activity.

Since this study deals with water vapor divergence, the extraction of water vapor from the atmosphere by any means must be considered as precipitation. Thus, the formation of dew and the capture or deposition of fog drops must be included in our definition of precipitation even though such amounts are generally small relative to the rainfall. In other words, the adiabatic cooling caused by ascending motions produces more precipitation than does the diabatic cooling of the atmosphere. The precipitation due to diabatic cooling is as difficult to measure as evaporation.

We shall consider evaporation as the addition of water vapor to the atmosphere by any means. In computing the annual mean precipitable water content, transport maps and divergence maps, it was assumed that the liquid or solid water content of clouds could be disregarded.

MATHEMATICS

The notations and derivations are the same as used by Peixoto[11] and others.

For a column of air one square centimeter in cross section extending from the surface of the earth to the top of the atmosphere, we have

$$\frac{\delta W}{\delta t} + \nabla \cdot \vec{Q_i} = E - P \qquad (1)$$

where

$$W = \frac{1}{g} \int_0^{p_0} q\,dp = \text{total water vapor in column}$$

$$\vec{Q_i} = \frac{1}{g} \int_0^{p_0} q\vec{V_i}\,dp = \text{integrated vector transport of water vapor}$$

q = specific humidity
p = pressure
p_0 = surface pressure
E = evaporation
P = precipitation
g = gravity.

Expanding eq. (1) in geographical coordinates (λ, ϕ, p, t),

$$\frac{\delta W}{\delta t} + \frac{1}{a \cos \phi} \frac{\delta Q_\lambda}{\delta \lambda} + \frac{1}{a} \frac{\delta Q_\phi}{\delta \phi} - \frac{Q_\phi \tan \phi}{a} +$$
$$\frac{\delta Qp}{\delta p} = E - P \qquad (2)$$

where a is the radius of the earth.

For our purposes $\delta W/\delta t$ is very small compared to the other terms, and

$$\frac{\delta Qp}{\delta p} = \frac{\delta}{\delta p} \int_0^{p_0} q\omega\,dp = 0$$

where $\omega \equiv dp/dt$. Hence we are left with the working equation

$$\nabla \cdot \vec{Q} = \frac{1}{a \cos \phi} \left[\frac{\delta Q_\lambda}{\delta \lambda} + \frac{\delta}{\delta \phi} (Q_\phi \cos \phi) \right] = E - P \qquad (3)$$

Using station data, values of Q_λ and Q_ϕ, the annual mean zonal and meridional transports of water vapor were computed for a number of Northern Hemisphere stations. Maps of Q_λ and Q_ϕ were analyzed and grid points were taken off and used to compute areal values of $\nabla \cdot \vec{Q}$, the divergence of water vapor.

Inspection of the $\nabla \cdot \vec{Q}$ maps shows that the major regions of convergence correspond to the large regions of heavy precipitation. Otherwise, the correspondence between annual convergence values and total annual precipitation is small due to the fact that the evaporation is of the same order of magnitude as the precipitation. A very detailed and interesting discussion of the 1950 divergence map and its relation to ocean salinity, arid regions and regions of heavy precipitation is given by Lufkin.[9]

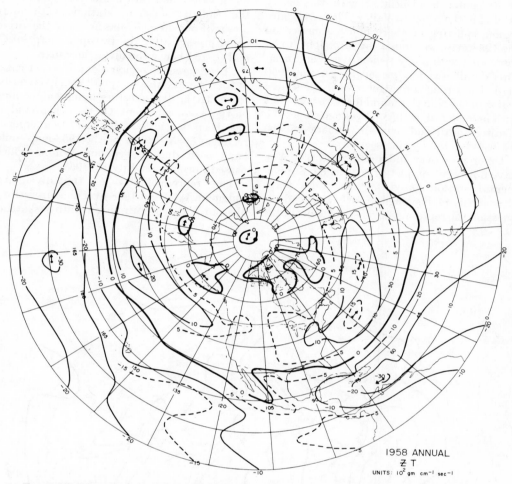

FIG. 1. Mean zonal transport of atmospheric water vapor over the Northern Hemisphere for the year 1958. Units: 10^2 gm cm^{-1} sec^{-1}.

DISCUSSION OF MAPS

Figure 1 shows the mean zonal transport, Q_λ, of water vapor over the Northern Hemisphere for the year 1958. Figure 2 shows the mean meridional transport, Q_ϕ, for 1958. Values at 285 stations were used to obtain these maps. Grid point values were taken at every 5 degrees from these two maps and were used to obtain the divergence field by using a finite difference form of eq. (3). The divergence field, $\nabla \cdot \vec{Q}$, obtained from Figs. 1 and 2 for 1958 is given in Fig. 3. Figure 4 shows the divergence field for 1950. Only 90 stations were used for the original 1950 study, and the

grid point values were taken every 10 degrees. The mean annual precipitable water vapor over the Northern Hemisphere for 1958 is given in Fig. 5.

The original data maps for 1958 (Figs. 1, 2, 3 and 5) were supplied by Crisi and were explained in greater detail in his paper which precedes this one. Figure 4, taken from Lufkin[9], was adapted from original data maps analyzed by Peixoto and the present author and first published by Peixoto[11].

Let us look at the similarities between Figs. 3 and 4. The strong region of convergence over northern South America in 1950 is repeated in 1958 with more detail. The convergence center is associated with the heavy rainfall in the Amazon Valley. The divergence region, splitting northern South America on the 1958 map, was found (by aftersight) to be associated with a dry region over Venezuela. This detail was not picked up on the 1950 map. The strong convergence over the source region of the Nile was found for both years but with more detail in 1958. Divergence over the Mediterranean and over the Sahara will be discussed in a following section.

Differences over India and Southeast Asia have not been completely reconciled. Supplemental stations used for the 1958 maps altered this analysis significantly and made us question the representativeness of some of the mean values used in the analysis. Because of the Indian monsoon, stations with more observations in one season than the other could greatly alter the transport maps of Q_λ and Q_ϕ and hence the divergence map.

The divergence region along the east coast of Russia and China on the 1950 map is consistent with the dry, moisture-hungry air coming off the Asian continent. On the other hand, it has been suggested that the convergence region at 30°N, 120°W on the 1958 map could have been due to typhoon Winnie which passed Formosa on July 15, 1958.

The reproducibility of the divergence tongue in 1950 and 1958 over the Mississippi-Missouri Valley, continuing up into Saskatche-

Fɪɢ. 2. Mean meridional transport of atmospheric water vapor over the Northern Hemisphere for the year 1958. Units: 10^2 gm cm⁻¹ sec⁻¹.

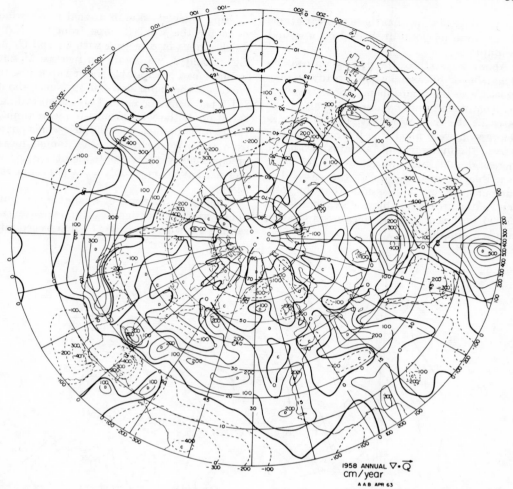

FIG. 3. Mean divergence of atmospheric water vapor over the Northern Hemisphere for the year 1958. Units: cm/year.

wan, is gratifying considering the coarseness of the grid used to compute the divergence patterns.

Where the data is adequate, the main features of the divergence field seems to repeat for the two years. Reasons for differences may be listed as

(1) Inadequate data to define the divergence field.

(2) Differences between the mean state of the circulation and moisture content for the two years.

(3) Action of hurricanes and typhoons. Since both the moisture and wind obtain large values in hurricanes, the yearly mean can be significantly affected. (Likewise annual total

precipitation can be dependent on just one storm).

(4) Differences in detail due to the difference in grid sizes used for the two years.

As an example of the use and interpretation of these divergence maps, we shall consider proposals for altering the weather by drying up the Mediterranean Basin and flooding the Qattara Depression in Egypt.

FLOODING THE QATTARA DEPRESSION

It has been suggested that the Qattara Depression in northern Egypt be filled with water from the Nile or the Mediterranean in order to increase the precipitation over

Egypt. We will show that these two variations of the same proposal are based on unsound assumptions.

About one-sixth of the depression consists of marshes or quicksand which already provide moisture to the atmosphere. These areas are fed from underground water which also feeds oases in the Sahara Desert. If the Qattara Depression were filled, the hydrostatic pressure in the underground "streams" would be increased and more water would be made available for evaporation at the oases. For our purposes, we shall assume that the total new water area available for evaporation is 15,000 km² and that the mean evaporation rate is 5 mm/day.[8]

Using Buch's[4] 850-mb annual mean wind value for the wind (3 mps from the NW) which agrees in direction with Q_λ and Q_ϕ in Figs. 1 and 2, we obtain an increase in the annual mean precipitable water vapor just to the east of the depression of 0.2 gm/cm², about a 10 per cent increase. Lateral spreading, variation of the wind from the mean annual value, and the fact that the dry winds come from the SW mean that the annual mean precipitable water vapor content would be increased at the most only a few per cent over Egypt.

Would this increase of available precipitable water vapor significantly increase the rainfall anywhere in Egypt? Almost certainly

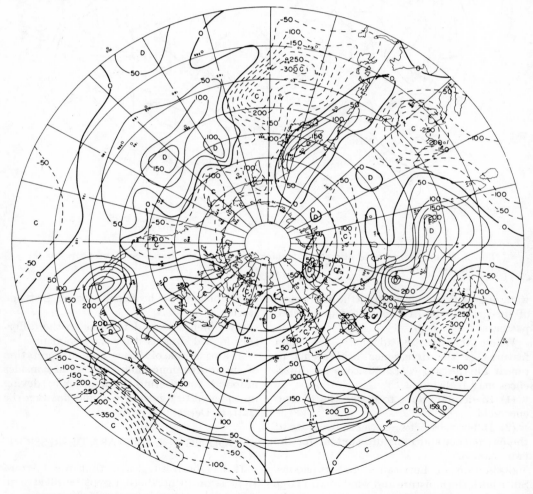

Fig. 4. Mean divergence of atmospheric water vapor over the Northern Hemisphere for the year 1950.[9] Units: cm/year.

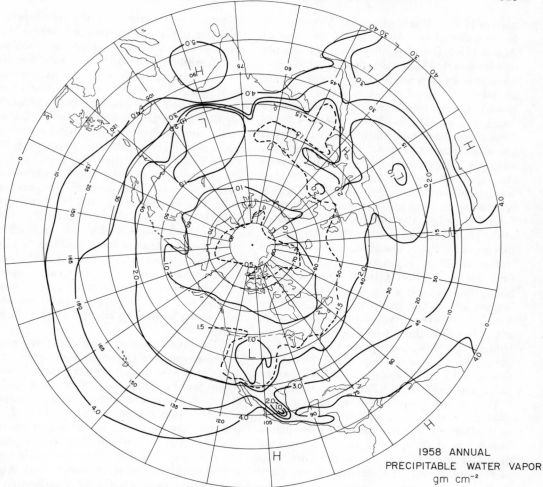

1958 ANNUAL
PRECIPITABLE WATER VAPOR
gm cm⁻²

FIG. 5. Mean precipitable water vapor content of the atmosphere over the Northern Hemisphere during the year 1958. Units: gm/cm².

it would not. Most of the water would be absorbed by dry air masses which would not produce local precipitation. Moist air masses bringing precipitation to the area would not absorb as much water when passing over the depression as would the dry air masses.

From Figs. 3 and 4 the mean distance between divergence and convergence centers is a couple of thousand kilometers. McDonald[10] in his article "The Evaporation-Precipitation Fallacy," states that the average water molecule drifts many hundreds of miles before precipitation terminates its residence period in the atmosphere. Thus, one would expect the water evaporated from the Qattara Depression to pass beyond the borders of Egypt

before coming back to earth as precipitation. On the other hand, local cooling of the air mass could possibly increase the precipitation within the borders. Orographic features which could produce ascending motions are the mountains in the Arabian and Nabian deserts along the Red Sea. Obviously, these ranges are not very effective in removing water vapor from the atmosphere.

Thus it would seem that the benefits to be derived from filling the Qattara Depression would not include a significant increase in the amount of precipitation anywhere in Egypt.

If we look closer at the two proposals to fill the depression, we find that on the average the daily evaporation would be 75 million cubic meters ($75 \times 10^6 m^3$) of water. According to Hurst's data,[8] the discharge of the Nile at Aswan is less than 75 million cubic meters per day from early March through the end of June. Since this water is needed in the lower Nile for irrigation, it would not be available to compensate for the evaporation from the Qattara during these months. There would also be considerable evaporation of the water as it traveled from Aswan to the Qattara. For example, every year between 1890 and 1902 the supply of the Nile during May and June was actually exhausted, no water at all being allowed to flow out into the Mediterranean.

In September, the average daily discharge of the Nile at Aswan reaches 700 million cubic meters, and there would be sufficient flood waters to effect a yearly balance with the evaporation in the Qattara. On the other hand, the flood waters are needed annually to deposit silt on the banks of the Nile. If the flood waters were diverted to the depression, not only would the silt be unavailable on the banks of the Nile, but the silt would settle in the calm waters of the depression, hinder the flow into the underground streams feeding the oases, and eventually fill the depression.

The second proposal, to build a 40-mile ditch and tunnel to bring Mediterranean water to the Qattara, also has its difficulties such as blowing sand filling the ditches, a two-hundred-foot mountain range on the north side of the depression, the salinity of the input water and the increasing salinity of the water in the depression due to evaporation.

DAMMING THE MEDITERRANEAN*

The Mediterranean Sea is almost completely landlocked, its only effective communication with the major oceans of the globe being through the Strait of Gibraltar. From Figs. 3 and 4 we see that there is a net divergence or removal of water vapor from the basin. This net loss of water is so great that, in spite of the inflow from the Nile and other rivers, a net eastward flow of water past Gibraltar is required in order to maintain the average water level. Actually, more cool

* Part of the material in this section was taken from an unpublished manuscript by Starr and Peixoto.

Atlantic water enters through the Strait of Gibraltar in the upper eastward current than exits as warm, saltier and denser, Mediterranean water in the lower westward current.

Let us consider the results of constructing a dam across the Strait of Gibraltar at its narrowest point, which is about ten miles. To begin with, the now completely landlocked sea would presumably become shallower at an initial rate of about half a meter per year. The water would recede from the present shore lines, the area covered by water would shrink, and the salt would become more concentrated. Both the smaller area and the increased salinity would act to decrease the total evaporation, although other climatic effects might occur. After a large number of years (perhaps two thousand), the most likely result would be an equilibrium between evaporation, drainage and precipitation with a much smaller sea. Let us suppose that the level would then be about a kilometer lower than it is now.

What might happen elsewhere in the world as a consequence? The entire atmosphere normally contains about 10^{13} metric tons of water. About four hundred times this much would be removed from our altered sea, and it is impossible to retain this in the atmosphere. If all this water were added to the major oceans, their average level would be increased about seven meters. It is difficult to predict the compensating geological adjustments that might result from such an altered distribution of weight of water, but undoubtably extensive flooding of coastlines in many regions of the world would result.

As far as general changes of climate are concerned one can say very little. If no readjustments were to occur in the shape of the present bottom contours and the water level dropped one kilometer, the Mediterranean would split into two major inland lakes with a substantial isthmus connecting Italy, Sicily and Tunisia, as was the case in earlier Quaternary times. The total water area would be reduced by about 45 per cent. Corsica together with Sardinia would form a new peninsula jutting out from the Tuscan coast in the vicinity of Elba. The entire upper Adriatic would disappear. There is some basis for supposing that the greater continentality engendered by this shrinkage of the sea area would result in hotter conditions, although this is far from a certainty.

If the general circulation of the atmosphere remained the same, there probably would be less precipitable water available downwind, to the east, of the Mediterranean. On the other hand, it is more likely that subtle and, at present, unpredictable changes in the general circulation of the atmosphere would be more important and would have world-wide affects.

The experiment might be irreversible due to some chance isostatic readjustment such as a buckling of the earth's crust creating a range of mountains in the southern Iberian Peninsula, Gibraltar and Morocco. On the other hand, an unplanned inundation from the Red Sea across the Isthmus of Suez could bring failure to the whole project.

CONCLUSIONS

The damming of the Mediterranean exemplifies an avenue of attack for attempts to control our large scale geophysical environment, and it is in the realm of possibility, but since the end results are unpredictable, the project is not advocated. Obviously, more effort should be put into obtaining knowledge and understanding of the workings of our atmosphere and, in particular, of the general circulation of our atmosphere so that the end results will be capable of being predicted before such major projects are undertaken.

Important facts about yearly mean precipitable water vapor, precipitation, water vapor divergence and large scale weather modification projects as touched on by this paper are summarized below.

(1) In order to have high precipitation, both large amounts of precipitable water vapor *and* cooling of the air mass are necessary.

(2) Precipitation is better correlated with water vapor convergence than with precipitable water vapor content, but the correlation is far from perfect since, in fact, the convergence is a measure of the precipitation minus the evaporation.

(3) Large-scale evaporation projects, such as filling the Qattara Depression, will not increase the local precipitation unless cooling of the moisture laden air can be effected.

(4) Major weather modification projects, such as damming the Mediterranean or melt-

ing the Artic icecap, should not be undertaken until it is possible to predict with some assurance the results such projects would have on the redistribution of land and sea surfaces, on the earth's climate and on the general circulation of the atmosphere.

Acknowledgments. The author wishes to thank Prof. Victor Starr of the Massachusetts Institute of Technology and Prof. José Peixoto of the University of Lisbon for their many hours of enlightened discussions which are reflected in these pages. We wish to acknowledge the help and guidance of Mr. Wayne Hering of the Air Force Cambridge Research Laboratories in our attempt to work with maps of annual precipitation. His expert knowledge in this field helped us avoid the many pitfalls associated with this subject.

This paper is intended to be complementary to "Hemispheric Water Vapor Balance During 1958" by Lt. Col. Alfred Crisi, U.S.A.F., which can be found on p. 502 of this volume. We are indebted to Col. Crisi for the original analysis of Figs. 1, 2, 3 and 5 and for the many discussions on our papers.

It is hoped that this study has in some sense satisfied two requests expressed by the keynote speaker at the 1963 International Symposium on Humidity and Moisture, Dr. J. H. Hollomon of the U.S. Department of Commerce. First, we have attempted to point out and work with the practical applications of some of our basic theoretical studies of the general circulation of the atmosphere by considering the ever important precipitation-evaporation field. Secondly, his request for a large scale outlook is met, we feel, not only by consideration of gross features over the Northern Hemisphere but also in the combination of such scientific disciplines as geology, hydrology, precipitation mechanics, numerical weather prediction, and the general circulation of the atmosphere.

References

1. Barnes, Arnold A., "The Energy Balance of the Stratosphere During the IGY," Ph.D. Thesis, Massachusetts Institute of Technology, 1962.
2. Benton, George S., Blackburn, R. T., and Snead, V. O., "The Role of the Atmosphere in the Hydrological Cycle," *Trans. Am. Geophys. Union*, **31**, 61–73 (1950).
3. Benton, George S., and Estoque, Mariano A., "Water Vapor Transport over the North American Continent," *J. Meteorol.*, **11**, No. 6, 462–477 (1954).
4. Buch, H., "Hemispheric Wind Conditions during the Year 1950," Final Report, Part 2, General Circulation Project, Massachusetts Institute of Technology, 1954.
5. Crisi, A. R., "Hemispheric Water Vapor Balance during 1958," M.Sc. Thesis, Massachusetts Institute of Technology, 1961.
6. Crisi, A. R., "Hemispheric Water Vapor Balance during 1958," in "Humidity and Moisture,"

Vol. II, p. 502, New York, Reinhold Publishing Corp., 1964.

7. Holzman, B., "Use of Aerological Soundings in Determining the Sources of Moisture for Precipitation," *Trans. Am. Geophys. Union*, **18**, 488–490 (1937).

8. Hurst, H. E., "The Nile," London, Constable and Company Ltd., 1952.

9. Lufkin, D. H., "Atmospheric Water Vapor Divergence and the Water Balance at the Earth's Surface," Scientific Report No. 4, General Circulation Project, Massachusetts Institute of Technology, 1959.

10. McDonald, J. E., "The Evaporation—Precipitation Fallacy," *Weather*, **17**, No. 5, 168–177 (1962).

11. Peixoto, J. P., "Hemispheric Humidity Conditions during the Year 1950," Scientific Report No. 3, General Circulation Project, Massachusetts Institute of Technology, 1958.

12. Starr, V. P., and Peixoto, J. P., "On the Global Balance of Water Vapor and the Hydrology of Deserts," *Tellus*, **10**, 188–194 (1958).

13. Starr, V. P., Peixoto, J. P., and Livadas, G. C., "On the Meridional Transport of Water Vapor in the Northern Hemisphere," *Geofis. Pura Appl.*, **39**, 174–185 (1958).

14. Wundt, W., "Das Bild des Wasserkreislaufs auf Grund Früherer und Neurerer Forschungen," *Mitt. Rerchsverb. Dtsch. Wasserwirtschaft*, Nr. **44** (1938).

64. Survey of Techniques for Measuring Dew

T. L. NOFFSINGER

U.S. Weather Bureau, Washington, D.C.

ABSTRACTS

Dew has attracted the interest and attention of man since the dawn of history. Reference to dew and dewfall occurs frequently in the writings of early man. Dew is mentioned more than a dozen times in the Old Testament.

Its role (1) in the maintenance of moisture balance of plants and soil; (2) in the incidence and spread of plant disease; (3) as a medium for insecticides and fungicides and (4) as a factor in corrosion of metals has contributed to a continued and growing interest in the measurement of both duration and amounts of dew.

A review of the literature reveals some 20 or more different instruments or pieces of apparatus which, according to the author, measure duration and/or amounts of dew.

The principles involved in the various methods of measuring dew amounts and dew duration are examined and instruments used for these measurements are reviewed and discussed.

"Hath the rain a father? or who hath begotten the drops of dew?" *Job 38:28*

INTRODUCTION

Dew has attracted the interest and attention of man since the dawn of history. It has figured in his literature, art and industry. Reference to dew appears numerous times in the Hebrew Bible. Prose and poetry of many nations abound with references to dew, dewfall and dewdrops. Works of Milton, Bacon and Shakespeare have numerous references to dew and dewfall.

Aside from its role in art and literature, dew plays an important part in activities associated with both agriculture and industry. The role of dew in the incidence and spread of plant diseases, in the maintenance of moisture balance in the soil and vegetative zone, its importance as a medium for the optimum reaction of pesticides, and its role in the corrosion of metals, have contributed to a growing interest in the measurement of the amount and duration of dew.

CLASSIFICATION OF DEW

Moisture found on leaves and other exposed surfaces which is generally classified as dew, can be separated into four categories:

(1) Dewfall, or condensation of water vapor from the atmosphere;

(2) Distillation, or condensation of water vapor from transpiring lower leaves or warmer moist soil;

(3) Fog interception by leaves or other exposed objects;

(4) Guttation, or exudation of liquid by portions of leaves.

Of the four categories, only the first three have a source of moisture outside the plant and, therefore, are of importance as an independent source of moisture for plant use. Only sources (1) and (3) represent a gain of water by the plant-soil system. Source (2), distillation, however, probably makes the greater contribution to dew amounts in most continental, mid-latitude areas. Condensation, sources (1), (2) and (3), is the evaporation process in reverse.

523

ROLE OF DEW IN THE MICRO-ENVIRONMENT

Industry

The corrosion rate of metals is dependent upon a number of factors among which is that of moisture. Although dew is only one of several sources of moisture which contribute to corrosion of industrial equipment, it does provide a medium for the solution of salts and the formation of bases or acids, thereby adding to the industrial problem of equipment and materials deterioration through rust and corrosion.

Agriculture

Dew or leaf wetness plays a decisive role in the life processes of pathogenic fungi which are so important in fruit, vegetable and field crop production throughout the world. The amount of water needed at any one time and the manner of action varies according to the particular fungus and upon the environmental temperature.

The effectiveness of pesticides, in the form of spray or dust, is frequently influenced by the condition of the vegetation, particularly the presence or absence of dew.

The importance of dew in the water economy of plants has been questioned by Angus.[2] He estimated that the maximum condensation of dew is probably no more than 10 per cent of the water transpired during the day. Dew may play two possible roles of benefit to plants.[2] The first of these is a passive role in which dew delays the rise in temperature and the onset of transpiration the following day. The second role is a possible active role in which dew is taken up by the plant and enters the dynamic liquid cycle.[25, 27, 28]

The value of dew as a source of moisture for plants is still a subject of controversy. The amount of dew which runs off the leaves and collects in the ground is too small to wet more than a few millimeters of soil. Many early experiments, which reported direct absorption of dew through the leaves, lacked conclusive evidence. A third possible mode of action of dew is its role in keeping the plant saturated at night. Since growth of most plants occurs at night, a water supply at night would be more effective than during the day.

Duvdevani[4] studied the importance of dew in the growth of agricultural type plants. He conducted an experiment in the coastal plain of Israel in which he compared two field plots of plants that were treated identically except that a canopy was placed over one plot between sunset and sunrise to prevent the formation of dew. The test showed that most plants grew twice as much when they received dew during the night.

Fowells and Kirk[8] showed that Ponderosa pine seedlings depleted soil moisture below the permanent wilting percentage and still survived. Stone, Went and Young[27] found that seedlings of *Pinus Coulteri* survived in dry soil below the wilting point in an atmosphere of high humidity.

The amount of nightly condensation was measured by actual weighing in an area of soil covered with various crops. Harrold and Dreibelbis,[11] using the weighing lysimeter at Coshocton, Ohio over a six-year period, found that an average equivalent of 9.1 in. of rain was deposited annually in the form of dew. This value was approximately 60 per cent of the 15 in. theoretically possible on a year of clear nights as computed by Went.[35]

In recent correspondence, Ekern and Harrold[7] have discussed a source of error in the Coshocton data; a report describing the erroneous operation of the lysimeter and errors in dew evaluation is being prepared. Ekern,[6] in Hawaii, found very few days of net gain of moisture in the lysimeter system. Davis weighing lysimeter data[20] seems to bear out the very few occasions when dew represents a net gain in moisture to the soil plant system.

Conditions for Dew Formation

In the classic "Essay on Dew," Wells[34] explained numerous experimental results in terms of the condensation of water vapor from the atmosphere. Aitkins[1] revised a concept of upward movement of moisture from the soil. In experiments with shallow trays of sod and bare soil he found that there was a loss of weight on occasions when dew was forming, and concluded that evaporation was occurring through diffusion of moisture to the surface from warmer moist soil. Studies by Monteith[14, 15] Ekern,[6] Deacon *et al.*[3] and Mukammal[16] have confirmed these findings.

The formation of dew is essentially a nocturnal occurrence which is dependent on radiation cooling of exposed surfaces. The temperature of the surfaces and eventually their vapor pressure is reduced to a value less than that of the adjacent air. The degree of cloud cover and wind speed are the two major factors in dew formation. Under favorable conditions of clear sky, light wind and high humidity, condensation may begin several hours before sunset and continue until sometime after sunrise.

Conditions favorable for dew formation are: (a) a radiating surface, well insulated from the heat supply of the soil; (b) a clear, still atmosphere with low specific humidity in all but the surface layers; and (c) high relative humidity in the surface air layers or an adjacent source of moisture.

Theoretically the process of dew formation is the reverse of the evaporation process and can be computed by the use of well-known principles of physics: (1) the vapor flux technique or (2) the energy balance technique.

METHODS OF MEASUREMENT

There is no simple way to distinguish between dewfall, distillation, and fog interception. Unless a sufficient area and depth of soil is weighed there is nothing to indicate the source of moisture gained by exposed surfaces such as leaves and branches. Weighing lysimeter techniques suggest the only means of distinguishing dewfall or fog interception from distillation. Although sensitive balances and careful measurements are required, successful measurements of dewfall have been carried out by Jennings and Monteith,[13] Ekern,[6] and Pruitt.[20] Lysimeters will not, however, provide a record of distillation or guttation since there is no change in weight of a system during their formation.

Theoretical

Since the factors that are involved in evaporation are also involved in condensation (dew formation) the theoretical approaches using the vapor flux technique or the energy balance technique offer possible means of computing dew deposit.

Vapor Flux Method. Dalton in 1802 expressed the equation for evaporation over a water surface as follows:

$$E = c\,(e_s - e_d) \tag{1}$$

where

E = evaporation

c = constant

e_s = saturation vapor pressure at the temperature of the evaporating surface

e_d = saturation vapor pressure at the dew-point temperature of the air.

For use in studying evaporation or condensation over land surfaces at ground level, the value of c varies between 0.3 and 0.8 depending on local geographic conditions. Conditions for condensation (dew) occur when e_s is less than e_d.

Thornthwaite and Holzman[32] treated water vapor flux as a turbulent transport problem. They used an integrated form of the one-dimensional transfer equation to compute mean hourly values of the flux at the surface.

Monteith[14, 15] comparing dew-balance traces with observations and direct measurements of moisture on grass (filter paper collection and lysimeter data) was able to distinguish three regimes in the diurnal exchange between the atmosphere, the soil and the grass. They were characterized by (1) a period of evaporation, (2) a transition period and (3) a condensation period. The condensation regime consisted of periods in which the source of moisture on the grass was (1) distillation from the soil below, (2) downward flux from the atmosphere and (3) a combination of (1) and (2).

Rate of distillation D was computed as follows.

$$D = K_v\,[T(0) - T(1)] \cdot \frac{(dx)}{(dT)_s} \tag{2}$$

where

K_v = 0·24 cm²/sec, (assumed) diffusion coefficient

$(dx)/(dT)_s$ = rate of change with temperature of saturated absolute humidity calculated at the mean of the surface temperature, $T(0)$, and the air temperature at 1 cm, $T(1)$.

From the calculation and from measurement using filter paper as a collector, it was concluded that the magnitude of the flux of water vapor upward from the soil could be estimated, to within a factor of two at least, from simply observed gradients of temperature and humidity.

Dewfall or the eddy flux of water vapor from the atmosphere to the surface was computed from the following equation.

$$F = \frac{k^2 z^2 \, (du/dz) \, (dx/dz)}{1 + \sigma \, Ri} \qquad (3)$$

where

k = Von Karman's constant = 0.4
du/dz = wind gradient at height z
dx/dz = specific humidity gradient
Ri = Richardson number or stability parameter.

It was assumed that $\sigma = 10$ from work by Pasquill[18] and Rider.[22] Observed and computed dewfall were compared, and it was concluded that dewfall over a short grass surface in saturated air can be estimated with an error of ± 30 per cent if wind and temperature gradients are known.

Energy Balance. Water-vapor exchange in terms of energy balance were investigated by Fransilla[9] and by Rider and Robinson.[21] Their findings indicated an appreciable portion of the radiative heat loss at night may be compensated by latent heat of condensation. Frost[10] assumed that heat conducted upward through the soil at night is small compared to heat brought to the surface by turbulent diffusion, and he showed that the heat released in dew formation would reduce nocturnal cooling by several degrees.

Dewfall and distillation can be regarded as fluxes of latent heat. Distillation represents heat transfer from soil to leaves. Dewfall represents heat transfer from the atmosphere to leaves. The heat balance equation representing the grass layer and air immediately above the soil surface can be written

$$Q \frac{dT}{dt} = R + G + C + \lambda F + M \qquad (4)$$

where

Q = heat capacity of the air-grass layer per cm^2
T = mean temperature of the layer
R = net incoming radiation flux
G = flux of heat from soil to surface
C = flux of sensible heat from air to surface
F = flux of water vapor from air to surface
λ = latent heat of vaporization

M = heat released by plant metabolism per cm^2.

One of the difficulties involved in the heat balance method of computing evaporation or condensation is that of measuring the parameters with sufficient precision, and another is the lack of simultaneity of values. Radiation balance values indicate the amount of heat supplied to the active surface at the time of measurement. Values for heat conduction, turbulent exchange and the expenditure of heat in evaporation occur at different times, thus introducing possible errors.

Mechanical

A survey of techniques for measuring duration and/or amounts of dew reveals numerous devices in use. A brief description of the mode of action and an evaluation of several instruments is included.

Weighing Dew Gauge. *Change in Weight Dew Recorder.* Kessler-Fuess Type: The sensitive element consists of a blackened aluminum plate of a flattened conical shape with its aperture directed upward. The weight changes resulting from dew deposited on the receptacle are mechanically transmitted to the recording beam. Mäde modified the recorder by replacing the aluminum plate by a (thermoplastic material) plate of equal size and shape. The thermoplastic material is reported to have a temperature correspondence much closer to that of material vegetation.

Evaluation: The instrument was designed to record the amount of dew and the duration. For dew or light rain, the record corresponds closely to duration of dew on plants. The water deposits on the smooth parts of leaves are the first to dry. Water remains in the deeper parts at the rim of the leaves. The evaporation of these deposits corresponds, in time, to the drying of dew or light rain deposits on artificial surfaces. The instrument, which was originally designed as a dew recorder, may be used for measuring moisture deposits caused by dew or light rain. The heavier the rain, the less representative are the records of leaf wetness period.

Change in Weight Dew Balance. Hiltner type (Fig. 1). The sensitive surface for dew and precipitation consists of a circular nylon filter which is fixed to the beam of the balance. All

FIG. 1. Dew balance—Hiltner type. (*Courtesy Science Associates, Inc.*)

changes of weight are mechanically transmitted to the recording drum.

Evaluation: The influence of the wind on the continuous record cannot be eliminated; therefore, the beginning and end of the period of dew cannot be easily distinguished.

Surface Wetness Recorder. Hirst and Mac-Dowell. The amount of moisture deposited in the form of precipitation or dew on a cylindrical test surface of polystyrene is determined by weighing. The change in weight is mechanically transmitted to a recording pen. The amount of moisture determines the curve. The oscillation of the beam caused by wind is reduced by an oil-damping system.

Evaluation: As with other instruments using the weighing principle, wind can oscillate the sensing element and give a recording which is difficult to interpret. Tests made in a potato field showed good agreement with the actually observed leaf wetness period of the lower part of the potato plants. It is reported that only a relationship between the recorded leaf wetness and that observed on natural leaves exists.

Surface Wetness Recorder. Hearn : The instrument is similar to the dew balance described by Hirst. It records the length of time that a polystyrene block retains surface moisture when exposed in the open air.

Evaluation: Wind tends to oscillate the polystyrene block, giving spurious results.

Weighing Lysimeter. Ekern Type: A lysimeter of sensitivity to detect moisture gains and losses of as little as 0.001 in. has been in operation in Hawaii since 1958. A box, 5 ft square and 1 ft deep, contains soil from which water may readily drain. One edge of the lysimeter is

pivoted on a 3-ft section of angle iron. The remainder of the box is supported by two water-filled innertubes. The water system in the tubes is interconnected. The weight of the lysimeter is measured by the height of the hydraulic head necessary to support the box. A float system gives a continuous record of the head change. (See also Harrold and Dreibelbis,[11] Monteith[14, 15] and Pruitt.[20])

Evaluation: Dewfall is recorded as a gain in weight on the recorder; however, leaf wetness from distillation is not recorded.

A sensitive lysimeter can be used to measure dewfall but is of little value in the measurement of distillation dew.

Volumetric Measurement. Hungerford and Edgerton experimented with collector gauges which theoretically were designed so that accumulated dew would run into a glass graduated cylinder and measure the accumulated dew volumetrically. This was the same basic approach as that of Potvin[19] except that plastic materials were used as the collector plate rather than glass as used by Potvin.

The plastic and expanded styrofoam proved difficult to shape into a uniform dew collecting surface. Work is continuing in the search for a satisfactory quantitative measurement without having to weigh each collector plate.

Scott[23] in New Zealand used plasticized nylon epoxy resins and detergents to encourage the drain of dew drops into the graduate.

Measurements made by Hungerford in Idaho during the summer of 1961, using 0.002-in. thick acetate plates, gave daily values which ranged from 0.001 to 0.290 mm.

Duvdevani Dew Gauge. The Duvdevani method of dew measurement (Fig. 2) consists in exposing a standardized painted block of wood (measuring $12.5'' \times 2'' \times 1''$) at about sunset and, around sunrise, observing the form and distribution of the dew deposit formed on it. The appearance of the dew deposit is matched with a set of photographs giving dew numbers from 0 through 8 (Table 1).

The set consists of sixteen photographs, some amounts of dew have more than one photograph because the same amount can appear in different forms. It is claimed that rainfall can easily be distinguished from the type of drops produced by dew.

FIG. 2. Duvdevani Dew Gauge. (*Courtesy Science Associates, Inc.*)

TABLE 1. QUANTITATIVE EQUIVALENTS
OF THE DEW SCALE NUMBERS

Dew Scale No.	Equivalent, mm
0	No dew
Tr	.01
1	.02
2	.045
3	.075
4	.11
5	.15
6	.20
7	.27
8	.35

Evaluation: The Duvdevani dew gauge is simple to use and relatively inexpensive per unit.

Careful attention is required relative to time of exposure and time of making observation. The painted surface deteriorates rapidly and requires frequent replacement by new blocks.

In this country, Newton[17] is experimenting with use of different types of paint and kinds of wood in order to provide a more durable sensor. Shaw[24] reports that the Duvdevani dew gauge gives a good measure of dew duration on broad-leaf crops, but for other crops the estimate is much poorer. The correlations found between duration of dew on a Duv-

devani gauge at the level of the plant surface and on the plant surface were 0.93 for grass, 0.82 for oats, 0.98 for soybeans and 0.93 for corn.

Change in Length of Sensing Element. *Dew-Duration Recorder.* Wallin-Palhemus Type (Fig. 3): The measuring element consists of a water-sensitive animal membrane (lamb gut) about 20 μ thick. When dew is deposited on the membrane, it expands and allows a spring to move a stylus which bears on a recording chart. The stylus maintains its position as long as dew is present. When the dew evaporates the element drys and contracts, withdrawing the stylus from the recording chart.

Evaluation: Although it is generally agreed that the animal membrane is influenced only by actual water deposit, there have been occasional reports of its being influenced by relative humidity conditions and therefore not completely representative of dew conditions.

Dewfall Integrator. New Zealand Type: The sensitive element consists of a folded strip of cellulose adhesive tape (Sellotape) which is incorporated in a conventional thermograph redesigned for the purpose. The instrument records the total amount of dew or rain up to about 0.5 mm.

Evaluation: The instrument is reported to be unaffected by temperature or small humidity changes. The instrument is calibrated by allowing water sprays to fall on the

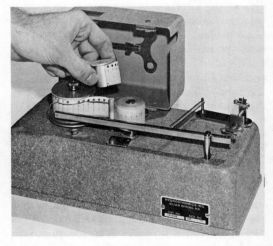

FIG. 3. Dew-duration recorder—Wallin-Palhemus type. (*Courtesy Hygrodynamics, Inc.*)

sensitive element and on adjacent glass squares on which the deposit can be measured by weighing.

Change in the Electrical Resistance. *Detecteur de Precipitation R-277A.* The sensitive element consists of a two-piece grid exposed in a horizontal position. The alternately teethed rods of both pieces are separated by very thin layers of non-conductive material. An electrical potential is placed across the two ends. A deposit of moisture on the grid completes the circuit and there is a flow of electrical current. After the moisture has dried, the electrical contact between the rods is interrupted. The contact period is a record of the wetness or dew period of the test surface.

Evaluation: The instrument is a modification of a heating conductor designed for another purpose. Further tests are needed before final evaluation can be made.

Dew Recorder. Crossan Type: The sensing element is an electrical grid.

A commercial grid is connected through a transistorized amplifier to a recorder. A low voltage electrical circuit is closed when dew forms on the grid and opens when dew or moisture is not present.

Evaluation: Height of exposure and type of surface on which the grid is exposed are important factors in use of this instrument.

Lemmons-Clark Type: The sensing element is similar to that used in the Crossan type. The major difference between the two systems is that the Crossan system incorporates a transistor amplifier in the detection circuit; the Lemmons-Clark system uses a bridge circuit.

Evaluation: Same as Crossan type.

Apparatus for Measuring Leaf Wetness. **Stuzka-Uhlir.** The sensitive element consists of a flat grid formed by parallel wiring. Alternate sets of even and uneven numbered wires form the two electrodes. The grid is put on a leaf. Deposits of dew or rain causes contact to be made between neighboring wires; upon drying the contact is interrupted.

Evaluation: Of the resistance type of dew meters, this one comes nearest to approximating natural vegetative surface conditions.

Change in Surface Characteristics. *Instrument for Recording Periods of Rainfall and Dew.* Theis and Calpouzos: The Theis-Calpouzos type dew recorder[31] is constructed

by modifying the standard 7-day hygrothermograph. A shaft extends from a hygrothermograph through the rainproof top of a ventilated box and connects to an arm holding an indelible pencil. The pencil makes a mark on a ground-glass plate on top of the box as the hygrothermograph drum revolves. The pencil makes a dark line on wet ground-glass surfaces but only a light, indistinct line on dry surfaces.

To determine the number of hours represented by each mark on a plate, a calibrated chart is used. The chart is prepared by making a circle with radii marked at 6-hour intervals, computed on the basis that hygrothermograph clocks rotate the drum 343 degrees in 7 days. The plates are superimposed on the chart and records of time of occurrence and duration of wet periods may be read directly.

Evaluation: Type of pencil used is very important in this instrument. Heavy rain destroys the record of a soft lead pencil. Hard lead fails to record deposits of very light dew. With proper choice of pencil, periods of dew duration can be recorded with a precision of approximately 15 minutes.

Humectograph. *Brazier type.* The sensing element of the humectograph is a paper tape 3 to 4 cm wide which moves horizontally from one roll to another at a speed of 1 cm/hr. A 10-cm section of the tape is exposed to the atmosphere so that rain and dew may be deposited and the tape may dry out. The paper disappearing in the instrument housing is contacted by a copying pencil which is under the lid of the housing. The pencil records a thin line on dry paper but a broader and darker line as the paper becomes moist from dew or rain.

Evaluation: It is reported that there is difficulty in finding a source of paper of consistent quality and that with continuing heavy rainfall the copying pencils are too quickly used up so that the end of the wetness period is often not recorded.

SUMMARY

A review of methods and techniques for measuring dew (dewfall and distillation) reveals that theoretical approaches, using either vapor flux or energy balance, give estimates of dew to ± 30 to 100 per cent of measured values.[3, 14–16] Greater refinement in instrumentation and a better understanding of meteorological factors involved will be required for a precise computation of dew deposits.

The proportion of dew deposited as dewfall and as distillate is dependent upon a complex of meteorological factors. Dewfall is frequently only a minor component of the total dew condensing at night. Under the most favorable conditions for dew formation, in the mid-latitudes, there is an upper limit of the order of 0.1 mm/hour. Actual deposition rates generally fall far below this value.

Total dew measured on artificial surfaces is roughly equal to that on a natural surface. A variety of methods, in addition to the turbulent transfer and energy balance approaches, are in use for dew quantity and dew duration measurements. Weighing lysimeters, weighing dew gauges and Duvdevani blocks provide a gross measure of dew quantity. Duration measurements (leaf wetness) are dependent upon a response to moisture deposits by (1) a change in weight, (2) a change in element length, (3) change in electrical resistance or (4) by a change in surface characteristics.

References

1. Aitkins, J., "On Dew," *Trans. Roy. Soc. Edinburgh*, **33**, No. 1, 9–64 (1885–86).
2. Angus, D. E., "Agricultural Water Use," *Advan. Agron.*, **11**, 19–35 (1959).
3. Deacon, E. L., Priestley, C. H. B., and Swinbank, W. C., "Evaporation and the Water Balance," Arid Zone Research, Climatology UNESCO, pp. 22–24, 1958.
4. Duvdevani, S., "Les Effets de la Rosée sur la Croissance des Plantes" (Effects of Dew on Plant Growth), *Meteorologie*, Ser. 4, 468–469 (1954).
5. Duvdevani, S., "Dew Observations and Their Significance—New Methods in Dew Estimation," Proceedings of the U.N. Scientific Conference on the Conservation and Utilization of Resources, pp. 45–47, Lake Success, N.Y., 1951. (Cited from Rigby, M., ed., "Meteorological Abstracts and Bibliography," Vol. 5, Boston, AMS, 1954.)
6. Ekern, P. C., "Dew Measurements at PRI Field Station (WAHIAWA)," *PRI News*, **6** (1958).
7. Ekern, P. C., Personal correspondence, 1963.
8. Fowells, S. A., and Kirk, B. M., "Availability of Soil Moisture to Ponderosa Pine," *J. Forestry*, **43**, 601–604 (1945).
9. Fransilla, M., *Mitt. Met. Z. Helsinki*, No. 20 (1936).
10. Frost, R., *Prof. Notes, Met. Office*, No. 95 (1948).
11. Harrold, L. I., and Dreibelbis, F. R., "Agricultural Hydrology as Evaluated by Monolith Lysimeters," *U.S. Dept. Agr. Tech. Bull.*, **1050** (1951).
12. Hungerford, Kenneth E., "The Ecology and Management of the Idaho Ruffed Grouse (Bonasa umbellus phaia)," Doctoral dissertation, University of Michigan, 1951.
13. Jennings, E. G., and Monteith, J. L., *Quart. J. Roy. Meteorol. Soc.*, **80**, 222 (1954).
14. Monteith, J. L., "Dew," *Q.J.R.M.S.*, **83**, No. 357, 322–341 (1957).
15. Monteith, J. L., *Neth. J. Agr. Sci.*, **4**, 34 (1956); Australia-UNESCO Symposium on Arid Zone Climatology, Canberra, 1956 Proceedings, 1957.
16. Mukammal, E. I., King, K. M., and Cork, H. F., "Dew Amounts and Measurements," 5th National Conference on Agricultural Meteorology, Lakeland, Florida. April 4–5, 1963 (unpublished).
17. Newton, O. H., Personal correspondence, 1963.
18. Pasquill, F., *Quart. J. Roy. Meteorol. Soc.*, **76**, 287 (1950).
19. Potvin, A., "A Simple Method of Dew Measurement," *Forestry Chronicle*, **25**, 52–53 (1949).
20. Pruitt, W. O., and Angus, D. E., "The Davis Weighing Lysimeter—An Introduction to Physical Microclimatology," University of California Syllabus No. 397, Appendix F., p. 129, 1959.
21. Rider, N. E., and Robinson, G. D., "A Study of the Transfer of Heat and Water Vapour above a Surface of Short Grass," *Q.J.R.M.S.*, **77**, No. 333, 375–401 (1951).
22. Rider, N. E., *Phil. Trans. Roy. Soc.*, **246**, 481 (1954).
23. Scott, D., "An Instrument Measuring Dew Deposition," *Ecology*, **43**, 342–343 (1962).
24. Shaw, R. H., "Comparison of Dew Duration on Duvdevani Dew Gauges and Several Crop-covers," Iowa State College, Department of Agronomy, Contract AF 19 (604)-589, 1954.
25. Slatyer, R. O., "Studies of the Water Relations of Crop Plants Grown Under Natural Rainfall in Northern Australia," *Australian J. Agr. Res.* **6**, 365–377 (1955).
26. Stone, E. C., "Dew as an Ecological Factor. I. A. Review of the literature II. The Effect of Artificial Dew on the Survival of Pinus Ponderosa and Associated Species," *Ecology*, **38**, 407–422 (1957).
27. Stone, E. C., Went, F. W., and Young, C. L., "Water Absorption from the Atmosphere by Plants Grown in Dry Soil," *Science*, **111**, 546–548 (1950).
28. Stone, E. C., Shachori, A. Y., and Stanley, R., "Water Absorbed by Needles of Ponderosa Pine Seedlings and Its Internal Redistribution," *Plant Physiol.*, **31**, 120–126 (1956).
29. Stone, E. C., and Shachori, A. Y., "Absorption of Artificial Dew; Ponderosa Pine Seedlings Demonstrate Ability to Reverse Usual Pro-

cedure of Plant Transpiration," *Calif. Agr.*, 8, 7–10 (1954).

30. Taylor, C. F., "A Device for Recording the Duration of Dew Deposit," *Plant Disease Reptr.*, **40**, 1025–1028 (1956).

31. Theis, T. and Calpouzos, L., "Seven-day Instrument for Recording Periods of Rainfall and Dew," *Phytopathology*, **47**, 746–7 (1957).

32. Thornthwaite, C. W., and Holzman, B., *U.S. Dept. Agr. Tech. Bull.*, **817** (1942).

33. Wallin, J. R., and Polhemus, D. N., "A Dew Recorder," *Science*, **119**, 294–295 (1954).

34. Wells, W. C., "Essay on Dew," 1815.

35. Went, F. W., "Fog, Mist, Dew and Other Sources of Water," *U.S. Dept. Agr. Yearbook*, **1955**, (water) 103–109.

65. Five-day Precipitation Patterns derived from Circulation and Moisture

William H. Klein

National Meteorological Center, U.S. Weather Bureau, Washington, D.C.

ABSTRACT

Five-day precipitation amounts observed during ten recent winters are assigned a numerical index according to the proportion of light, moderate, or heavy rain falling in a grid of 40 circles covering the United States. The relation between this precipitation index and preceding values of mean and daily circulation and moisture variables in North America and adjacent oceans is investigated by a stepwise method of multiple regression. Factors tested include height anomalies and changes at 700 mb, pressures at sea level, 700- to 1000-mb thicknesses, mixing ratios and relative humidities at 850 and 700 mb, and an index of present weather and cloud cover. Approximately 40 per cent of the variance of precipitation in the developmental sample can be explained by appropriate combination of these variables.

The synoptic climatology of precipitation is investigated by constructing correlation fields between the precipitation index in each circle and the anomaly of simultaneous 5-day mean sea level pressure at a grid of 70 points. These fields reveal the association between precipitation and such factors as wind direction, moisture source, curvature, local pressure, and position of the low center. Schematic models are then constructed showing preferred conditions for heavy and light precipitation in different parts of the nation.

INTRODUCTION

Each Sunday, Tuesday, and Thursday, the Extended Forecast Division of the United States Weather Bureau prepares a map showing the total amount of precipitation expected over the United States during the 5 days beginning the following evening[1]. These predictions are generally expressed in terms of three classes, heavy, moderate or light, which are defined from 36 years of climatological records so that each class normally occurs one-third of the time[2]. For example, at Washington, D.C. during the month of May, 5-day precipitation greater than .57 in. is considered heavy, less than .08 in. is light, and intermediate amounts are moderate. Of course the boundaries of the classes vary from place to place and month to month, and in arid regions no precipitation may be used in place of light or precipitation in place of heavy. An example of observed precipitation analyzed in terms of these classes for the 5 days from January 8 to 12, 1963, is shown in Fig. 1, which is based on daily reports from several hundred stations.

In a previous paper,[3] an objective method was developed for specifying 5-day precipitation from simultaneous values of 5-day mean 700-mb height. This method will be extended to the field of sea level pressure in the next section of the present paper. In the section on Prediction of Precipitation (p. 541) the relation

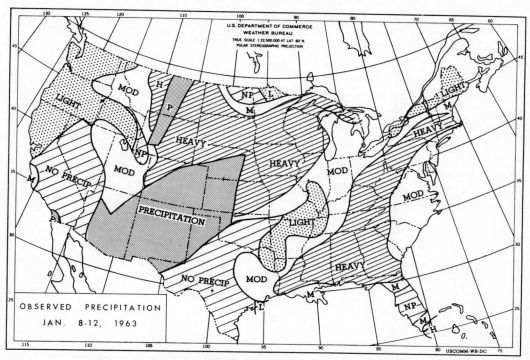

FIG. 1. Observed 5-day precipitation amounts for the period January 8–12, 1963, analyzed in terms of the 5 classes customarily used in extended forecasting: heavy (H), moderate (M), light (L), no precipitation (NP), and precipitation (P).

between 5-day precipitation and earlier, rather than simultaneous, values of various meteorological variables will be investigated in an effort to develop a more useful prediction scheme.

SPECIFICATION OF PRECIPITATION FROM SEA LEVEL PRESSURE

Since precipitation is discontinuous and localized in nature, a form of areal averaging was employed instead of single station reports, as illustrated in Fig. 2. The lines divide the United States into 40 climatologically similiar regions considered to be roughly homogenous on the basis of topography, Weather Bureau forecast districts, normal precipitation amounts, and drainage basins. For example, the vertical lines on either end represent the Appalachian and Cascade-Sierra Nevada mountain ranges, while the Continental Divide is delineated by the third line from the left. Near the center of each region are equal-area, non-overlapping circles,

approximately 230 miles in diameter. These circles consitute the basic units used in this study. Within each circle the observed 5-day precipitation class was tabulated from analyzed maps of the type shown in Fig. 1.

This was done with the aid of a numerical index illustrated in Fig. 3. Each case was placed in one of six categories which express the proportion of light, moderate, or heavy precipitation falling within each circle. In dry regions no precipitation was considered as light, and precipitation as heavy. The two extreme categories are 1 and 6, for which all portions of the circle must be analyzed as light or heavy, respectively. For categories 2 and 5, more than half, but not all, of the circle must be analyzed as light or heavy, regardless of the rest of the circle. The remaining two classes are both predominately moderate, with category 3 on the dry and category 4 on the wet side.

Figure 4 shows the grid of points at which sea level pressure was measured. A network of 70 points was used, at 10-degree intersections

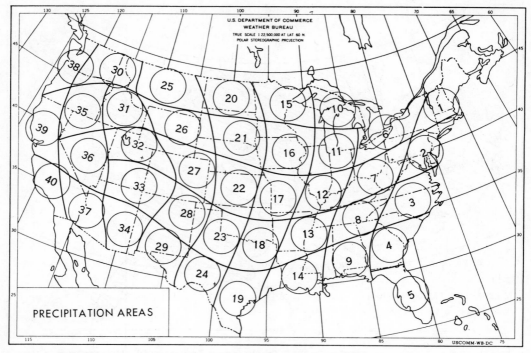

FIG. 2. Grid of 40 equal-area circles, each approximately 230 miles in diameter, at which the precipitation index was measured. Each circle is located near the center of climatologically similar areas delineated by the solid lines.

of latitude and longitude, extending from 30 to 70°N. and from 50 to 180°W. Forty maps were constructed giving the field of simple linear correlation coefficient between the precipitation index in each circle and the departure from normal of concurrent 5-day mean sea level pressure at each of these grid points. All data were taken for 140 five-day periods, one each week, during 10 winters from December 1949 to March 1959.

Of all 40 circles tested, the one where precipitation is apparently most sensitive to the simultaneous sea level circulation is in northern California, as illustrated by Fig. 5. Here the star locates the center of the circle, and the lines are isopleths of equal correlation between precipitation and pressure. The resulting correlation field indicates that winter precipitation in northern California is most closely related to sea level pressure about 100 miles off the coast of Oregon. The magnitude of the correlation is .73, and the sign is negative, thereby showing that low pressure off

Oregon is associated with heavy precipitation in northern California.

If we disregard the spatial variation of the

Definition of Precipitation Index

Category	Dominant class	Remaining class	Example
1	L	0	L
2	L	M or H	M / L
3	M	0 or mostly L	M / L
4	M	mostly H	H / M
5	H	M or L	M / H
6	H	0	H

FIG. 3. Definition of the precipitation index where symbols have the following meaning: H—heavy, M—moderate, L—light, 0—none.

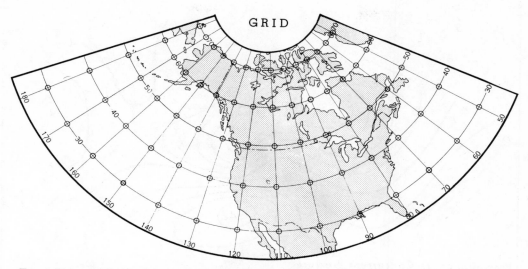

Fɪɢ. 4. Network of 70 grid points used to delineate the fields of sea level pressure, 700-mb height and height change, and 700- to 1000-mb thickness. Values were taken at even intersections of latitude and longitude, 10 degrees apart, marked by circles.

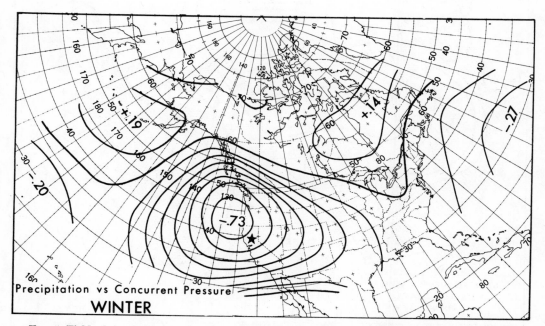

Fɪɢ. 5. Field of simple linear correlation coefficient between the precipitation index in circle No. 39 (located by star) and simultaneous 5-day mean sea level pressure anomaly at grid of points shown in Fig. 4 for 140 winter cases.

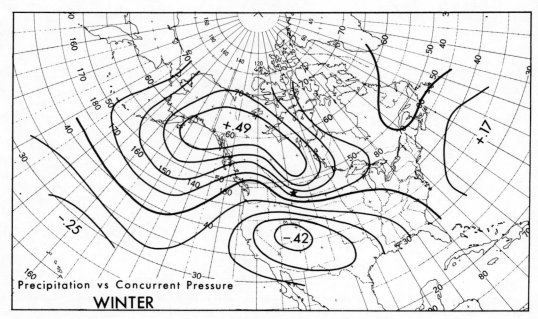

Fig. 6. Field of simple linear correlation coefficient between the precipitation index in circle No. 25 (located by star) and simultaneous 5-day mean sea level pressure anomaly at grid of points shown in Fig. 4 for 140 winter cases.

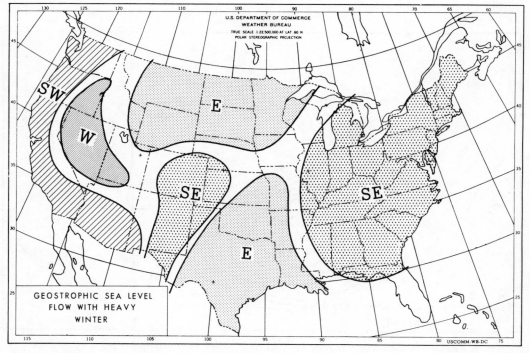

Fig. 7. Local component of geostrophic flow at sea level conducive to heavy precipitation in winter with symbols as follows: E—easterly, SE—southeasterly, SW—southwesterly, W—westerly.

standard deviation of sea level pressure and if we further assume that gradients of pressure on a normal chart are negligible* relative to gradients on 5-day mean charts, then the isopleths in this figure may be interpreted qualitatively as though they were isobars, representing streamlines of geostrophic flow.[4] This suggests that heavy precipitation falls in northern California when that area is in the southeast quadrant of a deep low. Likewise, other inferences may be drawn about the synoptic climatology of heavy winter rainfall in California such as:

(a) the direction of the gradient flow at sea level, from the southwest;

(b) the curvature of this flow, cyclonic;

(c) the origin of this flow and presumably of the moisture it carries, from the Pacific;

(d) the correlation between local pressure and precipitation, − .65;

---

* The reasonableness of this assumption may be verified by inspecting maps showing the field of normal sea level pressure during the winter months[13] and noting the very weak gradients which exist in the United States.

(e) the distance to the center of low pressure, about 400 miles.

Since we are working with linear correlation coefficients, exactly opposite conditions prevail for light precipitation, which is favored by high pressure and anticyclonic, northeasterly flow from the Continent.

A completely different type of synoptic climatology is illustrated by Fig. 6, which portrays the correlation field between 5-day precipitation in central Montana and the simultaneous sea level pressure pattern. Montana precipitation is poorly correlated with local pressure but quite sensitive to pressure in two other areas, one over northwest Canada and the other over the southern Great Basin. The sign and shape of the correlation isopleths suggest that heavy precipitation in Montana (usually in the form of snow) typically falls in a ridge of high pressure under anticyclonic, easterly, upslope flow about 700 miles north of a low center. Conversely, dry weather is frequently accompanied by cyclonic, westerly, downslope flow between a lee trough to the north and a Basin High to the south.

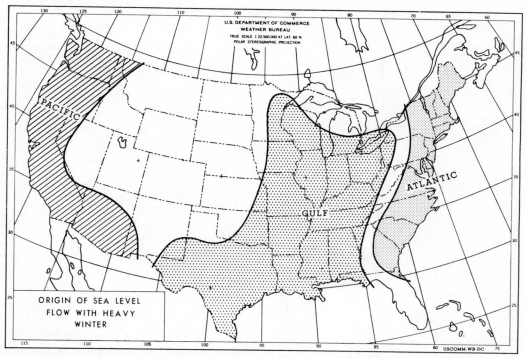

Fig. 8. The low level moisture source where the geostrophic flow at sea level favorable to heavy precipitation originates in winter. In unshaded areas, no single source of moisture predominates.

Similar reasoning to that illustrated in Figs. 5 and 6 has been applied to maps showing the correlation between the field of sea level pressure and the precipitation index in each of the other 38 circles, with results summarized in Figs. 7 through 13.

Figure 7 shows the local component of low level flow indicated by the correlation fields to be conducive to heavy precipitation in different parts of the country. Southwesterly winds are favorable not only in northern California, but also along the entire Pacific Coast. The preferred direction of flow is westerly or indeterminate in parts of the Great Basin. East of the Continental Divide, on the other hand, easterly components are universally favored, in agreement with earlier results of Kincer.[5] Here, further subdivision may be made between southeasterly winds east of the Mississippi and also in the southern Rockies, and easterly winds in both the Northern and Southern Plains.

Figure 8 gives the moisture source where the correlation fields suggest that the low level flow originates for heavy rain. This was obtained by following the correlation isopleth (assumed to represent the air trajectory) from the circle upstream to its first intersection with a large body of water. As shown by Stidd[4], primary sources are the Pacific for the West Coast, the Gulf of Mexico for most of the South and Mid-West, and the Atlantic for the East Coast. In the blank area on either side of the Rockies, the low level flow does not seem to originate in any well-defined source of moisture.

Figure 9 shows the local curvature of the sea level isobars conducive to heavy precipitation. As expected, it is cyclonic for most of the nation.[6] However, anticyclonic curvature favors heavy in the western Plains in a narrow belt extending from the Canadian to the Mexican border.

Figure 10 reveals similar information in the form of the correlation coefficient between the precipitation index in each circle and sea level pressure at that circle. In most of the country, heavy rains are accompanied by low pressure,

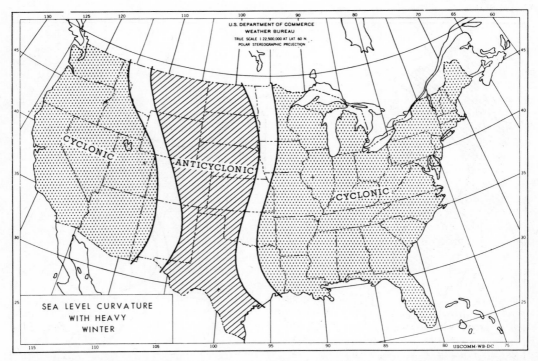

Fig. 9. Local isobar curvature conducive to heavy precipitation in winter. Heavy precipitation is characterized by anticyclonic flow at sea level in the Great Plains (hatched) but cyclonic curvature in the remainder of the country.

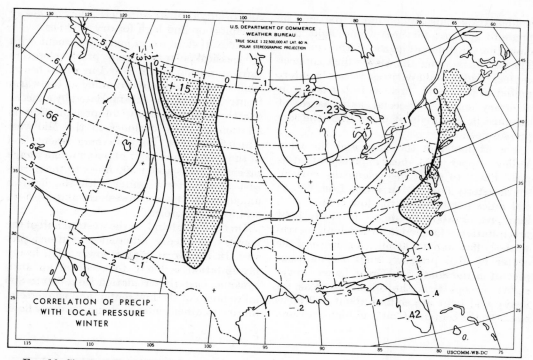

FIG. 10. Simple linear correlation coefficients between local values of the precipitation index in each circle and the simultaneous 5-day mean sea level pressure anomaly for 140 winter cases. Areas of positive correlation are shaded.

and dry weather by high pressure, as indicated by negative correlation coefficients which reach a maximum of .66 on the West Coast. On the other hand, the correlations are zero or slightly positive (shaded) in two narrow bands, one along the East Coast and the other on the eastern slope of the Rockies, thereby suggesting a slight tendency for heavy precipitation to go with high pressure and dry weather with low pressure.

In most cases precipitation can be directly related to a center of negative correlation in the vicinity of the reference circle. Figure 11 shows that the magnitude of this negative correlation varies from .18 near Lake Erie and in southern Texas to .73 in northern California. Here the precipitation circle is located at the tip of each arrow, and the point of highest correlation is shown by a solid dot. These dots lie north of the arrow tips in the Far West, thereby suggesting that westerly wind components favour heavy rains. In the remainder of the nation (except Florida), the dots are

south of the arrow tips, so that easterly components are preferred for heavy. The length of the arrows represents the distance to the center of correlation and is generally greater in the eastern than the western half of the country.

This information is given in greater detail in Fig. 12 which shows the distance in miles from the reference circle to the center of negative correlation. The maximum distance, over 800 miles, is found in the Middle Atlantic States, with a secondary maximum, over 700 miles, in the Great Plains. The minimum distance, under 200 miles, is found along the Gulf Coast and over the Great Basin with secondary minimum over the Upper Lakes.

The material presented in Figs. 7 through 12 is summarized in a qualitative sense in Fig. 13 in the form of four schematic models for winter precipitation. (Similar models for the 700-mb level have been presented earlier.[3]) The top of the Figure is north, the curves represent isobars at sea level, and the small shaded trapezoids are optimum portions of pressure systems for heavy and light precipitation in different parts of the country. The numbers along the axes which connect centers of high and low pressure can be interpreted in two ways: first, as isobar labels in arbitrary units; and second, as measures of distance in hundreds of miles from the low pressure centers.

For example, in the East and the Ohio Valley (upper left), heavy precipitation is most likely to occur in cyclonically curved, southeasterly flow at low levels from 600 to 800 miles northeast of the low center, with local pressure about average. Conversely, light precipitation is favored in anticyclonic, northwesterly flow about 700 miles northeast of the center of high pressure. Similar conditions prevail in the South and Great Lakes (upper right), except that the optimum areas for heavy and light are shifted about 400 miles closer to the centers of low and high pressure.

As a result, local pressure here is low for heavy precipitation and high for dry weather.

These models are in good agreement with the classical polar front concepts developed in Norway during World War I in which heavy rain is produced by overrunning at the warm front.[7] They are also substantiated by a recent Weather Bureau study[8] of precipitation in relation to daily cyclones in the Mid-west which found that "For the average orientation of the storm, the center of maximum average precipitation is about 300 miles to the northeast of the storm center with the lightest amounts in the southwestern and western sectors of the storm."

On the other hand, in the western half of the country markedly different conditions prevail. In the Great Plains (lower left), heavy precipitation is likely to occur in an anticyclonic, easterly circulation from 600 to 800 miles north of the low center, and conversely, for dry weather under cyclonic, westerly flow.

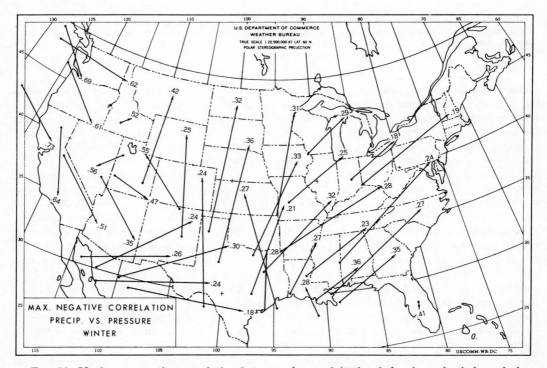

FIG. 11. Maximum negative correlation between the precipitation index in each circle and the simultaneous 5-day mean sea level pressure anomaly for 140 winter cases. The point of highest correlation is shown as a dot, the center of the reference circle is located at the tip of the arrow, and the value of the correlation coefficient is written next to each circle.

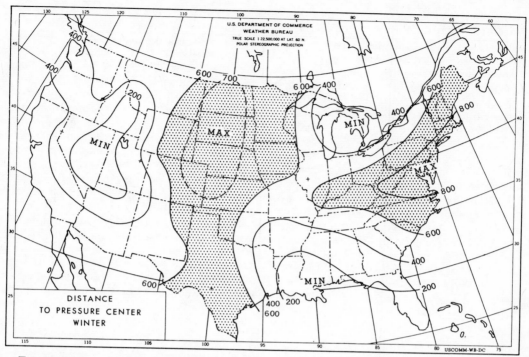

Fig. 12. Distance in miles to the center of maximum negative correlation between the precipitation index in each circle and the simultaneous 5-day mean sea level pressure anomaly for 140 winter cases. Centers of highest and lowest value are labelled MAX and MIN. Values greater than 600 miles are shaded.

Still another situation is found in the Far West (lower right). Here the optimum condition for heavy precipitation is low pressure with cyclonic, southwesterly circulation about 300 miles southeast of a storm center, and conversely for light rain under anticyclonic, northeasterly flow.

PREDICTION OF PRECIPITATION

We now turn to a more quantitative phase of this study. In order to develop prediction equations, which might be applied to numerical or conventional short-range forecasts, a stepwise method of linear multiple regression called screening was applied on the electronic computer[9]. This program selects (1) the predictor giving the simple correlation of greatest absolute magnitude with precipitation, (2) the predictor giving the highest partial correlation with precipitation after removal of the effect of the first predictor picked, (3) the predictor giving the highest partial correlation after

removal of the effect of the first two predictors selected, etc. After each selection, multiple correlation and regression coefficients are calculated.

The screening program was applied to the same 140 winter cases used previously to investigate the relation between the precipitation index in each circle and preceding values of various measures of circulation and moisture with which precipitation might be correlated. Figure 14 summarizes the results obtained from some of these factors measured on the day before the 5-day period begins (which is also the day after the 5-day forecast is prepared). The vertical axis gives the per cent of variance of the 5-day precipitation index explained by the number of predictors taken along the horizontal axis. The results are averaged over all 40 circles and are shown separately for six different variables. Sea level pressure anomaly, 700-mb height anomaly, and 700-mb height changes were measured at the grid of 70 points shown in Fig. 4; the

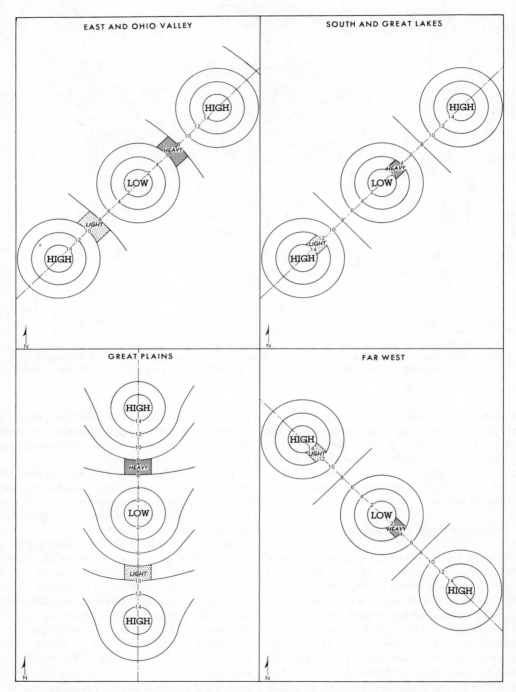

Fig. 13. Optimum regions for heavy and light precipitation in winter in different parts of the United States relative to schematic isobars at sea level. The numbers along the axes which connect centers of high and low pressure give both isobar labels in arbitrary units and distance in hundreds of miles from the low pressure centers.

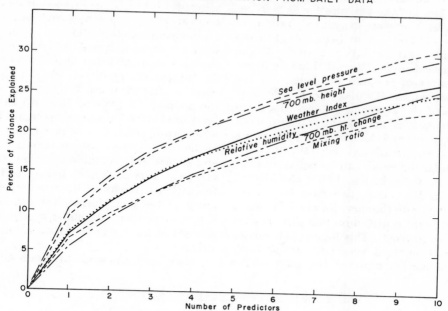

PREDICTION OF PRECIPITATION FROM DAILY DATA

Fig. 14. Per cent of the variance of the precipitation index explained by the number of daily predictors taken along the abscissa. The results are averaged over all 40 reference circles and are shown separately for the following six variables measured on the day before the 5-day period begins: sea level pressure anomaly; 700-mb height anomaly; present weather index; mean of 850- and 700-mb relative humidity; 24-hour, 700-mb height change; and mean of 850- and 700-mb mixing ratio anomaly.

present weather index was evaluated from cloud cover and instantaneous rainfall at each of the basic 40 reference circles (Fig. 2) by means of a classification scheme given in Fig. 15; the relative humidity and mixing ratio were computed from radiosonde observations at the 850- and 700-mb levels at a network of 39 upper air stations in the United States (Fig. 16). In Fig. 14, the mean of the two levels is presented in terms of departure from normal[10] for mixing ratio and actual percentages for relative humidity. The graph shows that the most effective predictors of 5-day precipitation are sea level pressure and 700-mb height, the least effective are 700-mb height change and mean mixing ratio anomaly, and intermediate values are given by the weather index and relative humidity. Similar results were found in earlier studies of daily precipitation in which better forecasts were obtained from the circulation pattern than from either 850-mb dew-point depression[14] or a code depicting several weather elements.[15]

In view of this finding, a further study was made of the relation between 5-day precipitation and daily departures from normal of both sea level pressure and 700-mb height (Fig. 17). The results are given for pressure (below) or height (above) on the middle day of the 5-day period (M−0), one day before the middle day (M−1), two days before (M−2), three days before (M−3) (used for Fig. 14), four days before (M−4) (the day 5-day forecasts are made), and five days before (M−5). The curves show that there is no appreciable lag between precipitation and either pressure or height, since in each case the explained variance is a maximum on the middle day (M−0) and then steadily decreases with increasing lag to a minimum on M−5 day. This behavior differs from that of surface temperature, which was found in an earlier study to be just as closely related to mean 700-mb height 2 days earlier as concurrently.[11]

On the whole there is little to choose between pressure and height as a predictor of precipitation. The 700-mb height explains slightly more of the variance for days 0 and −1, sea level pressure explains slightly more for days −4 and −5, and the two elements are about equal for days −2 and −3. The upper dashed curves labelled $\overline{M}$ are for 5-day mean values of pressure and height for the period of which M−0 is the middle day. Because of the averaging process, the mean for both pressure and height explains about 5 per cent more of the precipitation variance than does the middle day only (M−0).[4]

A similar difference can be noted by comparing the curve in Fig. 17 for the 700-mb height on M−2 day, two days before the middle day, with the curve for the 5-day mean 700-mb height centered on that day, plotted in Fig. 18 (dashed). This Figure summarizes the results obtained using measures of 5-day mean circulation centered two days earlier

than the precipitation itself. This period was selected because it gave good results in a previous study of temperature[11] and is used routinely in extended forecast operations[12]. Figure 18 shows that mean sea level pressure is slightly less effective than mean 700-mb height for the first two predictors but slightly more effective after the third. The third curve is for the anomaly of 700- to 1000-mb thickness (measured at the 70 basic grid points of Fig. 4), which is proportional to the mean temperature of the layer between approximately sea level and 10,000 ft. It is uniformly lower than the other two curves, thereby indicating that on the average, thickness does not explain as much of the precipitation variance as does height or pressure. A similar conclusion was reached in an earlier study of simultaneous values.[3]

An attempt was made to obtain improved

DEFINITION OF PRESENT WEATHER INDEX

INDEX	MEANING	EXAMPLE
1	100% of circle clear (0/10 to 3/10 sky cover)	
2	51 – 99% of circle clear	
3	More than 1/2 of circle partly cloudy (4/10 to 6/10 sky cover)	
4	More than 1/2 of circle cloudy (7/10 to 10/10 sky cover)	
5	Less than 1/8 of circle with precipitation	
6	1/8 to 1/4 of circle with precipitation	
7	1/4 to 1/2 of circle with precipitation	
8	More than 1/2 of circle with precipitation	

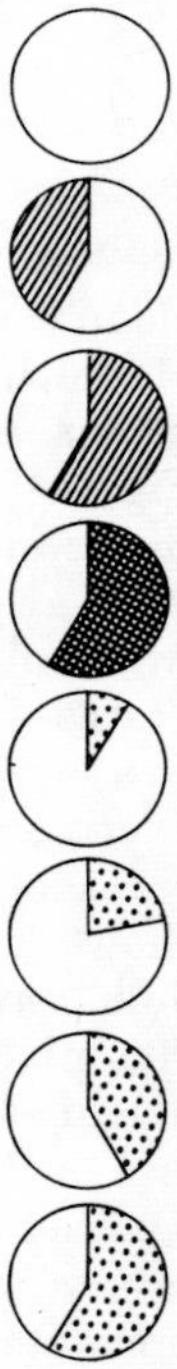

FIG. 15. Definition of the present weather index where hatching stands for partly cloudy skies (defined as four-tenths to six-tenths sky coverage), dark shading means cloudy (seven-tenths to overcast), and stippling represents precipitation falling at observation.

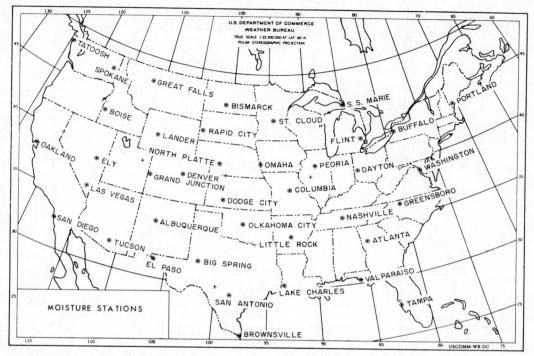

FIG. 16. Location of stations whose radiosonde observations were used to compute the relative humidity and mixing ratio variables plotted in Fig. 14.

results by combination of parameters (Fig. 19). The lower dashed curve gives precipitation as a function of the same 5-day mean 700-mb heights shown in Fig. 18, centered 2 days earlier than the period of the precipitation. The middle curve is for these heights in conjunction with the present weather index defined earlier (Fig. 15). The upper curve is for these heights and, in addition, the 5-day mean sea level pressures for the same period. This curve explains more of the variance of 5-day precipitation than any other variables tested so far in this study. It was therefore used to derive prediction equations by the screening procedure.

A typical equation is illustrated in Fig. 20, for the precipitation index in circle number 36

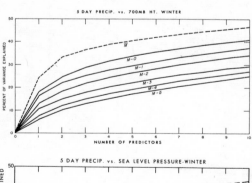

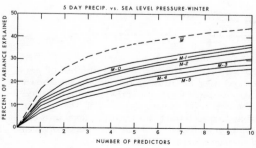

FIG. 17. Per cent of the variance of the precipitation index explained by the number of predictors taken along the abscissa. The results are averaged over all 40 circles and are shown separately for anomalies of sea level pressure (below) and 700-mb height (above). The results are given for pressure or height on the middle day of the 5-day precipitation period (M-0), one day before the middle day (M-1), two days before (M-2), three days before (M-3), four days before (M-4), and 5 days before (M-5). The upper dashed curves labelled $\bar{M}$ are for 5-day mean values of pressure or height for the period of which M-0 is the middle day.

PREDICTION OF PRECIPITATION FROM MEAN DATA

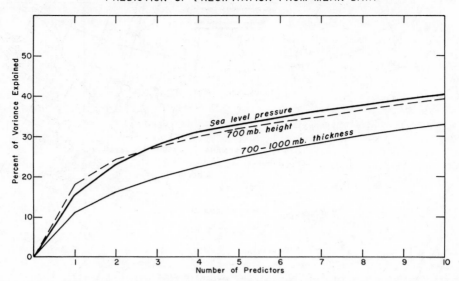

Fig. 18. Per cent of the variance of the precipitation index explained by the number of mean predictors taken along the abscissa. The results are averaged over all 40 reference circles and are shown separately for 5-day mean anomalies of sea level pressure, 700-mb height, and 700- to 1000-mb thickness, all taken for a period two days earlier than the 5-day precipitation.

PREDICTION OF PRECIPITATION (WINTER)

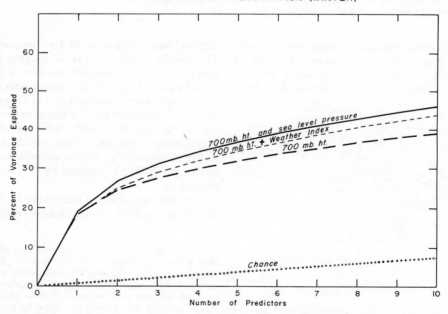

Fig. 19. Per cent of the variance of the precipitation index explained by the number of predictors taken along the abscissa. The results (averaged over all 40 reference circles) are shown separately for the 5-day mean 700-mb height anomaly centered two days earlier than the period of the precipitation taken (a) by itself—lower dashed curve; (b) in conjunction with the present weather index—middle dashed curve; and (c) in conjunction with the 5-day mean sea level pressure anomaly for the same period as the height—upper solid curve. The dotted line at the bottom gives the values expected by chance if the variables had been selected at random.

in Nevada. The most important single predictor of precipitation in this circle is mean sea level pressure 2 days earlier at the intersection of 40°N and 120°W, and the correlation between the two variables is − .58. The predictor contributing the most additional information is pressure at 30°N and 110°W. Combination of this pressure with the first one selected yields a multiple correlation of .60.

Combination of these two pressures with any additional predictor produces best results when the mean 700-mb height 2 days earlier at 30°N, 110°W is used, raising the multiple correlation to .64. This correlation can be raised to .67 by adding the height at 50°N, 120°W, but no other predictor is able to increase the explained variance by more than 2 per cent.

The screening process was therefore stopped at this point with the final prediction equation written at the top of Figure 20. The negative sign of the regression coefficient before the first predictor reflects the negative correlation between precipitation and local sea level

pressure demonstrated earlier on a concurrent basis (Fig. 10). This negative sign, taken in conjunction with the positive sign of the second regression coefficient, indicates that southwesterly flow, produced by low pressure in northern California and high pressure over northern Mexico, favors heavy rain in southern Nevada, and conversely for dry weather under northeasterly flow. The negative sign of the regression coefficient before the third predictor and the positive sign before the fourth suggest that heavy precipitation in Nevada is favored by a blocking[1] type of circulation aloft, in which a trough at low latitudes is surmounted by a ridge at high latitudes. The opposite signs before the second and third predictors imply that wet weather in Nevada is associated with abnormally cold air in northern Mexico 2 days earlier, produced by low thickness at 30°N, 110°W between high pressure at sea level and low heights at 700 mb.

Similar multiple regression equations were derived separately for each of the 40 circles. On the average, 39 per cent of the variance of

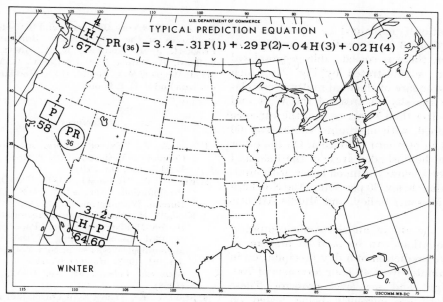

TYPICAL PREDICTION EQUATION

$$PR_{(36)} = 3.4 - .31\,P(1) + .29\,P(2) - .04\,H(3) + .02\,H(4)$$

Fɪɢ. 20. Multiple regression equation used in predicting the precipitation index (PR) in circle No. 36 (located by open circle) during the winter season as a function of the 5-day mean anomaly, two days earlier, of both sea level pressure (*P* in mb) and 700-mb height (*H* in tens of ft) at indicated points. The location of the predictor is given by the open brackets; the order of selection, by the number above the bracket; and the multiple correlation coefficient after inclusion of the given predictor, by the decimal below the bracket.

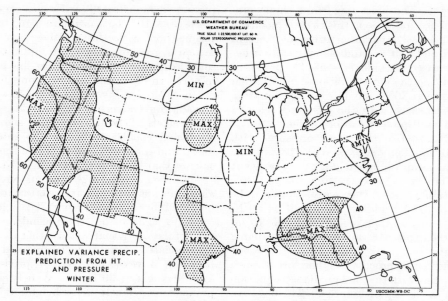

FIG. 21. Per cent of variance of the precipitation index explained by prediction equations of the type shown in Fig. 20. Analysis is based upon values at 40 circles on dependent sample of 140 winter cases from December 1949 to March 1959. Centers of highest and lowest value are labelled MAX and MIN. Values greater than 40 per cent are shaded.

precipitation is explained by equations containing from 3 to 8 predictors (mean 5.5). However, there is considerable geographical variation, as illustrated by Fig. 21, which gives the square of the final multiple correlation. In the shaded areas of the West and South better than 40 per cent of the variance is explained, with maximum values over 60 per cent in northern California. On the other hand, in the unshaded areas of the East and North the accuracy is much lower, with minimum values below 30 per cent in the Northern Plains, Missouri Valley, and Middle Atlantic States.

With the aid of an electronic computer, these equations can be used to prepare an objective prediction of 5-day precipitation in a few minutes from 48-hour forecasts of 700-mb height and sea level pressure. These predictions are currently being tested on independent data and results will be presented some time in the future.

Acknowledgment. The author is indebted for assistance received during the course of this investigation to Professors Jerome Spar and Willard Pierson of New York University and to the following employees of the U.S. Weather Bureau: C. W. Crockett, J. F. Andrews, R. A. Green, R. H. Gelhard, B. Ratner, T. Carpenter, C. R. McGuire, M. M. Wagner, M. C. Gould, H. M. Goddard, D. L. Jackson and S. E. Edmonds.

References

1. Namias, J., "Extended Forecasting by Mean Circulation Methods," U.S. Weather Bureau, Washington, D.C., 1947.
2. Brier, G. W., "Revised Limits for Five-Day Total Precipitation Forecasts." U.S. Weather Bureau, Washington, D.C., 1946.
3. Klein, W. H., "Specification of Precipitation from the 700-Millibar Circulation," Paper presented at 43rd Annual Meeting of the American Meteorological Society in New York, N.Y., on Jan. 21, 1963. *Monthly Weather Rev., Wexler Memorial Volume*, **91**, No. 10–12, 527–536 (1963).
4. Stidd, C. K., "The Use of Correlation Fields in Relating Precipitation to Circulation," *J. Meteorol.*, **11**, No. 3, 202–213 (1954).
5. Kincer, J. B., "Some Pressure-Precipitation Trend Relations," *Monthly Weather Rev.*, **69**, No. 8, pp. 232–235 (1941).
6. Smith, K. E., "Five-Day Precipitation Patterns in the United States in Relation to Surface and

Upper Air Mean Charts," Unpublished Masters' Thesis, Massachusetts Institute of Technology, Cambridge, Mass., 1942.

7. Bjerknes, J., and Solberg, H., "Meteorological Conditions for the Formation of Rain," *Geofy. Publikasjoner*, **2**, No. 3, (1921).

8. U.S. Weather Bureau, Office of Forecast Development, Staff Members, "Climatological Snowfall Patterns and the Synoptic Climatology of Precipitation of Winter Storms in the Central United States," Technical Note No. 10, Heavy Snow Project—Part I, Washington, D.C., 1962; also published in: Jorgensen, D. L.: "A Computer Derived Synoptic Climatology of Precipitation from Winter Storms," *J. Appl. Meteorol.*, **2**, 226–234 (1963).

9. Miller, R. G., "The Screening Procedure," Part II of "Studies in Statistical Weather Prediction," pp. 86–136, final report, contract No. AF19 (604)1590, Travelers Weather Research Center, Hartford, Conn., 1958.

10. Ratner, B., "Upper-Air Climatology of the United States, Part I—Averages for Isobaric Surfaces—Height, Temperature, Humidity, and Density," U.S. Weather Bureau Technical Paper No. 32, 1957.

11. Klein, W. H., Lewis, B. M., and Enger, I., "Objective Prediction of Five-Day Mean Temperatures During Winter," *J. Meteorol.*, **16**, No. 6, 672–682 (1959).

12. Namias, J., *et al.*, "Application of Numerical Methods to Extended Forecasting Practices in the U.S. Weather Bureau," *Monthly Weather Rev.*, **86**, No. 12, 467–476 (1958).

13. U.S. Weather Bureau, "Normal Weather Charts for the Northern Hemisphere," U.S. Dept. Comm. Tech. Paper, **21** (October, 1952).

14. Sellers, W. D., "Prediction of Daily Precipitation by Using Statistical Methods," in "Studies in Synoptic Climatology," final report of Synoptic Climatology Project, Department of Meteorology, M.I.T., Cambridge, Mass. pp. 102–114, March 1956.

15. Glahn, H. R., "An Experiment in Forecasting Rainfall Probabilities by Objective Methods," *Monthly Weather Rev.*, **90**, No. 2, 59–67 (1962).

RADIO PROPAGATION AND ATMOSPHERIC REFRACTION

66. Radio Refractometry and Its Potential for Humidity Studies

R. E. McGavin and M. J. Vetter

National Bureau of Standards, Boulder, Colorado

ABSTRACT

Radio refractometers have been in use for the past decade. Their primary use has been in the investigation of the refractive index structure as applied to radio-wave propagation. There has been considerable improvement in these devices in recent years and the present status of radio refractometry indicates broader application of these techniques. Since the radio refractive index is a function of pressure, temperature and humidity, these devices can be converted to hygrometers when suitable compensation for temperature and pressure is applied. This technique has been used successfully by a number of investigators. The results of some of these investigations are reviewed.

INTRODUCTION

The refractive index is defined as the ratio of the velocity of a wave through free space to its velocity through a particular medium. At optical frequencies the refractive index is essentially independent of water vapor; at radio frequencies, however, water vapor plays a significant role. The radio refractive index (i.e., the refractive index at radio frequencies) has been studied extensively, especially in recent years, due primarily to its applicability to radio propagation phenomena[1, 8, 11] The radio refractive index can be computed as a function of pressure, temperature and humidity. However, the lack of precision in the measurement of water vapor coupled with the necessary conversion of parameters led inves-

tigators to seek a direct method of measuring the radio refractive index. Since the refractive index and the dielectric constant are related, these investigators utilized the progress which had been made in the laboratory measurement of the dielectric constant of gases utilizing microwave refractometers. Early in the last decade, two instruments were developed independently and appeared almost simultaneously. In terms of the refractive index, these instruments are based on the relationship between the resonant frequency of a microwave cavity and the refractive index of the contents of the cavity.

$$\frac{\Delta f}{f} = -\frac{\Delta n}{n} \approx -\Delta n \tag{1}$$

where

f = original resonant frequency,
n = the refractive index corresponding to the resonant frequency f.

REFRACTOMETERS

Two microwave refractometers appeared in 1950. The Crain[5] refractometer, presented as an instrument to measure the refractive index of the air, was a refinement of a device proposed by the same author in 1948[4] to measure the dielectric constant of gases. The Crain refractometer heterodynes the frequencies of two microwave oscillators each of which is stabilized by a microwave cavity after the manner of Pound.[9] One cavity is sealed, hence the frequency of its oscillator is constant; the other cavity is open to the air, and the resonant

553

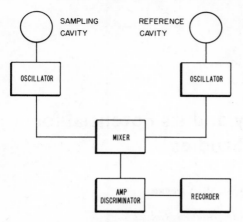

FIG. 1. The Crain refractometer.

of the klystron and, hence, is a function of the characteristics of the particular klystron in use. This problem was circumvented by Sargent[10], who modified the Birnbaum refractometer to operate as a microwave hygrometer. A servo system is used to tune the sampling cavity to the frequency of the reference cavity. The servo positions a tuning probe in the sampling cavity; the depth of penetration of the probe is a measure of the refractive index of the contents of the sampling cavity.

The work of Sargent with the Birnbaum refractometer was extended by Vetter[13] and resulted in the Vetter Absolute Refractometer.

frequency of its oscillator varies with the refractive index of the air passing through the open cavity. The difference frequency between the two oscillators is the measure of the refractive index of the air sample. The Crain refractometer is illustrated in Fig. 1.

The second instrument developed by Birnbaum[2] was proposed for use in dielectric measurements of gases. The Birnbaum refractometer uses two similar cavities, one sealed and one open to the air, as passive elements. Both cavities are excited by a single klystron. The frequency of the klystron is linearly swept through the resonant frequencies of the two cavities. The time difference between resonances is the measure of the refractive index of the air passing through the sampling cavity. Figure 2 illustrates the basic technique of the Birnbaum refractometer.

The accuracy of this instrument is dependent upon the linearity of the frequency sweep

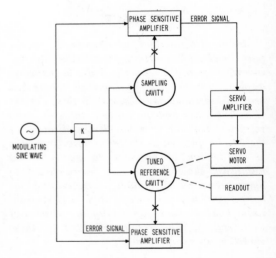

FIG. 3. The Vetter refractometer.

In this instrument, the klystron and the reference cavity are constrained to follow the resonant frequency of the sampling cavity (see Fig. 3). The Vetter refractometer has the capability of absolute calibration and, like Sargent's version of the Birnbaum refractometer, is virtually independent of electronic stability.

Lightweight refractometers having less accuracy than the aforementioned microwave refractometers, but superior to the radiosonde, have been developed for balloon-borne and drop-sonde use. Two examples of these lightweight refractometers can be cited. D. R. Hay[7] devised a refractometer at 10 Mc utilizing a capacitor of a Clapp oscillator as the sensing

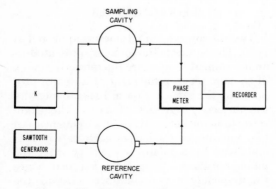

FIG. 2. The Birnbaum refractometer.

element, the air to be measured being the dielectric of the capacitor. Deam[6] developed a drop-sonde refractometer of the Pound type operating at 400 Mc.

THE RADIO REFRACTIVE INDEX AND HUMIDITY

The radio refractive index can be expressed:

$$N = (n - 1)10^6 = K_1 \frac{P}{T} + K_2 \frac{e}{T^2} \quad (2)$$

where

N = refractivity
n = radio refractive index
P = atmospheric pressure, mb
e = water vapor pressure, mb
T = temperature, °K

Smith and Weintraub[12] found that:

$$K_1 = 77.6 \ °K/mb$$
$$K_2 = 3.73 \times 10^5 \ (°K)^2/mb$$

It should be noted that one N unit is equal to 1 ppm in terms of the radio refractive index.

Assuming that the perfect gas laws apply, it can be shown that

$$N = K_1 \frac{P}{T} + K_3 \frac{\rho_w}{T} \quad (3)$$

or

$$\rho_w = K_4 (NT - K_1 P) \quad (4)$$

where ρ_w is the absolute humidity. In units of grams of water vapor per cubic meter,

$$\rho_w = 5.81 \times 10^{-4} NT - 4.51 \times 10^{-2} P \quad (5)$$

The water vapor pressure can be expressed in terms of the absolute humidity as

$$e = K_5 \ T\rho_w \quad (6)$$

when e is expressed in mb,

$$e = 4.615 \times 10^{-3} \ T\rho_w$$

The specific humidity, q, in grams of water vapor per kg of air is

$$q \approx 622 \frac{e}{P} \quad (7)$$

Then the humidity can be measured as a function of N, T and P, since these quantities are more amenable to observation than is the humidity.

It should be pointed out that these relationships are valid only in the absence of condensation, since no adjustment is made for the heat of fusion. The absence of condensation is also a requirement for proper operation of the refractometer since water droplets inside the cavity would have serious and indeterminate effects on the resonant frequency.

THE MICROWAVE REFRACTOMETER AS A HYGROMETER

The microwave refractometer is preferable to the lightweight refractometers from the viewpoint of accuracy. However, even here the ultimate limit of accuracy is determined by the characteristics of the cavities. The resonant frequencies of these cavities are functions of their linear dimensions, which are affected by the temperature. Present-day cavities are made of invar, having a temperature coefficient 1 ppm/°C. This is equivalent to 1 N unit/°C. Temperature compensation can reduce this coefficient to less than one-tenth of this; coefficients as low as 0.03 N/°C have been achieved. A temperature coefficient of 0.1 N/°C produces a change in the apparent refractive index which is equivalent to a humidity change of approximately 0.017 g/m³ under average sea level conditions. Hence, a change in temperature would appear as change in humidity even for constant humidity, due merely to changes in the cavity.

Equation (5) expresses the absolute humidity as a function of N, P and T. Two methods of measurement may be used:

(1) Precondition the air to constant temperature and pressure prior to its entry into the sampling cavity and measure the variations in N calibrated in terms of humidity.

(2) Measure the local temperature and pressure and apply corrections to the output of the refractometer.

Method (1) has been proposed by several experimenters. Sargent's microwave hygrometer was proposed as a secondary laboratory standard hygrometer. The air to be sampled is pumped through a duct to a heat exchanger where, by sufficient mixing, the sample comes to a uniform temperature and a reasonably stable pressure. Both cavities of the refractometer are contained in the same temperature

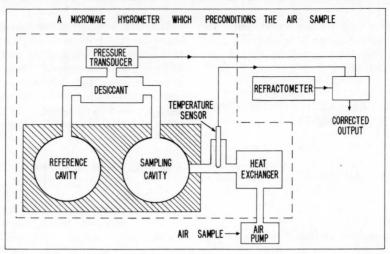

FIG. 4. A microwave hygrometer.

chamber. Second-order corrections can be applied to the output for small changes in pressure and temperature. An illustration of a representative system is shown in Fig. 4. One of the chief advantages of this technique is that the effect of the temperature coefficient of the cavities is reduced. With reliable temperature and pressure sensors, this system should approach an absolute hygrometer. This type of hygrometer would be ideal for single-point measurements of relatively long-term averages.

The alternate approach (2), that of correcting the output of the refractometer with measured values of the local temperature and pressure was used by Bunker[3] in an airborne application. A representative system is illustrated in Fig. 5. The system has the advantage of mechanical simplicity, better frequency response, and adaptability to gradient measurements. The degree of accuracy is limited by the thermal characteristics of the cavity. In the open atmosphere, the temperature can be expected to change at least over a limited range, which would be reflected as an apparent change in humidity.

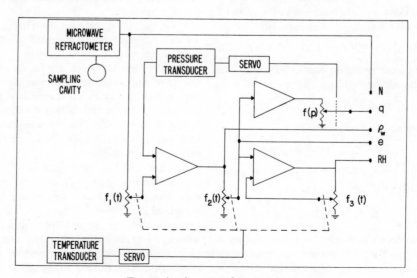

FIG. 5. A microwave hygrometer.

ANALYSIS OF THE ACCURACY OF A MICROWAVE HYGROMETER

From Eq: (5) the absolute humidity is expressed as a function of the refractivity, the temperature and the pressure.

$$\rho_w = f(N, T, P) \qquad (8)$$

Taking the total derivative:

$$d\rho_w = \frac{\delta\rho_w}{\delta N} dN + \frac{\delta\rho_w}{\delta T} dT + \frac{\delta\rho_w}{\delta p} dp \qquad (9)$$

Under average sea level conditions and assuming a relative humidity of 10 per cent ($N = 330$, $T = 288°$K, $P = 1013$ mb),

$$\Delta\rho_w = 0.167\Delta N + 0.185\Delta T - 0.045\Delta P \qquad (10)$$

which expresses the apparent change in the absolute humidity due to changes in the true value of N, T and P.

Figs. 6 to 9 illustrate the degree of accuracy to be expected in the measurement of the absolute humidity in terms of the accuracy of the refractometer and the accuracy in the measurement or control of temperature and pressure. The errors are assumed to be normally distributed and the curves exhibit the rms errors to be expected. Dotted lines are included to illustrate the maximum error, should the inaccuracies be additive. These curves

apply for average sea-level conditions, assuming a temperature of 288°K. To convert to another temperature, T, a factor of $288/T$ should be applied, where T is the absolute temperature. The maximum error will be experienced at sea level with accuracy improving when the elevation approaches the limit imposed by the refractometer. The limits imposed by the accuracy of the refractometer are:

Accuracy of Refractometer	Limit of Accuracy in the Measurement of $\rho_w(g/m^3)$
$\pm 2N$	± 0.334
$\pm 1N$	± 0.167
$\pm 0.5N$	± 0.084
$\pm 0.1N$	± 0.17

Then, if the refractometer accuracy is $\pm 1.0N$, from Fig. 7, it can be seen that an accuracy in ρ_w of ± 0.2 gm/m³ requires an accuracy in temperature and pressure found to the left of the curve labeled 0.2 gm/m³.

These curves can also be used as an approximate estimate of the errors in determining the vapor pressure and the specific humidity. For vapor pressure:

$$\Delta e = 0.036\Delta T + 1.33\Delta\rho_w \qquad (11)$$

$$\Delta e \approx 1.33\Delta\rho_w. \qquad (12)$$

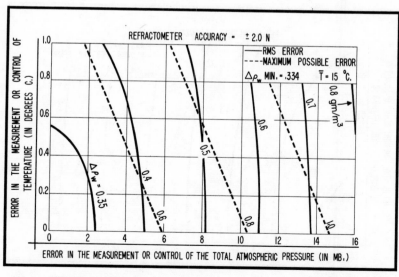

FIG. 6. The accuracy of the microwave hygrometer as a function of temperature and pressure control.

The temperature dependency can be ignored except in cases where extreme accuracy is desired. Where $\Delta\rho_w = \pm0.1$ g/m³, the maximum contribution of the temperature normally will be less than 3 per cent.

In terms of the specific humidity,

$$\Delta q = 0.022\Delta T - 0.006\Delta P + 0.818\Delta\rho_w \quad (14)$$

$$\Delta q \approx 0.818\Delta\rho_w \quad (15)$$

where q is measured in g/kg. Here also, the contribution of the temperature and pressure will normally be less than 3 per cent.

It should be noted that these error analyses assume average sea-level conditions. The constants in Eq. (11) are functions of altitude. Maximum values occur at sea level, and therefore, the expected absolute accuracy will improve with altitude approaching the limit im-

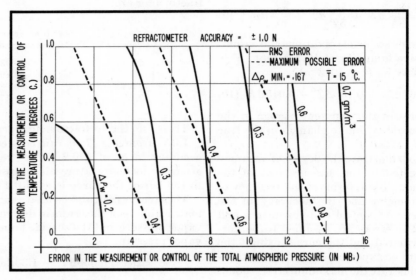

FIG. 7. The accuracy of the microwave hygrometer as a function of temperature and pressure control.

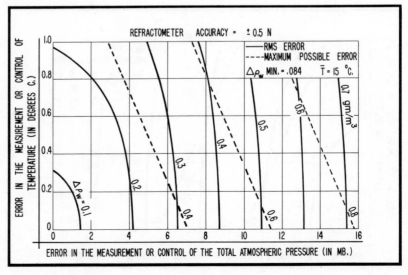

FIG. 8. The accuracy of the microwave hygrometer as a function of temperature and pressure control.

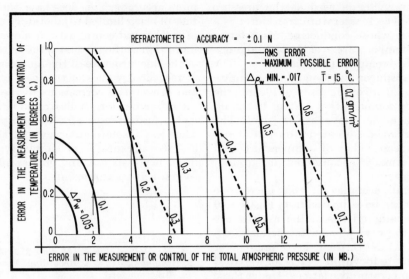

Fig. 9. The accuracy of the microwave hygrometer as a function of temperature and pressure control.

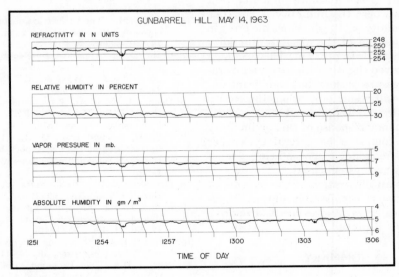

Fig. 10.

posed by the refractometer. It should be apparent also that the limit imposed by the refractometer will limit the altitude usefulness of the microwave hygrometer. Even if the refractometer has an accuracy of 0.1 N, this is equivalent to an rms error of approximately 0.02 g/m³.

APPLICATION

A preliminary model of a microwave hygrometer utilizing the method illustrated in Fig. 5 has been developed. The device has been used with the Vetter refractometer. A temperature compensated differential pressure potentiometer is used as the pressure transducer. The temperature transducer is a silicon diode whose conductivity is a linear function of temperature over the normal range of expected temperature variations. The pressure transducer was found to be accurate to within ± 2.0 mb over a range of 100 mb, the temperature compensation system to within $\pm 0.3°C$ over an ambient range of $\pm 15°C$. The hygrometer can be calibrated to operate at any arbitrary mean value of temperature and pressure normally encountered in ground-based operations.

The overall accuracy of this microwave hygrometer can be estimated from Figs. 6 to 9 when the characteristics of the cavities are known. If the cavity has a temperature coefficient of 0.1 $N/°C$, then the refractometer will be accurate to within ± 1 N for a $\pm 10°C$ range of temperature variations. Under these conditions (Fig. 4) the expected accuracy will be approximately ± 0.2 g/m³. Under average conditions at sea level, this represents an absolute accuracy of roughly 2 per cent in the measurement of the absolute humidity. For arid regions where the humidity is low (i.e., relative humidity < 10 per cent), the error in the determination of the absolute humidity may be as high as 15 per cent. This accuracy can be improved slightly with better temperature and pressure sensors, but significant improvement will result only when the cavity characteristics can be improved.

The frequency response of this preliminary model was found to be several cycles per second, the frequency response being a function of the servo systems used.

Fig. 10 is an illustration of the outputs of this hygrometer. Comparable output in refractivity, water vapor pressure and relative humidity are displayed.

SUMMARY

The radio refractometer can be used as a detector for water vapor. The limit of accuracy is determined by the accuracy in measuring or controlling the refractive index, the temperature and the pressure. If the air sample is preconditioned after the manner of Sargent, the microwave hygrometer approaches the optimum accuracy. This does have the disadvantage of being limited to laboratory use because of mechanical complexity; a more important limitation of the method is the smoothing out of the fine structure of the humidity. The use of measured values of the local temperature and pressure as corrections to the output of the refractometer, as illustrated in this paper, yields measurements of humidity of somewhat less absolute accuracy, but the method has the advantages of simplicity, adequate frequency response, and greater adaptability to gradient measurements.

References

1. Bean, B. R., "The Radio Refractive Index of Air," *Proc. I.R.E.*, **50**, 260–273 (March 1962).
2. Birnbaum, G., "A Recording Microwave Refractometer," *Rev. Sci. Instr.*, **21**, 169–176 (Feb. 1950).
3. Bunker, A. F., "An Airborne Microwave Refractometer Developed as an Hygrometer," Woods Hole Oceanographic Institution, Report No. 61–13, Tech. Report 45, ONR Contract Nono-1721(00)(NR-082-021), Woods Hole, Mass., 1961.
4. Crain, C. M., "The Dielectric Constant of Several Gases at a Wavelength of 3.2 cm," *Phys. Rev.*, **74**, 691–693 (Sept. 1948).
5. Crain, C. M., "Apparatus for Recording Fluctuations in the Refractive Index of the Atmosphere at 3.2 cm Wavelength," *Rev. Sci. Instr.*, **21**, 456–457 (May 1950).
6. Deam, A. P., "An Expendable Atmospheric Radio Refractometer," EERL Report 108, University of Texas, 1959.
7. Hay, D. R., and Bree, G. G., "Light Weight Refractometer, DRTE Report 1012, Defense Research Telecommunications Establishment, 1959.
8. Herbstreit, J. W., "Radio Refractometry," *Nat. Bur. Std. Tech. Note*, **66** (1960).
9. Pound, R. B., "Electronic Frequency Stabilization of Microwave Oscillators, *Rev. Sci. Instr.*, **17**, No. 11, 490–505 (1946).
10. Sargent, J. A., "Recording Microwave Hygrometer," *Rev. Sci. Instr.*, **30**, 348 (1959).
11. Saxton, J. A., "The Propagation of Metre Radio Waves Beyond the Normal Horizon," *Proc. Inst. Elec. Engrs.*, **98**, 360–378 (1951).
12. Smith, E. K., and Weintraub, S., "The Constants in the Equation for Atmospheric Refractive Index at Radio Frequencies," *Proc. I.R.E.*, **41**, 1035–1037.
13. Vetter, M. J., and Thompson, M. C. Jr., "An Absolute Microwave Refractometer," *Rev. Sci. Instr.*, **33** (1962).

67. The Use of the Radio Refractometer to Measure Water Vapor Turbulence

B. R. Bean and R. E. McGavin

National Bureau of Standards, Boulder, Colorado

ABSTRACT

The turbulent transport of the radio refractive index is studied theoretically. This study indicates that, under a wide range of conditions, the turbulent fluxes of the radio refractive index and of the absolute humidity are linearly related.

The initial results of an experiment specifically designed to check this conclusion are in agreement with the theoretical analysis.

INTRODUCTION

The radio refractometer shows considerable promise as a method of determining humidity content of the atmosphere. The previous paper (66) by McGavin and Vetter, has shown that, where response time is not important, one may determine the absolute humidity to within ± 0.02 g/m³ by preconditioning the air sample. The present paper will turn to the problem of utilizing the fast response of the radio refractometer to determine the turbulent flux of water vapor. To do this, the theory of turbulent transport is reviewed as it applies to the radio refractive index, emphasizing the conditions under which the refractive index and the absolute humidity fluxes are correlated. An experimental check of the expected relationship has been planned and initiated. The initial data from this experiment are in agreement with the above theoretical development.

THE FLUX OF THE RADIO REFRACTIVE INDEX AND ITS RELATION TO THE FLUX OF HUMIDITY

The radio refractive index of air can be expressed[1]:

$$N = (n - 1)10^6 = K_1 \frac{P}{T} + K_2 \frac{e}{T^2} \quad (1)$$

where

N = the refractivity
n = the radio refractive index
P = the atmospheric pressure
e = the water vapor pressure
T = the temperature.

Applying the perfect gas laws

$$N = K_3\rho + \frac{K_4}{T} \rho_w \quad (2)$$

where

ρ = the air density
ρ_w = the water vapor density.

If T does not vary more than several degrees over the interval of measurement

$$N \approx K_3\rho + K_5\rho_w \quad (3)$$

The refractivity can be considered as a passive parameter borne by the flow of air and a parameter α_N, the "specific refractivity" can be defined

$$\alpha_N = \frac{N}{\rho} = K_3 + K_5 \frac{\rho_w}{\rho} \qquad (4)$$

where α_N is in units of ρ^{-1}.

The vertical transport of a passive parameter across a horizontal unit cross section can be expressed[8].

$$\overline{A_z(\alpha_N)} = \overline{\rho \alpha_N w} = \overline{Nw} \qquad (5)$$

where $w =$ the vertical component of the wind, where $A(i) =$ the vertical transport of i, i.e., the mass of i transported through a unit cross section in unit time.

The instantaneous value of any variable is the sum of its mean value and its instantaneous departure from that mean value.

$$\rho = \bar{\rho} + \rho'$$
$$\alpha_N = \overline{\alpha_N} + \alpha'_N$$
$$w = \bar{w} + w'$$
$$N = \bar{N} + N'$$

then

$$Nw = [K_3(\bar{\rho} + \rho') + K_5(\bar{\rho}_w + \rho'_w)][\bar{w} + w'] \quad (6)$$

To determine $\overline{Nw}$, Reynold's averaging[3] can be applied if the process is a stationary

time series. This restriction limits the sample size to relatively short periods throughout the diurnal cycle avoiding those times of rapid transition such as near sunrise and sunset.[7] The minimum sample size reflecting all the essential characteristics of the flux has been determined by Swinbank.[9] At least at low levels, the average flux of momentum, water vapor and heat was shown to be essentially constant for samples in excess of 100 seconds. Thus a sample taken at midday or at midnight should satisfy both restrictions if the time is in excess of 100 seconds but less than one hour.

Applying Reynold's averaging, i.e.,

$$\bar{\bar{u}} = \bar{u}$$
$$\overline{\bar{u}v'} = 0$$
$$\overline{\bar{u}\bar{v}} = \bar{u}\bar{v}$$

Equation (6) becomes

$$\overline{Nw} = (K_3\bar{\rho} + K_5\bar{\rho}_w)\,\bar{w} + \overline{(K_3\rho' + K_5\rho'_w)\,w'} \quad (7)$$

also

$$\overline{Nw} = \overline{N}\overline{w} + \overline{N'w'}$$

then

$$\overline{N'w'} = K_3\overline{\rho'w'} + K_5\overline{\rho'_w w'} \qquad (8)$$

Fig. 1. Gunbarrel Hill field site.

K_3 and K_5 are constants whose values are (the air density and water vapor density are expressed in g/m³, and $T = 288°K$)

$$K_3 = .222$$
$$K_5 = 5.98$$

If the atmosphere can be considered incompressible, the first term on the right in Eq. (8) vanishes and

$$\overline{N'w'} \approx K_5\overline{\rho_w'w'} \quad (9)$$

which states that the eddy flux of the refractivity varies directly with the eddy flux of water vapor.

Under incompressible conditions N can be considered to be a linear function of ρ_w. From Eg. (2)

$$N = K_3\rho + \frac{K_4}{T}\rho_w \quad (10)$$

which for a limited temperature range can be expressed

$$\rho_w \approx AN + B \quad (11)$$

which indicates that not only is the flux of the refractivity well correlated with the flux of the absolute humidity, but that N and ρ_w themselves are linearly related.

The assumption of incompressibility can be evaluated by considering the total derivative of the refractivity as a function of ρ, ρ_w, and T [Eq. (2)]. Evaluating the partial derivatives for average sea level conditions ($T = 288°K$, $P = 1013$ mb, $RH = 60$ per cent)

$$\Delta N = 0.22\,\Delta\rho + 5.98\,\Delta\rho_w - 0.16\,\Delta T \quad (12)$$

where $\Delta\rho$ and $\Delta\rho_w$ are in units of grams per cubic meter, and ΔT is in units of °C. Comparison of ΔN determined directly with a radio refractometer and from its constitutent parameters by use of Eq. (12) indicates that $\Delta\rho$ may be set equal to zero without incurring an error of more than 3 per cent for the data used in this study. The published data from the Great Plains Turbulence Program yielded similar results.[5] Considering the small effect of compressibility, as well as the error of measurement of the various parameters, it appears reasonable at this point of the experiment to assume the atmosphere is incompressible, especially for the short sample times of 20 minutes.

Extending the classical formulation of turbulence theory to the radio refractivity

leads to the concept of exchange or turbulent transfer coefficients of N. This concept relates the average flux of a passive parameter to its vertical gradient

$$\overline{A_z(\alpha_N)} = -\bar{\rho}K_N\frac{\partial\overline{\alpha_N}}{\partial z} = -K_N\frac{\partial\overline{N}}{\partial z} \quad (13)$$

where K_N is the turbulent exchange coefficient. Then from Eq. (8)

$$K_N\frac{\partial\overline{N}}{\partial z} = K_3K_\rho\frac{\partial\bar{\rho}}{\partial z} + K_5K_{\rho_w}\frac{\partial\overline{\rho_w}}{\partial z} \quad (14)$$

where K_ρ and K_{ρ_w} are the turbulent exchange coefficients for dry air and water vapor respectively, which for incompressible atmosphere reduces to

$$K_N\frac{\partial\overline{N}}{\partial z} \approx K_5K_{\rho_w}\frac{\partial\overline{\rho_w}}{\partial z} \quad (15)$$

relating the exchange coefficient of refractivity to that of water vapor.

EXPERIMENTAL PROCEDURE

A 45-meter tower was erected northeast of Boulder, Colorado. The tower was instrumented at 15, 30 and 45 meters with electrical transducers to measure the temperature, humidity, pressure, wind and refractive index. (See Figs. 1 and 2). To insure the absence of

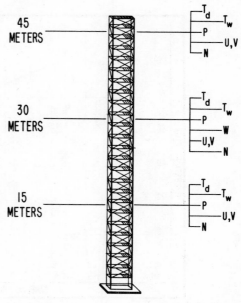

Fig. 2. Sensing levels, Gunbarrel Hill field site.

filtering due to the recording technique, all data were recorded on magnetic tape having a frequency response of better than 1 kc/sec. The temperature and humidity were measured using aspirated thermocouples with the reference temperature accurate to within ±0.05°C. The dry-bulb temperature sensing system exhibited a standard error relative to the true temperature of ±0.25°C. The time constant was 0.25 seconds. The wet bulb was supplied with precooled water and was compensated for radiation and conduction along the leads. The standard error in the wet-bulb temperature sensing system was slightly more than that of the dry-bulb system, and the time constant was approximately one second. During the time of observation, the mean value of the temperature sensing system was compared to the results of an Assman psychrometer having matched thermometers accurate to 0.1°C.

The pressure was measured at all levels using temperature compensated differential strain gauge transducers which were calibrated with a mercurial barometer. The standard error of the pressure transducers was within several tenths of a millibar; the time constant was sufficiently short to be ignored.

The horizontal wind was measured at all levels using cup anemometers and wind vanes.

The time constant was approximately 1.5 seconds for existing conditions. The accuracy of the wind velocity was ±½ m/sec, that of the wind direction approximately ±3 degrees. A bivane was mounted at the 30-meter level to measure the angle of attack of the wind from which was computed the vertical component.

The refractivity was measured using two types of refractometer. The turbulent aspects of the refractive index were measured at 30 meters using a Birnbaum refractometer having a time constant approaching 100 cps. The gradient of the refractive index was measured using the Vetter absolute refractometer at the 15- and 45-meter levels. The temperature of each cavity was monitored by thermocouples taped to the surface of the cavities.

PRELIMINARY EXPERIMENTAL RESULTS

After many attempts, two twenty-minute samples were obtained with coincident N, ρ, ρ_w and T data. It is these two samples that are presented as preliminary results. Fortunately, one was obtained during stable atmospheric conditions, the other during unstable conditions. To avoid biasing due to different time constants, all data were averaged over a period of 2.2 seconds; this interval, in excess of the maximum time constant of all measured vari-

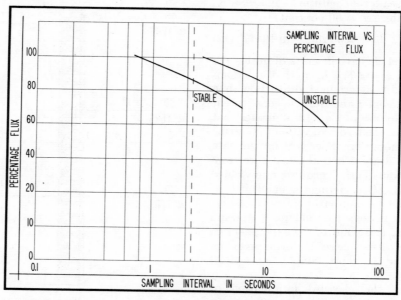

FIG. 3. Percentage of actual flux measured *vs* the sampling interval.

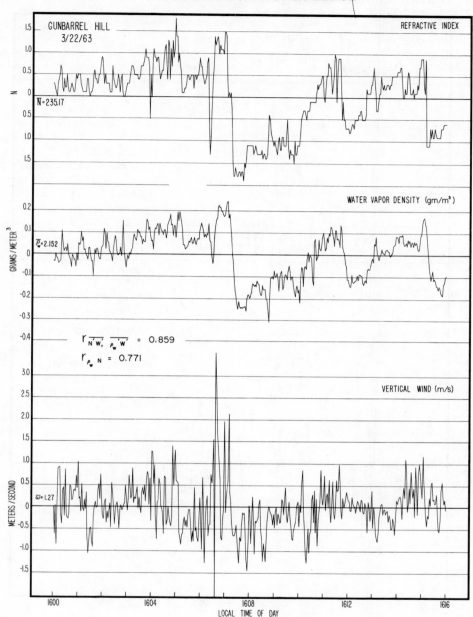

FIG. 4. Simultaneous variations in refractivity, absolute humidity and vertical wind (stable conditions).

ables, reduced all data to a common time constant. To determine the efficiency of this sampling interval, Priestley's estimate of the percentage of flux detected as a function of sampling interval was utilized.[8] In Fig. 3 it can be seen that for a 2.2 second interval, almost 90 per cent of the flux was detected for the stable case, whereas 100 per cent was detected for the unstable case.

Figures 4 and 5 are the results from two samples, the first was a stable case, the second an unstable case. The variations of the refractive index, the absolute humidity and the vertical wind are plotted as functions of time.

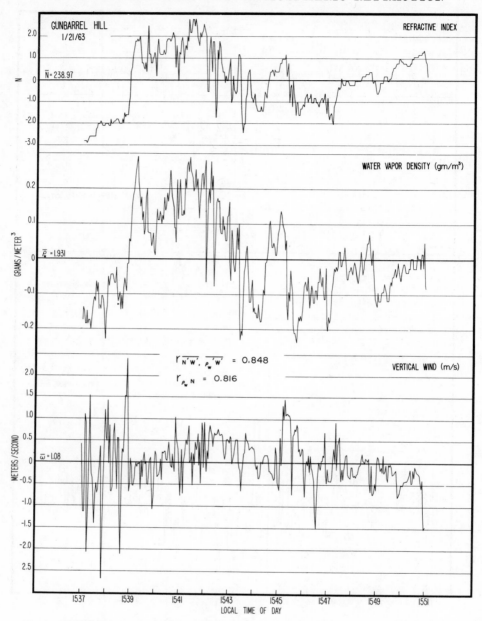

FIG. 5. Simultaneous variations in refractivity, absolute humidity and vertical wind (unstable conditions).

The correlation coefficient between the flux of the refractivity $\overline{N'w'}$ and the flux of the absolute humidity $\overline{\rho_w'w'}$ was found to be approximately 0.85 for both samples. The correlation coefficient between the refractivity and the absolute humidity was approximately 0.8.

Equation (9) predicts the fluxes of the refractivity and the absolute humidity to be linearly related with a correlation coefficient of unity, based on the assumption of incompressibility. For the samples presented here, the error due to this assumption would have the effect of reducing the true correlation coefficient by no more than 2 per cent, if this were the only source of error. On the basis of these preliminary data, it is too early to evaluate the range of correlation under varying conditions of stability, wind shear and thermal radiation. However, the present results are sufficient to encourage further work.

Applying standard statistical techniques,[4] it can be shown that with a true correlation coefficient of unity, the known errors of observation of ρ_w could easily produce the observed correlation of 0.85 tending to support the theoretical conclusion that N and ρ_w are linearly related, see Eq. (11).

SPECTRAL CHARACTERISTICS AND STABILITY

The spectra of the two samples can also be investigated in terms of atmospheric stability. Richardson's number is commonly accepted as an index of stability:

$$R_i = \frac{g}{\overline{T}} \frac{\partial \overline{T}/\partial z + \Gamma}{(\partial \overline{u}/\partial z)^2} \qquad (16)$$

where

$\quad g = $ acceleration of gravity

$\quad T = $ temperature

$\Gamma = $ adiabatic temperature lapse rate

$u = $ horizontal wind.

A positive value of Richardson's number indicates a stable system whereas a negative value indicates unstable conditions. One of the samples used in this analysis yielded a value for Richardson's number of $+0.6$ whereas the other sample yielded a value of -0.6, i.e., a stable condition and an unstable condition.

The two samples had been digitized using a 2.2-second sampling interval which, as has been mentioned, would result in the measurement of 90 per cent of the flux present. The Tukey Method[2] of spectral analysis was applied to these data, the results of which are illustrated in Fig. 6. Since the region of interest was the low-frequency end of the spectra, the Nyquist frequency cutoff of 0.23 cps was not a limitation for this analysis. (The unfiltered output of the refractometer is capable of an extended frequency range.) Figure 6 well illustrates the expected relationship between the spectrum of the refractivity and stability conditions. As would be expected, the effects of stability are most pronounced in the low-frequency range of the spectrum, that part of the spectrum where energy enters the system. Below 0.01 cps, the spectral density for the unstable case is con-

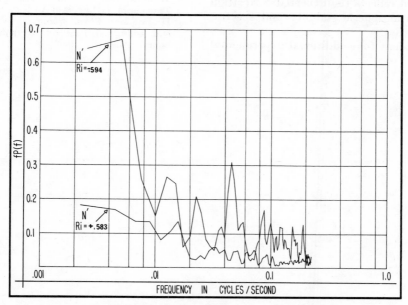

FIG. 6. Comparative power spectra for stable and unstable conditions in terms of Richardson's number.

siderably greater than that for the stable case. This is equivalent to stating that the contributions to the variance increases most rapidly at the lower frequencies ($f < 0.1$) as the degree of instability increases. In the low-frequency range, the difference between the spectral estimates of the two samples proved to be statistically significant for the 10 to 90 per cent confidence interval.

The nearly constant spectral density at the higher frequencies suggests either a limiting process of the atmosphere or self-induced turbulence from the cavity. The turbulence inducing properties of the cavity do not appear to have been treated in the literature.

SUMMARY

It has been demonstrated that the refractive index as measured by fast responding refractometers shows promise as a method to investigate humidity turbulence. Theoretical development indicates correspondence between the variability of the refractivity and the absolute humidity; preliminary experimental data appears to confirm this. A method of investigating the spectral characteristics of water vapor turbulence utilizing microwave refractometers has been demonstrated and reflects the expected correlation between atmospheric stability and spectral characteristics.

It is evident that additional experimental verification is required to confirm the relationships suggested by these preliminary data. Future efforts will include further application of turbulence theory to refractivity as a parameter to investigate water vapor turbulence.

References

1. Bean, B. R., "The Radio Refractive Index of Air," *Proc. I.R.E.*, **50**, 26–273 (March 1962).
2. Blackman, R. B., and Tukey, J. W., "The Measurement of Power Spectra," New York, Dover Publications Inc., 1959.
3. De Feriet, J. Kampe, "Averaging Processes and Reynolds Equations in Atmospheric Turbulence," *J. Meteorol.*, **8**, 358–361 (Oct. 1951).
4. Hald, A., "Statistical Theory with Engineering Applications," New York, John Wiley & Sons, 1952.
5. Lettau, H. H., and Davison, B., "Exploring the Atmosphere's First Mile," Vol. II, New York, Pergamon Press, 1957.
6. Pai, Shih-i, "Viscous Flow Theory," Vol. II, "Turbulent Flow," New York, D. Van Nostrand & Co., 1957.
7. Portman, D. J., Elder, F. C., Ryznar, E., and Noble, V. E., "Some Optical Properties of Turbulence in Stratified Flow Near the Ground," *J. Geophys. Res.*, **67**, 3223–3235 (July 1962).
8. Priestley, C. H. B., "Turbulent Transfer in the Lower Atmosphere," Chicago, University of Chicago Press, 1959.
9. Swinbank, W. C., "An Experimental Study of Eddy Transports in the Lower Atmosphere," Technical Paper No. 2, "A Study of Turbulent Transfer in the Layers of Air Near the Ground," Div. of Met. Phys., Commonwealth Scientific and Industrial Research Organization, Melbourne, Australia, 1955.

68. The Measurement of the Vertical Distribution of Water Vapor by the Differential Absorption of Scattered Energy from a Searchlight Beam

R. M. Schotland, E. E. Chermack, and D. T. Chang

Department of Meteorology and Oceanography,* New York University, New York, N.Y.

ABSTRACT

A remote sounding method has been developed for the determination of the vertical profile of water vapor in the lower troposphere. The technique used consists of the measurement of the side scattered energy from a xenon searchlight beam at wavelengths corresponding to the water vapor ρ band. The scattered energy is observed by a receiver located at a distance from the searchlight beam. Profile data are obtained by scanning the receiver vertically along the transmitted beam.

A theoretical analysis of this method, including a discussion of the effect of Rayleigh and Mie scattering components upon the observed signal strength is presented. Transfer functions, defined as the ratio of power received to that transmitted over a given wavelength interval, are derived. A method for the inversion of the data is developed.

An experimental evaluation of this method was performed at Brookhaven National Laboratory. Observations made during periods in August and October 1962 have been analyzed and comparisons between these data and the tower data are presented. Limitations of the method and the potential usefulness of this approach are considered.

* Contribution No. 11 from the Geophysical Sciences Laboratory, New York University.

GENERAL INTRODUCTION

One of the important problems which concerns the meteorologist is the determination of the vertical profile of water vapor. The existing systems, such as the radiosonde, are costly both in time and money. In addition, the positioning of radiosondes in the air poses some degree of hazard to aircraft. Recently, effort has been directed to the measurement of this quantity by "remote techniques." This implies that the sensing elements are located at a position away from the region of the atmosphere whose parameters are to be measured, and by definition the system does not require a physical probe at such a region.

This paper gives an analysis and some experimental results relating to water vapor of a class of active remote sounding methods. An active system is composed of an energy source and a receiver. The source is directed at the region of the atmosphere under investigation and through some transfer mechanism such as a scattering process, a portion of this energy is returned to the receiver. Referring to Fig. 1, when a source transmits an amount of energy per unit time of $F_\lambda \Delta\lambda$, only a portion of this energy will reach the level of intersection with the receiver beam due to the attenuation caused by scattering elements and absorbing gases distributed along the propagation path. A very small fraction of the energy at the

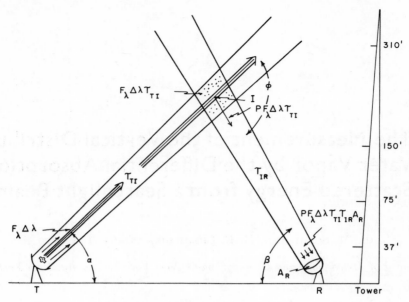

FIG. 1. Power flow diagram.

intersection volume will be side scattered into the receiver cone of acceptance. This energy will be further attenuated by scattering and absorption along the return propagation path length. As will be seen later, a study of the Differential Absorption of the Scattered Energy [DASE] as the receiver beam is scanned in elevation permits the specification of the vertical distribution of the absorbing gases.

ATMOSPHERIC SCATTERING AND ABSORPTION PROPERTIES

Rayleigh Scattering

The basic theory of Rayleigh scattering is discussed by many authors. As given by Sinclair,[5] the intensity of light scattered by a single scatterer is

$$E = \frac{9\pi^2}{2r^2} E_0 \left(\frac{m^2 - 1}{m^2 + 2}\right)^2 \frac{v^2}{\lambda^4} (1 + \cos^2\phi)$$

where

E = flux per unit area scattered
E_0 = flux per unit area incident
r = distance of observer from scattering element

m = refractive index of element with respect to the medium
v = volume of element
λ = wavelength of incident light
ϕ = scattering angle as measured from direction of incident radiation.

If many (n) scatterers of different size and composition are present and one assumes negligible secondary scatter, the light scattered from this aggregate is

$$E = E_0 \frac{9\pi^2}{2r^2} \frac{(1 + \cos^2\phi)}{\lambda^4} \sum n \left(\frac{m^2 - 1}{m^2 + 2}\right)^2 v^2 \quad (1)$$

The summation in Eq. (1) should take into account the number of particles of different sizes and compositions. The value m is dependent on particle composition and only slightly dependent on wavelength in the visible, near ultraviolet, and near infrared.

In the case of molecular scattering, Eq. (1) reduces to

$$E = \frac{E_0 2\pi^2 n\gamma^2 (1 + \cos^2\phi)}{r^2\lambda^4} \quad (2)$$

where $\gamma = [(\mu - 1)/n]$, and is nearly constant over the near ultraviolet, visible, and near infrared regions of the spectrum. The quantity μ is the bulk refractive index of the gas.

Mie Scattering

For particles exceeding a certain size with respect to incident wavelength, the more general theory of Mie must be used. Sinclair[5] gives the following expression for the light scattered from a large particle:

$$E = \frac{E_0 \lambda^2}{8\pi^2 r^2}(i_1 + i_2)$$

where i_1 and i_2 are proportional to the incoherent polarized components of the scattered light (i_1 and i_2 are highly angular dependent and generally describe the strong forward scattering characteristics of large particle scattering). Of great importance, however, is the fact that i_1 and i_2 are dependent upon size parameter $\alpha(= \pi D/\lambda)$ and m, where D is the particle diameter. As in the case of smaller particles and molecules, if many particles are encountered, the scattered intensity will be:

$$E = \frac{E_0 n \lambda^2 (i_1 + i_2)}{8\pi^2 r^2} \tag{3}$$

Attenuation by Scattering

When Eqs. (1), (2) and (3) are integrated with respect to direction over a sphere, one obtains the total energy scattered out of a beam by the aggregate molecule-particle system. The relationship thus arrived at is, in effect, an attenuation coefficient due to scattering per unit path length of scattering material.

$$k_s = \frac{32\pi^2 n \gamma^3}{3\lambda^4} \quad \text{molecular scattering attenuation} \tag{4}$$

$$k_s = 24\pi^3 n \left(\frac{m^2 - 1}{m^2 + 2}\right)^2 \frac{v^2}{\lambda^4} \quad \text{small particle attenuation} \tag{5}$$

$$k_s = n \pi a^2 K_s \quad \text{large particle attenuation} \tag{6}$$

where n in the last three equations is number density (length^{-3}); a is the radius of the large particles; and K_s is a dimensionless coefficient calculable from the Mie theory. As a grows very large, K_s approaches the value 2.

Attenuation by Absorption

Water vapor absorbs radiation to a greater or lesser extent in several bands (see Fig. 2). Several factors dictate the use of wavelength less than 1 μ. The intensity of scattered radia-

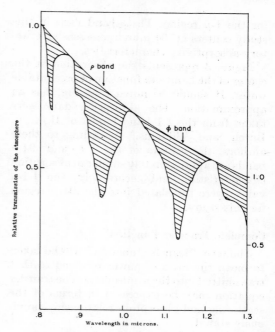

FIG. 2. Water vapor absorption bands between 0.8 and 1.3 μ.

tion generally falls off inversely with wavelength, and therefore it is desirable to use the shortest possible wavelength. A second point is that photomultiplier detectors are available

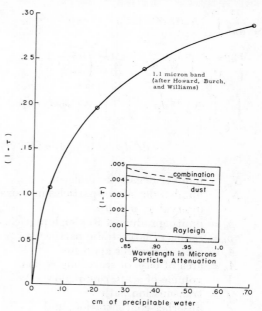

FIG. 3. Attenuation diagram.

for the 1-μ region. The ρ-band used in this study centers at .94 μ and possesses satisfactory absorptivity characteristics.

Figure 3 represents the absorption at the center of the band as a function of precipitable water. It should be noted that Fig. 3 is an approximation. The absorption data were taken from the 1.1 band model of Howard, Burch, and Williams.[3] According to these authors, the centers of the 1.1- and .94-μ bands are approximately similar in absorption characteristics, and accordingly, the 1.1-μ values were translated into the .94-μ region for this study.

Complete Transfer Function

The term "transfer function" will be taken to mean the ratio of power received to that transmitted into the atmosphere. The transfer equation may be expressed in terms of the scattering and absorption relationship previously stated.

The complete transfer function is

$$\frac{F_\lambda}{F_{T_\lambda}} = \frac{A_r V}{A_b r^2} \left[\frac{2\pi^2 N_m \gamma^2 (1 + \cos^2\phi)}{\lambda^4} + \right.$$

$$\frac{9\pi^2(1 + \cos^2\phi)}{2\lambda^4} \left(\frac{m^2 - 1}{m^2 + 2}\right)^2 \int_{p_\alpha}^{p_\beta} N_p V_p^2 \, dp +$$

$$\left. \frac{\lambda^2}{8\pi^2} \int_{p_\beta}^{p_i} N_p (i_1 + i_2)_p \, dp \right] \times \exp -$$

$$\left[\frac{32\pi^2\gamma^2}{\lambda^4} \int_0^\ell N_m \, d\ell + \frac{24\pi^3}{\lambda^4} \left(\frac{m^2 - 1}{m^2 + 2}\right)^2 \right.$$

$$\int_{p_\alpha}^{p_\beta} \int_0^\ell N_p V_p^2 \, dp + \int_{p_\beta}^{p_i} \int_0^\ell N_p \pi p^2 K_s(p)$$

$$\left. d\ell \, dp + \int_0^\ell \rho_k A_k \, d\ell \right] \quad (7)$$

N_m = number density of molecules
N_p = number density of particles in a size interval $p, p + dp$
p_β = limiting radius of Rayleigh particles
p_i = radius of largest Mie particles
A_r = area of receiver aperture
A_b = area of base of scattering region
V = volume of scattering region
ℓ = transmission path
ρ_k = absorber concentration, and
A_k = absorption coefficient.

Analysis of Non-molecular Terms

An attempt was made to study the effect of non-molecular scattering on the transfer function. Two scattering effects had to be considered in this evaluation. These are attenuation due to scattering and the angular distribution of scattered radiation. Attenuation due to particles appears as the second and third terms in the exponential of Eq. (7). The angular distribution of the scattered energy is represented by the phase functions $(1 + \cos^2\phi)$ and $(i_1 + i_2)$ in terms 2 and 3 of Eq. (7).

A particle size distribution was assumed based upon the values given in the "Handbook of Geophysics"[2] from the work of Junge. For simplicity this distribution was assumed invariant from 0 to 400 ft. Phase functions and scattering cross sections were determined for each size increment of the distribution from Lowan's tables[4] for an assumed particle refractive index of 1.55 and the phase function for the entire distribution obtained by summation. The ratio of forward to back scatter for this particle distribution was about 20 to 1. Although there is no unique correspondence between this ratio and visibility, it would appear from the work of Barteneva[1] that a ratio of 20:1 corresponds to visibilities less

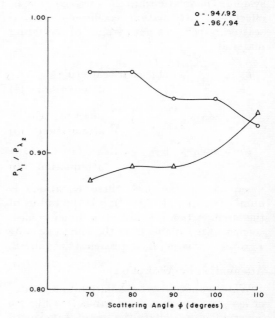

FIG. 4. Phase function ratios for non-molecular scattering.

than 5 km. Barteneva's work summarizes the results of field measurements of phase function and visibility made under various meteorological and geographical conditions over a period of several years.

In order to invert the basic DASE data into a water vapor profile, two restrictive assumptions are necessary:

(1) The attenuation due to scattering along the transmission path chosen and in the wavelength pair chosen, must be either negligible compared to the differential water vapor absorption along this path or the difference in attenuation between the wavelengths of the pair chosen must be small compared to the difference in water vapor absorption between the two wavelengths.

(2) The scattering phase function at the wavelengths chosen must maintain a constant ratio independent of the scattering angle.

Calculations were made of the phase functions and attenuation at .92, .94, .96 and .99 μ. The inset in Fig. 3 represents the extinction due to scattering as a function of wavelength over a 730-ft path. It can be seen that Rayleigh attenuation is quite small and that the particle attenuation, while of greater magnitude, is only slightly wavelength dependent. Thus it appears that even in a contaminated, poor visibility atmosphere, assumption (1) holds.

Figure 4 represents the ratios of the total phase function *vs* scattering angle for two wavelength pairs (.92-.94, .94-.96). The results of the calculations here indicate that assumption (2) fails when the atmosphere is dusty or contaminated, since the ratio of the phase functions varies greatly with scattering angle. One might expect that for cleaner atmospheres (or better visibility) where the Rayleigh component of the phase function will weigh more heavily, the angular variation of the ratio will decrease in amplitude.

Beam Shape Considerations

The quantity $V/A_b r^2$ is of primary importance in the transfer function equation. This factor is dependent upon the relative beam width of the transmitter and receiver. V/A_b can be roughly approximated by considering the beam to be square and of angular width θ_T and θ_R. Two significant cases arise that affect V/A_b. The first case is one in which

$\theta_R > \theta_T$ and the receiver beam is at all elevations greater than the transmitter beam width. In the second case $\theta_R < \theta_T$, such that the transmitter beam width is greater than the receiver beam at all elevations. Clearly the former arrangement is more desirable since none of the transmitter beam is wasted.

Analysis shows that for the wide receiver beam system

$$V \approx z^3 \, \theta_T^2 \, \theta_R \csc^2 \alpha \csc \beta \qquad [\text{if } \theta_R > \theta_T]$$

and

$$A_b = z^2 \, \theta_T^2 \csc^2 \alpha$$

so that

$$\frac{V}{A_b r^2} = \frac{\theta_R \sin \beta}{z} = \frac{\theta_R}{r} \qquad (8)$$

For a narrow receiver beam system, one obtains

$$V \approx z^3 \, \theta_T \, \theta_R^2 \csc \alpha \csc^2 \beta \qquad [\text{if } \theta_R < \theta_T]$$

and

$$A_b \approx z^2 \, \theta_T^2 \csc^2 \alpha$$

so that

$$\frac{V}{A_b r^2} = \frac{\theta_R^2 \sin \alpha}{\theta_T z} = \frac{\text{const}}{z} \qquad (9)$$

It can be seen that Eq. (8) remains almost constant with height while Eq. (9) varies inversely with height. It is desirable therefore

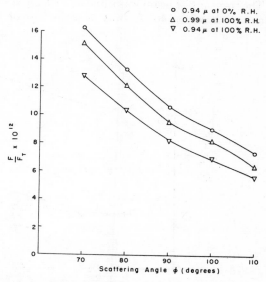

FIG. 5. Transfer functions (molecular and nonmolecular scattering).

to arrange the optics of the system so that the receiver beam is wide compared to that of the transmitter in order to obtain the maximum signal from a given scattering level.

Equation (7) was computed to a height z of 400 ft assuming Eq. (8). The atmosphere was divided into 20-ft slabs for this purpose, and N_m was assumed constant. A baseline between transmitter and receiver of 500 ft was chosen. The value of θ_v was assumed to be 1 degree and the receiver diameter 2 ft.

A standard atmosphere utilizing the dust model with 100 per cent humidity was considered as well as a dry atmosphere. The results of these calculations are shown in Figs. 5 and 6. Little or no water vapor information may be expected from the contaminated atmosphere since the variation in phase function tends to mask the absorption effect.

AN EXPERIMENT TO EVALUATE THE D A S E TECHNIQUE

The differential absorption technique was tested for several nights in the months of August, September, and October at Brookhaven National Laboratory at Upton, Long Island. This site was chosen principally because of the opportunity to check the system against known water vapor profiles.

Figure 1 represents the experimental setup. The transmitter beam was tilted at 45 degrees, and the receiver, 407 ft away near the base of the tower, was free to scan the transmitter beam in the vertical. Energy scattered from the beam was picked up by the receiver and transferred onto a filtered (0.941 and 0.995 μ) photomultiplier tube.

A calibration of the system was performed using Brookhaven's 420-ft meteorological tower. Carbon strip hygrometers were placed at the 37-, 75-, 150-, 300- and 410-ft levels. Temperature data were also taken at these levels. The precipitable water as a function of height was estimated by the readings (R, H and T) taken at these levels.

Figure 7 is a block diagram of the experimental apparatus.

System Design

Transmitter. *Source.* The source used was an 800-watt xenon compact arc lamp (Hanovia 418 c. g.) having an oval quartz envelope containing xenon gas under high pressure. When a discharge takes place between the tugsten electrodes located at either end of the tube, an extremely bright light is produced having a black body continuum radiation of approximately 5000°K. Superimposed on this are the spectral lines of xenon. The spectral energy distribution for the range 0.8 to 1.1 μ is given in Fig. 9. The lines applicable to the ρ-band system are centered at 0.9374 and 0.9513μ. More than 3 per cent of the electrical input to the source is radiated in the spectral range 0.93 to 0.96 μ.

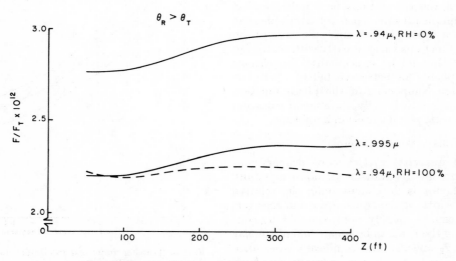

FIG. 6. Transfer functions (molecular scattering alone).

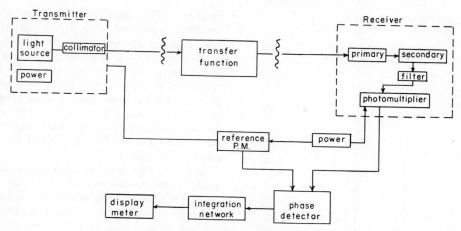

FIG. 7. Block diagram of DASE.

The lamp was modulated by its input power supply which, in this case, was operated by a gasoline powered generator with a frequency of 60 cps so that the emitted radiation had a modulated frequency of 120 cps.

The arc dimensions of the lamp are 2 mm by 4 mm with almost all of the radiation contained in a pattern symmetrically distributed about the arc axis at ± 55 degrees about the normal plane.

Optics. The xenon arc lamp was mounted at the focus of a parabolic reflector having a maximum linear aperture of 25 in and a focal length of 9.75 in. From photographs taken of the emitted beam with the optical axis of the camera at right angles to the axis of the beam, the divergence half angle of the transmitted beam between half power points, was determined to be 0°30′ in the plane perpendicular to the axis of the electrodes. The optical system had an *f* number approximately equal to 0.4.

A small spherical mirror was mounted along the optical axis of the system with its focus at the center of the arc of the lamp to collect the energy that would otherwise be radiated away from the primary reflector.

The reflecting surfaces of the system were polished "Hastelloy" which has a relatively low absorption coefficient in the near infrared so that transmission loss due to reflection was kept at a minimum.

Mount. The transmitter was mounted on a pedestal and the optical axis of the system was inclined at an elevation angle of 45 degrees. The whole system was fixed in position in line with the receiver.

It was anticipated that Mie particles in the form of flying insects would be attracted by the light, causing a scattering in the vicinity of the source. A metal wire screen on a wooden framework was placed over the whole transmitter. Figure 8 shows a schematic diagram of the transmitting system.

Receiver. *Optics.* The receiver optical system was Cassegrainian in design, consisting of a collector and a collimator. The radiation scattered from the beam by the atmosphere was collected by a concave parabolic reflector having the same characteristics as those of the primary of the transmitter. The

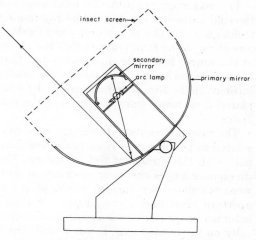

FIG. 8. Schematic diagram of transmitter.

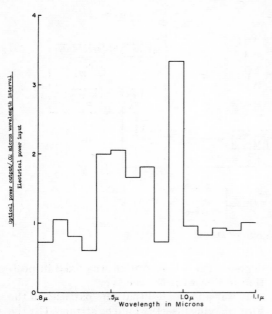

FIG. 9. Spectral distribution of xenon arc lamp between 0.8 and 1.1 μ.

received radiation, being essentially parallel, was brought to convergence at the focus of the collector, forming an image of the source.

Because wavelength selection was accomplished by means of interference filters, collimation of the convergent beam before detection was necessary. A parabolic secondary reflector which folded the beam back along the optical axis of the collector was chosen as collimator because of its simplicity.

The maximum aperture and focal length of the collimator was determined by ray tracing techniques. In the procedure, consideration was given to the requirements that the image of the source had finite dimensions and that the collimated beam should, ideally, be totally incident on the 2-in. diameter face of a detector placed 5 in. away from the focus of the collector.

The extreme points of the image were considered to be formed by rays emanating from points on the surface of the secondary. The divergence angles and their subtenses at 5 in. were calculated for various combinations of aperture sizes and focal lengths. With an assumed image size of 0.2 in. lying symmetrically on the optical axis, it was found that a parabolic reflector having a focal length of

0.85 in. and a maximum aperture of 2 in. would provide satisfactory collimation. The loss of energy due to the occulting effect of the secondary was approximately 10 per cent. However, since the divergence angle at the secondary of rays received from the primary is greatest for rays emanating from points on the primary near the optical axis, the energy loss due to the occulting would, in any case, be out of the 3-degree beam needed for transmission through the filters.

Detector. The detector used was a Dumont K2273 photomultiplier with an S-1 surface and an amplification factor of 10^6. The tube was a specially chosen tube having a cathode dark current on the order of 10^{-13} A at 20°C. The diameter of the end window photosensitive area was 1.6 in.

Filters. Energy measurements must be per-

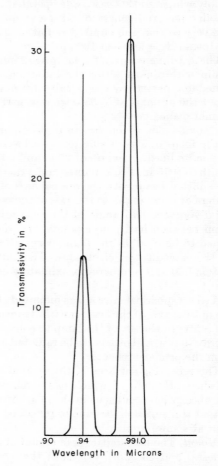

FIG. 10. Transmittivity of filters 0.94 and 0.99 μ.

formed in two wavelength intervals centered about the ρ absorption band of water vapor. The wavelengths chosen were 0.94 and 0.99 μ. The filters used to accomplish wavelength selection were interference filters with bandwidths approximately equal to 250 Å. These filters have steep slopes at the cut-on and cut-off wavelengths (see Fig. 10).

Filter-detector Assembly. The Dumont K2273 photomultiplier with its electrostatic shield was encased in a phenolic tube which had been threaded at the face end. The two filters were recessed in phenolic rings threaded to fit over the face of the photomultiplier. Wavelength selection was accomplished by changing the filters over the photomultiplier. The whole assembly was mounted along the optical axis of the receiver with the detector face 5 in. from the focus of the primary.

When in position, the solid angle which the detector views is nearly 2π steradians. Unless this angle is reduced, the detector would view the total length of the transmitted beam. A combination of a 2-in. tube in front of the detector and an 8-in. diameter disc behind the secondary mirror was used to step down this angle so that only the light reflected from the secondary was received.

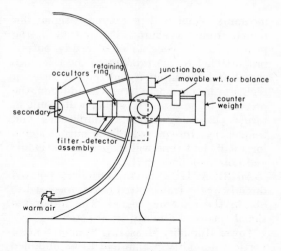

FIG. 12. Schematic diagram of receiver.

The receiver beam pattern was determined by moving a constant intensity light source perpendicular to the optical axis. The source was located 811 ft. from the receiver. A plot of the intensity pattern obtained is given in Fig. 11. The beam of the receiver was found to subtend a horizontal plane angle of 1 degree between half power points.

Mount. The receiver was mounted on a pedestal which permitted both azimuth and elevation scan. A remotely actuated motor drive was provided for automatic elevation scan. A calibrated potentiometer was attached to the elevation scan axis, and this permitted remote measurement of the elevation scan angle.

Jets of warm air were directed at the optical surfaces to prevent optical transmission loss due to condensation on the surfaces. A schematic of the whole receiver system is given in Fig. 12.

Detection System. The energy that is received by the detector is modulated by the supply frequency. The transfer function is small and in order that this energy be measurable, it is necessary to limit the bandwidth of the associated amplifiers to at least 0.1 cps. However, the primary power sources available in the field did not provide the frequency stability required. To overcome this difficulty, a phase locked detection mode was used which allowed for post-detection bandwidth compression.

The phase locked detector multiplies the

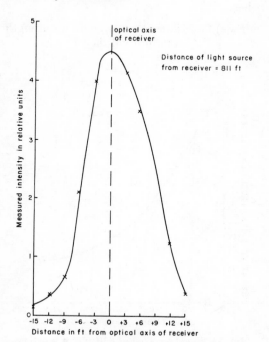

FIG. 11. Receiver beam characteristic curve.

incoming signal with a reference signal obtained from the source. The output of the phase detector consists of a steady output proportional to the product of the reference signal and the input signal, plus a series of higher order harmonic terms. In addition, the presence of noise in the signal will result in terms possessing random amplitudes and frequencies. Integration of the output signal for a sufficient time will reduce the harmonic and noise components.

An RCA IP28 photomultiplier, pointed directly at the transmitted beam, was used to obtain the reference signal. The integrated signal was read directly off a meter.

Tower Humidity Measuring System. Since a vertical humidity profile had to be obtained independent of the DASE system, humidity sensors were mounted on the 420-ft meteorological tower adjacent to the receiver.

The tower was originally instrumented for continuous wind and temperature measurements. The sensors chosen to instrument the tower for humidity were manufactured by Eltronics Corp., Warren, Pa. These sensors are based on the principle that the value of the electrical resistance of carbon deposited on an insulating sheet in an absorbing binder is a function of the relative humidity and temperature of the air passing over the carbon.

Although the commercial units used were specified by the manufacturer to have a 1 per cent accuracy, it was found that calibration was necessary. This was done by means of a standard humidity chamber.

The sensor signals were measured with an Eltronic ohmmeter calibrated in terms of relative humidity. Temperature corrections were made for the sensor readings for deviations from 77°F. This correction factor was given by the manufacturer to be −0.2 per cent for every degree Fahrenheit above 77 per cent and +0.2 per cent for every degree Fahrenheit below 77°F.

The calibrated sensors were shielded and mounted in perforated tubes. These were in turn mounted on units which allowed for switching to 1 per cent resistors, providing continuity checks and a means of checking the accuracy of the data telemetered through cable to the meter.

Sensor units were mounted at the 37-, 75-, 150-, 300- and 410-ft levels and were connected to the meter through a switch so that consecutive readings of the relative humidity at these levels could be made. The whole system was shielded from stray fields to prevent spurious readings.

ANALYSIS OF DATA

Inversion Technique

Experimental measurements were carried out on five nights during the months of August and September 1962. The runs were initiated a few hours after sunset and were restricted to those nights that were free from clouds. The data yielded only three pairs of runs that were satisfactory. The others had to be eliminated because of such problems as insect swarms, tower inoperation and sudden unpredicted rain.

The method of analysis applied to the data to obtain the vertical moisture profile follows directly from the previously described theory. An equation relating the power received at the detector may be expressed in functional form or

$$F_R(\lambda)\Delta\lambda = k_z F_T(\lambda_2) \cdot \rho(z) \cdot \phi(\lambda_1) \cdot$$
$$\gamma(\theta)\Delta\lambda T_\lambda(\theta, w) \quad (9)$$

where

$F_R(\lambda)\Delta\lambda$ = flux at receiver at wavelength λ in interval $\Delta\lambda$

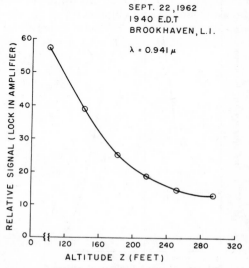

SEPT. 22, 1962
1940 E.D.T
BROOKHAVEN, L.I.

$\lambda = 0.941 \mu$

FIG. 13. Signal received at 0.94 μ as a function of height.

F_T = flux transmitted

$\rho(z)$ = density of scattering elements

$\phi(\lambda)$ = scattering wavelength dependency

w = precipitable water (cm)

$\gamma(\theta)$ = elevation angle dependency

$T_\lambda(\theta, w)$ = atmospheric transmissivity at wavelength λ.

Figure 13 is a plot of the signal received at .941 μ as a function of height. The two wavelengths used in this experiment were separated by 0.05 μ. It was assumed that the scattering property of the atmosphere remained constant over this interval, although, as has been seen, this represents a limiting assumption. The ratio of $F_R(\lambda_1)\varDelta\lambda$ (absorbed wavelength) to $F_R(\lambda_2)\varDelta\lambda$ unabsorbed) defined to be $R(\theta, w, \lambda_1, \lambda_2)$ is

$$R = \frac{k_1}{k_2} \cdot \frac{F_T(\lambda_1)}{F_T(\lambda_2)} \cdot \frac{\phi(\lambda_1)}{\phi(\lambda_2)} \, T_\lambda\,(\theta, w) = KT_\lambda(\theta, w) \quad (10)$$

When the experiment was first planned it was thought that K would be determined by directing the receiver horizontally and then measuring $T_\lambda(0^\circ, w)$ by means of auxiliary equipment. However, it was found in field tests that this procedure was not workable because the searchlight illuminated surrounding foliage at elevation angles below 20 degree. The procedure was then revised, and K was determined using $T(20^\circ, w)$ obtained from the tower humidity equipment and the relation $A = 43.5w + 14.5$. This relation differs from the absorption of the 1.1 μ band which

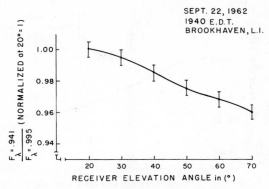

FIG. 15. Normalized spectral ratios (September 22, 1962, 1940 EDT).

was used for the calculation of the transfer function, by a factor 1.23. It was thought that the inclusion of this factor would better approximate the absorption due to the ρ-band since the ratio between the total absorptions in the ρ-band and the 1.1-μ band as given by Howard, Burch, and Williams[3] is roughly that amount.

The data taking procedure employed in this experiment was as follows:

(1) Meteorological observations

(2) Tower humidity measurement (300, 150, 75, 37, 0)

(3) F_R (0.941 μ) 20, 30, 40, 50, 60 and 70 degrees

(4) F_R (0.995 μ) 20, 30, 40, 50, 60 and 70 degrees

(5) Tower humidity measurement.

The data obtained were normalized to $R(20^\circ, w) = 1$,

$$\frac{R(\theta, w)}{R(20^\circ, w)} = \frac{T(w, \theta)}{T(w, 20^\circ)} \quad (11)$$

Measurements on the nights of August 29, and September 22, 1962 are presented in Figs. 14, 15, and 16. The horizontal visibility on these nights was estimated to be greater than 15 miles.

Results

The inversion of Figs. 14, 15, and 16 was accomplished by using the 1.1-μ absorptivity curves and are given in Figs. 17, 18, and 19 together with the tower checkpoints. The vertical bars represent the estimate of the uncertainty in the DASE measurements and

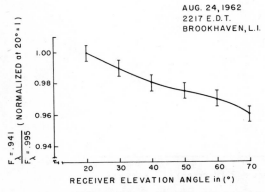

FIG. 14. Normalized spectral ratios (August 24, 1962, 2217 EDT).

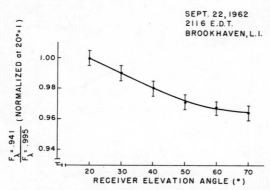

SEPT. 22, 1962
2116 E.D.T.
BROOKHAVEN, L.I.

FIG. 16. Normalized spectral ratios (September 22, 1962, 2116 EDT).

the tower data. The DASE flux measurements were considered accurate to 1.5 per cent. However, when this uncertainty was translated to water vapor uncertainty, this yielded a spread of approximately ± 15 per cent in w in the range of w at 0.18 cm H_2O.

It can be seen that there is general agreement between the DASE determination and the tower data within the uncertainty of the DASE measurements. In addition, it must be noted that the uncertainty shown for the tower data is a minimum estimate, since the tower data shown are interpolated values from the sensor level measurements.

CONCLUSIONS

The active system which has been described will provide measurements of water vapor up to 400 ft on clear nights only. It has been shown by calculations that the invariance of the phase function with scattering angle is valid only under extremely clear conditions, and moderate amounts of particulate matter will introduce energy fluctuations of the order that would mask the effects of water vapor absorption. A further limitation imposed on this system is the assumption of horizontal slab symmetry.

However, the system as described is usable at higher elevations where the Rayleigh approximation more closely describes the

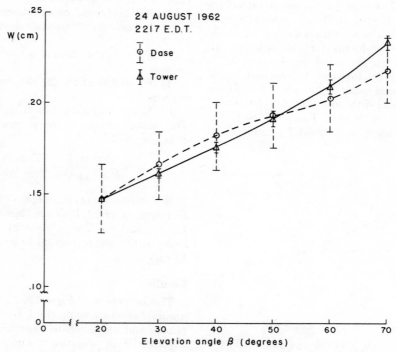

24 AUGUST 1962
2217 E.D.T.

⌀ Dase
△ Tower

FIG. 17. Comparison of the DASE and tower measurements (August 24, 1962, 2217 EDT).

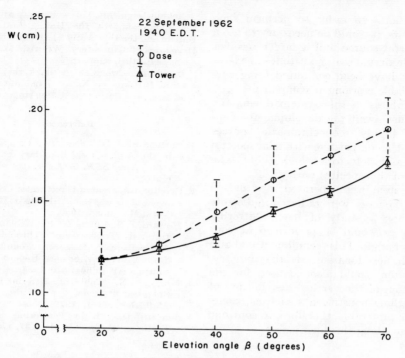

FIG. 18. Comparison of the DASE and tower measurements (September 22, 1962, 1940 EDT).

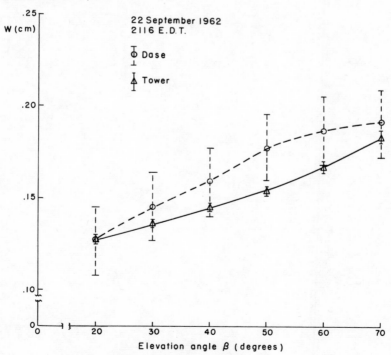

FIG. 19. Comparison of the DASE and tower measurements (September 22, 1962, 2116 EDT).

phase function. In order to perform such measurements, it would be necessary to use a more powerful source and a larger receiver aperture. Maximum search altitudes in excess of 30,000 ft have been computed using currently available equipment components.

The usefulness of this system during the daytime must await the development of intense and highly monochromatic sources which would be competitive with solar spectral irradiance and detectors which could take advantage of this spectral purity.

If the system were operated in a pulsed mode, i.e., if energy were radiated in discrete bundles, then a study of back scattering characteristics would be performed at constant scatter angle. This technique would also eliminate the need for assumed slab symmetry. Such a system could also be used for the determination of the vertical distribution of other absorbing constituents such as ozone. It would be preferable, therefore, to continue development along this line.

Acknowledgments. This work was performed under the sponsorship of the United States Weather Bureau and the U.S. Army Electronics Research and Development Laboratory. We wish to thank these agencies for their support.

In addition, we wish to thank the Meteorology Staff at Brookhaven National Laboratory for their kind assistance during the testing stages of this work.

References

1. Barteneva, O. D., "Scattering Functions of Light in the Atmospheric Boundary Layer," *Izvest. Akad. Nauk SSR, Geof. Ser.* (trans.) 1237–1244 (1960).
2. Geophysics Research Directorate, USAF, "Handbook of Geophysics," Revised Edition, New York, Macmillan, 1960.
3. Howard, J. N., Burch, D., and Williams, D., "Near Infrared Transmission Through Synthetic Atmospheres," Research Foundation, Ohio State University, Science Report No. 1 under contract AF 19(604)-516, 1954.
4. Lowan, A. N., "Tables of Scattering Functions for Spherical Particles," *Natl. Bur. Std., Appl. Math. Ser.*, No. 4, (1949).
5. Sinclair, D., "Light Scattering by Spherical Particles," *J. Opt. Soc. Am.*, **37**, 475–480 (1947).

69. On the Eddy Transfer of Water Vapor above an Outdoor Surface*

D. R. Hay, H. C. Martin and E. V. Pemberton

Department of Physics, University of Western Ontario, London, Canada

ABSTRACT

Fluctuations in the refractive index of the air above a laboratory roof have been examined by a 180-ft microwave interferometer. The observed standard deviations of refractivity were less than 10^{-6}. These deviations were associated with instability of the air at the interferometer path, but not with instability of the air immediately above it. Smaller refractivity deviations occurred for weak eddy transfer of water vapor downwards through moist air in the radio path; intermediate deviations were associated with strong eddy transfer of vapor upwards through drier air in the path. The largest refractivity deviations were observed for less vigorous upward transfer of water vapor from the surface. It is suggested that the more vigorous eddies disperse the entrained water vapor more rapidly into smaller eddies than do the less vigorous eddies; and hence, lesser local fluctuations in air refractivity appear along an extended path that is highly unstable than along the same path under conditions of somewhat greater stability. The study that was begun in this pilot experiment is being extended through several modifications; the equipment has been transferred to a field site, at the ground, and a rapid-response refractometer and a temperature sensor are located adjacent to the interferometer path, to provide information on the profiles of temperature and vapor pressure within the turbulent eddies.

* The research for this paper was supported in part by the Defence Research Board of Canada, grant number 2801-12, and in part by the National Research Council of Canada, grant number T-1141.

Studies over the past years at our laboratory have added to the growing body of evidence that it is possible to obtain radar reflections from a visually clear sky.[1] It has further been indicated that there is a marked correlation between these occurrences and the dampness condition of the ground. This correlation, then, suggests that the moisture at the surface of the earth must be transported into the atmosphere to heights where these reflections might occur. An experiment was therefore undertaken to investigate this transport of humidity in the atmosphere. The study was confined to the first few meters of the atmosphere and the center of interest was concentrated on the transport of humidity by the mechanism of turbulent diffusion.[2]

The experimental apparatus located on the roof of the laboratory is shown in Fig. 1. The microwave interferometer measures variations in electrical path length integrated along the 180-ft path. These variations in the electrical path length are directly proportional to variations in refractive index. The metal reflector confines the vertical range of the interferometer to the first meter of the atmosphere.* An instrument tower is located at the center of the path and just to one side of the interferometer beam. This tower is equipped with cup anemometers and thermistors at each of three levels. These instruments provide information on the vertical gradients in wind velocity and temperature centered about the

* Care in aligning the antenna, and the use of an absorbing barrier at the ground in the center of the interferometer path have suppressed reflections in the neighborhood of the reflector.

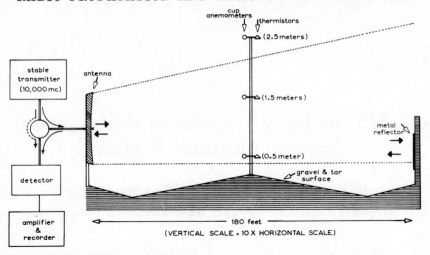

FIG. 1. Vertical section through the microwave interferometer.[2]

one meter level and the two meter level. A manually operated hygrometer was used to obtain the humidity gradient in the first one and one-half meters. Thus three main groups of parameters characteristic of the air under study were obtained from this instrumental array:

(a) Continuous records of refractive index fluctuations

(b) The humidity gradient centered about the one meter level

(c) The wind velocity and temperature gradients centered about the one meter level and the two meter level.

Equation (1) indicates how the temperature and wind velocity gradients are used to obtain a measure of air stability:

$$Ri = \frac{g(\Delta T/\Delta Z + r)}{T(\Delta \overline{u}/\Delta z)^2} \qquad (1)$$

where

g = gravitational acceleration
T = air temperature (°K)
z = height above surface
r = adiabatic lapse rate
$\overline{u}$ = mean horizontal wind speed.

Ri is the familiar Richardson's index. Positive values of Richardson's index are associated with a stable atmosphere while negative values are associated with a tendency towards unstable atmosphere.

Figure 2 presents the association between refractivity deviations at the interferometer path and the stability of the air centered about the one meter level in the lower graph or the two meter level in the upper graph. Both graphs use refractivity deviations along the interferometer path. The top graph uses Richardson's numbers calculated from the temperature and wind velocity gradients centered about the 2-meter level. The bottom graph, on the other hand, is a plot of the Richardson numbers calculated from temperature and wind velocity gradients associated with the one meter level.

The most notable feature of the upper graph is the lack of association between the deviations in refractivity and the stability of the air just above the interferometer path. The lower graph displays a more positive association between Richardson number and the refractivity deviations. For well-developed instability, that is an atmosphere tending towards turbulence, the deviations in refractivity are generally greater than 0.2×10^{-6}. It is apparent that as the atmosphere becomes more stable, the refractivity deviations are generally less than 0.2×10^{-6}.

These two graphs suggest a close relationship between refractivity deviations at the earth's surface and the stability of the air in this range whereas there appears to be no apparent relationship between the refractivity fluctuations at the surface and the stability of the air centered two meters above the surface. Furthermore, the lower graph suggests that large refractivity deviations are associated

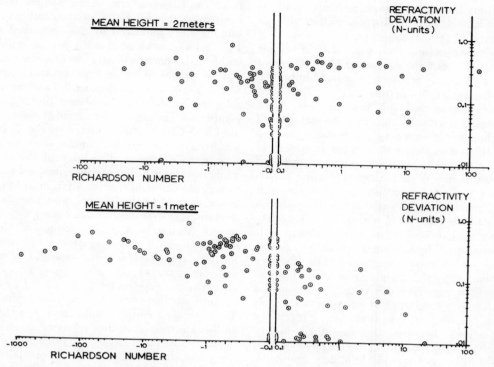

FIG. 2. Association between refractivity deviation at the interferometer path and the stability of the air at mean height 1 meter (lower graph) or at mean height 2 meters (upper graph).[2]

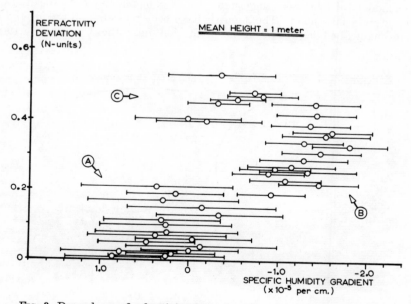

FIG. 3. Dependence of refractivity deviation at the interferometer path upon the vertical gradient in specific humidity of the air.[2]

with an unstable atmosphere while small re-fractivity deviations are associated with an essentially stable atmosphere.

A closer examination was made of the air centered about the one meter level. Figure 3 is a plot of the gradient in specific humidity *vs* the deviations in refractivity. Transport theory states that the flux or transport of humidity in the atmosphere is directly related to the specific humidity gradients. A positive gradient indicates a downward transport of water vapor, whereas a negative gradient indicates an upward transport of water vapor. Three groups of points are apparent. Group A is characterized by small refractivity devia-tions. It is associated with a mild, sluggish, downward flux of water vapor. Group B is characterized by moderate refractivity devia-tions and a vigorous upward flux of water vapor. Group C, which is characterized by the largest refractivity deviations, is associated with only a mild upward flux of water vapor. One might suspect that, as refractivity deviations increase, the specific humidity gradient increases and C should be associated with still larger specific humidity gradients. Thus one must conclude that deviations in refractivity over an extended path are not governed by the specific humidity gradient in a simple way.

Figure 4 is a model which has been suggested to help explain this last point. The figure depicts two mechanical eddies above the sur-face. The thatched arrows indicate the mean horizontal wind. High concentrations of humidity are indicated by dots. Group A (of Fig. 3) was associated with an essentially stable atmosphere where horizontal stratifica-tion is prevalent. This type of atmosphere tends to suppress turbulent eddies and the two cells in Fig. 4 would be absent under these conditions. The atmospheric conditions associ-ated with Group C are depicted by Fig. 4. Dry air from the mean horizontal wind curves downward at the leading edge of the eddy while the trailing edge carries entrained water vapor into the atmosphere. An interferometer beam, normal to this Figure, would see large deviations in refractivity associated with ad-jacent trailing and leading edges of these eddies. Group B was characterized by inter-mediate refractivity deviations and a very vigorous transport of water vapor. This sug-gets that the large eddies in Fig. 4 are broken up into smaller eddies under this condition. These smaller eddies would have less inter-surface contrast, resulting in lesser refractivity deviations as observed by the interferometer. They are, however, capable of transporting large quantities of water vapor into the atmos-phere.

This pilot experiment has been a precursor to the program presently under way. The interferometer and its associated equipment have been relocated on the ground at a Field Station near the University campus. Con-

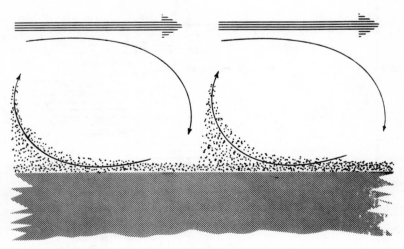

Fig. 4. Simplified model of vapor transfer between the ground and the adjacent air, within turbulent eddies.

tinuously recording humidity sensors have been added to the instrument tower on one side of the interferometer path; on the opposite side is an instrumented boom. This boom carries a capacitor-type refractometer[3] and a platinum thermometer[4] vertically up and down in the lowest 10 ft of the atmosphere. Axial rotation of these two instruments insures continual flushing. The instruments have a response time of less than 1/100 of a second or a spatial resolution of approximately 2 cm.

Equation (2) indicates how small fluctuations in temperature, refractive index, total pressure and partial vapor pressure near the ground are related by the differential form of the familiar Debye equation:

$$\Delta N = 4.3\Delta e - 1.2\Delta T + 0.26\Delta p \qquad (2)$$

where

n = refractive index
$N = (n - 1)10^6$
e = partial vapor pressure (mb)
T = air temperature (°K)
p = total air pressure (mb).

In this experiment it is assumed that the fluctuations in total air pressure over short periods of time may be neglected. Equation (2) then allows rapid fluctuations in humidity to be determined from the measurement of the rapid fluctuations in refractivity and air temperature.

This program will provide information on the structure of the humidity profile within turbulent eddies above the ground.

References

1. Hay, D. R., and Reid, W. M., "Radar Angels in the Lower Troposphere," *Canadian J. Phys.*, **40**, 128 (1962).
2. Hay, D. R., and Pemberton, E. V., "On the Eddy Transfer of Water Vapour Above an Outdoor Surface," *Canadian J. Phys.*, **40**, 1182 (1962).
3. Hay, D. R., Martin, H. C., and Turner, H. E., "A Lightweight Refractometer," *Rev. Sci. Instr.*, **32**, 693 (1961).
4. Turner, H. E., and Hay, D. R., "Fine Structure of Temperature and Refractivity in the Lower Troposphere," *Canadian J. Phys.*, **41**, 1732 (1963).

70. Influence of Water Vapor on the "Feuillet" Structure of the Atmosphere[*]

P. MISME

National Center for the Study of Telecommunication, ISSY-LES-Moulineaux, France

ABSTRACT

The author proposes the use of water vapor as a natural "tracer" in the atmosphere instead of smoke. The observation of this tracer is easier when one considers the calculations for the index of refraction of the air. Present experiments lead to an acceptance of a "feuillet" or "leaflet" structure of the atmosphere. Hence, one calculates the horizontal speeds caused by irregularities, due to water vapor, albedo, or radiation, and concludes that the atmospheric feuillets have distinctly flat lower surfaces. These results are generalized for all altitudes even though water vapor may not be the preponderant cause.

INTRODUCTION

The study of the fine structure of the atmosphere has been attempted from time to time by analyzing the trajectories of a "tracer," the latter often being smoke. This method is similar to that used in the aerodynamic research on wind currents. In the free atmosphere, however, this method has definite limitations particularly when one considers the difficulty of discharging the tracer into the atmosphere as well as the difficulty in observing its diffusion. These problems would be simplified if one of the constituents of the atmosphere could play the role of the tracer. Analysis of the different gases as found in the air shows that certain ones, such as oxygen, nitrogen, argon, etc., are present in constant proportions, whereas others, such as water vapor, exhibit wide variability in concentra-

tion. In this paper, we will study some of the conclusions resulting from the variable concentration of water vapor in the atmosphere.

THE APPROACH THROUGH ELECTROMAGNETIC PROPERTIES

It is well to remember that in physics it is unusual to compare a measurement directly with a standard. With the exception of certain lengths and weights, one parameter normally is measured in terms of another, the latter more amenable to observation. This, of course, assumes that the law joining the two parameters is well known. In the case of the measurement of humidity, in spite of the numerous efforts of many years, the results leave something to be desired.

A new method of calculation, still little used, is the index of refraction, n, for wavelengths greater than several millimeters. Using the specific humidity, s, measured in grams of water vapor per kilogram of air, n, can be expressed in the following implicit form:

$$(n-1)10^6 = N = 77.6 \frac{P}{T}\left(1 + 7.73\frac{s}{T}\right) \quad (1)$$

where

P = the atmospheric pressure, mb
T = the temperature, °K
N = the coindex.[*]

[*] In certain English texts, N is called the "Refractivity." The consideration of the meaning of words formed by adding "ity" (in English) and "ite" (in French) has led the French speaking authors to prefer the word "coindex."

[*] Translation by J. B. Reubens, NBS.

or

$$s = \frac{T}{7.73}\left(\frac{TN}{77.6P} - 1\right) = f(P, T, N) \quad (2)$$

The measurement of s then depends upon that of P, T and N.

One obtains an estimate of the precision of the measurement by writing the total differential. From Eq. (2),

$$ds = \frac{\delta f}{\delta P}\,dP + \frac{\delta f}{\delta T}\,dT + \frac{\delta f}{\delta N}\,dN \quad (3)$$

It can be shown that the partial derivatives are constant to within 10 per cent. Then the above expression can be approximated by:

$$\Delta s = 0.14\Delta N - 0.043\Delta P + 0.15\Delta T \quad (4)$$

in terms of the above units.

With a device such as the refractometer, N can be measured to within 0.1 N; P can be measured to within 0.1 mb, and T to within 0.1 degree. Hence the measurement of s should reflect an absolute accuracy on the order of 0.02 g/kg. For a value of s in the neighborhood of 10 g/kg, the relative precision

is on the order of two parts in 10^3. A measurement to within one part in 10^2 does not require any special precautions. Note that an error of $7°$ in T corresponds to an error of 1 g/kg in s. One might say that s is measured by N corrected by the approximate values of P and T. Hence the study of the variations in N becomes a study in the variations of humidity. The role of water vapor as a tracer, as was mentioned above, can then be detected through the medium of N.

THE SUBJECT OF THIS STUDY

Apart from an academic point of view, at times it is necessary to study the flow pattern of the atmosphere both in a general way and under special conditions. The lack of boundaries, the inhomogeneity of the environment, and the compressibility of the air, all tend to lessen the applicability of classical hydrodynamics. However, some of the concepts of this scientific field do apply. In particular, one should retain the concept of one or more types of turbulent and laminar flow. This study will touch on these problems.

It may be noted that atmospheric turbulence has given rise to numerous works, many of which are statistical and are concerned with the search for a spatial autocorrelation function of some measured parameter (speed, temperature, index of refraction). In certain cases, smoke emission has been used.[1, 2]

Methods of Observation

Two methods of observation are possible.

(1) Make measurements of the index of refraction at fixed points.

(2) Utilize telemetered measurements of the index of refraction starting from a fixed point.

In either case the specific humidity will be determined.

The disadvantage of the first method is that, in general, it would be impossible without a large number of instruments, the measurements are not taken simultaneously, and one must take account of a theoretically predetermined time variable.

But when using the second method one is not sure he is measuring the true gradient of the refractive index. All he is sure of is that the sudden variations measured in the gradient of

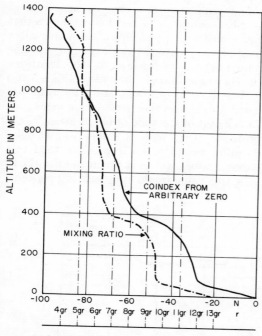

FIG. 1. Radiosonde flights, August 24, 1600 UT, 1955, Mediterranean area (1 measurement/12 meters).

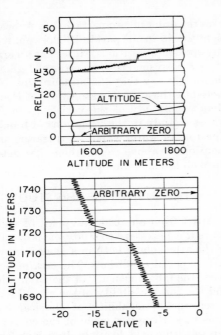

FIG. 2. Refractometer soundings, June 6, 0937 UT, 1957, Orleans, France.

the refractive index are related to variations in the gradient of the specific humidity.

The Vertical Sounding Radar used by Saxton,[3] is certainly the best approach to the latter method. One can show that the intensity of the echo is a function of the steepness of the gradient of the refractive index. Such radars have localized gross variations in the gradient of the index of refraction to regions on the order of 15 meters thick.

Principal Results Obtained

Measurements made by an airborne refractometer yield results similar to those in Figs.

2 and 3. The interpretation of these results is not easy.

The hypothesis has often been made that all of these fluctuations belong to a single ensemble which can be represented by a single cumulative distribution or by a single autocorrelation function, the Fourier transform of which is the spectrum.

Unfortunately, it is not clear that this hypothesis is well-founded. First it is necessary to investigate from the viewpoint of physics whether or not the nature of these fluctuations is unique. One of the methods adopted has been the verification by example of the permanence of certain fluctuations in space. To do this, recourse has been had to the two types of measurements pointed out above, (a) and (b).

Measurements have been made using special radiosondes capable of detecting variations on the order of $3N$.[4] By using a captive balloon, wiresonde, or helicopter, it is possible to make vertical soundings over a short interval as shown in Figs. 4(a) and (b). It can be seen [Fig. 4(b)] that certain irregularities produced by variations in relative humidity remain at a quasi-constant level.

Independent of this type of measurement vertical soundings by radar have shown that zones with strong gradients of refractive index (and hence, strong gradients of specific humidity) can last an hour or more whatever the time or season of observation (Figs. 5 and 6). Results from one radar study indicate that a definite echo level existed during more than 75 per cent of the time of observation.[3a] It is probable that, with a radar whose pulse duration would make it possible to detect strong gradients over a much smaller thickness, this value would approach 100 per cent.

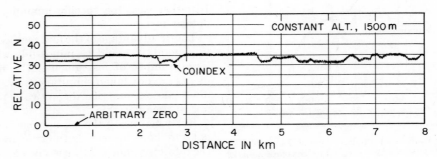

FIG. 3. Orleans, France, April 6, 1957, 0930–1030.

These experimental facts show that a least two families of fluctuations exist: one, quasi-persistent in position, the other practically random; the terms "persistent" and "random" are relative to a duration on the order of one hour. Hence, any statistical presentation should stress these two families of different nature, regardless of the amplitude of the fluctuations considered.

Theoretical Interpretation

The problem is simplified if, as in hydrodynamics, it is assumed that there are no sources or sinks of water vapor in the atmosphere. It is further assumed that there is neither condensation nor rain, and that there is no contribution to the water vapor by any horizontal movement.

The preceding experimental results show the existence of thin zones of the atmosphere characterized by a steep gradient of specific humidity; these can be termed "feuillets" or "leaflets." One is led to seek a theoretical explanation for them. From the principles of turbulence theory, beginning with Richardson, it is known that a parcel of air when subjected to a turbulent system breaks up while displacing itself. In this case, the diffusion of water vapor is increased and the specific humidity tends to be constant. On the contrary, in a volume of air, free from internal movements, water vapor diffuses from bottom to top much more slowly than in the preceding case. The steep gradient of the humidity which characterizes the "feuillets" is therefore the indicator of a change in the flow-system.

Let us consider in a calm atmosphere, two neighboring points at ground level A and B, subject to the same pressure, P_0 (Fig. 7).

It is known* that at an altitude z, the pressure will be

$$P = P_0 \exp\left[-\int_0^z \frac{g}{RT}\, dz\right] \qquad (5)$$

where

g = the acceleration of gravity
T = absolute temperature
R = the particular gas constant.

---

* This proof is valid for any height, provided that the air can be considered as a continuous environment, for which it suffices to say that an elementary particle should contain a very large number of molecules.

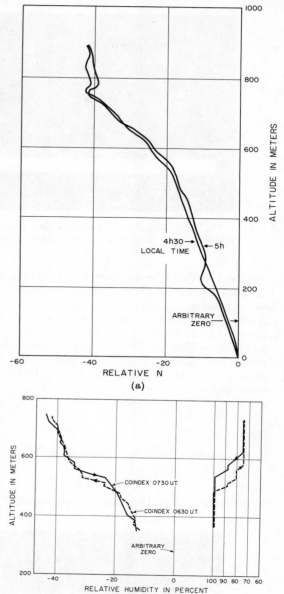

FIG. 4. (a) Radiosonde, August 27, 1955, Mediterranean area. (b) Radiosonde by helicopter, June 25, 1958, St. Andre de l'Eure, France.

The variation of g with altitude is independent of the nature of the air. Here g is assumed constant.

It is further known that the atmosphere is the mixture of two gases: dry air (of constant chemical composition) and water vapor. For

Fig. 5. Vertical sounding 10-cm radar. Height-time record for period 1200–1215 hours on 30/4/59. Height markers at 1-km intervals. Note "feuillet" at 1.5 km.

specific humidity, the constant R is fixed and does not depend on z. If the vertical variation in temperature $T(z)$ is the same above points A and B, all points at the same height will have the same pressure, and the atmosphere will be in equilibrium. It is also known that if a particle of mass, m, is displaced vertically a distance, h, it is subjected to a settling force equal to:

$$mgh \frac{\gamma_a - \gamma_t}{T} \qquad (6)$$

where

γ_a = temperature gradient for an adiabatic process

γ_t = the true temperature gradient.

In general, $\gamma_a < \gamma_t$. The force is in opposition

to h, i.e., the atmosphere is in stable equilibrium. $\gamma_a \geqq \gamma_t$ is the unstable condition, rarely achieved, leading to a generalized turbulence whose movements have a vertical component.

Let us now suppose that a source of water vapor is located at A and that the diffusion of this water vapor reaches the level H at a given moment. The composition of the gases along the verticals AH and BH is different, hence the absorption of the solar or terrestrial energy increases over AH, and the temperature is not identical at the same altitude above A and B. In the same way, R, which depends upon the nature of the gas, increases in value; Eq. (5) shows, however, that if RT varies, the points at the same altitude are not subject to

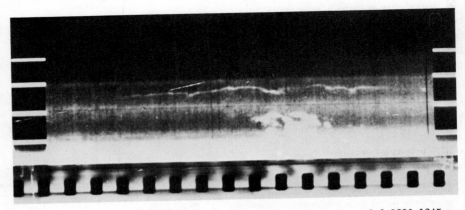

Fig. 6. Vertical sounding 10-cm radar. Height-time record for period 1230–1245 on 10/6/59. Height markers at 1-km intervals. Note "feuillet" at 2.5 km. Echos below have unknown origin.

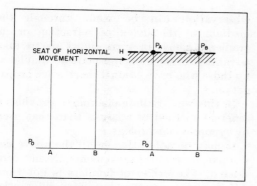

Fig. 7. Formation of a "feuillet." If $(RT)_A \neq (RT)_B$, then $P_A \neq P_B$.

the same pressure. Hence there is a difference of pressure in the horizontal plane, giving rise to a horizontal movement which tends to mix the air between AH and BH.* Layers at greater altitudes, however, are not affected. At level H, a discontinuity arises in the distribution of specific humidity, and this discontinuity extends horizontally above A and B. One can thus explain the formation of a "feuillet" which then will persist while rising very slowly as a function of the upward diffusion of water vapor.

If the entire body of air shifts or the system of evaporation at A and B modifies itself, another "feuillet" can form, but the first will last a long time, its destruction being tied to the vertical diffusion of water vapor.

Finally, let us notice that between feuillets the formation of a turbulent system is not unusual. In certain cases, it is a question of important vertical movements, in others, of horizontal movements. It is probable that the two must often coexist, but it is not clear that their statistical characteristics are the same at such times. Here one notes once again the complexity of atmospheric turbulence.

In a general way, every irregularity of temperature, radiation, albedo, or chemical composition modifies the product RT and induces the formation of "feuillets." For example, it is known that the difference in

* One may recall that the breezes (of earth, sea, and valley) are horizontal movements produced on a grand scale by a phenomenon comparable to that explained here for the difference in albedo between two neighboring regions. For the same reasons, an atmospheric duct often develops above breezes.

salinity in the oceans is one cause of the production of currents. In the ionosphere, it is probable that "feuillets" exist, but the "tracer" will no longer be water vapor but ionized particles, and the principal cause may well be variations in albedo from the atmosphere below.

It follows from the foregoing explanations that the horizontal dimensions of a "feuillet" are determined by the irregularities of the ground. On the contrary, the dimensions of "layers" which eventually form an atmospheric duct, are much greater. A zone of subsidence, for example, is linked to an anticyclone and its formation corresponds to atmospheric subsidence caused by movement from top to bottom, which is a less perturbed movement than that from bottom to top.

Study of Discontinuity

This problem can be approached mathematically.

A particle of unit mass, assumed in equilibrium in the horizontal plane will be subjected to:

(1) a pressure force

$$\frac{1}{\rho}\frac{dP}{dx}$$

where dP/dx is the horizontal variation in pressure and ρ is the density of the air.

(2) a force of resistance to movement in the manner of

$$-18\frac{\nu}{L^2}\frac{dx}{dt}$$

where

   18 = an approximation of 6π
   ν = kinematic viscosity
   L^2 = the cross section of the particle of any form
dx/dt = the velocity.

The Coriolis force will be ignored.

The equation of motion may then be written as

$$\frac{d^2x}{dt^2} + 18\frac{\nu}{L^2}\frac{dx}{dt} - \frac{1}{\rho}\frac{dP}{dx} = 0 \qquad (7)$$

To integrate, let us suppose that dP/dx is constant, and let us choose $x = 0$ when $t = 0$. Integration yields the velocity

$$\frac{dx}{dt} = v = \frac{1}{\rho}\frac{dP}{dx} \cdot \frac{L^2}{18\nu}\left[1 - \exp\left(-\frac{18\nu}{L^2}t\right)\right] \tag{8}$$

v rapidly approaches its maximum value:

$$v_M = \frac{L^2}{18\rho\nu}\frac{dP}{dx} \tag{9}$$

The smallest dimensions for L^2 obtained from the turbulence theory are, let us say, several cm^2, and a mean value for dP/dx is on the order of 0.1 mb for 10 meters, corresponding to experimental values obtained by microbarographs over a short distance. [A similar value can be found from Eq. (5).] For v, an order of magnitude of 0.1 m/sec is found. This order of magnitude proves that it is possible to ignore the Coriolis force.

It should be noted that the clearly indicated horizontal speed is much greater than the vertical speed of the diffusion of water vapor. The lower surface will then be very sharp; the formation of a single "feuillet" does not permit the study of the upper surface.

It has been seen that another modification of the product RT results in the formation of a new "feuillet." Its upper surface could be studied in the same way, but the speed to be taken into consideration will then be the difference between the horizontal speeds of two super-imposed layers. One could continue this analysis using the well-known study of gravitational waves, which has been done for the troposphere and for the ionosphere.[6]

CONCLUSIONS

It has been shown that the study of the distribution of water vapor leads to the acceptance of a very general model for the atmosphere in which, in the midst of a turbulent environment, one finds elements, more or less horizontal, which are zones of great stability.

Observation can be made through the medium of the index of refraction or its gradient, which in turn allows us to take advantage of the numerous data accumulated by those who have studied short-wave propagation.

In this way, radio meteorology provides a different method of analysis than that used by synoptic meteorology.

It may be noted that in all the above development, vertical movements are not considered. The origin of feuillets is not from differential convection but from differential temperature or gas constant in a stable atmosphere.

Thermal energy, given by the difference in temperature between hot and cold points, is transformed to kinetic energy in turbulent layers. On this particular point, in relation to vorticity, more explanations are given in a recent paper [Misme, P., *Annales des Télécommunications* (January-February 1964)].

References

1. Sutton, O. G., "Micrometeorology," New York, McGraw-Hill Publishing Co., 1953.
2. Saissac, J., "On the Atmospheric Diffusion of Particles," *C. R. Acad. Sci.*, **T247**, 1371 (1958).
3. Saxton, J., "Some Reflections on the Propagation of Radioelectric Waves through the Troposphere," *Onde Electrique*, **400–401**, 505–515 (July-August, 1960).
3a. Saxton, J., Private communication.
4. Misme, P., "Method of Thermodynamic Measurement of the Index of Refraction of the Air; Description of the M.D.I. Radiosonde," *Annals of Telecommunications*, **T11**, No. 4, 81–88 (April 1956).
5. Castel, F. du, Misme, P., Spizzichino, A., and Voge, J., "Partial Reflections in the Atmosphere and Propagation at Great Distance," *Edition de la Revue Optique*, (1960).
6. Hines, C. O., "Theoretical Survey of Motions in the Ionosphere," *XIIIth General Assembly of URSI*, **Doc. III, 3**, (1960).

71. Potential Use of Passive Probing of Atmospheric Structure by Thermal Emissions at Radio Frequencies

B. R. Bean, E. R. Westwater and R. L. Abbott

National Bureau of Standards, Boulder, Colorado

ABSTRACT

Microwave resonance lines of water vapor ($\nu = 22.235$ Gc/sec) and oxygen (50 Gc/sec $< \nu < 65$ Gc/sec) give rise to strong thermal emissions by the atmosphere in the microwave region. The intensity of these emissions depends on the water vapor and temperature distributions within the atmosphere. This paper explores the possibility of using ground-based radiation measurements of these thermal emissions to determine the gross water vapor and temperature profiles of the lower atmosphere.

INTRODUCTION

This paper considers the possibility of determining the gross water vapor and temperature profile of the atmosphere by means of ground-based radiometer measurements in the microwave region. The presentation here is primarily concerned with the radiative properties of the atmosphere that will determine if the method of passive probing is possible under the assumptions of horizontal homogeneity of atmospheric structure. The approach used here involves the careful calculation of radiative emission along the expected path of a radio ray (assuming, again, horizontal homogeneity and the availability of high side lobe rejection antennas) and comparison of this calculated value with that expected in a standard atmosphere. The above is presented with the usual reservations concerning the practical problems

of available antennas; extrapolation of laboratory determination of absorption coefficients, line widths and their pressure and temperature dependence to the real atmosphere. This passive technique may be possible in the microwave frequency region because of the strong microwave absorptive and emissive properties of the oxygen and water vapor molecules, and because of the absence of other competing sources which are present in adjacent frequency regions. For such a technique to yield significant information about atmospheric structure, it would be necessary to utilize the frequency dependence of the various thermal emissions, the angular dependence of antenna measurements, and the surface values of standard meteorological parameteres in conjunction with the radiometer measurements.

For the sake of completeness and clarity in understanding the problem at hand, background material on radiative transfer through a non-scattering medium is briefly discussed. In particular, the concept of brightness temperature is introduced and related to the more familar quantity, radiation intensity.

The next section covers atmospheric absorption due to oxygen and water vapor. It summarizes the present state of the art in regard to pressure and temperature dependence of line widths and absorption intensity factors.

Finally, calculations of brightness temperatures for various climatic profiles are presented and discussed.

BACKGROUND

All substances with temperatures above absolute zero emit thermal radiation. The distribution of this energy throughout the frequency spectrum is characteristic of the temperature of the source and of the constituent materials of the source itself. For our purposes the source of radiation is the atmosphere; the frequency region is the microwave region from 5 to 60 Gc/sec.

For substances in thermal equilibrium, general laws of thermodynamics relate the absorption characteristics of the material to those of emission. Good absorbers of radiation are also good emitters, and vice versa. Thus, one may describe quantitatively both emission and absorption by the same parameter. The standard choice for this parameter is the absorption coefficient.

A useful comparison when dealing with thermal emissions from real bodies is the radiation from a black body, a substance which absorbs completely all radiation of any frequency which falls on its surface. The emission of a black body depends only on the frequency and its temperature. This emission is independent of the composition of the black body. The fact that the spectral distribution of the emitted energy uniquely determines the temperature of a black body is the basis of many spectroscopic temperature measurements, since the radiation from many real bodies approximates, more or less, that from a black body.

In the microwave region, the noise energy emitted by a blackbody in thermal equilibrium with its surroundings is given by the Rayleigh-Jeans law

$$\psi_\nu = 8\pi k T \left(\frac{\nu}{c}\right)^2 \tag{1}$$

where

- ψ_ν = emitted flux density per unit frequency.
- ν = frequency
- k = Boltzmann's constant (1.38044×10^{-6} ergs/K°)
- T = absolute temperature, K°
- c = speed of light.

The emissions from bodies not in thermal equilibrium can similarly be described by means of a source function. For the micro-

wave region the source function is approximated by the Rayleigh-Jeans function. This approximation is valid because of conditions of local thermodynamic equilibrium which exist in the earth's atmosphere.

The thermal emissions from a real body may be related to those of the ideal black body by means of the mass absorption coefficient, κ_ν (absorption per unit length per unit density of absorbing material at the frequency ν), through Kirchhoff's law[5]. This law may be written

$$j_\nu = \kappa_\nu \psi_\nu \tag{2}$$

where j_ν is emitted intensity per unit mass per unit frequency. This law expresses in quantitative form the well-known physical fact that good absorbers of radiation are good emitters, and vice versa.

The transmission of radiation through an absorbing and radiating medium may be described as follows: consider a small cylindrical element of volume, with unit cross-sectional area and height ds. Neglecting scattering, the change of radiation intensity, dI_ν, between opposite ends of this cylinder will be given by the difference of radiation emitted and radiation absorbed within this volume:

$$dI_\nu = \kappa_\nu \rho \psi_\nu ds - \kappa_\nu \rho I_\nu ds \tag{3}$$

where ρ is the density of the medium and I_ν is the incident intensity at the frequency ν. In terms of the absorption coefficient, γ_ν, ($\equiv \kappa_\nu \rho$), this may be written

$$\frac{dI_\nu}{ds} = \gamma_\nu \psi_\nu - \gamma_\nu I_\nu \tag{3a}$$

The general solution to Eq. (3a) is

$$I_\nu = \sum_i I_{\nu,i} \exp\left(-\int_0^{S_i} \gamma_\nu ds\right) + \int_0^\infty \gamma_\nu \psi_\nu \exp\left(-\int_0^s \gamma_\nu ds\right) ds \tag{4}$$

where the summation extends over the discrete sources in and beyond the atmosphere, $I_{\nu,i}$ is the unattenuated intensity due to the ith source, and S_i is the distance of this source from the point of reception of energy. The terms in the summation represent the intensity contributed by discrete sources attenuated by the intervening atmosphere while the integral represents the contribution

$$T_b \left(\nu, \theta_0 \right) = \int_0^\infty \gamma(r)\, T(r) \left(e^{-\int_0^r \gamma(r')\, dr'} \right) dr$$

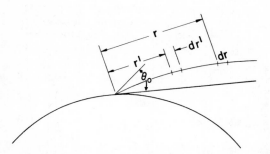

FIG. 1. Thermal noise integral and associated geometry. θ_0 is the antenna elevation angle.

due to the continuous distribution of sources within our atmosphere.

Equation (4) cannot in principle be integrated even if the absorption coefficient and source function are known functions of position within the atmosphere. The dependence of the integral upon the ray trajectory makes it imperative that the refractive properties of the atmosphere be known as well.

In analogy with the Rayleigh-Jeans law, which relates the emitted radiation intensity to the actual temperature, it is convenient to describe the intensity received at a point by an equivalent temperature. This is done by a relation identical in form to the Rayleigh-Jeans equation:

$$I_\nu = 8\pi k T_b \left(\nu \right) \left(\frac{\nu}{c} \right)^2 \tag{5}$$

where the quantity $T_b(\nu)$ is called the brightness temperature. This quantity is also commonly referred to as the thermal noise temperature, or simply noise temperature. This terminology will be used interchangeably in the following sections of this paper.

Combining (1), (4), and (5) we get

$$T_b(\nu) = \sum_i T_{b,i}(\nu) \exp\left(- \int_0^{S_i} \gamma_\nu ds \right) + \int_0^\infty \gamma_\nu T \exp\left(- \int_0^s \gamma_\nu ds \right) ds \tag{6}$$

which is the basic equation of our study.

In Eq. (6), $T_{b,i}(\nu)$ is the brightness temperature (unattenuated) of the ith discrete source. Figure 1 shows the thermal noise integral for continuous sources only and its associated geometry.

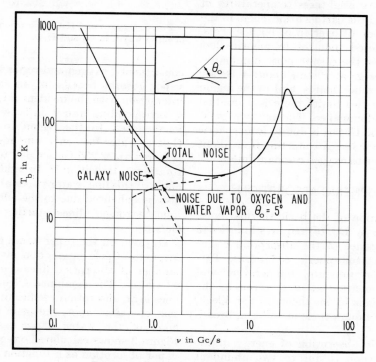

FIG. 2. Cosmic and atmospheric noise.[9]

Insight into the physical significance of noise temperature may be gained by observing that the noise temperature of a radiating medium will always be less than or equal to its actual temperature, the equality holding only if the medium is a black body. It is apparent that thermal noise temperature expresses quite concisely the effectiveness of a radiating medium as compared to its kinetic temperature.

Atmospheric thermal noise as measured by an antenna will depend explicitly on two variables—the frequency and the antenna elevation angle—and will depend implicitly on the atmospheric profile giving rise to the radiation. The basic problem of this study, then, is to employ the frequency and angular dependence of ground-based antenna measurements to reconstruct the actual profile. A similar technique has long been employed to study the galaxy by means of cosmic noise receivers that have been perfected in the frequency region of cosmic radiation. With the recent advent of sensitive receivers in the microwave region, it is becoming increasingly possible to study the thermal radiation characteristics of our atmosphere. Figure 2[9] shows brightness temperatures of the cosmos and the earth's atmosphere in the frequency region of overlap of both sources. It is to be noted that for frequencies less than 0.5 Gc/sec the cosmic noise dominates, for frequencies greater than about 4 Gc/sec the atmosphere dominates, and in the region between these two limits there is a gradual transition of dominance. The relative maximum at 22.235 Gc/sec is due to atmospheric water vapor; the increase starting from about 35 Gc/sec is due to oxygen resonant lines.

ATMOSPHERIC ABSORPTION

The evaluation of the basic thermal noise integral given by Eq. (6) requires knowledge of the dependence of the absorption coefficient, γ_ν, on atmospheric conditions. This dependence on pressure, temperature and water vapor concentration is given in the microwave region by the theory of Van Vleck, based on the assumptions of collision broadening.

Atmospheric absorption of energy in the microwave region is due to two abundant

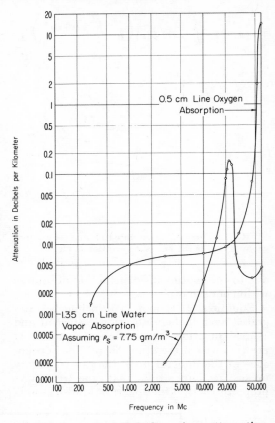

FIG. 3. Oxygen and H_2O absorption—attenuation of radio waves in O_2 and H_2O.

constituents, oxygen and water vapor. Water vapor absorbs because of an electric dipole interaction with the incident microwave with a corresponding transition between its rotational states. In the region from 10 to 60 Gc/sec, water has only one resonance line, centered at 22.235 Gc/sec due to the 6_{-5}-5_{-1}, rotational transition.[14] In addition to the effect of this line, water vapor absorption will also be enhanced due to the effect of several much stronger, lines starting around 200 Gc/sec.

Oxygen, on the other hand, absorbs via a magnetic dipole interaction giving rise to a number of absorption lines centered around 60 Gc/sec. The combined effect of all these lines is an absorption coefficient greater than that of water vapor, except in the neighborhood of the water vapor resonance line. Figure 3 shows calculated oxygen and water vapor absorption as a function of frequency.

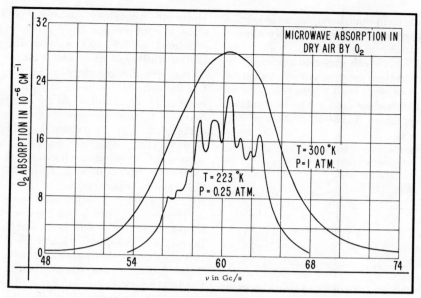

FIG. 4. $\gamma(O_2)$ for $P = 1$ atm and $P = \frac{1}{4}$ atm.

Quantitatively, the oxygen absorption coefficient, $\gamma(O_2)$, (decibels per kilometer), is given at $T = 293°K$ and standard atmospheric pressure by the following expression, valid for frequencies below 50 Gc/sec[13]

$$\gamma(O_2) = \frac{0.34}{\lambda^2} \left\{ \frac{\Delta\nu_1}{(1/\lambda)^2 + \Delta\nu_1^2} + \frac{\Delta\nu_2}{(2.0 + 1/\lambda)^2 + \Delta\nu_2^2} + \frac{\Delta\nu_2}{(2.0 - 1/\lambda)^2 + \Delta\nu_2^2} \right\} \quad (7)$$

where λ is the wavelength (cm) for which the absorption is to be determined and $\Delta\nu_1$ and $\Delta\nu_2$ are the line width factors with dimensions of cm^{-1}. Physically, the line width is the breadth of the spectral line when the absorption is half of its maximum value. The term involving $\Delta\nu_1$ in Eq. (7) describes the non-resonant absorption arising from the zero frequency line of the oxygen molecules; the terms involving $\Delta\nu_2$ describe the effect of several natural resonant absorptions of oxygen occurring in the vicinity of 60 Gc/sec [$(1/\lambda) = 2.0$ cm^{-1}]. Figure 4 shows the measured oxygen absorption in the 60 Gc/sec range at 1 atm and $\frac{1}{4}$ atm pressure.[1] Although this frequency region contains some 25 individual resonant lines, at 1 atm the pressure broad-

ening of the individual lines has so obscured the individual line structure that the absorption appears to be due to a single line centered at 60 Gc/sec (called the centroid frequency). The individual lines begin to be resolved with decreasing pressure as can be seen from the lower curve. Even though at this pressure the individual lines are predominant, the net shape of the line is such that it may be described by a centroid frequency in the region below 45 Gc/sec.

The water vapor absorption at 293°K arising from the 1.35-cm line (22.235 Gc/sec), $\gamma(H_2O)_R$, is given by

$$\frac{\gamma(H_2O)_R}{\rho} = \frac{3.5 \times 10^{-3}}{\lambda^2} \left\{ \frac{\Delta\nu_3}{[(1/\lambda) - (1/1.35^2)] + \Delta\nu_3^2} + \frac{\Delta\nu_3}{[(1/\lambda) + (1/1.35)^2] + \Delta\nu_3^2} \right\} \quad (8)$$

where ρ is the absolute humidity (g/m^3), and $\Delta\nu_3$ is the line width in cm^{-1}. The additional absorption arising from the higher frequency absorption lines is described by

$$\frac{\gamma(H_2O)_{NR}}{\rho} = \frac{.05\Delta\nu_4}{\lambda^2} \quad (9)$$

where $\Delta\nu_4$ is the effective line width of the absorption bands above the 1.35-cm line. The nonresonant term has been increased by a factor of 4 in order to better satisfy experimental results.[3]

Although Van Vleck gives estimates of the various line widths, more recent experimental determinations were used whenever possible. The line width values used in the calculations are summarized in Table 1.

TABLE 1. LINE WIDTH FACTORS USED TO DETERMINE ATMOSPHERIC ABSORPTION

Line Width	Temperature (°K)	Value (cm⁻¹atm⁻¹)	References
$\Delta\nu_{1,2}$	293	0.018	10
$\Delta\nu_{2,0}$	300	0.049	1
$\Delta\nu_{3,0}$	318	0.087	3
$\Delta\nu_{4,0}$	318	0.087	3

The preceding expressions for gaseous absorption are given as they appear in the literature and do not reflect the pressure and temperature sensitivity of either the numerical intensity factor or the line widths. This sensitivity must be considered for the present application since it is necessary to consider the manner in which the absorption varies with temperature and pressure throughout the atmosphere. The dependence of intensity factors upon atmospheric pressure and temperature variations was considered to be that given by the Van Vleck theory. The magnitude and temperature dependence of the line widths is a question not completely resolved. Both theory and experiment indicate the line width to vary as $1/T^x$, $x > 0$.

Different laboratory measurements on the same line of oxygen have given values of x ranging from 0.71 to 0.90 with differences in the magnitude of $\Delta\nu$ of about 20 per cent.[8-12] The major disagreement is in the resonant line width factor for oxygen, $\Delta\nu_2$. The laboratory determinations of Birnbaum and Maryott[10] and Gordon[7a] give impressive agreement with a centroid value of $\Delta\nu_2 = 0.05$ cm⁻¹, whereas equally impressive agreement is obtained with outdoor measurements by Straiton and Tolbert[11] and Bell Telephone Laboratories[4] with a value of $\Delta\nu = 0.02$ cm⁻¹. The physical reason for the differences between laboratory and outdoor measurements has not been clarified in the literature. The line widths used for the calculations of this paper are those given in Table 1. Part of the reason for the choice of the laboratory values is that a clear delineation of the contributions of both resonant absorption and the effect of the wings of absorption lines at higher frequencies is made, a factor not treated by Tolbert and Straiton. Experiments have also clearly indicated that the line width changes from line to line, with maximum fluctuations of about 15 per cent. In the frequency region here considered (10 to 45 Gc/sec), the centroid frequency approximation for oxygen is valid and a mean line width can be used with good accuracy, but in the region of the resonant frequencies of oxygen, the line-to-line line width variations must be taken into account. The expressions used to calculate the absorptions are given in Table 2. In Table 2, T is the

TABLE 2. VALUES USED IN THE CALCULATION OF ATMOSPHERIC ABSORPTION

Absorption* (db/km)	Intensity Factor	Line Width ($\Delta\nu$)
$\gamma(O_2)$	$\dfrac{.34}{\lambda^2}\left(\dfrac{P}{1013.25}\right)\left(\dfrac{293}{T}\right)^2$	$\Delta\nu_{1,0}\left(\dfrac{P}{1013.25}\right)\left(\dfrac{293}{T}\right)^{3/4}$ and $\Delta\nu_{2,0}\left(\dfrac{P}{1013.25}\right)\left(\dfrac{300}{T}\right)^{3/4}$
$\dfrac{\gamma(H_2O)_R}{\rho}$	$\dfrac{.0318}{\lambda^2}\left(\dfrac{293}{T}\right)^{5/2}\exp\left(-\dfrac{644}{T}\right)$	$\Delta\nu_{3,0}\left(\dfrac{P}{1013.25}\right)\left(\dfrac{318}{T}\right)^{1/2}(1+.0046\rho)$
$\dfrac{\gamma(H_2O)_{NR}}{\rho}$	$\dfrac{.05}{\lambda^2}\left(\dfrac{293}{T}\right)$	$\Delta\nu_{4,0}\left(\dfrac{P}{1013.25}\right)\left(\dfrac{318}{T}\right)^{1/2}(1+.0046\rho)$

* ρ is water vapor density in g/m³.

absolute temperature and P is the pressure. The reference temperatures given are those at which the appropriate experimental determinations were made, and the pressures are to be expressed in millibars. A detailed discussion of the theoretical aspects of the pressure and temperature dependence is given by Artman[1].

By taking into account the temperature and pressure dependence of the line widths. it is seen that for a given quantity of water vapor, the attenuation is proportional to

$$P^{-1} \text{ and } T^{-2} \exp\left(-\frac{644}{T}\right)$$

at the resonance line; to

$$P \text{ and } T^{-3} \exp\left(-\frac{644}{T}\right)$$

at the sides of the curve; and to P and $T^{-3/2}$ well away from resonance. In applying the above considerations to absorption approx-

imations, it also must be remembered that for a given relative humidity, the density will vary considerably with temperature.

The behavior of water vapor attenuation near the resonant line is very remarkable, as can be seen by inspecting Eq. (8). Since $\Delta\nu_3$ is small compared to $1/\lambda$, it may be neglected in the denominator of Eq. (8) for non-resonant wavelengths. The attenuation per unit density is thus directly proportional to $\Delta\nu_3$ and hence to the total pressure for these frequencies. But at the resonant frequency, the dominant term in the expression is proportional to $1/\Delta\nu_3$, and thus inversely proportional to the pressure. In the atmosphere, the water vapor density is proportional to the total pressure. Therefore, the attenuation is independent of pressure at the resonant frequency and now depends only on the fraction of water vapor present. For practical purposes, this means that attenuation can occur at high altitudes with the same

TABLE 3

Gas	ν(Mc)	$\gamma_{max.}$(db/km)	% by Volume at Ground	γ(db/km) at Ground
SO$_2$	12,258.17	1.9×10^{-1}		$(0\text{-}1.9) \times 10^{-7}$
	12,854.54	8.7×10^{-1}		$(0\text{-}8.7) \times 10^{-7}$
	23,433.42	1.2×10^{-1}		$(0\text{-}1.2) \times 10^{-7}$
	24,304.96	2.3		$(0\text{-}2.3) \times 10^{-6}$
	25,398.22	2.1	$(0\text{-}1) \times 10^{-6}$	$(0\text{-}2.1) \times 10^{-6}$
	29,320.36	3.3		$(0\text{-}3.3) \times 10^{-6}$
	44,098.62	5.2		$(0\text{-}5.2) \times 10^{-6}$
	52,030.60	9.5×10^{-1}		$(0\text{-}9.5) \times 10^{-7}$
N$_2$O	24,274.78	2.5		1.25×10^{-6}
	22,274.60	2.5	0.5×10^{-6}	1.25×10^{-6}
	25,121.55	2.5		1.25×10^{-6}
	25,123.25	2.5		1.25×10^{-6}
NO$_2$	26,289.6	2.9	$(0\text{-}2) \times 10^{-8}$	$(0 \text{ to } 5.8) \times 10^{-8}$
O$_3$	10,247.3	9.5×10^{-2}	Summer $(0 \text{ to } .07) \times 10^{-6}$	$(0 \text{ to } 6.3) \times 10^{-9}$
	11,075.9	9.1×10^{-2}	Winter	$(0 \text{ to } 6.3) \times 10^{-9}$
	42,832.7	4.3×10^{-1}	$(0 \text{ to } .02) \times 10^{-6}$	$(0 \text{ to } 2.8) \times 10^{-8}$

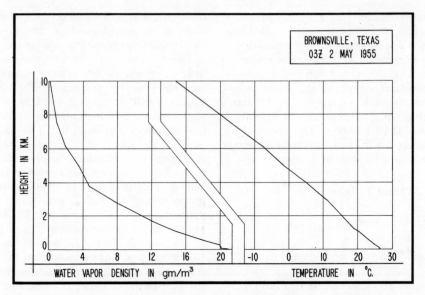

FIG. 5. Water vapor and temperature profile for Brownsville, Texas.

effectiveness as in the lower, denser layers if the mixing ratio is the same.

In addition to oxygen and water vapor, there are a number of other atmospheric gases which have absorption lines in the microwave region from 10 to 50 Gc/sec. These gases normally constitute a negligible portion of the general composition of the atmosphere, but could conceivably contribute to attenuation. Table 3 shows the resonant frequencies, maximum absorption coefficients at 300°K (attenuation coefficient if the fraction of molecules present were equal to unity), expected concentration in the atmosphere, and expected absorption coefficients due to these trace constituents. The data on molec-

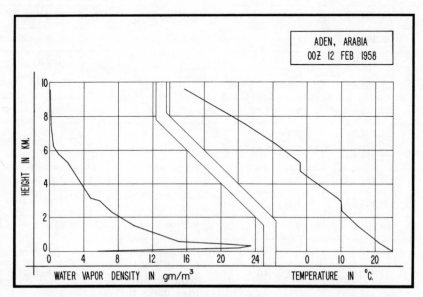

FIG. 6. Water vapor and temperature profile for Aden, Arabia.

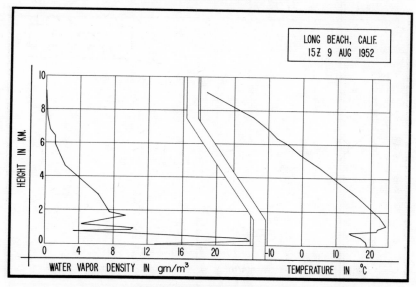

FIG. 7. Water vapor and temperature profile for Long Beach, California.

ular absorption coefficients were taken from Ghosh and Edwards[7] and those on concentrations were from the Compendium of Meteorology[6]. It is readily seen that the attenuation due to these sources is negligible compared to the high absorption due to oxygen and water vapor.

RESULTS AND ANALYSIS

We present here calculations determining the frequency and angular dependence of thermal noise temperatures for four varied climatic profiles. The numerical results are given in Figs. 9 through 16. These profiles were chosen because they exemplify extremes in climatic conditions which vary from hot-humid to cold-dry.

The actual temperature and water vapor height profiles of these stations are given in Figs. 5 through 8. Two of these (Brownsville, Texas, and Aden, Arabia) were chosen because of nearly identical profile structure over most of the height intervals. Only in the first 500 meters, where Aden has a large humidity gradient, do the two profiles appreciably differ. For heights above 500 meters, both profiles conform closely to standard temperature and absolute humidity lapse rates. Long Beach, California, exhibits devious

low-altitude behavior in both temperature and humidity, while Bismarck, N.D., typifies a cold, dry profile.

Figures 9 through 12 give the angular spectrum of noise temperatures calculated for the four profiles for resonant, near resonant, and off resonant wavelengths—1.35, 1.429, and 3.00 cm respectively. The first two wavelengths may be considered as the "wet" contribution, whereas the third gives the "dry" contribution to the noise. It is to be noted that for the humid profiles, Brownsville, Aden, and Long Beach, a condition of noise saturation exists for the "wet" wavelengths at low antenna angles. This occurs when the brightness temperature is constant with angle and is equal to the actual surface temperature of the ground. Under these conditions, the atmosphere is radiating as a black body. This is due, of course, to the large total path attenuation which occurs. At higher elevation angles, where the rays spend a smaller fraction of the total distance traveled in the lower more dense, strongly radiating portions of the atmosphere, the noise is correspondingly less.

The slope of the 3-cm brightness temperature is approximately the same for all of the stations, although the magnitudes of the noise temperatures differ considerably. The

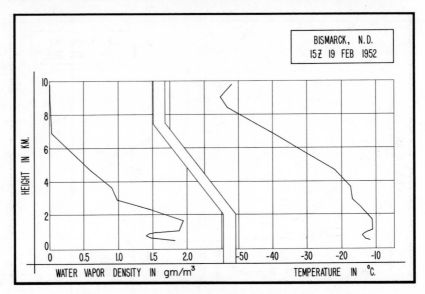

FIG. 8. Water vapor and temperature profile for Bismarck, N.D.

slope similarity in this case is due to strong dependence on pressure which exhibits the same height decay for all stations.

The influence of water vapor and the individual differences between stations are much clearer in Figs. 13 through 16 where the departures from calculated brightness temperatures for zero humidity standard atmospheres are plotted as a function of elevation angle for three frequencies. The magnitude of

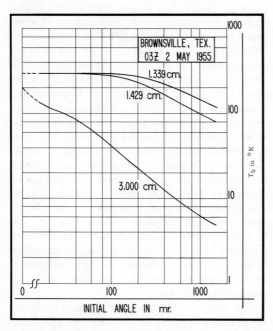

FIG. 9. Brightness temperature *vs* antenna elevation angle for several wavelengths at Brownsville, Texas.

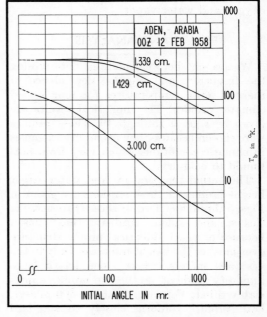

FIG. 10. Brightness temperature *vs* antenna elevation angle for several wavelengths at Aden, Arabia.

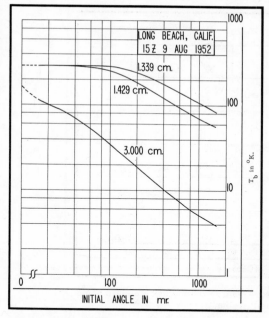

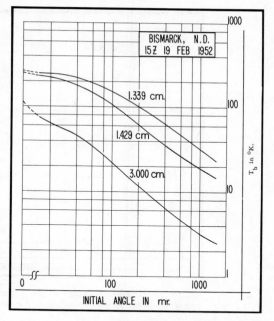

FIG. 11. Brightness temperature *vs* antenna elevation angle for several wavelengths at Long Beach, California.

FIG. 12. Brightness temperature *vs* antenna elevation angle for several wavelengths at Bismarck, N.D.

these differences ranges from about 240°K at the low angles to 40°K at the vertical for the humid stations as compared to a difference range about half as large for the dry, cold, Bismarck.

More subtle differences appear when one compares, for example, the noise figures from Aden and Brownsville, which, for heights above 1 km, have similar profiles and radically different ones below this height. We recall that

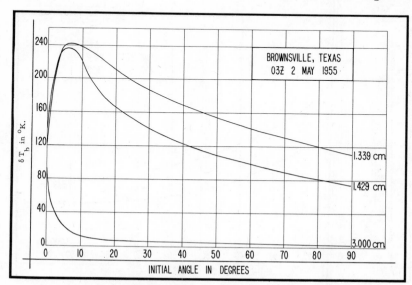

FIG. 13. Brightness temperature departure from zero humidity standard atmosphere *vs* antenna elevation angle for Brownsville, Texas.

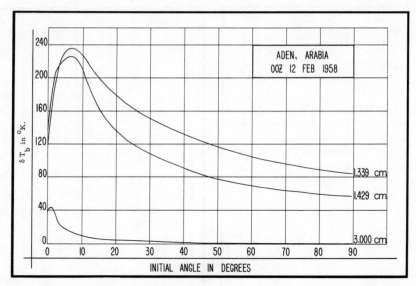

FIG. 14. Brightness temperature departure from zero humidity standard atmosphere *vs* antenna elevation angle for Aden, Arabia.

Aden has the humidity "bump" around 1 km, while Brownsville has near standard distribution. This difference shows up even at the dry 3.000-cm wavelength: Aden has a maximum displaced from zero initial angle, whereas Brownsville displays a monotonic decreasing angular dependence. This is due to a humidity refractive effect rather than any absorption. The resonant behavior of the two indicates profile similarities and dissimilarities as shown by the difference in slopes and positions of the maxima.

A very promising method utilizing thermal noise measurements to resolve the open quest-

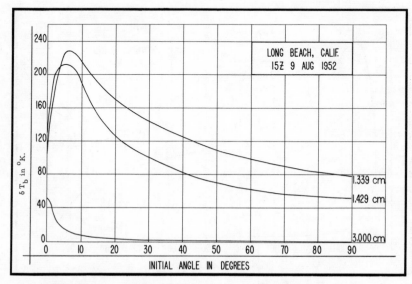

FIG. 15. Brightness temperature departure from zero humidity standard atmosphere *vs* antenna elevation angle for Long Beach, California.

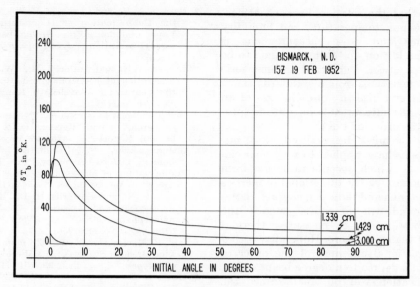

Fig. 16. Brightness temperature departure from zero humidity standard atmosphere *vs* antenna elevation angle for Bismarck. N.D.

ion of high altitude water distribution was discussed in a recent article by Barrett and Chung.[2] They propose noise measurements with a vertical receiving antenna operating at the resonance frequency of water, 22.235 Gc/sec. The line profile is drastically affected by the high altitude distribution, as may be seen from Fig. 17. The "spike" is due to the pressure independence at the resonance line of the absorption coefficient. It should be mentioned that the effect of oxygen has been neglected in Fig. 17, which gives rise to a noise temperature lower than one which would actually be measured. This does not, however, affect the presence of the spike, if the high altitude water is present.

SUMMARY

It has been seen that the atmospheric noise temperature varies considerably with respect to climatological conditions, particularly with water vapor content. This, indeed, suggests its potentialities as a probe for, at least, the gross water vapor structure of the lower atmosphere. Significant information about high altitude water vapor might also be gained by this method.

An intrinsically more difficult problem remaining to be solved is that of reconstruct-

ing the profile, as much as is possible, from the set of frequency and angular measurements which would, in practice, be available. The assumption here, and one which is far from

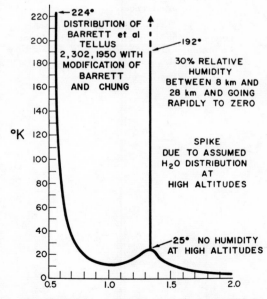

Fig. 17. Brightness temperature for high altitude water vapor distribution—effect of different assumptions as to water distribution at very high altitudes.

trivial, is that the relation between atmospheric pressure, temperature, and humidity distributions and noise measurements is unique. In addition, for such a method to be used in practice, significant atmospheric structural deviations from a standard atmosphere must give rise to noise changes of an experimentally measureable magnitude (probably on the order of 1°K).

Finally, it must be realized that our considerations have applied to a very special antenna: one which accepts radiation from one direction only. The directional properties of a real antenna and radiation characteristics of the ground will, of course, modify the angular distribution of measured thermal noise from that given here. Hopefully, with a highly directional antenna, of the order of fractions of a degree to a degree beam width, the modification will be small. Since the maximum departures from standard occur at 5 to 10 degrees elevation angle, it appears that sufficient angular resolutions and the elimination of ground effects is practiable.

It might be mentioned in passing that certain variants of this passive method could be useful in studying cloud structure and in studies of horizontal turbulence.

References

1. Artman, J., "Absorption of Microwaves by Oxygen in the Millimeter Wavelength Region," Columbia University Radiation Laboratory Report, 1953.

2. Barrett, A. H., and Chung, V. K., "A Method for the Determination of High-altitude Water Vapor Abundance From Ground-based Microwave Observations," *J. Geophys. Res.*, **67**, 4259 (1962).

3. Becker, G. E., and Autler, S. H., "Water Vapor Absorption of Electromagnetic Radiation in the Centimeter Wavelength Range," *Phys. Rev.*, **70**, 300 (1946).

4. Bell Telephone Laboratories, "Millimeter Wave Research," Final Report, ONR Contract 687(00), Report No. 24261-15, May 1955.

5. Chandrasekhar, S., "Radiative Transfer," London, Oxford University Press, 1950.

6. "Compendium of Meteorology," Boston, Mass., American Meteorological Society, 1951.

7. Ghosh, S. N., and Edwards, H. D., "Rotational Frequencies and Absorption Coefficients of Atmospheric Gases," *Air Force Surveys in Geophysics*, No. 82 (1956).

8. Hill, R. M., and Gordy, W., "Zeeman Effect and Line Breadth Studies of the Microwave Lines of Oxygen," *Phys. Rev.*, **93**, 1019 (1954).

9. Hogg, D. C., and Mumford, W. W., "Effective Noise Temperature of the Sky," *Microwave J.*, **3**, 80 (1960).

10. Maryott, A. A., and Birnbaum, G., "Microwave Absorption in Compressed Oxygen," *J. Chem. Phys.*, **32**, 686 (1960).

11. Straiton, A. W., and Tolbert, C. W., "Anomalies in the Absorption of Radio waves by Atmospheric Gases," *Proc. IRE*, **48**, 898 (1960).

12. Tinkham, M., and Strandbert, M. W. P., "Line Breadths in the Microwave Magnetic Resonance Spectrum of Oxygen," *Phys. Rev.*, **99**, 537–539 (1955).

13. Van Vleck, J. H., "The Absorption of Microwaves by Oxygen," *Phys. Rev.*, **71**, 413 (1947).

14. Van Vleck, J. H., "The Absorption of Microwaves by Uncondensed Water Vapor," *Phys. Rev.*, **71**, 425 (1947).

72. Moisture Analysis by Use of Microwaves

Gillis Johansson

Institute of Analytical Chemistry, University of Lund, Lund, Sweden

ABSTRACT

Two microwave cavities are used to measure the humidity of gases. One cavity is an empty reference cell and the other is the measuring cell. A klystron generates power which is divided between the two cavities. Differences in the Q-value or resonant frequency of the cavities will result in an output to the detector. Cavities ranging from 1.4 to 65 ml in volume have been used.

The measuring cavity is mechanically tuned to zero output of the microwave detector when the cavity is filled with a reference gas mixture. This reference may be dry gas or a mixture with predetermined humidity content.

The equipmnet is quite reliable and trouble-free. The accuracy of the measured deviation is better than 2 per cent. The range depends on the Q-value of the cavities; 0 to 2 per cent and 0 to ½ per cent water vapor in nitrogen have been used.

Microwave cavities have been used as sensing elements for the measurement of moisture in gases. A diagram of the apparatus is shown in Fig. 1. The microwave power source, a klystron, is isolated from the load by a ferrite isolator. The microwave power is divided by means of a magic T. When the impedances of the side arms are identical, the power is equally divided and there is no power in the detector arm. The output is zero. This condition is established if the two cavities are identical, i.e., they have the same Q-value and are tuned to the same resonant frequency. Further, the wave guides connecting the cavities to the magic T must have the same length. If the cavity tuning is very fine and the components have small tolerances, the zero signal will be very small. The gas inlet and outlet from the measuring cavity will of course introduce some changes in the characteristics of this cavity. There is no problem, however, in compensating for these changes so that a sufficiently small zero output signal is obtained.

A change in the dielectric constant of the gas inside the measuring cavity will produce a detuning of this cavity, resulting in an output of microwave power into the detector arm. The klystron is frequency modulated so that the cavity resonant frequency is passed twice each modulation cycle. The output waveform will then represent the impedance difference between the cavities vs frequency. The output is an AC current. This current is amplified, rectified and recorded.

The power level can be controlled either as shown in the figure by an auxiliary detector or by detuning one cavity and measuring the voltage at the main output.

Figure 2 shows a calibration curve for water vapor in nitrogen using a small cavity operating in a hybrid mode. This cavity has a Q-value of about 2000; its volume is 1.4 ml. The klystron frequency is about 9000 Mc. This cavity is suitable when a small cell volume is essential or when a great measuring range is desired. (The cavity is made by Sivers Lab, Stockholm 42, model SL 7596.)

TE_{011} cavities have also been used. They have a volume of 65 ml, the Q-value for these cavities is about 10,000. The sensitivity to changes in moisture is 8 to 10 times higher than for the hybrid cavities. These cavities are suitable when a small range is used and the large volume can be tolerated.

Temperature differences between the two

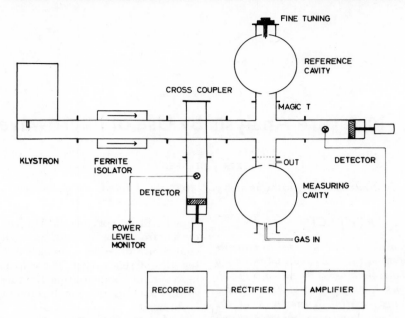

FIG. 1. Schematic diagram of microwave hygrometer.

cavities will cause a zero drift. By mounting the cavities close together, most of those variations can be cancelled. Both temperature and pressure changes, will however, change the dielectric constant of the gas. A calibration curve must be made for this hygrometer. The calibration is very stable, after several months it has been found to be unchanged.

The hygrometer described has a stability and noise which is less than 2 per cent of the measured quantity. Most of the variations are due to variations in the klystron power output. The temperature has been constant to $\pm 1°C$, and the pressure has been atmospheric.

This type of microwave hygrometer is very rugged and troublefree and the circuit is simple. The more complex servo-operated microwave hygrometers described earlier[1-2] have a higher accuracy.

A servo-operated version of this hygrometer is under development. A thermoregulator which can be set at any temperature between 30 and 150°C to an accuracy of $\pm 0.01°C$ has been developed. At present no data are available for this version of the apparatus.

Acknowledgment. The author thanks K. J. Karrman for his advice and interest. The work is supported by grants from the Swedish Technical Research Council.

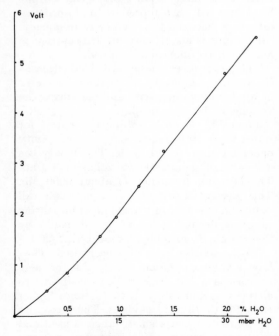

FIG. 2. Calibration curve for the microwave hygrometer using hybrid cavities.

References

1. Sargent, J., *Rev. Sci. Instr.*, **30**, 348 (1959).
2. Vetter, M. J., and Thompson, M. C., **Jr.**, *Rev. Sci. Instr.*, **33**, 656 (1962).

73. Refractometer Measurements at High Relative Humidities[*]

D. R. HAY AND H. E. TURNER

Department of Physics, University of Western Ontario, London, Canada

ABSTRACT

The measurement of refractive index of a gas by the microwave refractometer or by the capacitor-type (Hay) refractometer is subject to error due to water vapor adsorption on the sensing element. It is well-known that the rate of vapor adsorption upon metal or dielectric surfaces increases rapidly at humidities approaching saturation. The paper describes a detailed study of this physical process as it affects refractivity measurements, through the use of an environmental wind tunnel in which air temperature and relative humidity are variable throughout the range found in the troposphere.

INTRODUCTION

Two techniques for the precise measurement of changes in air refractivity within the troposphere have been examined. These are the microwave refractometer which uses a ventilated metal cavity as the sensing element, and the Hay refractometer whose sensing element is an air capacitor. The effects of water vapor adsorption and condensation upon the sensing elements of these instruments at high relative humidities make the interpretation of such soundings uncertain, in view of the conflicting evidence of previous workers. This work is concerned with a laboratory study of the interaction between the refractometer sensors and the air humidity.

EXPERIMENTAL

Preliminary measurements upon the adsorption of water vapor on isolated quartz and invar plates have been carried out with the aid of an optical ellipsometer. With a ventilation speed of 800 fpm, the depth of the adsorbed layer on flat quartz plate increased as relative humidity increased beyond 20 per cent; the increase became very rapid and erratic for relative humidities greater than 50 per cent. However, no detectable adsorption was found on the flat invar plate, for relative humidities up to saturation.

An experimental wind tunnel of special design was constructed to provide a controlled environment for further adsorption studies. This tunnel contains a homogeneous jet of 8-cu ft volume, in which wind speed is approximately 800 fpm and in which temperature can be varied between -20 and $+50°C$ for relative humidities variable up to saturation, at surface atmospheric pressure.

The refractive index of the air in the jet was ascertained from measurements of wet- and dry-bulb temperature and air pressure. A hygrometer was developed for this purpose to indicate temperature with a precision of

[*] The research reported in this paper was sponsored by the Air Force Cambridge Research Laboratories, Office of Aerospace Research, U.S.A., under Contract AF 19(628)-444.

The material in this paper has been published in greater detail in the Final Report on Contract AF 19(628)-444, "Investigation of Refractometer Measurements in the Atmosphere at High Relative Humidities and Temperatures," by D. R. Hay and H. E. Turner, July 1963.

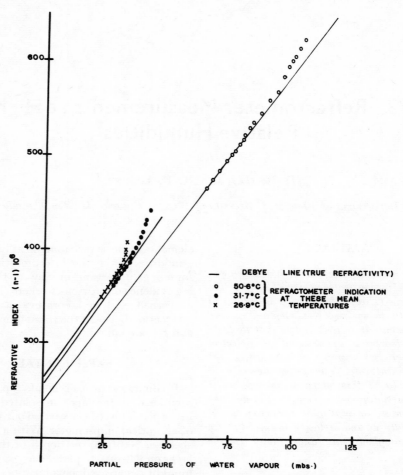

Fɪɢ. 1. Comparison between indicated and true refractivity—the microwave refractometer.

± 0.01°C. Air refractivity was computed, with an accuracy of one part in 10^6 through the Ferrel form of the psychrometric equation and the Smith-Weintraub form of the Debye equation. This information was compared with the refractometer indications, as relative humidity was varied for different fixed temperatures.

REMARKS

It has been found that adsorption occurs at high relative humidities in both the microwave refractometer cavity and in the Hay refractometer sensor, in amounts which cause apparent refractivity errors well in excess of

1 ppm. In the former, the apparent error increases approximately linearly with vapor pressure, beginning at a minimum relative humidity whose value depends upon the air temperature (Fig. 1); in the latter, the apparent error increases nonlinearly with vapor pressure, beginning at approximately 50 per cent RH for a wide range of air temperatures (Fig. 2). The amount of refractivity error in the capacitor-type sensor decreases with decreasing amount of quartz in the capacitor (Fig. 3); a further decrease in error results from the application of some types of hydrophobic materials to the sensor surface (Fig. 4). A significant improvement in the capacitor sensor has been obtained by elimination of

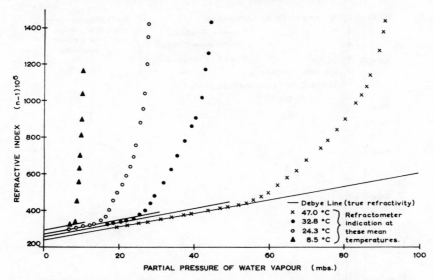

FIG. 2. Comparison between indicated and true refractivity—the capacitor-type refractometer. (Invar capacitor with six quartz spacers, uncoated.)

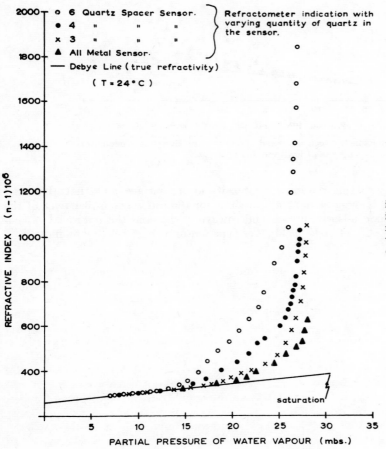

FIG. 3. Comparison between indicated and true refractivity—the capacitor-type refractometer. (Invar capacitor with variable number of quartz spacers, uncoated.)

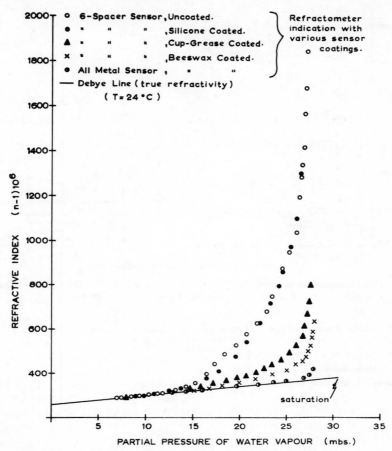

FIG. 4. Comparison between indicated and true refractivity—the capacitor-type refractometer. (Effects of hydrophobic coatings.)

the quartz spacers and by coating the invar surface with beeswax. It is suggested that the process of water vapor adsorption on metals is governed by the electric field intensity at the surface and that this may account for the difference in behavior of the microwave cavity and the improved capacitor-type sensor at high relative humidities.

74. The Microwave Refractometer used as a Humidity Sensor in Cloud Physics

ROBERT M. CUNNINGHAM

Air Force Cambridge Research Laboratories, Bedford, Massachusetts

ABSTRACT

This paper discusses the equation used for computation of moisture values from refractive index measurements obtained using a modified University of Texas refractometer. Hysteresis and aging errors caused by the variable coefficient of expansion of the not completely temperature compensated cavity are discussed. The refractometer becomes inoperative when there is a deposit of liquid water inside the cavity. The internal mounting of the cavity and the external cloud drop separator used on the AFCRL C-130 aircraft installation to alleviate this problem are illustrated and explained.

Examples of the fine grain humidity structure found in, and at the edge of, clouds are shown. The use of this type of data to monitor the decay of clouds and the study of entrainment is illustrated.

The detailed refractive index or moisture structure of a dry line is strikingly shown by refractive index data taken with the AFCRL C-130 while flying with the National Severe Storms Project (NSSP).

INTRODUCTION

The microwave refractometer has been used for many years by people in the radio propagation field to measure refractive index changes in the atmosphere. Perhaps because of its cost, its somewhat complex electronics, and difficulties involved in obtaining the absolute index of refraction during field operations, it has not been extensively used by meteorologists for obtaining moisture values. Also, the requirements for extremely rapid response has not been requested by most meteorologists. In the area of research in cloud dynamics and cloud physics, however, the need exists for very high speeds of reponse for both temperature and moisture measurement. Fortunately in this area the difficulty of obtaining absolute moisture values from refractive index measurements taken on cloud probing flights can be largely overcome by assuming that maximum values of refractive index within thick clouds correspond to regions of water vapor saturation.

REFRACTIVITY AND HUMIDITY

The refractive index (n) or refractivity (N) of the atmosphere is a function of the pressure (P), absolute temperature (T), and water vapor pressure (e), of the air. The liquid water content in the case of a cloudy atmosphere, according to Enenstein, affects the refractive index to a minor extent[1,2]. Its effect will be ignored in this paper which is directed toward the measurement of humidity. The instrument is arranged so that liquid water is eliminated from the measurement in flight through cloud. Experimental work is needed to verify Enenstein's formulations before the present sampling methods can be completely valid for the measurement of radio refractive index in clouds.

The relationship between refractivity or refractive index and atmospheric variables is, according to Smith and Weintraub,[3]

$N = (n - 1) \times 10^6$

$$= \frac{77.6\,P}{T} + \frac{3.73 \times 10^5\,e}{T^2} \quad (1)$$

If the value of N of an air sample is measured by a refractometer and the pressure and temperature of the sample are known, the water vapor content of the sample can be computed. For instance the relative humidity (RH) in per cent is obtained from the following expression where e_s is the saturation vapor pressure at temperature T.

$$RH = 2.68 \times 10^{-4} \frac{T}{e_s}\,(TN - 77.6P) \quad (2)$$

A change in the measured value of refractivity can be related to a change in relative humidity if the pressure and temperature have remained constant as follows:

$$\Delta RH = 2.68 \times 10^{-4} \frac{T^2}{e_s}\,\Delta N \qquad (3)$$

This latter relation is shown in Fig. 1 for a change of one N unit. Except in the case of special installations, refractivity changes measured from aircraft of less than $\frac{1}{2}$ to $1\,N$ unit are suspect. This low order of residual noise of the refractometer measuring system (refractometer, duct and external probe) has been estimated from flights at several airspeeds at high altitude where the residual small noise was found to be related to aircraft airspeed and engine power setting and not to ambient index changes. These residual effects

are probably due to rapid changes of flow in the boundary layer around the aircraft and around the intake probe. Sound waves from propeller tips may also cause low amplitude noise in the refractometer system. These phenomena, essentially pressure effects, could theoretically be compensated for with rapid response pressure measuring equipment. This refinement is not found to be practical, therefore, as indicated by Fig. 1, the refractometer as presently used is not too useful a humidity sensor below temperatures of -10 to $-15°C$.

THE REFRACTOMETER

The microwave refractometer has several forms, the particular type used by the AFCRL Cloud Physics Branch is a modified University of Texas instrument. This particular unit was originally described by Crain and Cronenwett.[4] The modification of this unit to eliminate circuits susceptible to drift has been described by Shaw and Cunningham.[5] This latter modification replaces the discriminator and DC amplifiers by counting circuits. The resulting unit is stable electronically to 0.02 N units.

Much larger values of drift remain, however, when the whole system is considered. The measuring cavity must remain a constant size in order to have a completely stable instrument. Cavities are made from invar in order

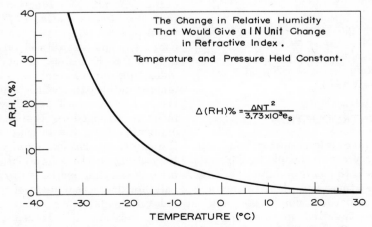

Fig. 1. Sensitivity of the refractometer as a relative humidity source.

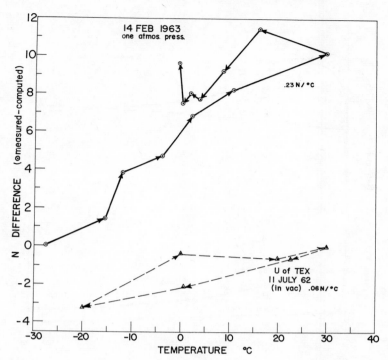

FIG. 2. Results of two calibration runs on a University of Texas refractometer cavity. N difference scale has an arbitrary zero. N for the February 14
case, run at AFCRL, at ΔN of zero was 320. ΔN for the July 11 case, run at
University of Texas is the equivalent in N units of a frequency change.

to minimize size change due to changes of the
temperature of the air flowing through and
around the cavity. To further minimize this
temperature effect, a steel disc is placed inside
the cavity so made that the small expansion
of the invar with temperature is compensated
by the expansion of the disc inside the cavity.
This compensation can not be accomplished
perfectly. The data plotted in Fig. 2 illustrate
the residual effect of temperature on the
refractive index measurement. Both sets of
data are for the same cavity. The earlier set
was obtained at the University of Texas by
evacuating the cavity, sealing it, and immer-
sing it in a temperature controlled bath. Seven
months later the cavity was checked again,
this time at AFCRL in its mount used for the
aircraft installation. Temperature and
pressure were measured of dry air circulated
through and around the cavity. The difference
between the measured and computed refractive index value results in this second plot of
the temperature effects on this cavity. These

curves in Fig. 2 illustrate the magnitude and
complexity of this temperature compensation
factor. A hysterisis loop is involved in the
correction for temperature effect in the short
term, hours, and a drift of the average correction factor is probable over a long term of many
months (i.e., July to February).

The data plotted in Fig. 2 were taken over
some six hours, so that the cavity is very
close to being at thermal equilibrium with its
surroundings for each plotted point. Rapid
changes in temperature (in a few seconds)
have a more marked effect in terms of the
error introduced. Figure 3 illustrates the
results of a test using the same refractometer
cavity and duct work but suddenly sending
cold air through the cavity. A thermocouple
on the cavity outside surface under a screw
and washer was considered to give a rough
measure of the temperature of the body of the
cavity, other thermometers (resistance wire)
were used to give a record of the air temperature entering and leaving the cavity. The

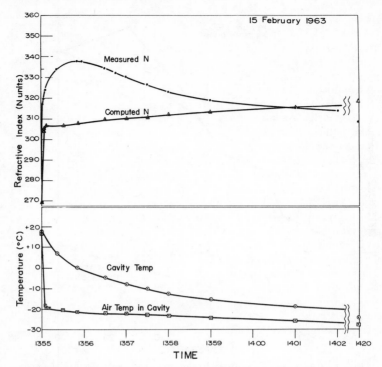

FIG. 3. Effect of a sudden change in temperature on the refractometer output. Time in minutes and seconds.

outside cavity temperature (cavity temp) and
the average of the air temperature before and
after flowing through the cavity (air temp
in cavity) are plotted in Fig. 3. The initial
sudden change in measured refractive index
is due to a real change of index caused by the
rapid flushing of the cavity with cold air in
$\frac{1}{100}$ to $\frac{1}{50}$ of a second. No measurable change
in temperature of the cavity parts occurs
during this short period. The computed N
did not quite follow the measured N value
since the thermometer used did not have a
high enough time of response. The marked
overshot of the refractivity values as measured by the refractometer is presumably
caused by the more rapid cooling of the
compensation disc than of the much more
massive cavity walls. The cavity temperature
coefficient (Fig. 2) has not been used to correct
these data so at the end of twenty five minutes
the measured N value is lower than the
computed N value. The very large temperature jump used here to test this compensator
lag effect is not encountered in the free

atmosphere. One-twentieth of this jump
change (i.e., about 2°C) occurs on rare
occasions at the edge of clouds; an approximate 2-N overshot in the refractivity value
will then be recorded. The measurements
could be corrected for this effect, but it is not
practical to do this until the data is programmed into a computer. It probably is
possible to relocate the compensation steel
disc inside the cavity so that it changes
temperature in closer harmony with the invar
portion of the cavity.

AIRCRAFT INSTALLATION

For most measurements of humidity, a
response time of one second is rapid. For
measurements above the ground, where one
searches for horizontal as well as vertical
humidity structure, the aircraft is the most
practical mode of travel. With aircraft speeds
of 300 fps or so, one is interested in response
times of the order of $\frac{1}{100}$ of a second (a
resolution of about 3 ft in horizontal distance).

The refractometer is at present the only practical instrument used today that will meet this requirement at least for temperatures above −10°C. The limiting factor in the speed of response of the refractometer is the time required to flush the cavity. Moderate ventilation of the cavity is therefore required. The AFCRL C-130 installation has a flow rate of about 30 fps through the duct leading to the cavity. Step changes which may not have been square edged have been observed with this installation at the edges of clouds where at least 66 per cent of the change has occured in $\frac{1}{100}$ of a second. This flushing time, which gives an outside sampling distance of about 3 ft, has been found adequate for most of the present studies in cloud physics. In order to verify theories which attempt to explain radar angles by the presence of appreciable refractive index changes over one wavelength, it would require measurements of N gradients over centimeters rather than meters.

In using a refractometer, or for that matter almost any other instrument, to measure structure in and around clouds, the effect of cloud or precipitation particles on the sensor must be considered. In the case of the refractometer, a moderate air flow must be maintained. Direct exposure of the refractometer to the airstream gives sufficient ventil-

ation, but inside clouds the deposition of particles on the walls of the cavity stops the operation of the instrument. The arrangement found to be satisfactory on the C-130 used by the AFCRL Cloud Physics Branch is shown in Fig. 4. Figure 5 shows the position of the intake probe on the left hand forward section of the C-130, on the forward cargo door. Air and cloud flow at static pressure through the paralleled discs. A small portion of this air is drawn off at right angles and taken inside the aircraft, small holes on the low pressure side of the duct bleed to the outside any water that has collected on the inside tube walls. A small pocket in the wall also helps to prevent water from running further down the tube. The air flowing through this duct is at a higher temperature than the ambient air because of aerodynamic and frictional heating which occurs on sampling. This temperature difference is 3 to 4°C at C-130 flight speeds so that the humidity in the duct is close to 80 per cent when flying through an ambient saturated atmosphere. The walls of the tube are usually somewhat warmer than the air in the duct being heated by conduction from their supports and through the insulation surrounding them. The cabin temperature is usually above the ambient temperature. Loss of moisture to the duct walls is therefore an

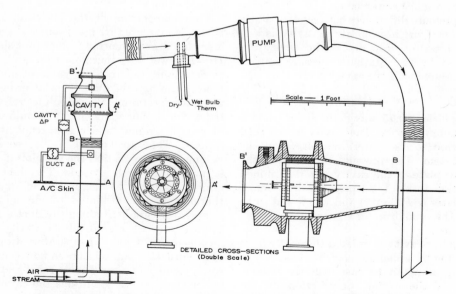

Fig. 4. Refractometer system installation in AFCRL-ESD's C-130 No. 3133.

Fig. 5. Refractometer intake and outlet probes on C-130, intake No. 3, outlet No. 4. Other meteorological probes shown are: (1) electric field mill, (2) reverse flow temperature and humidity probe, (5) rotating disk icing-rate meter, (6) Rosemount temperature probe, (7) liquid-water-content probe, (8) tangential vortex temperature probe.

unusual condition occurring only momentarily on very rapid descent from cold high altitudes into warm moist lower layers.

The pressure differences between true static and the pressure in front of the cavity as well as the pressure drop across the cavity are measured by two Statham pressure gauges. The pressure inside the cavity is given by

$$P_{\text{cavity}} = P_{\text{ambient}} - \Delta P_{\text{duct}} - 0.75 \, \Delta P_{\text{cavity}}$$

The coefficient 0.75 was determined using a brass dummy cavity. This cavity with a tube connection to its center was placed in the duct system. The pressure drop across the entrance plate of the cavity was determined in relation to the total pressure drop across both plates (ΔP cavity) and was found to be 0.75 of the total drop for all normal operating conditions.

The invar cavity is isolated thermally from its housing by a phenolic ring. Many groves in this ring allow air to pass over the outside surface of the cavity. Contraction due to temperature changes of the mounting parts

will not cause a mechanical stress on the cavity as it is not held tightly inside the phenolic ring.

The temperature of the air entering the cavity is measured by a resistance thermometer placed in the entrance duct (not shown). Dry- and wet-bulb thermometers can be read to determine the absolute value of moisture flowing through the duct. This latter figure is used to determine the absolute refractive index during horizontal flight in uniform air or on the ground under nonturbulent conditions. The air pump is a constant-volume flow type so that the ventilation speed is maintained with altitude. The duct from aircraft skin up to the wet- and dry-bulb thermometers is insulated to minimize the temperature gradient along the duct and the thermal stresses placed on the cavity. This arrangement of inertial separator, drop-trap and ventilating pump has been flown through thick cloud and very heavy rain, and even under these severe conditions the cavity has not been effected by water.

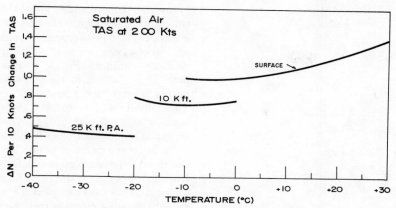

FIG. 6. Effect of small airspeed changes on refractive index measured in C-130 duct system at the surface, at 10,000 ft pressure altitude and at 25,000 ft.

The pressure and temperature changes that occur on the way to the cavity make it awkward to compute the ambient refractive index moisture values. For purposes of studying the horizontal refractive index changes, the measurements made at the cavity are used directly. An absolute value of refractive index is assigned to the measurement taken while passing through a thick cloud. This absolute value is computed from the measurement of the true ambient temperature by a large tangential vortex thermometer and from the measurement of static pressure and by assuming saturated conditions at the temperature measured. Short-term fluctuations of pressure in the system caused by atmospheric turbulence or aircraft speed changes are generally disregarded in our normal analysis procedures as only several N unit changes are usually considered of interest. Two plots (Figs. 6 and 7) show the effect of airspeed fluctuations on the measurement of refractive index at the cavity. These are computed values using derivatives of Eq. (1)

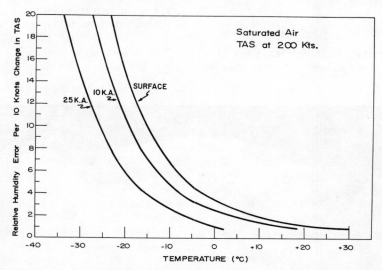

FIG. 7. The error in relative humidity computed from refractive index, if a 10-knot airspeed change was disregarded for three altitudes—surface, 10,000 ft pressure altitude, and 25,000 ft pressure altitude.

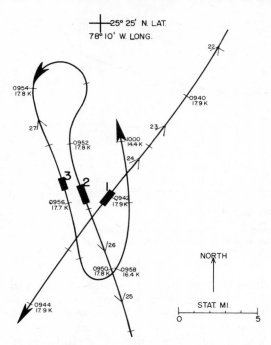

25° 25' N. LAT.
78° 10' W. LONG.

22

0954
17.8 K

0940
17.9 K

27

0952
17.8 K

1000
14.4 K

23

24

3 **2** **1**

0956
17.7 K

0942
17.9 K

0944
17.9 K

26

0950
17.8 K

0958
16.4 K

25

NORTH

STAT. MI.

0   5

FIG. 8. Flight track, photo and cloud pass positions.

and the relation between duct pressure. temperature change, and airspeed change found from speed runs made by the C-130. Again, if the data are to be processed by a computer, this analysis shortcut would not necessarily be made.

EXAMPLES OF USE

Several illustrations follow to show that there are some very sharp moisture changes

in the atmosphere and to show the response of this refractometer installation to these sharp changes. The first Figures present data taken on three successive passes through the same chimney cumulus. Figure 8 shows the flight path and position of cloud passage and the points from which photographs were taken. The cloud drifts to the west-northwest because the wind at lower levels is stronger from the east than at flight altitude.

Figure 9 is a print of photo No. 24 showing the cloud to be sampled just before penetration (the nearer cloud on the right hand side of the picture). This pass sampled the top of a new rapidly growing cloud turret. Figure 10 gives the refractometer trace and vortex thermometer traces for this first pass. These traces are a direct copy from the original record; instead of converting the refractometer measurements to show a humidity trace, two values of humidity—50 and 100 per cent—have been shown. The 100 per cent line represents the changes in refractivity that would occur at the measured temperature for a saturated atmosphere. At a constant humidity of 50 per cent, the moisture term in the refractive index computations just cancels the effect of the dry temperature term resulting in a straight line for the 50 per cent value of relative humidity at this pressure.

The sharp edge recorded by the refractometer upon entrance and exit to the cloud is typical of data taken on clouds as they actively grow through flight altitude. However, it is unusual to find such warm temperatures throughout the cloud. This cloud was

FIG. 9. Photo No. 24 taken before pass 1. Aircraft penetrated nearer cloud, right-hand bubble.

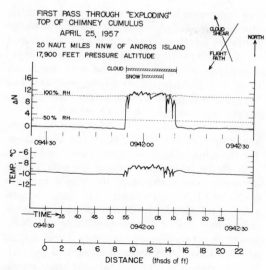

FIG. 10. Refractive index and temperature trace for pass 1. Time in hours, minutes and seconds.

snow, the snow in this case being in the form of pellets (graupel). It is rather remarkable that snow pellets would be found in so young a cloud at a rather warm temperature. Very heavy icing on the aircraft and pilot's window was encountered on this pass, suggesting the existence of many large cloud drops.

The necessity of a fast response humidity sensor for studying the structure of cumulus clouds is self-evident after examining a humidity trace such as shown by Fig. 10. The degree of mixing of dry ambient air can, to a certain extent, be quantized, and the size of the turbulent cells involved in the mixing process can be measured. However arguments can be started in this case over the reasons for the existence of the relatively dry warm spot in the cloud center.

Certain characteristics of a cloud pass trace are helpful in assessing the characteristics of the present measuring system. For instance, note should be made of the slight difference in the shape of the refractive index record at the beginning of the cloud and at the end. A sudden jump in the record is evident at the beginning, the record is slightly rounded at exit from the cloud. This difference is presumably an instrumental effect rather than a

apparently penetrated just as this portion of a larger lower cloud mass was starting its "explosion" upward. The cross-hatched bars at the top of the Figure mark the time and indicate that the observer noted (by throwing an on-off switch) the presence of cloud and/or

FIG. 11. Photo No. 26 taken just before pass 2. Aircraft penetrated at the cloud center slightly above height of apparent horizon.

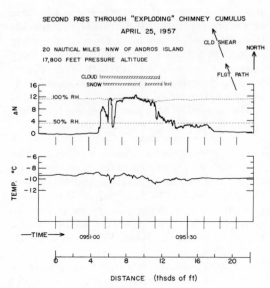

FIG. 12. Refractometer and vortex thermometer record for pass 2.

real effect. A small per cent of the cavity volume probably does not flush as rapidly as the rest, this effect would give a trace as shown. There are 2 ft of 2-in. pipe between the intake from the ambient airstream and the cavity, a thin layer of air along the inside walls of this pipe lags behind the main volume of air in passing through the system, this process would also tend to smooth out the measured value for the last few per cent of a sudden change.

The aircraft made a long leg to the south of the cloud being probed in order to let the ice collected melt before heading back on a heading to the north west, Fig. 8. The cloud was penetrated for the second time, nine minutes after the first pass. Measurements from a photo (Fig. 11) indicate the cloud top at photo time had reached a height of 25,000 ft, a growth of about 7000 ft. The records from the refractometer and vortex thermometer through the middle of this cloud are shown in Fig. 12. Considerable mixing appears at cloud edge in eddies of 500 to 1000 ft in the upshear (entrance) side, while a longer trailing finer scale mixing appears to be occuring at the down wind (exit) side. A solid saturated cloud center still exists but with little buoyancy remaining. (The effect of the higher water

vapor content inside the cloud in reducing the cloudy air density can be assumed to be canceled by the weight of liquid water and snow in the cloud volume so that the temperature trace remains an indicator of cloudy air density.) Precipitation (snow pellets) has spread throughout the cloud and to a little extent outside the visible cloud.

Just before entering the cloud on its downshear side, photo No. 27 (Fig. 13) was taken. By the time of this last pass, the cloud top is well above 30,000 ft. Falling snow is visible at cloud edges although the cloud appears quite solid in the center. The pass record (Fig. 14), however, indicates that only a very small (about 600-ft) portion of the cloud is still at saturation. Mixing with a wide range of eddy sizes has destroyed most of the cloud. Evaporation has cooled almost the whole cloud area to below the ambient temperature. Note that the observer has indicated that the plane is passing through cloud while the refractometer measures 80 per cent humidity. This condition has been frequently experienced in rapidly dissipating clouds.

A final example of the usefulness of a rapid response humidity sensor to the study of atmospheric structures other than clouds is given in Fig. 15. Here, a cloud line that formed along a so-called dryline was probed at various elevations. These data were collected by the AFCRL C-130 aircraft while participating in the National Severe Storms Project. This pass was made at 1000 ft above the ground and about 3000 ft below cloud base. As the plane flew below the cloud line, which was north to south, the humidity jumped from 16 to 65 per cent in about 300 horizontal ft. Jumps in clear air of up to 14 per cent RH in 6½ ft are recorded. This sharp humidity jump was not an isolated momentary atmospheric feature but was characteristic of a line 500 miles long from northern Oklahoma to mid-Texas. Severe storms were forming along this line fifty miles south of this point of measurement. Study of the various turbulent and wave structures that develop along such a line can only be accomplished in detail if high response equipment is employed. Part of the refractometer record is missing for this pass. The sudden change in refractive index caught the instrument monitor off-guard, he did not get the recorder back on scale for

FIG. 13. Photo No. 27 taken just before pass 3. Aircraft penetrated just above apparent horizon and in cloud center.

15 seconds. A record of a carbon strip humidity element (dashed line) is substituted for the missing refractive index data. This substitution allows one to compare the response of these two types of humidity sensors. The real variations in humidity presumably continued to oscillate as first indicated by the refractometer record. The carbon strip unit, normally considered a fast response humidity sensor, gives a smooth average trace. The existence of this dry line was detected by the WSR-57 radar at Oklahoma City, 50 miles to the east, as a "thin" line. Current radar theory would indicate that within the gradients measured here by this system which resolves gradients to about 3 ft. there must be appreciable gradients over distances smaller by an order of magnitude or two. For certain studies therefore, there is room for even higher response times (helped by probings at slow speed) than given by the 3-cm type of refractometer that has been discussed in this paper.

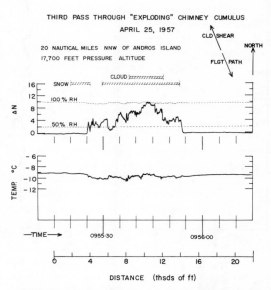

FIG. 14. Refractometer and thermometer record for pass 3.

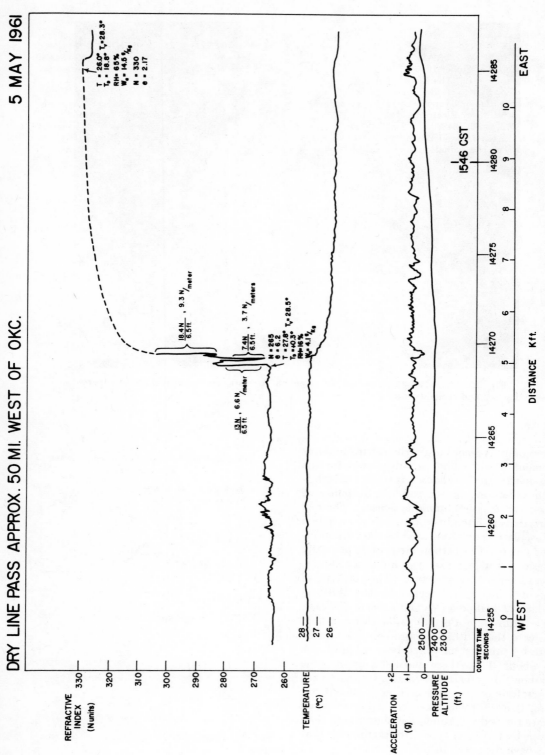

Fig. 15. Refractometer, thermometer, pressure and q meter trace for a dry line intercept.

References

1. Cunningham, R. M., Plank, V. G., and Campen, C. F., "Cloud Refractive Index Studies," AFCRC-TR-56-210; AD-110259 *Geophys. Res. Papers*, **51** (October 1956).
2. Enenstein, N. H., "The Effect of Water Droplets on the Index of Refraction," Proceedings, Symposium on Tropospheric Wave Propagation, U.S. Navy Electronics Laboratory Report No. 173, p. 52, 1948.
3. Smith, E. K., Jr., and Weintraub, S., "The Constants in the Equation for Atmospheric Refractive Index at Radio Frequencies," *Proc. IRE*, **41**, No. 8, 1035 (August 1953).
4. Crain, C. M., and Cronenwett, W. T., "Engineering Report on the Type VIII-GRD Microwave Refractometer," Rpt No. 6-20, Electrical Engineering Research Laboratory, University of Texas, April 15, 1957.
5. Shaw, R. H., and Cunningham, R. M., "A Microwave Refractometer With Fast Response and Absolute Digital Recording," AFCRL-62-298, Instrumentation For Geophysics and Astrophysics No. 20, Air Force Cambridge Research Laboratories, March 1962.

Author Index

Subject Index